JAMES R. [illegible]

TECHNICAL AERODYNAMICS

The quality of the materials used in the manufacture of this book is governed by continued postwar shortages.

TECHNICAL AERODYNAMICS

BY

KARL D. WOOD, M.E., M.S.
Professor and Head of Department of Aeronautical Engineering,
University of Colorado

SECOND EDITION

NEW YORK AND LONDON
McGRAW-HILL BOOK COMPANY, INC.
1947

TECHNICAL AERODYNAMICS

PRINTED IN THE UNITED STATES OF AMERICA

THE MAPLE PRESS COMPANY, YORK, PA.

PREFACE

Twelve years ago the first edition of this title was published. Because of the many important developments in this field in the last 12 years, this edition resembles the first edition only in the chapter headings and topics covered. This text is supplemented in the design field by the author's lithographed text "*Airplane Design*," 8th ed., distributed by the University Book Store of Boulder, Colo.

Not only has the fund of technical information expanded; college instruction in this field has also been extended. Whereas the first edition was intended to be covered in a single three-credit course of about 45 lessons, this book is intended to supply material for two such courses. The student is assumed to have completed four 16-week terms of college instruction in engineering and to have a good background in physics and mathematics, including at least one course in calculus, before undertaking this study. He may profitably also have taken courses in fluid mechanics and thermodynamics, though these courses are not necessarily prerequisite, since the fundamentals of these subjects needed for the understanding of this text are covered in Chap. 1.

This edition is dedicated to the students at Cornell, Purdue, and Colorado, who asked the questions and made the author help them find the answers—especially to the University of Colorado V-12 students who suffered with the author through the preliminary second edition. Particular thanks are due to Mrs. Louise H. Beattie for assistance in preparation of the manuscript.

K. D. Wood.

Boulder, Colo.,
June, 1947.

CONTENTS

CHAPTER 10

CHAPTER 11

APPENDIX 1

APPENDIX 2

APPENDIX 3

APPENDIX 4

APPENDIX 5

APPENDIX 6

NOTATION AND ABBREVIATIONS

a = acceleration $= dy/dt$, ft per sec; lift-curve slope = slope of graph C_L vs. α.

a_0 = infinite-aspect-ratio lift-curve slope.

a_t = lift-curve slope of horizontal tail.

a_v = lift-curve slope of vertical tail.

a.c. = aerodynamic-center distance from leading edge, ft or fraction of c.

$(a.c.)'$ = effective aerodynamic-center location taking account of fuselage and nacelle effects.

A = area of the wind-tunnel throat, sq ft; cross-sectional area, sq ft.

A_f = area of fan disk $= \pi D^2/4$.

$A.F.$ = activity factor.

Æ = aspect ratio $= b^2/S$.

$Æ_e$ = effective aspect ratio $= eÆ$.

$Æ_{eq.d}$ = equivalent monoplane aspect ratio for equal induced drag.

$Æ_t$ = aspect ratio of horizontal tail.

$Æ_v$ = aspect ratio of vertical tail.

b = wing span, ft; propeller width at any radius r.

b_s = slot width.

Btu = British thermal unit = ft-lb/778; a constant $= Q_0 dx/2\pi$; ft^4 per sec (used in source and sink problems).

Bhp = brake horsepower = 550 ft-lb per sec.

c = chord of wing, ft; critical velocity, ft per sec; geometric mean chord; length or distance, ft.

c_1 = critical velocity at some local point in a flow pattern, ft per sec.

c_{d0} = section, or profile, drag coefficient for an airfoil section $= dD/qdS$.

c_l = section lift coefficient $= dL/qdS$.

c_{la} = additional lift coefficient.

c_{la1} = constant of proportionality in equation for additional lift.

c_{lb} = basic lift coefficient.

c_{l0} = lift coefficient for an airfoil section $c_{l0} = dL/qdS$.

c_m = mean wing chord $= S/b$, ft.

c_{ma} = mean aerodynamic chord.

$c_{m\ a.c.}$ = pitching-moment coefficient for airfoil section about aerodynamic center $c_{m\ a.c.} = dM/cqdS$.

c_{mg} = mean geometric chord $= S/b$, ft.

c_n = normal force coefficient.

c_{nb} = normal force coefficient, basic.

c_0 = critical velocity for conditions in free stream flow; ft per sec.

c.p. = center of pressure, distance from leading edge, ft.

c_p = specific heat at constant pressure $= \Delta Q_P/W\Delta t = Kc_v$, Btu (lb) (deg F).

c_r = chord at the root of tapered wings.

c_t = chord at the tip of tapered wings.
c_t/c_r = taper ratio.
c_v = specific heat at constant volume, Btu (lb) (deg F).
c.g. = center of gravity.
c.g.n.s. = center of gravity for neutral stability.
C_D = drag coefficient = drag/qS.
C_{Di} = induced drag.
C_{De} = effective profile-drag coefficient.
$C_{De\ min}$ = effective minimum profile-drag coefficient of a wing $= C_D - C_L^2/\pi e A\!\!R$.
$C_{De\ int}$ = intercept of the graph of C_D *vs.* C_L; also called the effective minimum profile-drag coefficient.
C_{Dpe} = effective parasite-drag coefficient.
$C_{D\pi}$ = proper drag coefficient.
C_f = skin-friction coefficient $= \dfrac{F/S}{\rho V^2/2}$.
C_h = rate of climb.
$C_{h\ max}$ = maximum rate of climb.
$C_{h0\ max}$ = maximum rate of climb at sea level.
C_L = lift coefficient = L/qS.
$C_{L\ max}$ = maximum coefficient of lift for a wing, or stalling lift coefficient.
$C_{L\ opt}$ = optimum lift coefficient.
C_M = pitching-moment coefficient = M/cqS.
$C_{Ma.c.}$ = moment coefficient about aerodynamic center; slope of graph C_P *vs.* $1/C_L$.
C_P = location of lift and drag forces = c.p./c.
C_r = rolling-moment coefficient.
$C_{r\Psi}$ = slope of rolling-moment-coefficient graph *vs.* angle of sideslip, or yaw.
C_{ry} = slope of rolling-moment-coefficient graph *vs.* angular-velocity ratio in yaw.
C_y = yawing-moment coefficient.
C_{yy} = slope of yawing-moment-coefficient graph *vs.* angular-velocity ratio in yaw.
C.F. = centrifugal force.
d = diameter, ft; length or distance, ft.
D = drag = $C_D qS$, lb; fan diameter, ft; diameter of circle in which propeller blade tips revolve.
D_i = induced drag $C_L^2/\pi e A\!\!R$, lb.
D_P = profile drag, lb.
e = induced-drag efficiency factor $= \dfrac{1/\pi A\!\!R}{dcD/dC_L^2}$.
e_w = induced-drag efficiency factor for wing.
E = ratio of the semiperimeter to the span of an ellipse; ratio of elevator chord to horizontal tail chord
EHTS = effective helical tip speed.
E.R. = energy ratio for wind tunnel.
f_e = equivalent flat-plate area for minimum drag of a wing or airplane.
F = force, lb.
F_e = free-elevator factor.
F_r = Froude number for waves in liquid V^2/gb.
F_r = free-rudder factor.

F_t	= tail force.
g	= acceleration due to gravity = 32.2 ft per sec^2.
g.m.c	= geometric mean chord.
Gr	= Grashof number (heat transfer).
h	= convective-heat-transfer coefficient Btu/(hr)(sq ft)(deg F); vertical location of the horizontal tail relative to the zero-lift chord of the wing.
h_1	= distance.
H	= enthalpy of a gas = $U + (P\vec{V}/778)$, Btu per lb.
H_f	= aerodynamic hinge moment of the movable surface.
H_{abs}	= absolute ceiling.
H_{serv}	= service ceiling.
HTS	= helical tip speed.
i_s	= stabilizer incidence.
Ihp	= indicated horsepower.
J	= advance ratio for propellers = V/nD.
k	= circulation constant for a vortex = $\Gamma/2\pi$; Munk span factor; pressure-loss coefficient for wind tunnels = Δ_P/q_t; ratio of specific heats = C_P/C_v.
k_c	= thermal conductivity = $\Delta Qx/S\Delta T\Delta t$, Btu/(hr) (ft) (deg F).
k_y	= radius of gyration of the airplane around the span axis.
K_x	= engineering-drag coefficient = D/Sv^2.
l_t	= tail length, c.g. to elevator hinge, ft.
L	= distance or length, ft; lift = C_LqS, lb; maximum median camber location, fraction of chord.
L_f	= fuselage length.
L_v	= tail length, c.g. to a.c. of vertical tail.
m	= lift-curve slope per radian; mass per second of air handled; mass of fluid flowing per second = dM/dt slugs per sec; maximum median camber.
$-m_q$	= rotational damping factor.
M	= mass in slugs, lb-sec^2 per ft; pitching moment = C_McqS, ft; Mach number = V/c.
M_1	= local Mach number.
M_0	= free-stream Mach number = V_0/c_0.
$M_{0\ cr}$	= critical free-stream Mach number.
M_y	= yawing moment, lb-ft.
n	= revolutions per second.
n_e	= number of engines.
N	= rotative speed of engine or propeller per minute = rpm.
Nu	= Nusselt number.
p	= angular velocity of roll; local pressure unit, lb per sq ft.
P	= ratio p/q at any point on the chord of a wing; absolute pressure = F/S lb per ft; brake power of engine, ft-lb per sec; period of vibration, sec.
p.i.	= power index.
P_1, P_2, P_3	= pressure at some local point in a flow pattern; lb per sq ft.
P_a	= atmospheric pressure, lb per sq ft.
P_f	= surface-pressure coefficient.
P_g	= gauge pressure, lb per sq ft.
P_{iw}	= engine power corrected for altitude and gross weight.

P_l = lower surface pressure.
P_0 = pressure distribution at zero lift; pressure of free stream; lb per sq ft.
Pr = Prandtl number (heat transfer).
P_u = upper surface pressure.
$-P_{u\,max}$ = maximum upper surface pressure.
q = dynamic or impact pressure $= \rho V^2/2$, lb per sq ft.
q_t = dynamic pressure at tunnel throat $= \rho V_t^2/2$, lb-ft.
Q = torque or moment, lb-ft; volume of air flow, ft per sec; heat energy, Btu or Btu per lb.
Q_c = centrifugal torque.
Q_f = friction torque.
Q_0 = source and sink strengths, cu ft per sec.
$Q_{0\,max}$ = full-throttle torque at sea level.
Q_s = quantity of fluid flowing, cu ft per sec.
r = angular velocity of yaw; radius, ft.
r_{min} = minimum radius.
R = radius; universal gas constant, ft per deg F abs
Re = Reynolds number.
s = specific humidity, lb H_2O per lb dry air.
S = entropy $= \int dQ/T$; wing surface, sq ft.
S_f = side area of fuselage, sq ft.
S_v = vertical tail area, sq ft.
S_π = proper area, plan or frontal.
S.L. = sea level.
$(\ )_S$ or $(\ )_s$ = stall condition.
t = airfoil thickness, ft; thickness ratio, Fahrenheit temperature, deg F; time, sec.
t/c = thickness ratio.
T = absolute temperature on Fahrenheit (Rankine) scale $= t + 460°F$; propeller thrust or other force, lb.
Thp = thrust horsepower delivered by the propeller $= \eta$ Bhp.
T_{NF} = final net thrust at take-off.
T_{NI} = initial net thrust at take-off.
u = fan tip speed $= \pi nD$; velocity in x direction, ft per sec.
U = internal energy $= \int c_v dT$.
v = velocity, mph.
v_c = best climbing speed, mph.
v_{cr} = cruising speed, mph.
v_L = maximum level high speed, mph.
v_{L0} = maximum level-flight speed at sea level.
v_{min} = minimum landing speed, mph.
v_{s0} = stalling speed at sea level $= 19.75 \sqrt{\frac{W/S}{C_{L\,max}}}$, mph.
v = velocity, ft per sec; volume, cu ft.
$\bar{V}$ = specific volume $= 1/w$, cu ft per lb.
V_f = mean fan-disk velocity.
V_i = true indicated air speed.
V_{iw} = indicated air speed corrected for gross weight.
V_{min} = minimum speed $= \sqrt{\frac{2W/S}{\rho C_{L\,max}}}$, ft per sec.

V_t = velocity at throat, ft per sec.
V_x = velocity component in x direction, ft per sec.
V_y = velocity component in y direction, ft per sec.
V_I = actual indicated-air-speed reading.
V_{STO} = take-off stalling speed.
V_{TO} = take-off velocity.
w = specific weight, lb per cu ft.
W = weight, lb.
W = gross weight, lb.
W_0 = design gross weight.
W_s = standard reference gross weight.
x = distance, length, or thickness, ft.
$x_{a.c.}$ = aerodynamic-center location.
x_c = climbing distance.
$x_{c/4}$ = fore-and-aft location of the quarter chord of the element dS.
x_g = ground run.
x_t = transition distance.
x_{TO} = total take-off distance.
X = excess horsepower.
X_b = braking distance.
X_g = glide distance.
X_r = free rolling distance.
X_t = transition distance.
X_L = landing distance.
y = length or distance, ft; spanwise distance on wing, ft.
z = liquid pressure head, ft; vertical distance, ft.
α (alpha) = angle of attack of wing, deg; absolute angle of attack
α_a = absolute or aerodynamic angle of attack.
α_{ir} = induced angle of attack, radians $= C_L/\pi A\!\!\!R$.
α_{l0} = angle of attack for zero lift of wing section.
α_{L0} = angle of attack for zero lift of wing.
α_{0r} = angle of attack for infinite aspect ratio, radians $= \alpha_r - (C_L/\pi A\!\!\!R)$.
β(beta) = propeller-blade angle measured from plane of rotation of propeller, deg.
$\beta_{0.75R}$ = propeller-blade angle measured at 0.75 propeller radius R.
γ (gamma) = angle between lift component and the resultant forces.
Γ (Gamma) = circulation $= 2\pi K = \rho V_0 b/L$, sq ft per sec.
Γ or Γ° = dihedral-angle degrees.
δ (delta) = angle, deg.
δ_e = elevator angle, deg.
δ_f = flap angle, deg.
δ_r = rudder angle, deg.
δ_t = trim-tab angle, deg.
Δ (Delta) = increment or increase in a quantity.
ϵ (epislon) = angle of twist, deg; angle of down-wash deg.
ϵ_r = angle of down-wash, radians.
ζ (zeta) = dynamic-stability factor.
η (eta) = propeller efficiency = Thp/Bhp; propulsive efficiency; wind-tunnel fan efficiency $= Q\Delta P/550$ Bhp.
η' = airfoil efficiency factor or lift-curve-slope efficiency factor.
θ (theta) = angle of glide path with horizontal.

λ (lambda) = 0.00356 for standard air, slope of graph of temperature *vs.* altitude.

μ (mu) = dynamic viscosity = Fx/SV, lb-sec per sq ft or poises; rolling-resistance coefficient.

$-\mu m_\alpha$ = static-stability factor.

ν (nu) = kinematic viscosity = μ/ρ, sq ft per sec.

π (pi) = 3.1416.

ρ (rho) = air density, slugs per cu ft.

ρ_0 = air density at sea level, slugs per cu ft.

σ (sigma) = air-density ratio ρ/ρ_0.

τ (tau) = unit shearing stress between layers of fluid flow = $\mu du/dy$ = lb per sq ft.

ϕ (phi) = flow coefficient; angle of bank, deg.

Ψ (psi) = pressure-rise coefficient; angle of yaw, deg.

Ψ' = dynamic-stability coefficient.

ω (omega) = angular velocity = $2\pi n$, radians per sec.

TECHNICAL AERODYNAMICS

INTRODUCTION

Students familiar with popular literature in the general field of aeronautics will find this collection of photographs and sketches and the accompanying description and discussion a very simple review of the important superficial aspects of aircraft. Its value for college students is in building up a common background of descriptive vocabulary among a group undertaking a study of the technical aspects of aircraft. The instructor is advised to check the student's understanding of aircraft nomenclature by means of an examination based on the questions at the end of this introduction before proceeding further in the study.

I:1. Types of Aircraft.—Aircraft are machines for transportation of persons and things through the air. They are of two major types:

Fig. I:1.—Lighter-than-air aircraft. U.S. Navy K-type airship made in 1944 by the Goodyear Aircraft Corporation. Used effectively for antisubmarine escort of surface vessels. (*Courtesy Aviation.*)

(1) lighter-than-air aircraft, which are supported in the air by aerostatic buoyant forces, such as the semirigid dirigible balloon shown in Fig. I:1; (2) heavier-than-air aircraft of the various types shown in Fig. I:2. Heavier-than-air aircraft are supported in the air by the aerodynamic forces resulting from their movement or the movement of their parts, relative to the air. The *airplane* (Fig. I:2*a*) is a heavier-than-air craft in which the lifting surfaces are fixed in position during flight. The autogyro is, in effect, a type of airplane that uses a windmill for a wing. It is propelled by means of an engine and propeller, but the windmill is not connected to the engine, except for starting, being rotated by air forces. The helicopter (Fig. I:2) is also known as a "rotary-wing" aircraft; but the *rotor* or *rotors* are driven by means

of the engine, and forward flight is obtained by tilting the rotors slightly from the horizontal plane of rotation. The means used for tilting the rotor are discussed later.

These are the principal types of aircraft in current use. Many others have been tried, but none have been found as satisfactory as

a. Airplane. Taylorcraft Model 15 four-place airplane of 125 hp. (*Courtesy Aviation, February,* 1945.)

b. Autogyro. Pitcairn Model PA-36, two-place autogyro of 165 hp. (*Courtesy Aero Digest.*)

c. Helicopter. U.S. Army R-6 helicopters built in 1944 by Nash-Kelvinator from Sikorsky design. (*Courtesy Aviation, February,* 1945.)

Fig. I:2.—Heavier-than-air aircraft.

those described above. Much effort has been devoted to attempting to build a flying machine that would sustain itself by flapping its wings as a bird does, but none of these has thus far been successful as a transportation vehicle, although numerous satisfactory models have been built.

Other types of aircraft have been built using rotating cylinders as lift surfaces or wings or paddles on rotating cylinders, but the few successful models have been found uneconomical compared with those already listed.

The airplane is the principal type that will be considered in this text although some attention will be given to the helicopter because

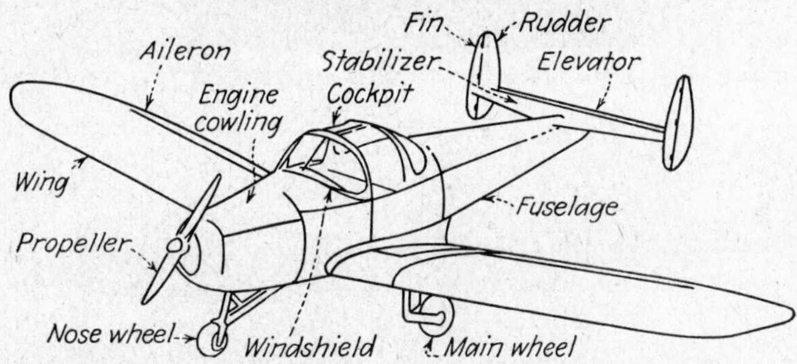

Fig. I:3.—Ercoupe Model 415-C light airplane, with principal external parts labeled to show nomenclature.

of its current promise of an important future. The helicopter can take off and land vertically; the airplane cannot.

I:2. Types of Airplanes.—Airplanes are commonly classified either according to the *purpose* for which they are used or according to the *arrangement* of their principal parts. The principal external parts of a particular light airplane, the Ercoupe, are shown in the labeled sketch (Fig. I:3). For classification according to purpose this airplane could be called a private airplane, a light airplane for private flying, or a personal airplane. It is shown in Fig. I:4*d*. Other types of airplanes classified by purpose are the bomber (Fig. I:4*a*), for which the military purpose is to drop bombs and destroy enemy ground installations and personnel in time of war; the fighter or pursuit ship (Fig. I:4*b*), for which the military purpose is to destroy enemy aircraft in time of war; and the commercial transport airplane (Fig. I:4*c*), the purpose of which is to transport persons and things from one place to another for profit to the owners of the airplane.

Other types of airplanes, classified according to the arrangement of principal parts, are shown in Fig. I:5. Figure I:5*a* is known as a *biplane* because it has two main lifting surfaces. All the other types shown in Fig. I:5 are *monoplanes*. The biplane appears to be becoming obsolete for most purposes. Monoplanes are further classified as *low-wing* as in Fig. I:5*c*, or *high-wing*, as in Fig. I:5*b*, depending on the position of the wing relative to the fuselage. Many airplanes have the wing going approximately through the middle of the fuselage, as

a. Bomber. Boeing B-29 Superfortress. (*Courtesy Aviation, February*, 1945.)

b. U.S. Army Air Forces pursuit airplanes. Left: P-51, North American Mustang. Right: P-63, Bell Kingcobra.

c. Commercial transport airplane, the Lockheed Constellation, in production for several air lines in 1945. (*Courtesy Aviation, February*, 1945.)

d. Ercoupe light airplane for individual ownership and personal transportation. (*Courtesy Aviation, February*, 1945.)

Fig. I:4.—Types of airplanes. Classification by use.

in Fig. I:4*a*, and are known as *mid-wing* models. Another major arrangement classification is according to the landing gear. Airplanes equipped with wheels for landing on land are known as "landplanes." Most landplanes have three wheels, two side by side and a third at the tail or at the nose. If the third wheel is at the tail, this type of landplane is known as the *conventional three-wheel landplane* as in the biplane in Fig. I:5*a*. If the third wheel is in front, as in Fig. I:4*d*, the landing gear is known as the *tricycle* or *nose-wheel type*. If the wheels are replaced by floats, as in Fig. I:5*c*, the airplane is known as a *seaplane;* or if the body is designed as a boat hull, it is known as a flying boat. If a flying boat is also equipped with wheels for landing

a. Biplane. British Fairey Swordfish torpedo and rocket airplane. (*Courtesy Aviation, February*, 1945.)

b. Monoplane. Luscombe Silvaire. (*Courtesy Aviation, February*, 1945.)

c. Seaplane. Japanese Paul 11 Navy Reconnaisance. (*Courtesy Aviation, February*, 1945.)

d. Amphibian. Republic Sea Bee four-place amphibian. Without wheels, this would be known as a "flying boat."

e. "Tail-first," or forward-stabilizer type, proposed Naugle N-6. Estimated high speed 185 mph with Lycoming 125-hp engine. (*Courtesy Aviation, February*, 1945.)

f. Tailless Northrop XB-35, with counterrotating three-blade pusher propellers. Lateral controls and elevators are at wing tips. (*Courtesy Aviation, May*, 1946.)

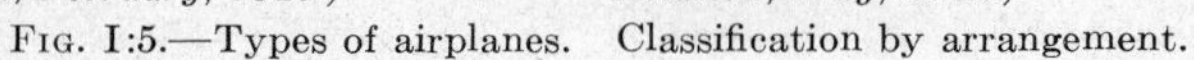

Fig. I:5.—Types of airplanes. Classification by arrangement.

on land, it is known as an *amphibian*, as in Fig. I:5*d*. Airplanes are also classified according to the up-and-down control surfaces, the stabilizer and elevator. If these surfaces are on the rear end of the fuselage or on booms behind the wing, the airplane is said to have conventional tail surfaces. If the horizontal control surfaces are in

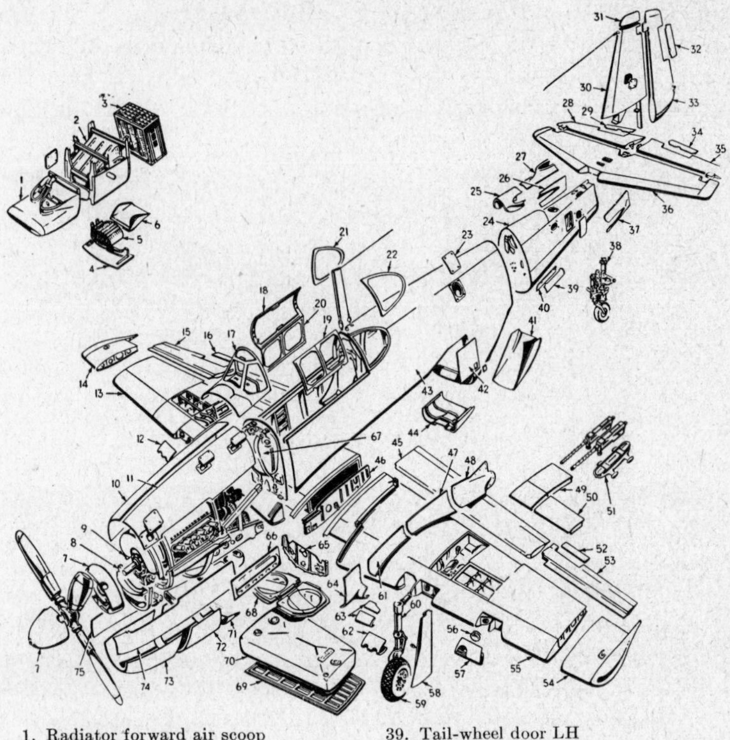

1. Radiator forward air scoop
2. Radiator forward air duct
3. Coolant-radiator assembly
4. Oil radiator cover
5. Oil radiator
6. Oil-cooler air-inlet door
7. Spinner assembly
8. Engine-mount front-frame assembly
9. Engine-mount assembly
10. Engine top cowling RH
11. Engine top cowling LH
12. Wing-nose assembly
13. Wing panel RH
14. Wing tip RH
15. Aileron RH
16. Aileron-trim tab
17. Windshield
18. Cockpit exit hatch
19. Cockpit exit-hatch panel LH
20. Cockpit exit-hatch panel RH
21. Radio-access window RH
22 Radio-access window LH
23. Oxygen-access door
24. Oxygen rear door
25. Fillet
26. Fillet
27. Fillet
28. Elevator
29. Elevator-trim tab
30. Vertical stabilizer
31. Vertical stabilizer
32. Rubber-trim tab
33. Rudder
34. Elevator-trim tab
35. Elevator
36. Horizontal stabilizer
37. Fillet
38. Tail-wheel unit assembly
39. Tail-wheel door LH
40. Tail-wheel door RH
41. Radiator aft air scoop
42. Cover
43. Fuselage forward section
44. Coolant-radiator-access cover
45. Wing flap
46. Wing center rib
47. Wing-to-fuselage fillet
48. Wing-to-fuselage fillet
49. Gun-bay door
50. Ammunition-bay door
51. Bomb rack
52. Aileron-trim tab LH
53. Aileron LH
54. Wing tip LH
55. Wing panel LH
56. Landing light
57. Landing-light cover
58. Landing-gear fairing
59. 27-in. smooth-contour wheel
60. Main-landing-gear shock strut
61. Wing-to-fuselage fairing
62. Wing-nose assembly
63. Main-landing-gear access cover
64. Intermediate-rear-engine cowling
65. Wing center bulkhead
66. Exhaust-stock fairing
67. Firewell assembly
68. Main-gear fairing door
69. Fuel-tank door
70. Fuel tank
71. Engine lower aft cowling
72. Engine lower intermediate cowling
73. Engine lower forward cowling
74. Engine intermediate cowling LH
75. Engine intermediate cowling RH

Fig. I:6.—Nomenclature of parts of P-51 Mustang. (*Courtesy Aviation.*)

front, as in Fig. I:5*e*, the airplane is known as a canard or *tail-first* type. If the horizontal control surfaces are on the ends of the wing, the airplane may be known as *tailless* or as of the *flying-wing* type.

Airplanes are usually propelled by means of one or more propellers of one or more blades each, driven by internal-combustion engines. If a propeller is in front of its engine, it is known as a *tractor propeller*. If it is behind, it is known as a *pusher*. Some airplanes have both tractor and pusher propellers. The engines, described in detail later, usually burn gasoline. If they are kept from overheating by means of a blast of air blowing directly on the engine, they are known as "air-cooled." If, as in an automobile engine, water or other liquid is circulated around the engine and the liquid is cooled by means of a *radiator*, they are known as "liquid-cooled" engines.

A more complete list of parts and an exploded sketch of an important present-day liquid-cooled pursuit airplane, the North American P-51 Mustang, is shown in Fig. I:6. A similar list and exploded sketch for the Lockheed Constellation is shown in Fig. I:6.1.

I:2.1. Types of Helicopters.—Helicopters, like airplanes, may be classified according to *use* or *arrangement*.

The *uses* of helicopters are similar to those of airplanes except insofar as the helicopter is limited in high speed to speeds considerably lower than those of airplanes. Accordingly, a *transport helicopter* would probably be used chiefly for transportation of passengers and baggage from larger city airports to downtown rooftop landing areas or for transportation between closely spaced cities without airports.

Helicopters are classified principally according to arrangement of the rotors. Four satisfactory arrangements are shown in Fig. I:6.2. The single main rotor arrangement shown in Fig. I:6.2*a*, with a small antitorque rotor at the rear, is the most satisfactory type at present for small sizes.

Some details of the Sikorsky YR-4 helicopter are shown in Fig. I:6.3. Sketches *a* and *b* of this figure show the means by which the angle of the blades with the plane of rotation (the *pitch* of the blades) is varied throughout the cycle of rotation by means of connections between the pilot's *control stick* and the *swash plate*. Sikorsky's successful development of this "cyclic pitch control" was largely responsible for the rebirth of the helicopter, which was for many years an unsatisfactory vehicle because of lack of adequate control.

I:3. Performance of Airplanes.—The purpose of an airplane is to transport persons and things from place to place in a short time. To do this it must *take off* from the land or water, *climb* to a desired flying *altitude*, cruise the desired *distance* in the desired direction, under the control of the pilot, *maneuvering* as necessary to avoid obstacles, and descend and land at the destination. An airplane is considered to have merit insofar as it does these things quickly, safely, and

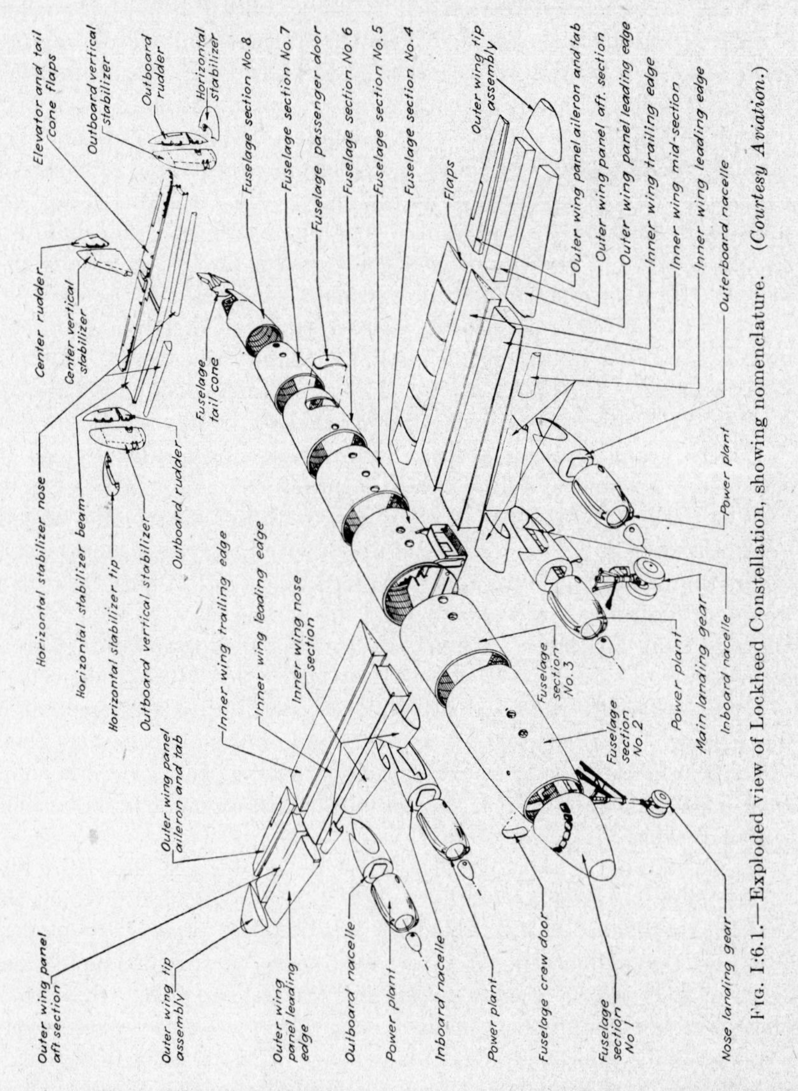

Fig. I:6.1.—Exploded view of Lockheed Constellation, showing nomenclature. (*Courtesy Aviation.*)

comfortably. The quantitative measure of the way it performs these functions is known as the *performance* of the airplane. The principal items of performance are, therefore, the take-off time or distance, the angle and rate of climb, the maximum altitude that can be reached (the "ceiling"), the cruising speed and distance, the maximum speed of level flight with full power, the angle and rate of descent, the minimum radius in which it can turn, the speed at which it lands, and the distance it must run on landing.

The airplane is supported in the air by means of the relative motion between the wing and the air; and with a given wing surface S,

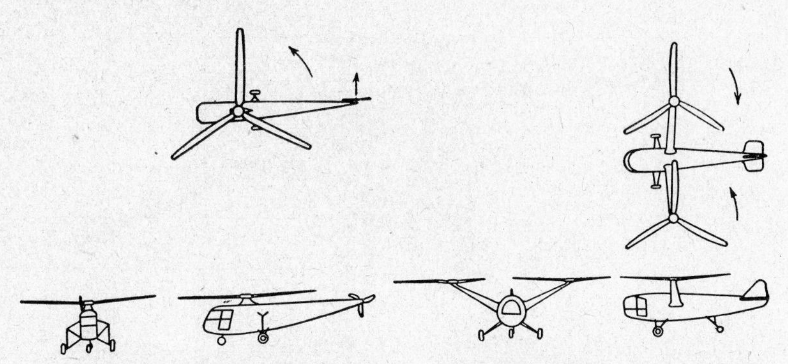

a. Three-view illustration of single-rotor helicopter with antitorque propeller, typical of Sikorsky, Young (Bell), Piasecki, Kaiser, and Higgins designs.

b. Biaxial-type helicopter with rotors laterally disposed, as built by Focke in Germany and Platt-LePage in United States, is shown here in three-view aspect.

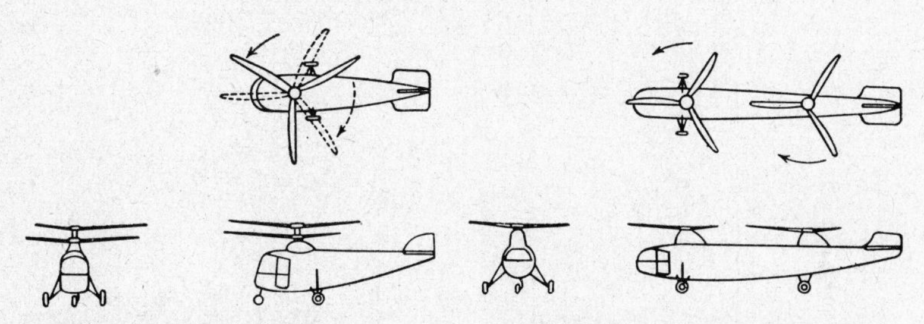

c. Coaxial-type helicopter as constructed by De Bothezat and by Hiller. Antitorque propeller is eliminated.

d. Biaxial-type craft shown here has rotors longitudinally disposed, in contrast with rotors shown in Fig. I:6.2*b*.

FIG. I:6.2.—General arrangement of helicopters. (*Courtesy Aviation.*)

usually measured in square feet, a certain maximum weight can be supported at a given speed for a given type of airplane wing. The greater the weight of the airplane W per square foot of wing surface S, the faster it must go to take off or land. The ratio of weight to wing surface W/S is known as the *wing loading*, and the wing loading for a given type of wing determines the *minimum landing speed*, also called the stalling speed for reasons to be explained later.

To travel fast, a large amount of power must be supplied by the engine and propeller; and the resistance to forward motion, or drag, depends on the size and shape of the wing and the size and shape of the fuselage and other external parts. The skin friction of the wing and the drag of the other parts of the airplane are commonly expressed

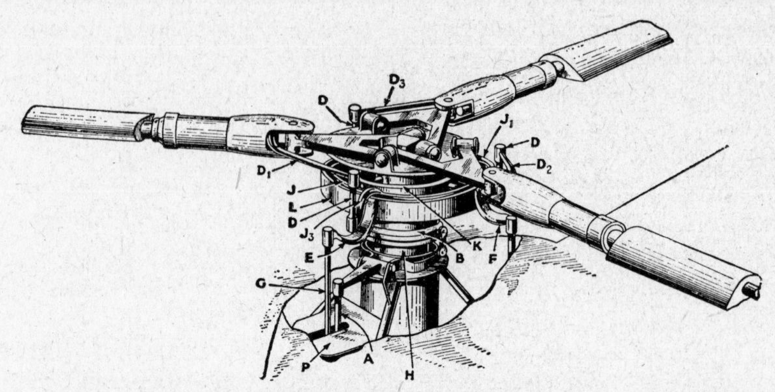

a. Perspective sketch of cyclic pitch-control mechanism. (*Courtesy Aviation.*)

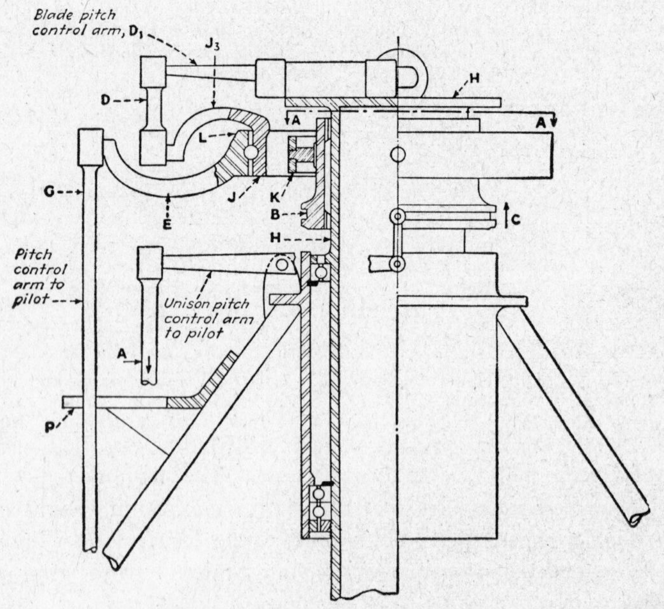

b. Side view of cyclic pitch-control mechanism of helicopter. (*Courtesy Aviation.*)

FIG. I:6.3.—Helicopter details.

in terms of the number of square feet of a thin flat plate (f), perpendicular to the wind, that would have the same drag. The *level high speed* of the airplane is determined principally by the ratio of the power delivered by the propeller (thrust horsepower = Thp) to the equivalent flat-plate area.

The aerodynamic "cleanness" of an airplane as measured by the ratio of the parasite flat plate f to the wing surface S is known as the "effective minimum drag coefficient" C_{De}. For a given aerodynamic cleanness and a given propeller efficiency (η = the ratio of the power delivered by the propeller to power supplied by the engine) the level high speed of the airplane will be determined by the ratio of the engine horsepower (brake horsepower = Bhp) to the wing surface S.

In order to climb well an airplane must "bite" on a large amount of air, and this is determined by the *span* of the wing (the maximum horizontal dimension perpendicular to the direction of flight). It must also have a large amount of power delivered by the propeller. The ratio of the airplane weight W to the square of the span of the wing is known as *span loading* (W/b^2). The span loading and power loading are the principal factors determining the maximum rate of climb and the ceiling of the airplane. The ratio of the square of the span to the wing surface (b^2/S) is known as the *aspect ratio* of the wing.

TABLE I:1.—MAJOR PERFORMANCE ITEMS FOR THE CONSTELLATION AND ERCOUPE AIRPLANES, SHOWN IN FIG. I:4c AND d*

	Constellation	Ercoupe
Gross weight, lb., W	86,250	1,260
Maximum power, Bhp	8,800	65
Wing surface, sq ft, S	1,650	142.6
Wing span, ft, b	123	30
Aspect ratio, $\frac{b^2}{S}$	9.18	6.31
Span loading, lb per sq ft, $\frac{W}{b^2}$	5.70	1.40
Wing loading, lb per sq ft, $\frac{W}{S}$	52.2	8.8
Power loading, lb per Bhp, $\frac{W}{Bhp}$	9.8	19.4
Parasite flat plate, sq ft (est.), f	25.4	4.3
Minimum drag coefficient, $\frac{f}{S}$	0.0154	0.030
Minimum landing speed, mph, v_{min}	80	48
Maximum rate of climb, ft per min, C_h	1,800	500
Cruising speed, mph, v_{cr}	300	100
Maximum level high speed, mph, v_L	350+	117
Service ceiling, ft (100 ft per min rate of climb), H_S	35,000+	13,000

* Data from *Aviation*, February, 1946.

Performance data and specifications on many other airplanes in use in 1946 are given in Table A, a loose sheet in the back of the book. Performance data on current helicopters are given in Table B, a loose sheet in the back of the book.

The aspect ratio is also the ratio of the span to a mean chord of the wing [determined by dividing the wing surface by the wing span ($c_m = S/b$)].

Power loading is the principal factor in determining the take-off run of the airplane. *Wing loading* is the principal factor in determining the turning radius, landing run, and various other flight maneuvers.

Performance of the typical nonmilitary airplanes shown in Fig. I:4*c* and *d* is given in Table I:1.

A tabular review of the relationships stated in this article between the physical characteristics of airplanes and their performance is given in Table I:2.

TABLE I:2.—RELATION BETWEEN PHYSICAL CHARACTERISTICS AND PERFORMANCE

Physical Characteristics		Performance Item Determined
Wing loading, $\frac{W}{S}$	determines	Minimum speed, power off, $v_{\min}$
Power loading, $\frac{W}{Bhp}$ Span loading, $\frac{W}{b^2}$	determine	Maximum rate of climb, C_h Ceiling, H
Thrust horsepower, η Bhp (η = propeller efficiency) Parasite flat plate, f	determine	Maximum level high speed, v_L

Cruising speed (v_{cr}) is any speed at which it is desired to cruise. Considerations of economy generally limit v_{cr} to $0.85v_L$.

Service ceiling (H_s) is the altitude at which the rate of climb has dropped to some arbitrary small value, usually 100 ft per min for commercial airplanes, sometimes 350 ft per min for military airplanes flying in formation, in which case it is called "formation service ceiling."

I:4. Operation of Airplanes.—An airplane performs the functions described in Art. I:3 only if the pilot can make it do as he wishes and can know from instruments that it is doing so. The means for travel under the control of the pilot accordingly merits further amplification. The pilot's cockpit is equipped with numerous handles and pedals for the control of the airplane, engine, and propeller and with numerous instruments that inform him whether or not his control movements are having the desired effect.

The motions of an airplane are usually referred to the three axes shown in Fig. I:6.4, where it is noted that the ailerons control the *rolling* about the *longitudinal, or x, axis,* the *elevators* control the *pitching about* the *lateral, or y, axis,* and the *rudder* controls the *yawing* about the *normal, or z, axis,* the positive directions of angles and the symbols used to designate them being shown in the figure. The ailerons and elevators are usually connected to a control stick (or to a control wheel) on a movable column, like an automobile wheel free to move front and back. The rudder is usually hooked up to foot pedals so that pushing the right rudder pedal yaws the airplane to the right and pushing the left rudder pedal yaws the airplane to the left (just the opposite from steering a sled). Some airplanes, like the Ercoupe in Fig. I:3, have no rudder pedals or any independent control of the rudder, the rudders being mechanically connected to

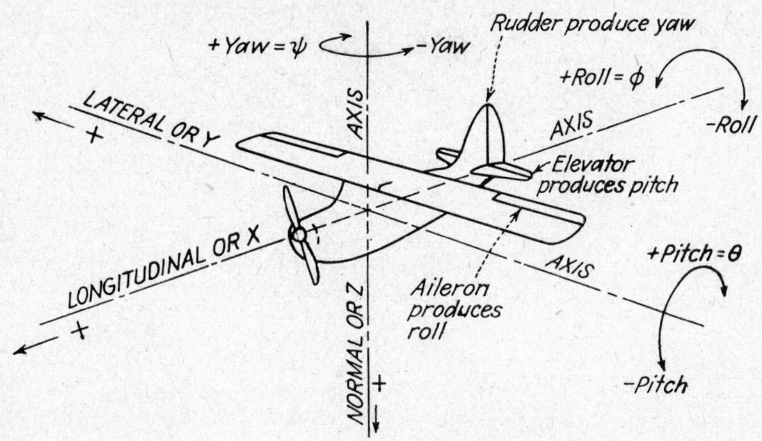

FIG. I:6.4.—Axes of airplane.

the ailerons so that they move together in making turns in the airplane. Airplanes so equipped can never make perfectly banked turns and are capable of fewer kinds of maneuvers but, in general, are considerably safer for amateur pilots and therefore promise to come into wide use. The movements of the stick or wheel and the corresponding movements of the airplane are "natural" in that leaning the stick to the right leans the airplane to the right and pushing forward on the stick pushes the nose of the airplane down.

A typical mechanism connecting the stick and ailerons is shown in Fig. I:7.1, which also shows a mechanism for the adjustment of aileron trim tabs. On this particular airplane, the Mustang, the right trim tab is adjustable only on the ground, to compensate for minor errors in the alignment of the wing, while the left trim tab is adjustable in the air to compensate for variations in propeller torque. Details of the trim-tab adjustment are shown in detail sketches A and B, and the details of the connection between the control-stick arm and aileron cable pulley are shown in sketch C. If, in flight, the ship tends to lean to one side or the other or requires continuous pressure on the control stick to one side or the other in order to keep it level, the left aileron trim tab is adjusted by means of the knob on the instrument panel. The rudder pedals are connected to the rudder in the manner shown in Fig. I:7; the same cable that moves the rudder also steers the tail wheel. Note that the rudder trim-tab control is on the floor of the cockpit. Detail *B* shows the provision for locking the tail

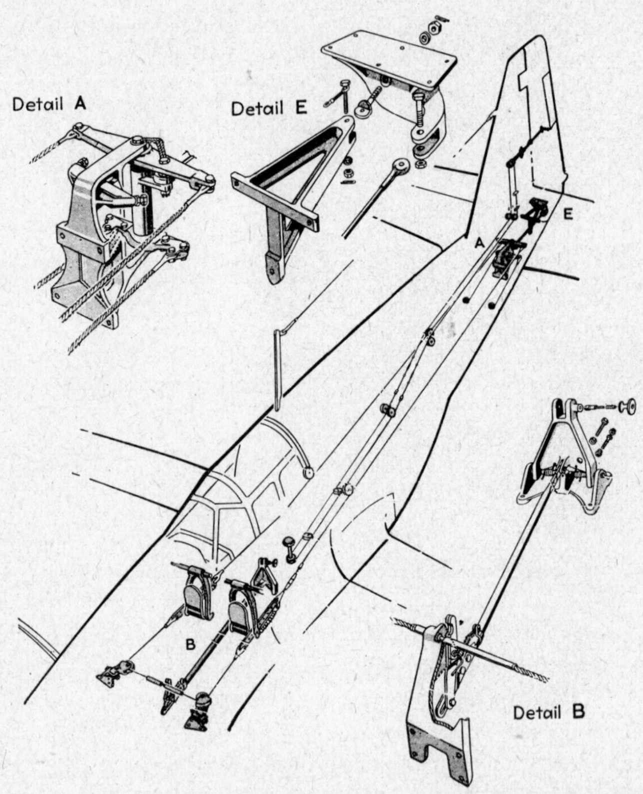

Fig. I:7.—Connections between rudder pedals and rudder and rear wheel of P-51 Mustang. (*Courtesy Aviation, July,* 1944.)

wheel into a fixed fore-and-aft position to avoid ground looping (uncontrollable changes in direction on the ground after landing). The connection of the control stick to the elevators, which is similar to the connection to the ailerons, is not shown in the sketches. Wing flaps for the purpose of increasing the lift and drag of the wing during landing are commonly controlled electrically or hydraulically by means of a small lever on the instrument panel, where there is also a flap-position indicator that shows whether the flaps are up or down.

Instruments commonly used on light airplanes are shown in Fig. I:7.2; additional instruments used on larger airplanes are shown in Fig. I:7.3. The instrument panel is necessarily more elaborate than that of an automobile because the airplane will do so many more things

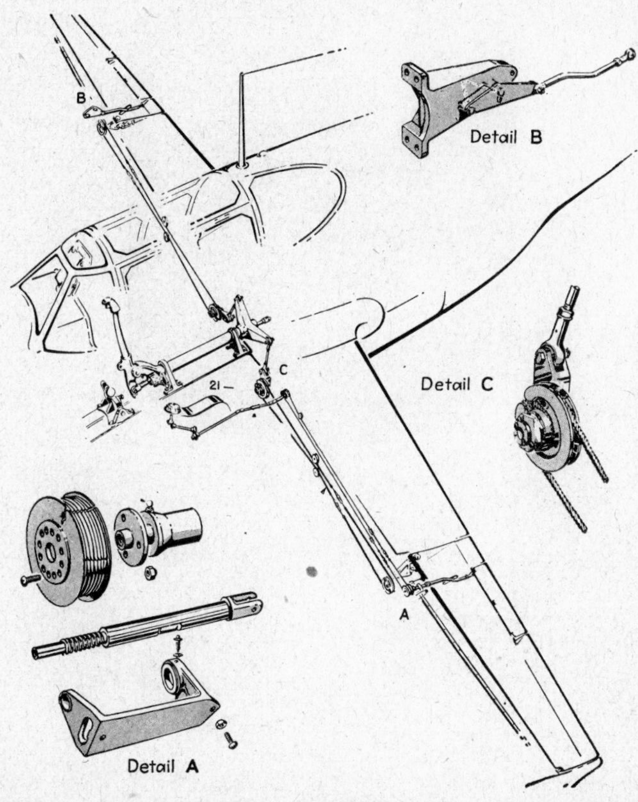

FIG. I:7.1.—Connections between control-stick ailerons. Aileron- and trim-tab controls. Detail *A* shows operating mechanism of left-hand tab, controlled from cockpit by turning knob. Travel of cables is restricted by stops, and adjustments are made by means of turnbuckles. *B* is detail of right aileron-tab adjustment set on ground and shows method of attaching and actuating aileron cables by link from stick attachment.

than an automobile. The engine instruments are those of an automobile plus additional instruments for a supercharger, if any (there is usually a supercharger). In place of the speedometer of the automobile there must be two instruments, one to show engine speed and the other to show airplane speed since the airplane engine is not "geared to the road" as the automobile engine is. The essential elements of a *centrifugal tachometer* for measuring engine rpm are shown in Fig. I:7.2*e*. Centrifugal force on the weights *W* compresses the spring, and the position of the hand on the dial is the measure of the amount of compression on the spring and hence of the rpm of the

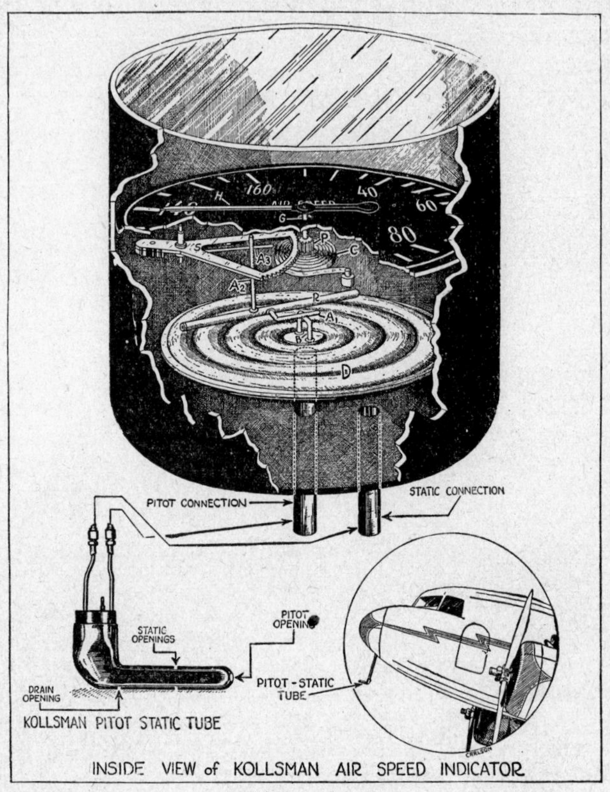

a. Air-speed meter.

Fig. I:7.2.—Instrument panel for light airplanes, with sketches of the mechanism of the principal instruments.

engine. Other types of tachometers use the magnetic drag on an aluminum disk as the actuating force that balances a spring. Others are essentially voltmeters driven by generators and calibrated in rpm. Others (chronometric) are combinations of a clock, a revolution counter, and an adding machine; this last type is used for maximum accuracy. The essential elements of an *air-speed meter* are shown in Fig. I:7.2*a*. The external elements are a pitot and static tube. The air blowing on the front of the open tube builds up an impact pressure that actuates a diaphragm and mechanism that is virtually a very sensitive pressure gauge. This pressure gauge is calibrated in terms of sea-level air velocity. The pressure on the front of the tube depends on the density as well as the velocity of the air, and since the density is considerably less at high altitudes, this type of instrument cannot read true air speed; its reading is called "indicated air speed."

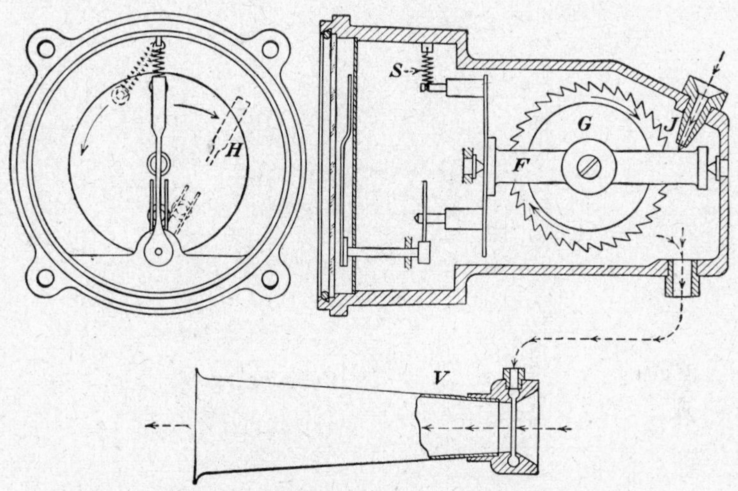

b. Gyroscopic bank and turn indicator.

c. Instrument panel.

Fig. I:7.2.—*Continued.*

The airplane has an additional dimension of travel beyond that of the automobile (the vertical dimension); it must therefore be equipped with an altimeter and preferably also with a *rate-of-climb* indicator. The mechanism of these instruments is shown in Fig. I:7.2*h* and *d*, respectively. The altimeter is essentially an aneroid barometer using a metallic diaphragm capsule element to measure changes in the pressure of the outside air. The rate-of-climb indicator is essentially

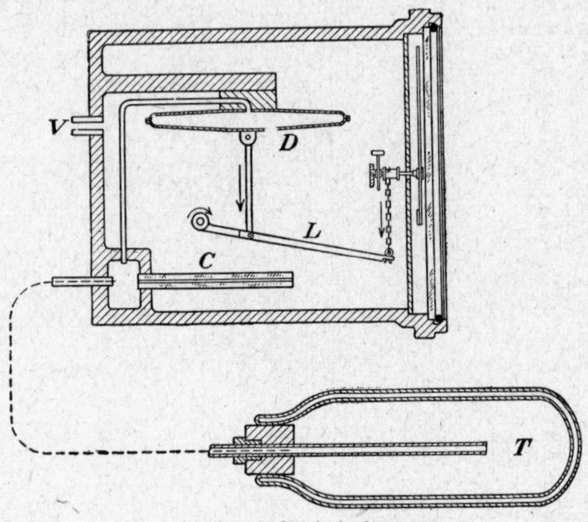

d. Rate-of-climb indicator.

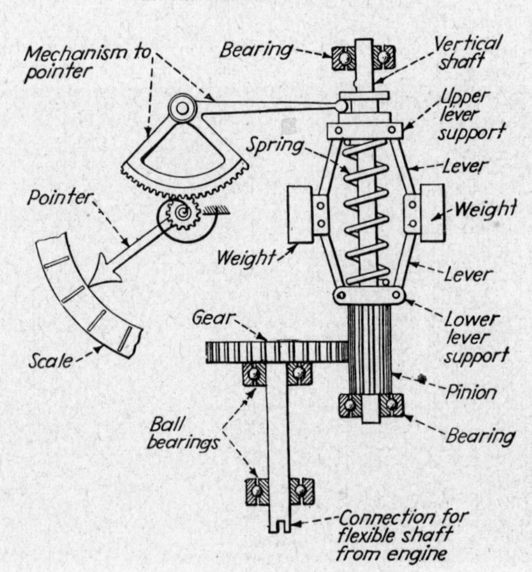

e. Centrifugal tachometer.

FIG. I:7.2.—*Continued.*

a punctured altimeter with a very small (capillary) leak; the greater the rate at which the pressure changes, the faster will be the pressure drop across the leak tube. This pressure drop is transferred to a dial reading that is calibrated in rate of climb or descent in feet per minute.

Since the airplane is not confined to roads as the automobile is, the pilot needs a compass to tell him in which direction he is heading. On light airplanes, a simple magnetic compass is provided; but since this type of instrument oscillates wildly in turns or rough air, it is of

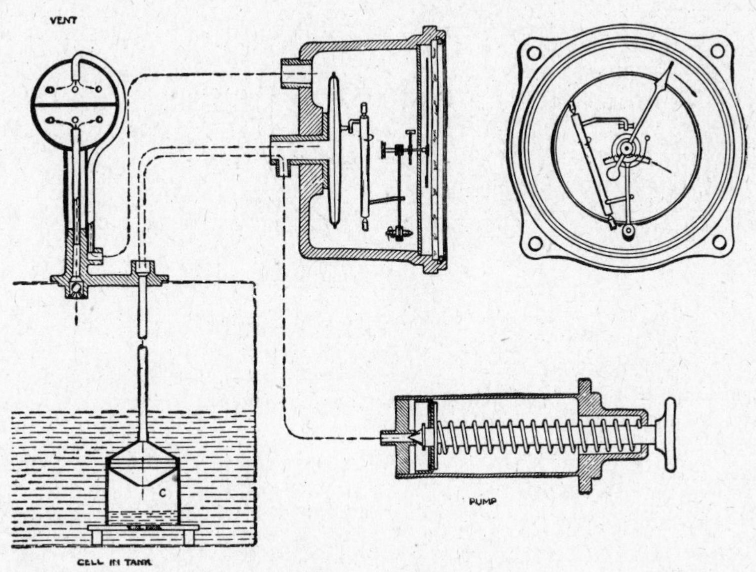

f. Fuel-level gauge.
FIG. I:7.2.—*Continued.*

little use by itself and must be supplemented with a turn indicator actuated by a gyroscope, the gyroscope being driven by an air jet provided by the intake manifold vacuum. The turn indicator is usually combined with a pendulum or spirit-level type of bank indicator into a single instrument, as shown in Fig. I:7.2*b*; this arrangement is known as a "bank and turn indicator."

The foregoing instruments are not suitable for flying through fog and clouds, although they are all that are usually provided on a small airplane intended primarily for fair-weather use and "contact" flight when the ground is visible at nearly all times. For any appreciable amount of blind flying additional instruments must be provided. On civilian airplanes in times of peace, various radio devices are the principal aid to blind flying. With suitable radio devices men can fly airplanes when birds have to walk. The subject of radio aids to navigation is too extensive to be undertaken at this point, but some of the newer nonradio aids to blind flying are described below.

To keep the airplane headed in the right direction a new type of

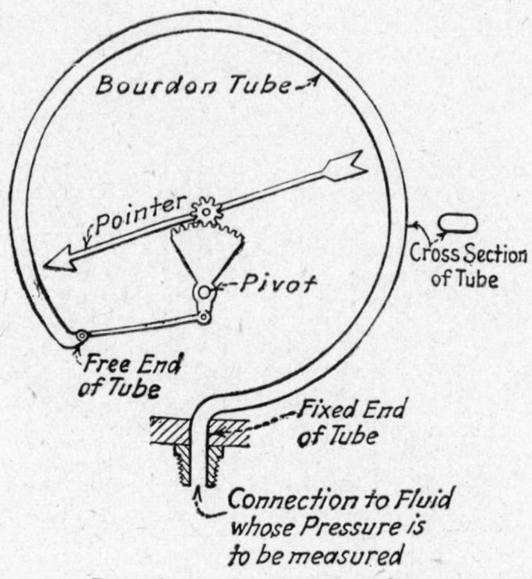

g. Bourdon-tube pressure element.

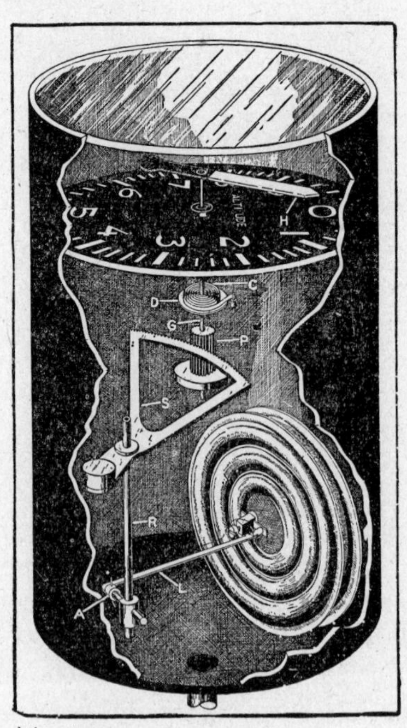

h. Sensitive altimeter.

Fig. I:7.2.—*Continued.*

electric gyroscopic compass has been developed, known as the "gyrosyn" and shown in Fig. I:7.3*c*. This compass, combined with a gyro horizon (Fig. I:7.3*b*), which is essentially a gyroscopic bank and pitch

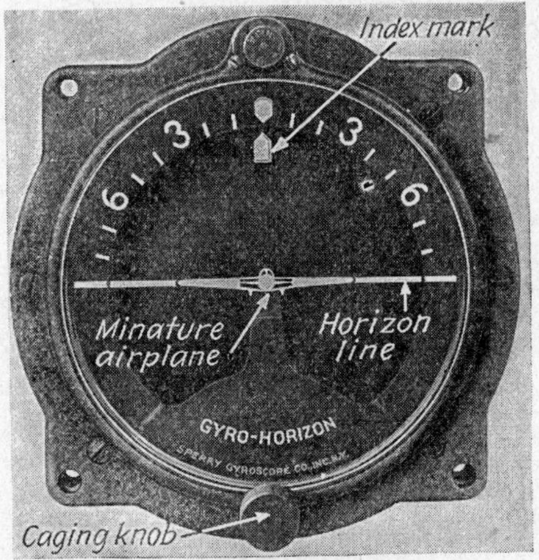

a. Dial of gyro horizon.

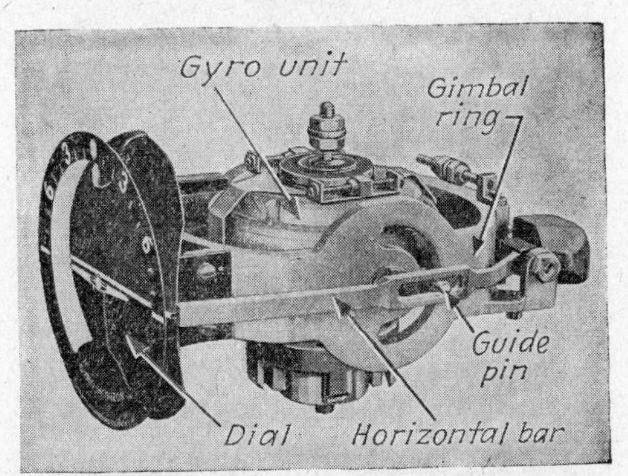

b. Electric gyro horizon. (*Courtesy Sperry Gyroscope Co.*)
FIG. I:7.3.—Instruments used on larger airplanes.

indicator, permits the pilot to orient himself properly with respect to motion about all three axes.

To relieve the pilot of the task of correcting his air-speed-meter reading for air density, which depends on pressure and temperature, a new type of air-speed meter known as a *true air-speed meter*, incorporating barometric pressure and air temperature as well as air-impact-pressure elements, has been developed.

Once an accurate true air-speed meter and an accurate and sensitive compass had been developed, it was possible to combine these two instruments with a calculating machine that would show how far and in what direction the pilot had traveled relative to the air. Such an instrument is the *air-position indicator*, shown in Fig. I:7.3*d*. Note

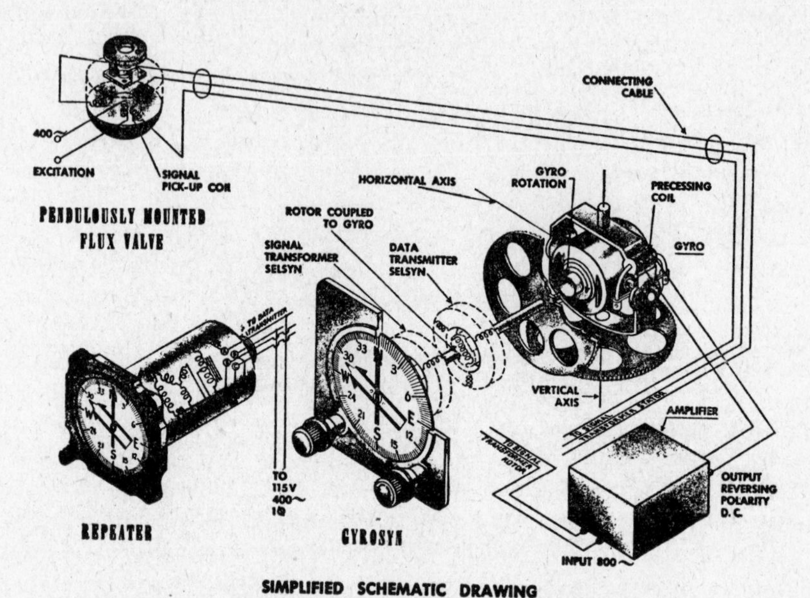

c. Electric gyroscopic compass. (*Courtesy Sperry Gyroscope Co.*)

d. Air-position indicator. A combination of air-speed meter, electric compass, and calculating machine that records changes in latitude and longitude, neglecting drift due to wind. One of the newest aids to navigation in 1945; used on B-29 bombers for Pacific Ocean missions. (*Courtesy Aero Digest.*)

FIG. I:7.3.—*Continued.*

that it reads in *latitude* and *longitude*. If, at the start of a trip, the pilot sets the dials at the known latitude and longitude of the starting point, this instrument reads continuously the latitude and longitude of his new location as well as the distance traveled relative to the air. If the air velocity and direction are known, as they can be either from radio information or by sighting on the ground (by *drift meter*), the pilot can calculate accurately his geographical position at all times with a minimum of labor.

Flying an airplane in the air does not require exceptional skill. Most people who have driven automobiles can fly an airplane the first time they go up, with only a few minutes' instruction. In most airplanes, however, considerable practice is required with a competent instructor before the student feels safe in landing the airplane by himself. If the rudder pedals are eliminated and certain other hazards removed in the design of the airplane (such as "spinning," to be described later), the average person of sound mind and body is usually permitted to fly alone (solo) after four or five hours' dual instruction, chiefly practice in landings and take-offs. The technique of landing an airplane is simple to describe, although difficult to achieve in practice. To land, it is simply necessary to head into the wind, close the throttle of the engine, point the nose slightly downward in a steady glide at a speed 20 or 30 per cent above the minimum speed, and bring the airplane in on a flight path tangent to the ground with the wheels a foot or two above the ground. If then the pilot tries to keep from landing, the airplane will land itself.

I:5. Construction of Principal Parts of Airplanes.—While this text is concerned, not primarily with airplane structures as such but chiefly with the aerodynamics of flight of airplanes, the proper place of aerodynamics as a contribution to the function of the complete vehicle must not be overlooked. The aerodynamics of airplane flight is important only if the airplane is structurally adequate. Hence, some idea of the structural problems is necessary to understanding the compromises that the aerodynamicist has to accept. It is therefore appropriate at this time to make note of the principal materials and types of construction and the way in which the parts of an airplane are put together.

The principal structural materials used in airplanes are wood, steel, and aluminum alloys. Wood was almost abandoned for many years except for very light and cheap airplanes, for adequate means had not been found to prevent deterioration due to moisture absorption. Recent developments in plastic impregnation and protection of woods have made them more desirable than metals for many installations. The three materials, wood, steel, and dural, have about the same ratio of strength to weight, although, in members that carry compression loads only, wood is usually stronger per pound than any metal. There has been considerable improvement in both steel and aluminum alloys in recent years, and they are in close competition for use in aircraft, with aluminum alloys at present preferred. Magnesium is also fairly widely used in castings and weighs only two-thirds as much as aluminum. Beryllium may also have aircraft applications of importance, for it is considerably lighter than magnesium, but most beryllium alloys thus far tried have turned out to be as brittle as glass. Though spun glass, in fine strands and impregnated with a suitable plastic, has been found a very advantageous structural material for some aircraft applications, it is possible that spun beryllium or some new plastic as yet undiscovered may eventually come to dominate the field.

Various types of wing construction are shown in Figs. I:8 and I:9. A wing consists primarily of structural members to take the load and a smooth surface of the proper shape to give maximum lift and minimum drag. Structural members that run lengthwise, or spanwise, of the wing are known as *spars* or *spar members*. The fore-and-aft, or chordwise members are known as *ribs*. Figure I:8*a* is a very efficient wing in which the principal structural element is a corrugated-dural box spar. Figure I:8*b* shows the wing construction of the Ercoupe airplane sketched in Fig. I:3. This wing, unlike most other wings, has no chordwise members but uses diagonal ribs to get exceptional resistance to twisting and carries most of the bending loads in a single main spar. Wing structures of the Mustang and Lightning Army fighter airplanes are sketched in Fig. I:9. The Mustang wing is essentially a two-spar conventional wing with pressed-dural ribs. In the Lightning wing most of the bending strength is in the corrugated-dural box spar in the rear portion of the wing, the leading edge being used for a fuel tank and taking little bending load.

Typical metal tail-surface construction is shown in Fig. I:9.1. The fixed surfaces (fin and stabilizer) are usually covered with sheet metal in the interests of rigidity. The movable surfaces (rudder, elevator, and ailerons) are usually made of a very light framework covered with doped fabric; this construction makes it possible to have the center of gravity very close to the hinge line with a minimum of weight, and this center-of-gravity location is desirable to avoid vibration and flutter trouble. Wing flaps, however, are usually moved by an irreversible mechanism and are not required to move rapidly and are therefore usually covered with sheet metal.

Figure I:10 shows details of the Mustang fuselage, which is a combination of dural extrusions and dural sheet.

The wheels of an airplane landing gear are like automobile wheels,

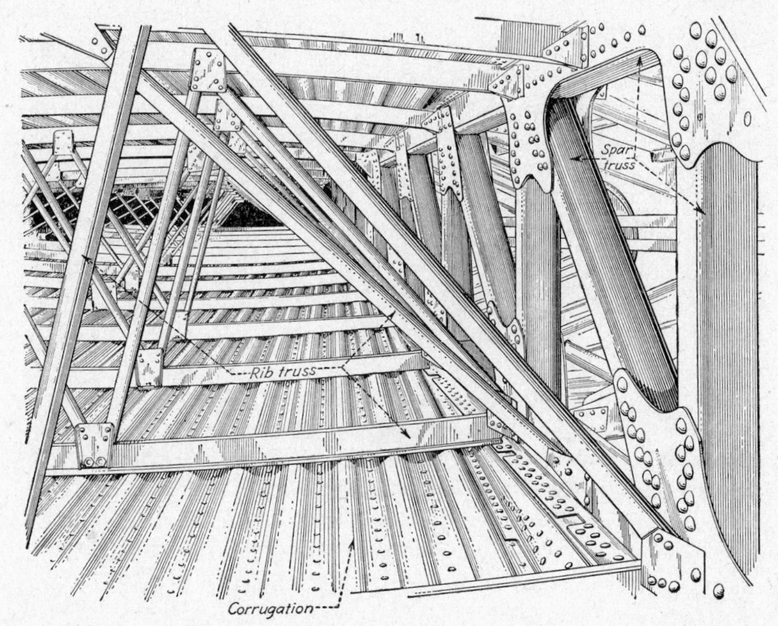

a. Corrugated dural wing structure. (*Photograph from Trans. A.S.M.E.*)

b. Wing structure of Ercoupe. Monospar wing is braced torsionally by diagonal bulkheads. Ribs are omitted. (*Sketch from Aviation, November*, 1940.) Wing weight 1 lb per sq ft; wing loading 7.8 lb per sq ft, span 30 ft. Thickness ratio −13 per cent.

Fig. I:8.—Wing construction.

only lighter, and with longer spring travel and shock absorbers. Figure I:11 shows the landing gear of the Ercoupe, which is not retractable. The nose wheel is a more difficult design problem than the main wheel, for it must be steerable and must have a long oleo (oil shock-absorber strut) travel. The lightest mechanism to meet this requirement has usually been found to involve concentric cylin-

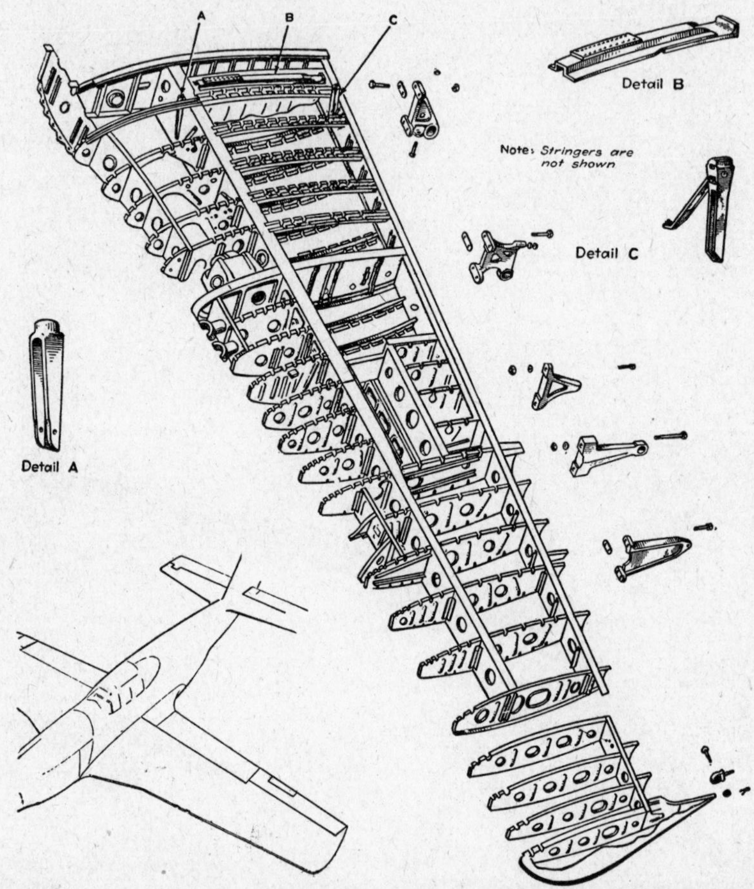

a. Mustang two-spar wing. Wing panels built up on 19 pressed ribs and two spars of 24ST Alclad. Insert shows proportion of wing surface taken up by flap and aileron. Wing tip has single spar and pressed end. Details are forgings. Detail *A* is front spar-to-fuselage connecting bracket; *B* is pilot's footrest and seat bracket; *C* is rear spar-to-fuselage connecting bracket. Others are aileron and flap hinge brackets.

Fig. I:9.—Types of wing construction.

drical tubes with a "nutcracker," or "scissors," device for making the wheel turn with the shaft, as in the Ercoupe or remain fixed with the shaft, as in the Mustang main landing gear shown in Fig. I:11*d*. Retracting the wheels, as in the Mustang, adds weight and expense but enormously reduces the drag.

Various types of aircraft engines are shown in Fig. I:12. For small airplanes, the four- or six-cylinder opposed type of engine and the five- or seven-cylinder radial type of engine, as shown in Fig.

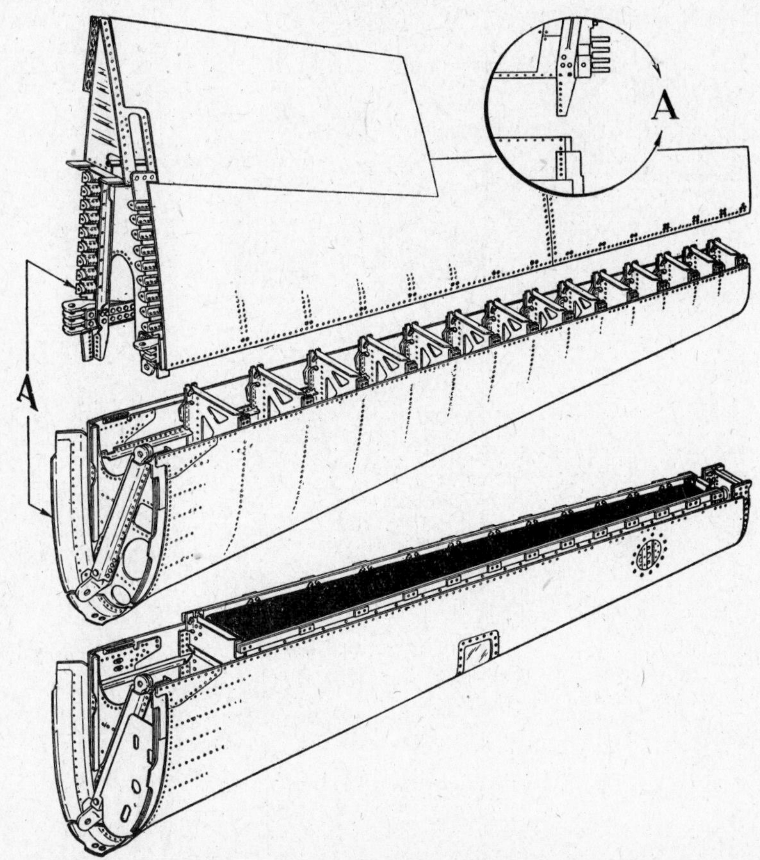

b. Wing construction of Lockheed Lightning. Alternate leading edge incorporating fuel tank below. Leading edge of wing, housing intercoolers in earlier models of P-38, now carries fuel cell (black in lower view), has no ribs, and is made up of formed inner skin and shallow chordwise 24ST corrugations.

FIG. I:9.—*Continued.*

I:12*b* and *e*, are in common use. In sizes over 1,000 hp, shown in Fig. I:12*a* and *c*, both liquid-cooled and air-cooled types are used. Practically all engines over 1,000 hp and many smaller ones incorporate a reduction gear in the nose of the engine, so that the propeller shaft runs at a considerably slower speed than the crankshaft of the engine. This has been found necessary to get both an efficient engine and an efficient propeller.

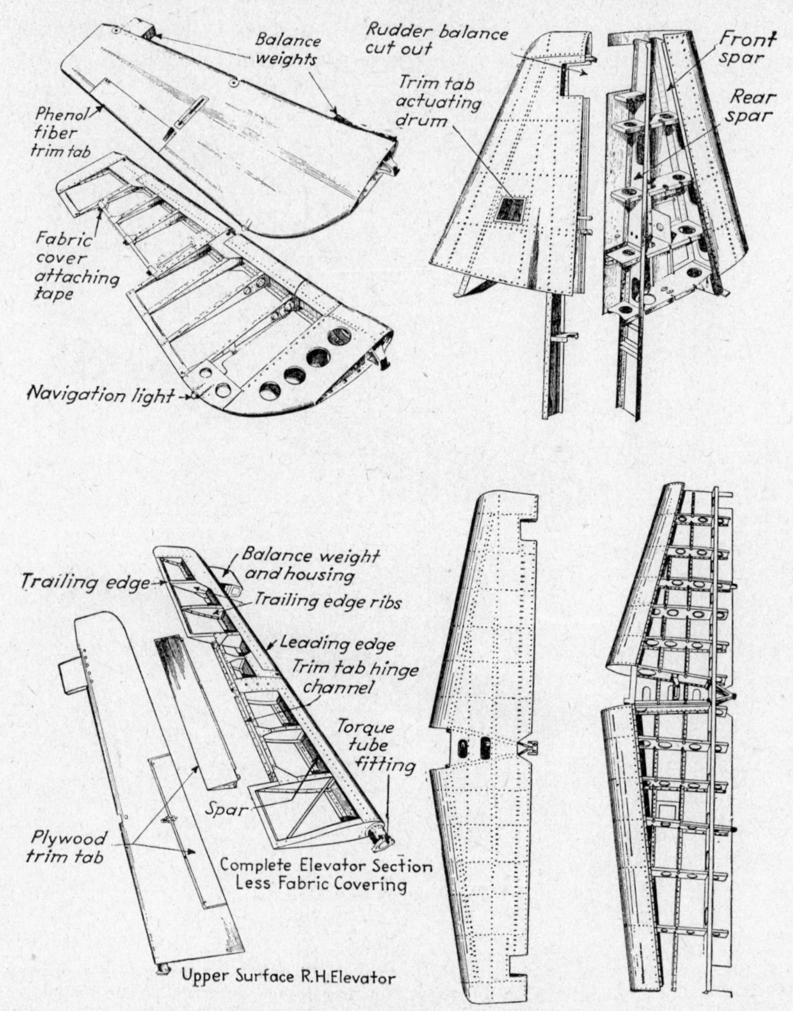

FIG. I:9.1.—Tail-surface construction of Mustang airplane.

Upper left: Rudder is fabric-covered 24ST leading edge under fabric. Plastic tab is carried on three hinges. Rudder-operating horn is a forging (shown at bottom of rudder, both views). Upper right: Two views of fin. This is built of 24ST with rolled stringers and is covered with Alclad sheet.

Lower left: Elevator is built of 24ST frame with fabric covering. Leading edge is 24ST under fabric. Trim tab, made of plywood, is operated by horn near center. Balance weights are concealed in stabilizer. Elevator control is through three-bolt coupling of inside end. Lower right: Stabilizer is full cantilever type with Alclad frame and covering. Half-hard 52S is used for the tips built on two ribs.

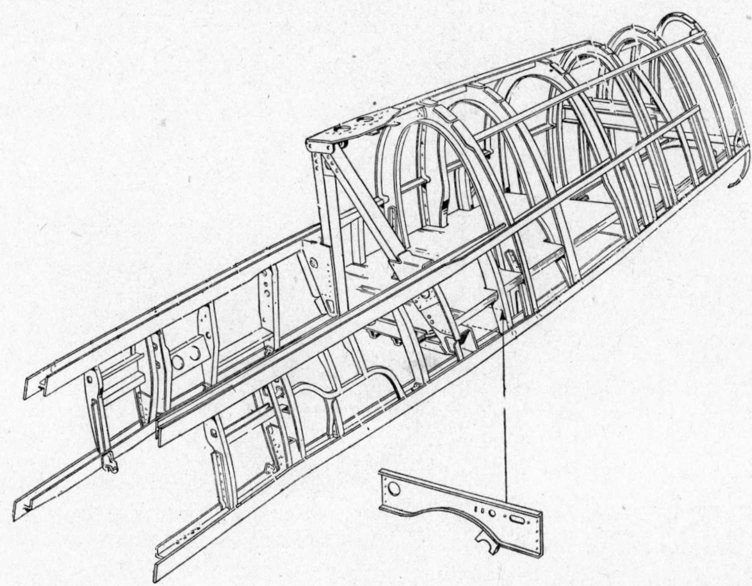

a. Main fuselage is built on four extruded 24ST longerons with heavy frames and a few light stringers. Turnover truss is built of 24ST extrustions and sheet for pilot protection. Web assembly is shown on bottom.

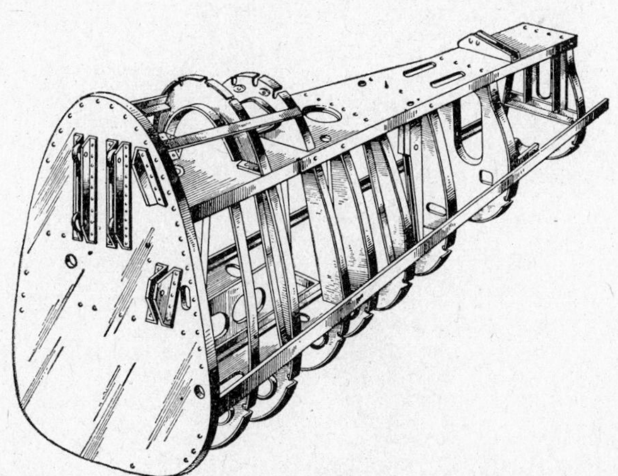

b. Fuselage rear frame, with diagram giving positions of elevator- and rudder-control frames and fin-attachment forging.

FIG. I:10.—Mustang fuselage construction of extruded dural longerons and bulkheads.

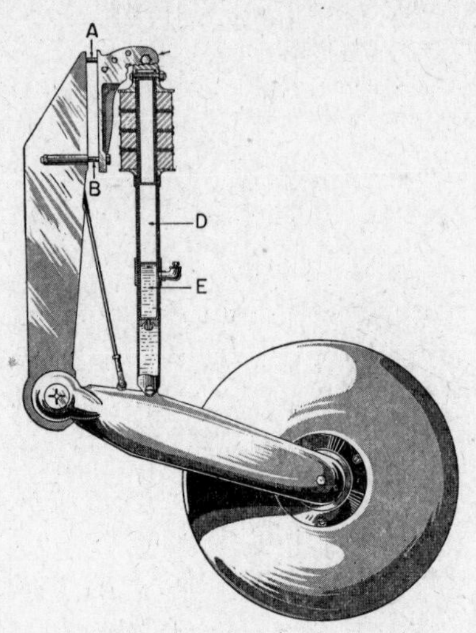

a. Main wheels of Ercoupe tricycle landing-gear units attach to front spar by bolts *A* and *B*, with oleo support *C* aft of the beam. Air chamber of shock strut is at *D*; fluid is at *E*.

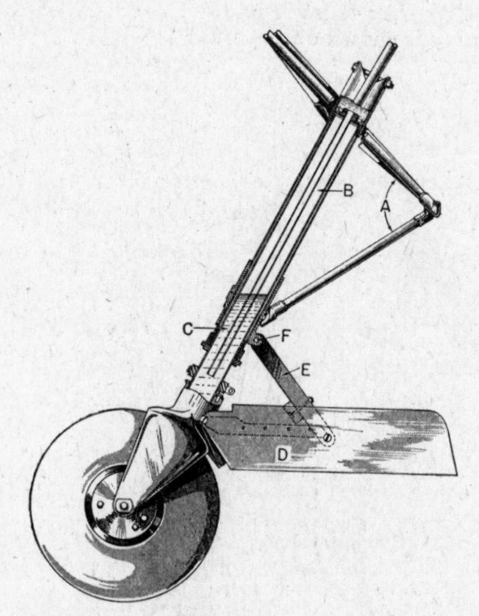

b. Phantom view of Ercoupe nose-wheel installation. Engine-mount members are at *A*; air chamber at *B*; fluid at *C*; fairing *D* dropped to horizontal position to reveal torque scissor *E*, connection *F*.

FIG. I:11.—Landing-gear details of Ercoupe (*a*) and (*b*), Lightning (*c*), and Mustang (*d*).

For small airplanes, a small, inexpensive, two-blade wooden propeller with the blades at a fixed angle (or pitch) is usually considered satisfactory. A two-blade propeller moving in the direction of its axis of rotation is symmetrical in respect to the wind; but if it has any component of upward or sidewise velocity, it presents a different aspect to the wind in the horizontal and vertical positions and is therefore

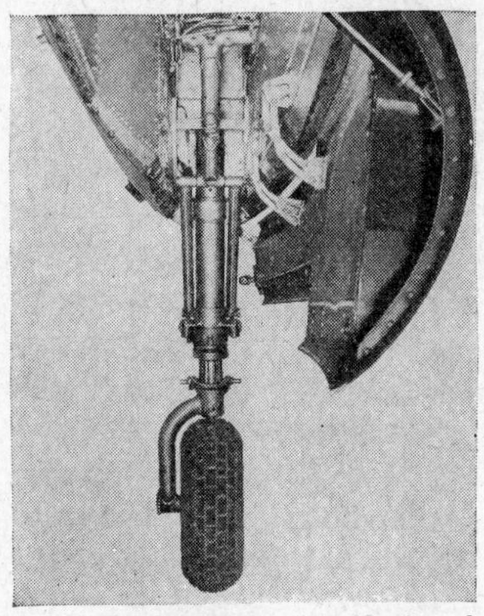

c. Retractable nose wheel, viewed from aft of well under fuselage showing heavy, built-up construction of fairing door, built to withstand speeds and hard field service.

d. Left standing wheel of Mustang. (1) Shock strut; (2) fairing; (3) wheel with dust cap; (4) 27-in. tire.

FIG. I:11.—*Continued.*

subject to force variations and bad vibrations, so that three or more blades are necessary for satisfactory operation of large propellers. Typical propellers are shown in Fig. I:13, which also shows details of the mechanisms for hydraulic and electric control of the blade angles as well as a sectional view of the Curtiss electric pitch-control mechanism.

All the foregoing items are means to an end, which is that the airplane should serve its designed function. In the case of commercial airplanes the function is to carry persons and goods; thus, the *seats* and *cargo space* represent the reason for building the airplane. In the case of military airplanes the reason for building the airplane is to carry *armament.* Typical armament installations are shown in Fig. I:14. Current military airplanes are equipped chiefly with machine guns, cannon, bombs, and rocket launchers. Rocket launchers have thus far always been external to the airplane. Bombs may be carried either externally, or internally, in a *bomb bay* with doors that can be

a. Packard-built 12-cylinder liquid-cooled Rolls-Royce Merlin 1,500-hp engine used in the P-51 Mustang.

b. Continental four-cylinder opposed engine for light airplanes. This type is used in the range from 65 to 125 hp.

FIG. I:12.—Types of engines. For technical data, see Table B.

opened before dropping the bombs. Machine guns of fighter airplanes are usually fixed relative to the airplane, and the guns are sighted by heading the airplane in the desired direction, having the sights fixed

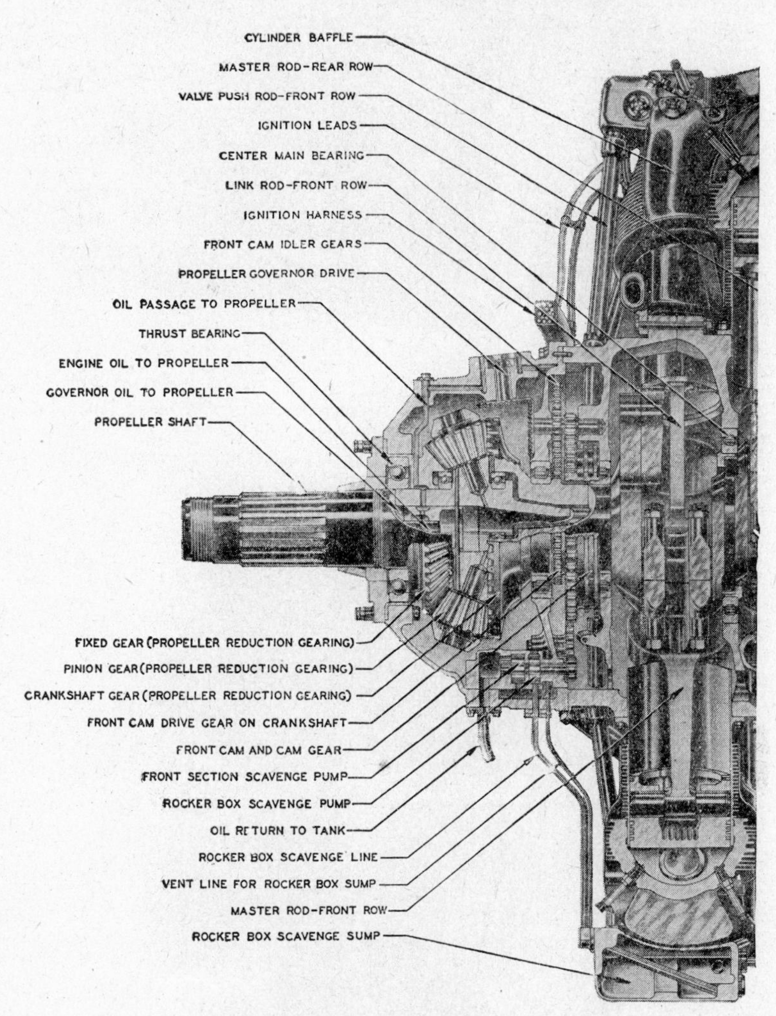

c. Longitudinal section through radial engine.
FIG. I:12.—*Continued.*

on the fuselage. Fighter airplanes equipped with cannon, like the Bell Kingcobra (Fig. I:4*b*), sight the cannon in the same way. Larger bombers are usually equipped with flexibly mounted guns; some are sighted with the mechanism shown in Fig. I:14*a* and *b*.

Ranger 12-cylinder inverted V-type air-cooled engine. Newest (1945) models develop 700 hp and weigh 780 lb.

e. Warner seven-cylinder radial engine.

FIG. I:12.—*Continued.*

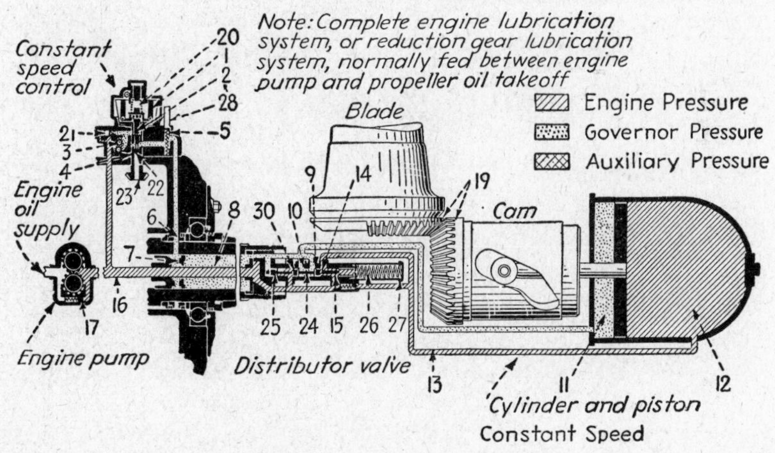

a. Hamilton standard three-blade propeller and sketch of hydraulic pitch-control mechanism.

Fig. I:13.—Types of propellers.

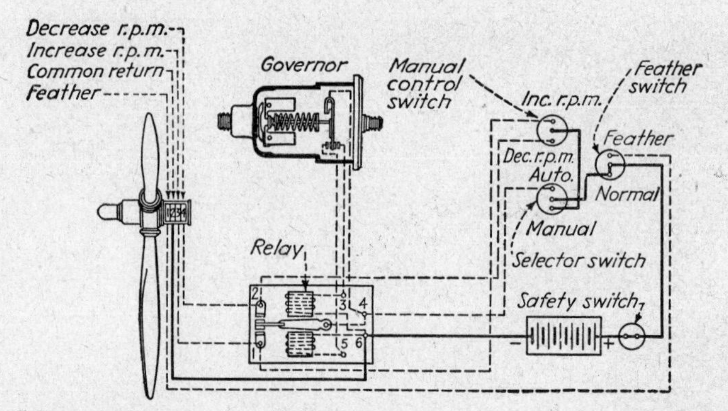

b. Schematic diagram of typical control system of Curtiss electric propeller.

c. Aeromatic eight-blade contrarotating propeller.

FIG. I:13.—*Continued.*

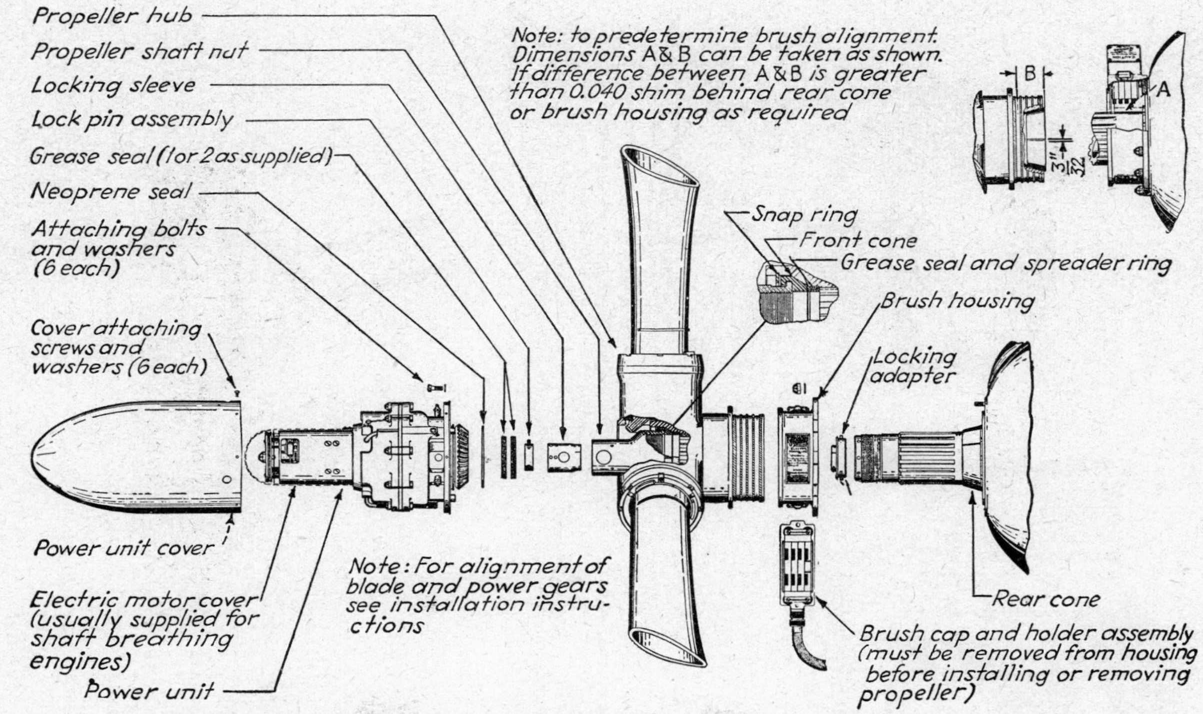

d. Sectional view showing control mechanism of Curtiss-Wright electric variable-pitch propeller. Electric motor controls pitch of blades through planetary spur gears and bevel gears. (*Courtesy Aero Digest.*)

FIG. I:13.—*Continued.*

a. Basic units of central electric gunnery-control system used in B-29. Gunner, occupying seat *A*, sights through unit *B* and, when ready, presses triggers on grips *C*. Electric impulses are carried through cables *D* to unit shown in center (but which can be located anywhere in airplane), which compensates for speed, distance, gravity, and parallax to operate through cables to turret shown at right.

b. Exterior view of upper portion of Boeing B-29 Superfortress showing gun-sight station and remote-controlled gun turret with twin 50-caliber machine guns. The gunner can fire, not only this turret, but two others, guns of which will be aimed at same target.

FIG. I:14.—Armament installations. (*Courtesy Aviation.*)

I:6. Review Questions and Problems

1. Into what major classes may aircraft be divided?

2. What are the principal external parts of an airplane?

3. Name the three axes of the airplane, the word that describes the rotation about each axis, and the control surface that controls the rotation about each axis.

4. Is an airplane steered like a bobsled?

5. What control-stick movements are used for banking and pitching?

6. Why does an airplane need both a tachometer and an air-speed meter?

7. What is the essential difference between an autogyro and a helicopter?

8. State the essential difference between a seaplane, a flying boat, and an amphibian.

9. What does a tachometer measure, and how does it work?

10. State the fundamental principle of an air-speed indicator.

11. When the altimeter reads 10,000 ft, does the air-speed indicator indicate greater or less than when the altimeter reads 5,000 ft, if the true air speed and temperature are the same in both cases?

12. What are the principal elements of an altimeter?

13. If a wing was properly banked for a turn, would a plumb bob in the cockpit point vertically toward the ground?

14. Why might a pilot wish to know the temperature of the air through which he is flying?

15. State the basic principle of operation of the gyrosyn compass, the true-air-speed meter, and the air-position indicator.

16. An airplane wing has a span of 35 ft and an area of 180 sq ft. What is its aspect ratio? What is its mean chord?

17. An airplane weighs 1,400 lb, has a wing area of 180 sq ft, and is powered by an engine of 130 lbs. Calculate the wing loading and power loading.

18. The airplane in Probs. 16 and 17 has an effective minimum drag coefficient of 0.040. Calculate the equivalent flat-plate area.

19. Name the principal structural members of a wing.

20. Explain why the fixed tail surfaces of an airplane are usually covered with sheet metal, whereas the movable tail surfaces are covered with fabric.

I:7. Suggested Additional Reading.—Elementary treatments like the foregoing, but considerably more comprehensive, may be found in the following books. Study of these books is recommended if the foregoing treatment is found excessively condensed. Additional bibliography is given in these references.

1. SEARS, W. R.: "The Airplane and Its Components."
2. POPE, FRANCIS, and ARTHUR S. OTIS: "Elements of Aeronautics."

CHAPTER 1

MECHANICS AND THERMODYNAMICS OF AIR

This chapter outlines briefly the fundamental principles of fluid mechanics and thermodynamics that are most important in the study of air and the aerodynamics of aircraft. Even though the student may have taken courses in fluid mechanics and thermodynamics, he may well review this chapter, for it collects the most important applications in a single brief treatment that serves as a reference guide to later parts of the book.

1:1. Fluids: Liquids and Gases.—Figure 1:1 shows a portion of material subjected to shear forces. If the material deforms con-

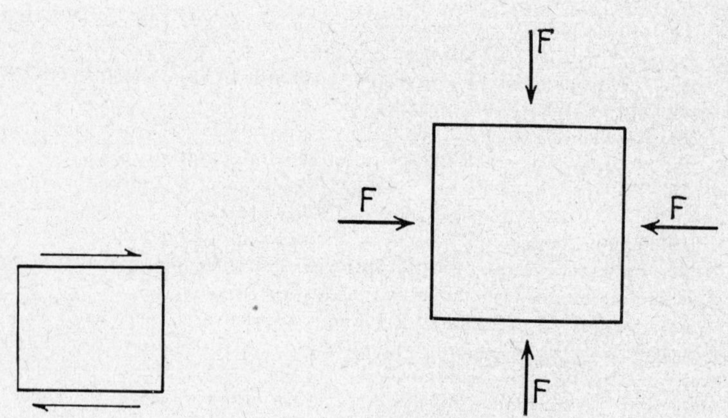

FIG. 1:1.—Material subjected to shear forces.

FIG. 1:2.—Material subjected to compressive forces.

tinuously when subjected to such forces, no matter how small, it is called a *fluid*. If it does not, it is called a *solid*.

If a fluid can be kept in a vessel and have a free surface, it is called a *liquid*, like water or gasoline. If it completely fills any closed container in which it is placed, it is called a *gas* or *vapor*, like air or steam.

A material of a given chemical composition may exist as a solid, a liquid, or a vapor, depending on the pressure and temperature. Figure 1:2 represents a portion of material subject to compressive forces. The compressive force F per unit surface S is known as the *pressure*, is designated in this text by P, and is measured in pounds per square foot unless otherwise specified (for conversion factors to other units, see page 378, Table VI in Appendix 1). Thus

$$P = \frac{F}{S} \tag{1:1}$$

All bodies at the surface of the earth are subjected to a pressure due to the weight of the atmosphere which is called atmospheric pressure, the average, or standard, pressure at sea level being 2,116 lb per sq ft. A mechanism for measuring pressure is known as a *pressure gauge*. The working elements of one type of pressure gauge are shown in Fig. I:7.2*g*. As the pressure in the pipe connected to the gauge is changed, the bent tube deforms and moves the pointer, which points to a number on a graduated dial. Pressure so measured is known as *gauge pressure*, designated by P_g. The absolute pressure P is the gauge pressure plus the atmospheric pressure P_a, or

$$P = P_a + P_g \tag{1:2}$$

At standard atmospheric pressure, the condition that determines whether a material of a given chemical composition will be solid, liquid, or gas is known as the *temperature*. When ice begins to change to water, or vice versa, the temperature is said to be 0° centigrade (C); when water begins to change to steam, the temperature is said to be 100°C. These temperatures are known, respectively, as the freezing and boiling points of water. For most engineering work these temperatures are measured on the Fahrenheit scale, so defined that 0°C = 32°F and 100°C = 212°F. Equations for conversion from one scale to the other are given in Appendix 1, Table XI. In molecular theory, it is considered that temperature is a measure of molecular kinetic energy. The condition for zero molecular kinetic energy is considered to be an *absolute zero* of temperature, and absolute zero has thus been located at −459.6°F or −273°C. Temperatures measured above absolute zero are known as *absolute temperatures*. In this text absolute Fahrenheit temperatures will be designated by T. If t = Fahrenheit temperature,

$$T = t + 459.6 \approx t + 460 \tag{1:3}$$

Boiling and freezing points of various substances that are liquids at 68°F (20°C) are given in Appendix 2, Table XIII.

If a vessel of liquid is agitated by stirring, the work done in stirring causes the temperature to rise. If 778 ft-lb of work is thus done on 1 lb of water at 63°F, the temperature will rise to 64°F, and this mechanical energy is said to have been converted to thermal energy. This amount of change of thermal energy is known as 1 *British thermal unit,* designated Btu. More exactly, a Btu may be defined by the statement that 180 Btu is the heat necessary to raise the temperature of 1 lb of pure water from 32° to 212°F. If Δ work is the frictional work done on a body in foot-pounds and ΔQ is the heat added in Btu, then

$$\Delta Q = \frac{\Delta \text{ work}}{778} \tag{1:4}$$

For most liquids other than water, addition of 1 Btu of heat to 1 lb of the liquid will raise the temperature more than 1°F. For a weight of W lb of the liquid, the heat added for a given temperature rise Δt is given by the equation

$$Q = c_p W \Delta t \tag{1:5}$$

where c_p is known as the *specific heat* of the liquid, the subscript p implying that the *pressure* on the liquid is kept constant while the heat is being added and that the volume of the liquid is not prevented from expanding (as most liquids do when heated). If the experiment is run by keeping the volume constant and letting the pressure rise, the specific heat thus measured is known as the *specific heat at constant volume* and is designated by c_v. For gases, both specific heats are of importance.

Specific heats of a few liquids are given on page 381. For example, the mean specific heat of gasoline in the temperature range from 32 to 104°F is there listed as 0.57. This means that 0.57 Btu of heat must be added to 1 lb of gasoline to raise the temperature 1°F. Specific heats (c_p and c_v) of a few common gases are given on page 382; both c_p and c_v vary somewhat with the temperature, but the ratio

$$\frac{c_p}{c_v} = k \tag{1:6}$$

is nearly independent of the temperature and a constant for a particular gas. For oxygen, note that $k = 1.40$.

The weight of a unit volume of a substance is known as its unit weight or *specific weight,* designated by w.

$$w = \frac{\text{weight}}{\text{volume}} \tag{1:7}$$

In engineering work w is usually measured in pounds per cubic foot; conversion factors to other units are given in Appendix 1. Specific weight is sometimes called *density,* but this term is preferably reserved for *mass per unit volume*, where

$$\text{Mass in slugs} = \frac{\text{weight in lb}}{32.2}$$

Mass density, or just *density* (symbol ρ), is usually measured in slugs per cubic foot. Thus

$$\rho = \frac{w}{g} = \frac{\text{mass in slugs}}{\text{volume in cu ft}} \tag{1:8}$$

For many problems involving gases, it is more convenient to deal with the volume of a pound instead of the weight of a cubic foot. The volume of unit weight of the substance is known as the *specific volume*, designated by $\bar{V}$, and usually measured in cubic feet per pound. From equation (1:7),

$$\bar{V} = \frac{1}{w} \tag{1:9}$$

Specific weight, specific volume, and density of fluids depend on the pressure and temperature of the fluid. Specific weights of several liquids and gases at atmospheric pressure and various temperatures are given in Appendix 2.

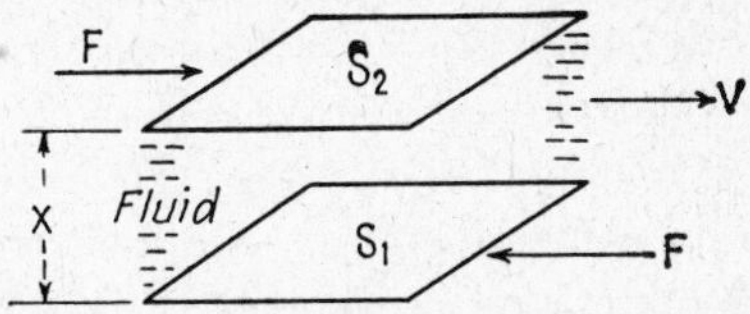

FIG. 1:3.—Sketch used in defining viscosity.

Another physical property of fluids of importance in engineering calculations is the *viscosity*, or resistance to shearing motion. If two flat plates, each of surface S (square feet), are separated by a thickness x of fluid, as shown in Fig. 1:3, and are moved relative to each other at a velocity V (feet per second), then the force F necessary to maintain steady motion is proportional to S and V and inversely proportional to x. The constant of proportionality is known as the *dynamic viscosity* and is designated by μ (mu) in the equation

$$F = \mu \frac{SV}{x} \tag{1:10}$$

In the foot-pound-second engineering system of units, μ has dimensions determined by

$$\mu = \frac{Fx}{SV} = \frac{\text{lb} \times \text{ft}}{\text{sq ft} \times \text{ft/sec}} = \frac{\text{lb-sec}}{\text{sq ft}}$$

In the cgs system, the unit of viscosity is known as the "poise." 1 centipoise = 0.01 poise = 0.01 dyne-sec/sq cm. Unit-conversion factors are given in Appendix 1. Viscosities of common fluids are very small numbers in pound-seconds per square foot; therefore, in

Appendix 2, viscosities are given in pound-seconds per million square feet. For most fluids, viscosity is a function of temperature only and is practically independent of pressure; an exception is furnished by vapors (gases at temperatures near the boiling point), for example, steam, which has considerably higher viscosity at 600 lb per sq in. than at 100 lb per sq in. In Appendix 2, note that the viscosity of water is 37.5 lb-sec per million square feet at 32°F and drops to 5.92 lb-sec per million square feet at 212°F. Note also that the viscosity of gases *increases* with temperature, whereas the viscosity of liquids decreases.

The ratio of *dynamic viscosity* μ to the *density* ρ is known as the "kinematic viscosity" and is designated by ν (nu). Thus

$$\nu = \frac{\mu}{\rho} = \mu \frac{g}{w} = \frac{\text{lb-sec}}{\text{sq ft}} \frac{\text{ft cu ft}}{\text{sec}^2 \text{ lb}} = \frac{\text{sq ft}}{\text{sec}} \tag{1:11}$$

When layers of a fluid slide on each other, as shown in Fig. 1:3, the force F does *work* on the fluid, raises its temperature, and therefore changes its viscosity, so the condition of constant viscosity is the exception rather than the rule in engineering work. The condition of uniform temperature across the distance x is also exceptional. If Δt is the temperature difference between the liquid at the surface S_1 and that at the surface S_2, heat is conducted through the fluid at a rate determined by a characteristic of the fluid known as the "thermal conductivity," designated by k_c, defined by the equation

$$\frac{\Delta Q}{\text{Time}} = k_c \frac{S}{x} \Delta t \tag{1:12}$$

and, in engineering units,

$$k_c = \frac{\Delta Q/\text{hr}}{(S/x)\Delta t} = \frac{\text{Btu/hr}}{(\text{sq ft/ft}) \text{ deg F}} = \frac{\text{Btu}}{\text{hr-ft deg F}}$$

Thermal conductivity of liquids and gases, like viscosity, depends chiefly on temperature and is practically independent of pressure.

The thermal conductivity, viscosity, and specific heat are frequently combined into a single factor known as the Prandtl number, designated Pr, so that

$$Pr = \frac{3{,}600 c_p \mu g}{k_c} \tag{1:13}$$

The factor 3,600 is included to change the time unit in k_c from hours to seconds. The Prandtl number is a dimensionless characteristic of a fluid. For monatomic gases, $Pr \approx 0.67$; for diatomic gases (N_2, O_2, etc.), $Pr \approx 0.70$; for triatomic gases, $Pr \approx 0.89$; for water at 65°F.

$Pr \approx 7.3$. Values of Pr for other liquids can be calculated from equation (1:13) and the data given in Appendix 2.

1:2. Problems

1. The average pressure due to the weight of the atmosphere at sea level is 2,116 lb per sq ft. Using Table VI in Appendix 1, calculate the pressure (*a*) in pounds per square inch, (*b*) in kilograms per square centimeter.

2. A pressure gauge reads 20 lb per sq in. If the atmospheric pressure is 1,800 lb per sq ft, find the absolute pressure.

3. The temperature of 10 lb of gasoline is raised 10°F by means of mechanical work (stirring). Find the number of foot-pounds of work that must be done.

4. Using the data in Appendix 2, find the specific weight and specific volume of turpentine at 32°F and atmospheric pressure.

5. Using the data in Appendix 2, find the specific weight and specific volume of oxygen at 32°F and atmospheric pressure.

6. Using the data in Appendix 2, calculate the kinematic viscosity of water at 32°F.

7. Using the data in Appendix 2, calculate the Prandtl number for air at atmospheric pressure and 32°F.

1:3. Statics of Liquids: Manometers, Barometers.—In a body of any fluid, whether liquid or gas, the relationship between pressure and elevation can be obtained from the free body sketch shown in Fig. 1:4. If the height of the element sketched is any small distance Δz over which the specific weight w can be considered constant, then

$$\Delta P = -w\Delta z \qquad (1:14)$$

the minus sign indicating that the positive z direction is *up* and that the pressure increases as you go *down* in the fluid. For liquids, the specific weight w is usually considered constant for the usual depths involved in engineering equipment (although for great depths, as at the bottom of the ocean, the compressibility of the water must be considered); hence, between any two points $(\ )_1$ and $(\ )_2$ in a liquid, the relation between pressure and depth is

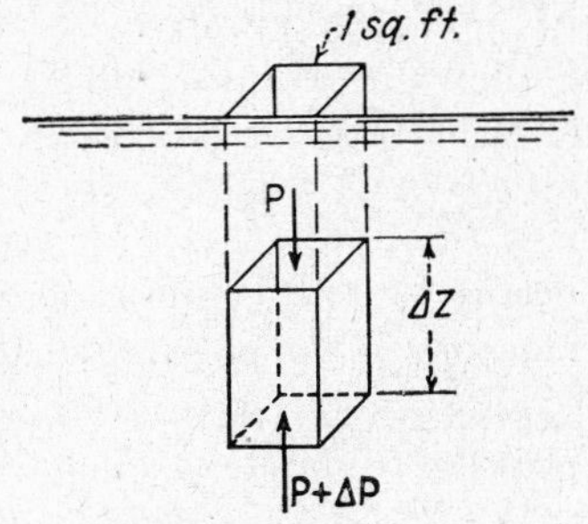

FIG. 1:4.—Free-body sketch of portion of 1-sq-ft column of liquid.

$$P_2 - P_1 = -w(z_2 - z_1) \qquad (1:15)$$

For any given liquid, equation (1:15) states that the increase in pressure is proportional to the increase in depth; the difference in depth is commonly called the *pressure head*. Pressures may thus be expressed not only as force per unit area but also as heights of liquid of known specific weight. Pressures in meters and inches of mercury and in meters, inches, and feet of water at atmospheric pressure and specified temperatures are given on Table VI, Appendix 1, page 378. These conversion factors are based on the specific weights of mercury and water, which appear in Table XIII, Appendix 2, page 381.

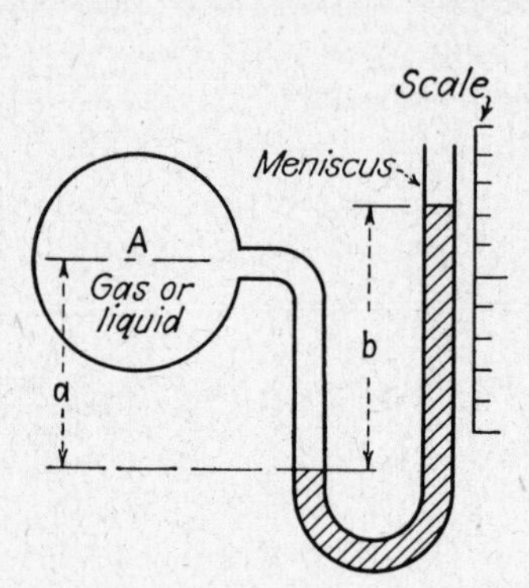

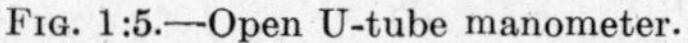

Fig. 1:5.—Open U-tube manometer.

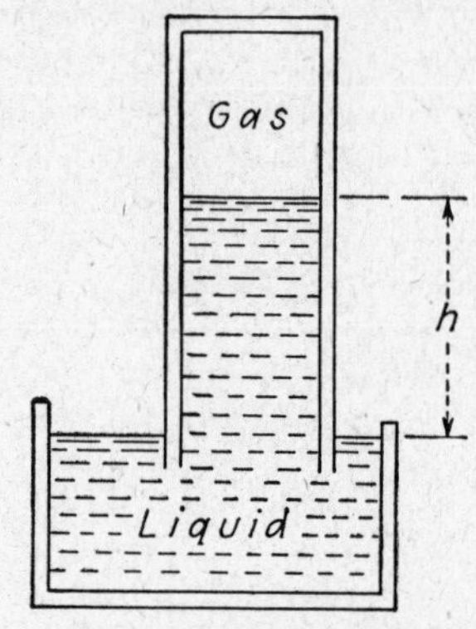

Fig. 1:6.—Straight-tube manometer.

A device in which a column of liquid is used to measure pressure is known as a *manometer* or *piezometer*. One type of manometer is shown in Fig. 1:5 and another type in Fig. 1:6. If a manometer of the type shown in Fig. 1:6 is filled with mercury and the gas above the mercury is only the vapor of mercury at room temperature, the pressure of which is negligible compared with atmospheric pressure, this type of manometer is known as a *barometer* because the height of the column of mercury is the measure of the pressure of the atmosphere.

For more accurate readings of small pressure differences such as are common

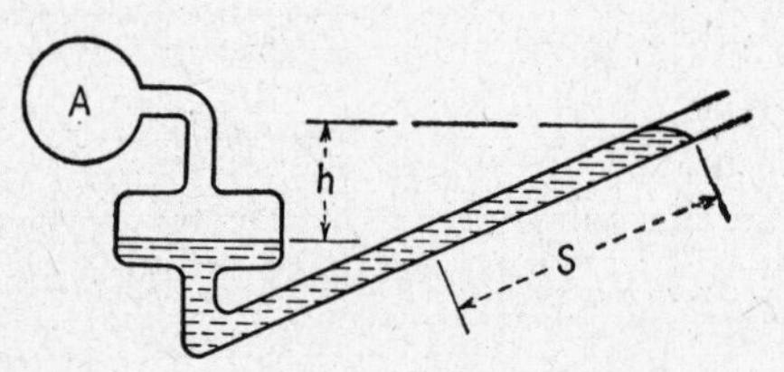

Fig. 1:7.—Inclined-tube manometer.

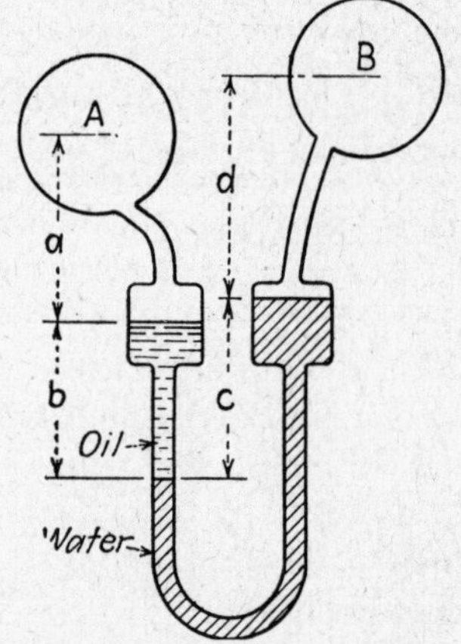

Fig. 1:8.—Differential manometer.

in experimental work involving air flow, it is common practice either to use an inclined manometer, as in Fig. 1:7, with a gauge liquid of a refined light oil, frequently colored red or blue, or to use a differential manometer, as shown in Fig. 1:8. In the differential manometer, two liquids that do not mix, such as oil and water, and that have nearly equal specific weights are balanced against each other so that the equivalent single fluid U tube is one using a fluid of density equal to the difference of the densities of the two gauge fluids.

For any given manometer, a constant can be calculated that relates the manometer reading to the pressure change.

In calculating such a constant on a manometer of unfamiliar design, it is recommended that the student follow through the pressure changes from one point to another, bearing in mind these three simple rules that follow from equation (1:15):

1. When you go down in a fluid, the pressure increases.
2. When you go up in a fluid, the pressure decreases.
3. At a given height in a given body of fluid, the pressure is the same at all points in the apparatus.

Example.—Given a manometer, as in Fig. 1:8, with the following dimensions: $a = 12$ in., $b = 15$ in., $c = 17$ in., $d = 19$ in. Specific weight of the oil is 57 lb per cu ft and of the water 62.3 lb per cu ft. Find the pressure difference between air pipes A and B.

Solution.—Proceed through the apparatus from A to B systematically, noting that pressure increases as you go down and decreases as you go up. The resulting equation is

$$P_A + {}^{15}\!/_{12} \times 57 - {}^{17}\!/_{12} \times 62.3 = P_B \qquad (1:16)$$

This equation assumes that the weight of a small depth of air is negligible compared with a depth of water or oil of the same order of magnitude. Equation (1:16) can be solved for $P_A - P_B = 17.0$ lb per sq ft or $P''_A - P''_B = 0.118$ lb per sq in.

1:4. Problems[1]

1. A vertical glass U tube is used to measure the pressure of air in a pipe. The water in the arm of the tube open to the atmosphere stands 7.5 in. higher than that in the arm connected to the pipe. Barometric pressure is 30.2 in. Hg, and the temperature of the water is 60°F. What is the absolute pressure in the pipe?

2. For the arrangement shown in Fig. 1:9, determine the gauge pressure at A. The kerosene has a specific gravity of 0.82,* and $t = 68$°F.

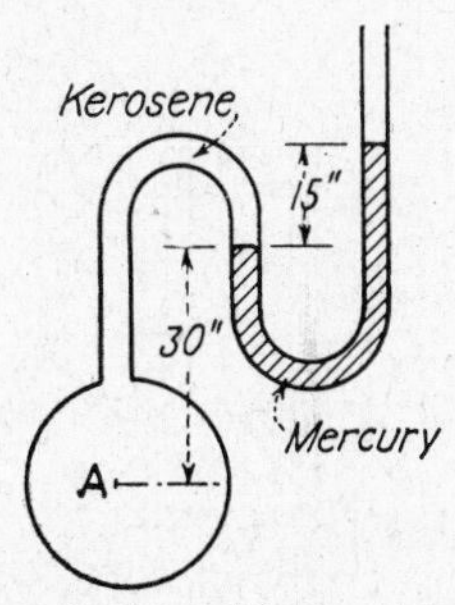

FIG. 1:9.—Manometer.

[1] These problems were suggested by Dr. R. C. Binder's text, "Fluid Mechanics," which is recommended for a more comprehensive study of this subject.

* Specific gravity = specific weight/specific weight of water.

3. For the inclined tube-draft gauge shown in Fig. 1:10, compute the gauge pressure at B if leg A is open to the atmosphere. The oil specific weight is 54.3 lb per cu ft.

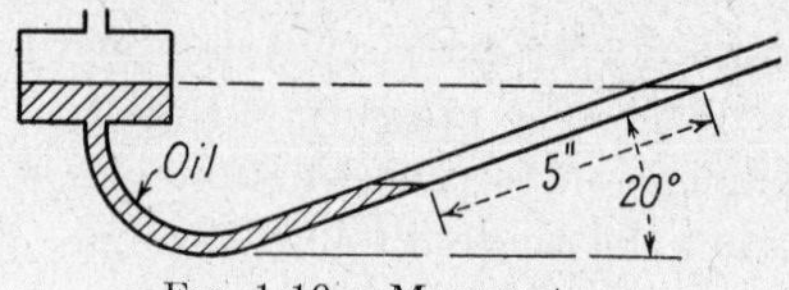

FIG. 1:10.—Manometer.

4. For the arrangement in Fig. 1:11, calculate the pressure difference between points A and B. The specific weight of the oil is 53.0 lb per cu ft.

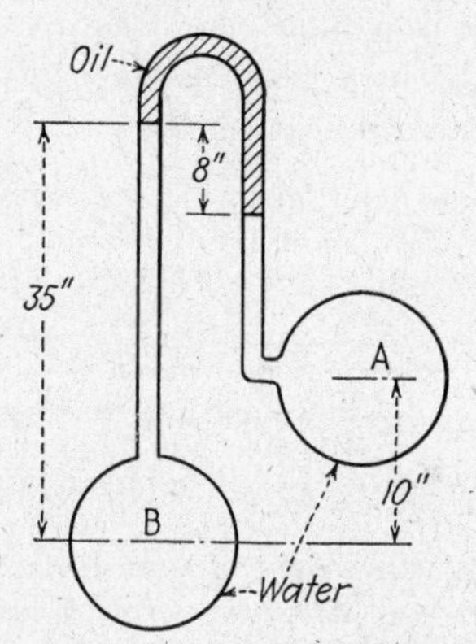

FIG. 1:11.—Manometer.

5. For the apparatus shown in Fig. 1:12, calculate the pressure difference between A and B. $t = 68°F$.

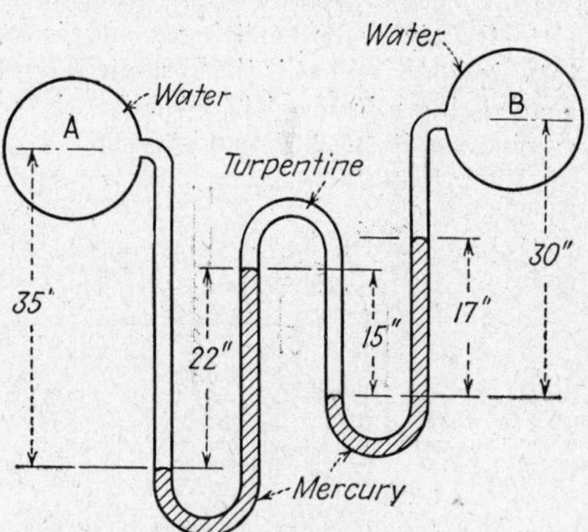

FIG. 1:12.—Manometer.

1:5. Statics of Gases: Perfect Gas Laws.—The laws of Charles and Boyle, strictly applicable only to a "perfect," or "ideal," gas, are close approximations to the actual behavior of the gases found in air.

They may be combined in the equation

$$P\bar{V} = RT \tag{1:17}$$

where R = 53.3 for air (see Appendix 2 for other gases)
P = absolute pressure, lb per sq ft
T = absolute temperature = $t + 460$

Equation (1:17) may be considered as stating the physical factors determining the specific volume (or specific weight) of air. Thus, for air

$$\bar{V} = \frac{1}{w} = \frac{53.3T}{P} \tag{1:18}$$

Any one of the factors P, V, or T, may be changed a small amount dP, dV, or dT. If such changes are made, the relationship between the changes is expressed by writing equation (1:17) in differential form thus:

$$Pd\bar{V} + \bar{V}dP = RdT \tag{1:19}$$

Equation (1:19) points out that if the temperature is changed an amount dT, there must also be either a pressure change dP during which the specific volume $\bar{V}$ is constant or a specific volume change $d\bar{V}$ during which the pressure P is constant, or both.

If the temperature rises because of the addition of heat of amount dQ and the *pressure is constant* ($dP = 0$), the heat added to 1 lb of gas is

$$dQ_{(p=\text{const.})} = c_p dT \tag{1:20}$$

and it appears as external work PdV, or, from equation (1:19),

$$dQ_{(p=\text{const.})} = \frac{c_p}{R} Pd\bar{V} = \frac{c_p}{R} d\text{ (work)} = dH \tag{1:21}$$

where H is known as the "enthalpy" of the gas.

If the temperature rises because of the addition of heat of amount dQ and the specific volume $\bar{V}$ is constant ($d\bar{V} = 0$), the heat added to 1 lb of gas is

$$dQ_{(\bar{V}=\text{const.})} = c_v dT \tag{1:22}$$

Since no external work is done on or by the gas in this case, it is customary to say that the heat energy has been *stored inside the gas* (as kinetic energy of molecules) or that there has been an increase in *internal energy* (here designated by the symbol U, usual units Btu per lb). Hence

$$dQ_{(\bar{V}=\text{const.})} = c_v dT = dU \tag{1:23}$$

These two common cases of heat addition are represented by Figs. 1:13 and 1:14.

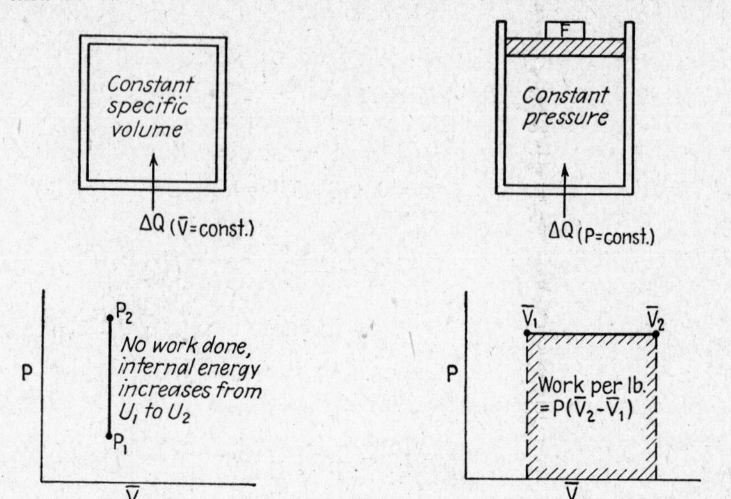

FIG. 1:13.—Constant-volume addition of heat.

FIG. 1:14.—Constant-pressure addition of heat.

The heat added per pound of gas dQ is commonly expressed as a dimensionless ratio by dividing by the absolute temperature T, and the resulting factor dQ/T is called *change of entropy*. Entropy is usually designated by the symbol S; thus

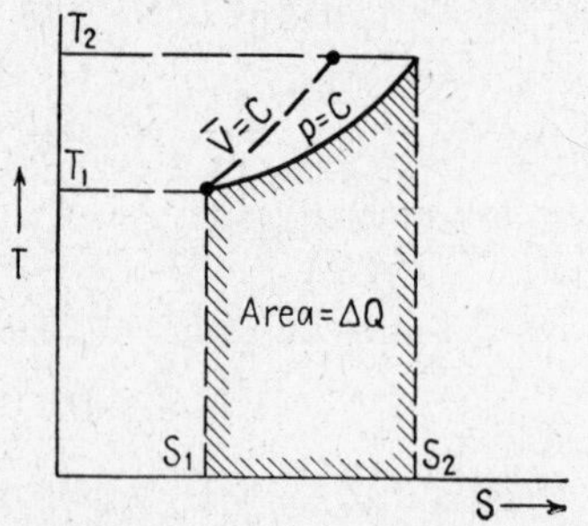

FIG. 1:15.—Representation of heat added as an area on temperature-entropy diagram.

$$dS = \frac{dQ}{T} \tag{1:24}$$

Since integrating equation (1:24) gives

$$Q = \int TdS \tag{1:25}$$

it follows that on a graph of T plotted against S, as in Fig. 1:15, the area under the graph between two constant-entropy lines is heat added. Entropy may thus also be defined as a quantity that, when plotted against temperature, gives heat added as an area. Figure 1:11 shows typical constant-pressure and constant-specific-volume changes on a T-S diagram. From the foregoing definition, it follows that *if no heat is added* (*or removed*), the entropy is constant; this process is described as *isentropic*.

Isothermal (constant temperature) and *isentropic* changes of a given mass of gas (1 lb) are represented by the sketches and graphs of Figs. 1:10 and 1:17.

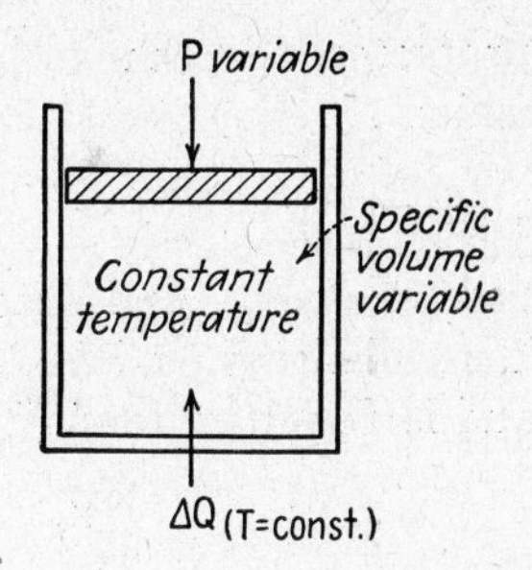

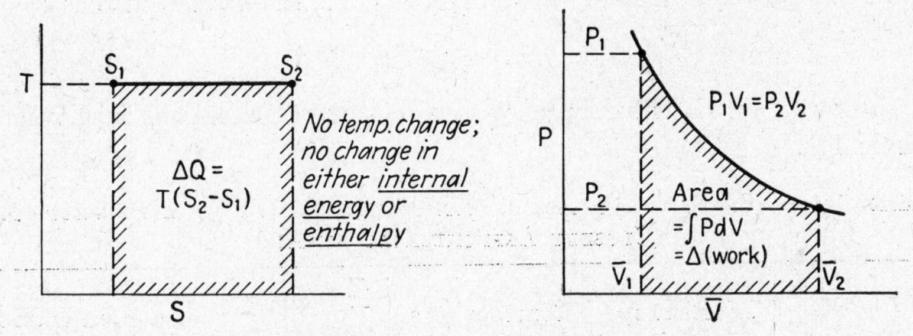

FIG. 1:16.—Gas changes at constant temperature.

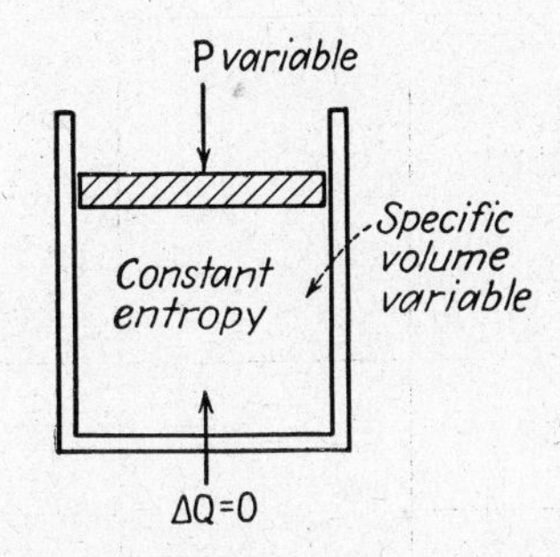

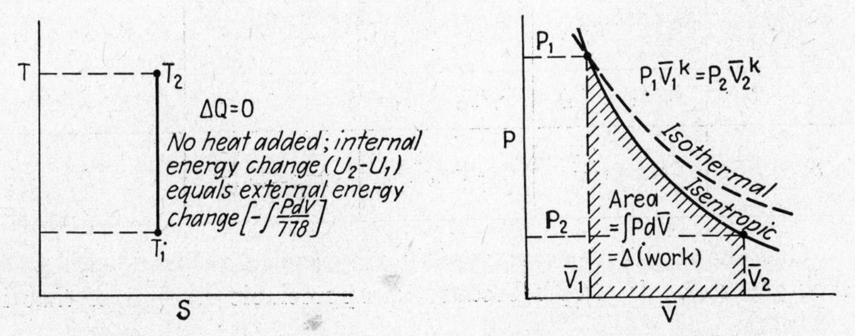

FIG. 1:17.—Gas changes at constant entropy (no heat added).

In all the above processes, the change in internal energy is considered to be that specified by equation (1:23), so that by integration

$$U_2 - U_1 = c_v(T_2 - T_1)$$

The sum of the internal energy and external work (converted to Btu per pound) is often called the *total heat*, *heat content*, or *enthalpy* (the preferred term) and is designated by H. Thus

$$H = U + \frac{P\bar{V}}{778} \tag{1:26}$$

In all the above processes (not only the constant-pressure process)

$$H_2 - H_1 = c_p(T_2 - T_1) \tag{1:27}$$

A summary of all the foregoing perfect-gas relationships is given in Table 1:1.

TABLE 1:1 —NONFLOW-PROCESS RELATIONSHIPS FOR 1 LB OF A PERFECT GAS (CLOSELY APPROXIMATED BY AIR)

Process	Constant specific volume $V = C$	Constant pressure $P = C$	Constant temperature (isothermal) $T = C$	Constant entropy (isentropic) $S = C,\ dQ = 0$
P,V,T relations	$\bar{V}_2 = \bar{V}_1$ $\frac{T_2}{T_1} = \frac{P_2}{P_1}$	$P_2 = P_1$ $\frac{T_2}{T_1} = \frac{\bar{V}_2}{\bar{V}_1}$	$P_1\bar{V}_1 = P_2\bar{V}_2$ $\frac{T_2}{T_1} = 1$	$P_1V_1^k = P_2V_2^k$ $\frac{T_2}{T_1} = \left(\frac{V_1}{V_2}\right)^{k-1}$ $\frac{T_2}{T_1} = \left(\frac{P_2}{P_1}\right)^{(k-1)/k}$
$\int_1^2 Pd\bar{V}$	0	$P(\bar{V}_2 - \bar{V}_1)$	$P_1\bar{V}_1 \log_e \frac{\bar{V}_2}{\bar{V}_1}$	$\frac{P_2\bar{V}_2 - P_1\bar{V}_1}{1 - k}$
$U_2 - U_1$	$c_v(T_2 - T_1)$	$c_v(T_2 - T_1)$	0	$c_v(T_2 - T_1)$
ΔQ	$c_v(T_2 - T_1)$	$c_p(T_2 - T_1)$	$\frac{P_1\bar{V}_1}{778} \log_e \frac{\bar{V}_2}{\bar{V}_1}$	0
$H_2 - H_1$	$c_p(T_2 - T_1)$	$c_p(T_2 - T_1)$	0	$c_p(T_2 - T_1)$
$S_2 - S_1$	$c_v \log_e \frac{T_2}{T_1}$	$c_p \log_e \frac{T_2}{T_1}$	$\frac{R}{778} \log_e \frac{\bar{V}_2}{\bar{V}_1}$	0

Gas changes that occur *rapidly* are usually assumed with good accuracy to be *isentropic* because an appreciable amount of *time* is required for the addition of heat. The $P, \bar{V}, T$ relationships for an isentropic change are derived as follows:

Since no heat is added or subtracted, the changes in internal energy and external work are equal and of opposite sign, or

$$dU + \frac{Pd\bar{V}}{778} = 0 = c_v dT + \frac{Pd\bar{V}}{778} \tag{1:28}$$

From equation (1:19),

$$dT = \frac{Pd\bar{V}}{R} + \frac{\bar{V}dP}{R} \tag{1:29}$$

Substituting equation (1:29) in (1:28),

$$0 = c_v \frac{Pd\bar{V}}{R} + c_v \frac{\bar{V}dP}{R} + \frac{Pd\bar{V}}{778} \tag{1:30}$$

Collecting the V and P terms for integrating gives

$$\left(\frac{c_v}{R} + \frac{1}{778}\right) PdV = -\frac{c_v}{R} \bar{V}dP$$

or

$$\left(c_v + \frac{R}{778}\right) \frac{d\bar{V}}{V} = -c_v \frac{dP}{P}$$

This integrates, between limits $(\ )_1$ and $(\ )_2$, to

$$\left(c_v + \frac{R}{778}\right) \log_e \frac{\bar{V}_2}{\bar{V}_1} = -c_v \log_e \frac{P_2}{P_1} \tag{1:31}$$

which may also be written in the form

$$\frac{P_2}{P_1} = \left(\frac{\bar{V}_1}{\bar{V}_2}\right)^k \tag{1:32}$$

where $k = \dfrac{c_v + (R/778)}{c_v}$. It is shown below that $c_v + (R/778) = c_p$, and thus $k = c_p/c_v = 1.405$ for air. For *any nonflow process*,

$$dQ = dU + \frac{PdV}{778} \tag{1:33}$$

and from equation (1:23), also for *any nonflow process*, dU is defined by

$$dU = c_v dT$$

For a constant-pressure process, by using equations (1:20) and (1:33),

$$dQ_{(P=\text{const.})} = c_p dT = c_v dT + \frac{Pd\bar{V}}{778} \tag{1:34}$$

and from equation (1:19), with $dP = 0$ (constant pressure),

$$Pd\bar{V} = RdT;$$

thus, equation (1:34) gives

$$c_p dT = c_v dT + \frac{RdT}{778}$$

or

$$c_p = c_v + \frac{R}{778} \tag{1:35}$$

Relationships like equation (1:32) involving nonintegral exponents are frequently plotted on logarithmic graph paper (slide-rule scales), as shown in Fig. 1:18, which shows the isentropic expansion of air from

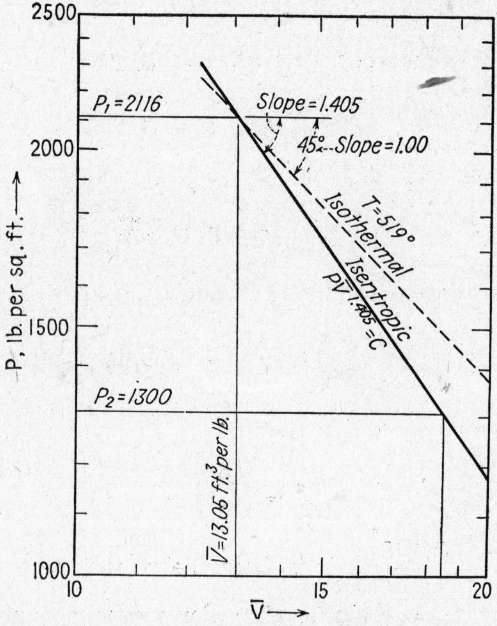

FIG. 1:18.—Logarithmic plot of isentropic expansion of air.

an initial expansion condition of $P_1 = 2{,}116$ lb per sq ft, $\bar{V}_1 = 13.05$ cu ft per lb, corresponding to an initial temperature of 519°F abs. (59°F). On such a graph, the isentropic line has a slope of k; the isothermal line has a slope of 1.00. Actual air processes involving small additions of heat frequently follow straight lines of slope $1 < n < k$ given by the equation

$$PV^n = C$$

For values of $n \neq k$, the expansion is known as *polytropic*.

All the equations in this article are written for 1 lb of air; for W lb of air, all terms of all equations should be multiplied by W.

1:6. Problems[1]

1. Heat is added to 1 lb of air at a constant pressure of 2,116 lb per sq ft, and the temperature rises from 60 to 90°F. *Find* (*a*) the change in internal energy, (*b*) the volume of the air before and after heat is added, and (*c*) the external work done by the air as it expands.

2. Five cubic feet of air at 30 lb per sq in. abs. pressure and 60°F is heated in a closed tank until the pressure becomes 40 lb per sq in. abs. Find (*a*) the heat added to the air and (*b*) the change in internal energy.

3. Seven cubic feet of air expands isothermally from 120 lb per sq in. abs. to 70 lb per sq in. abs. Find (*a*) the work done by the air, (*b*) the heat flow, (*c*) the change of internal energy, and (*d*) the change in entropy.

4. Ten cubic feet of air at 150 lb per sq in. abs. and 180°F expands isentropically to a final pressure of 60 lb per sq in. abs. Find (*a*) the final volume and temperature, (*b*) the work done, (*c*) the heat flow, (*d*) the change of internal energy, and (*e*) the change of entropy.

5. For the isentropic expansion of air shown in Fig. 1:18, find V_2, w_2, $U_2 - U_1$, $\int PdV$, $H_2 - H_1$, and T_2, and sketch a $T - S$ diagram to scale.

6. For the isothermal expansion of air shown in Fig. 1:18, find V_2, w_2, ΔQ, $\int PdV$, and S_2, assuming $S_1 = 0$, and sketch a $T - S$ diagram to scale.

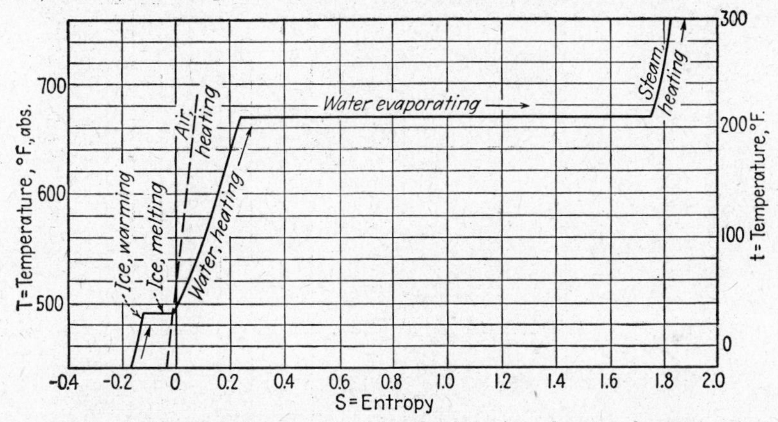

FIG. 1:19.—Comparison of heat involved in air and water changes.

1:7. Moist Air.—Since about three-quarters of the earth's surface is covered with water and exposed to the radiant heat of the sun, the water evaporates into the air, and air always has a small amount of water vapor in it. The small amount of water vapor makes a large difference in the behavior of the air with changes in altitude because of the relatively large amounts of heat involved in changes of temperature of air and water vapor, as shown in Fig. 1:19, which is a comparative temperature-entropy diagram for air and water.

[1] Suggested principally by Young and Young, "Elementary Engineering Thermodynamics."

Thus, while air usually contains less than 1 per cent moisture by weight, the heat exchanges are of the same order of magnitude, and the water, in the form of vapor (invisible), fog, clouds, snow, or hail, is the principal determining factor in the air conditions under 50,000 ft altitude.

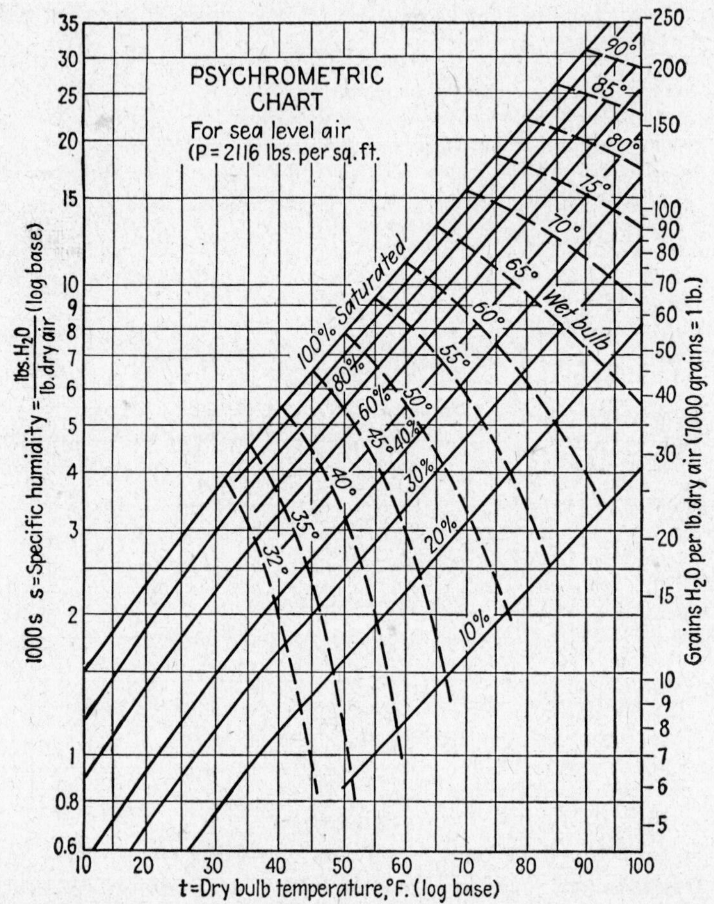

FIG. 1:20.—Humidity chart for sea-level air. (*Data from Mackey, "Air Conditioning Principles," and Byers, "Synoptic and Aeronautical Meteorology."*)

The term humidity refers to water vapor in the air. The term *specific* humidity (s) has the quantitative technical meaning of the weight of water vapor per pound of dry air. At a given air temperature, the air will hold just so much water vapor without condensing out in the form of a fog or cloud. When the air is full of water vapor, it is said to be *saturated.* The saturation specific humidity of air is shown as a function of temperature by the upper line in Fig. 1:20.

The *relative humidity* is the ratio of the actual specific humidity to the saturation specific humidity. Lines of constant relative humidity in per cent are also shown in Fig. 1:20.

Humidity is usually measured by comparison of readings of two thermometers. One of them is kept moist and is known as the "wet bulb." The other is the "dry bulb." Figure 1:20 is to be read as follows: When the dry-bulb temperature is 60°F and the wet-bulb temperature is 50°F, the relative humidity is read at the intersection of these two lines on the graph and is seen to be 50 per cent; the specific humidity is read on the left-hand scale and is seen to be about 6 lb of water vapor per 1,000 lb of dry air. The physical sensation of temperature is more nearly a function of the wet-bulb temperature than of the dry-bulb temperature.

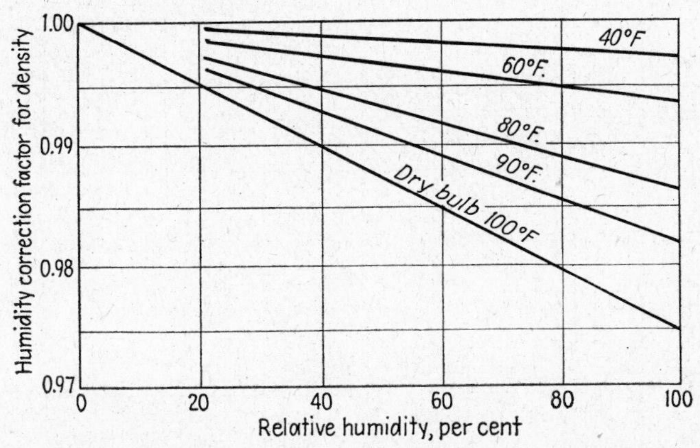

FIG. 1:21.—Humidity-correction factor to obtain density of moist air. (*Data from Marks, "Mechanical Engineers Handbook."*)

Since the water vapor is lighter than the air, the moist air is lighter than dry air by the amount shown in Fig. 1:21. This factor must be taken into account in accurate measurements in wind tunnels or in flight under conditions of high temperature and humidity.

The saturation specific humidity is a function of pressure as well as temperature, as shown by Fig. 1:22.

If 1 lb of sea-level air is raised quickly to a high altitude, as it often is by winds blowing toward mountains, it follows approximately an isentropic change because insufficient time is available for the addition or removal of much heat. If the sea-level air were perfectly dry, it would follow the line in Fig. 1:23 labeled "dry isentropic," which can be calculated from the perfect-gas laws in the preceding article. On the other hand, if the air at sea level were completely saturated with

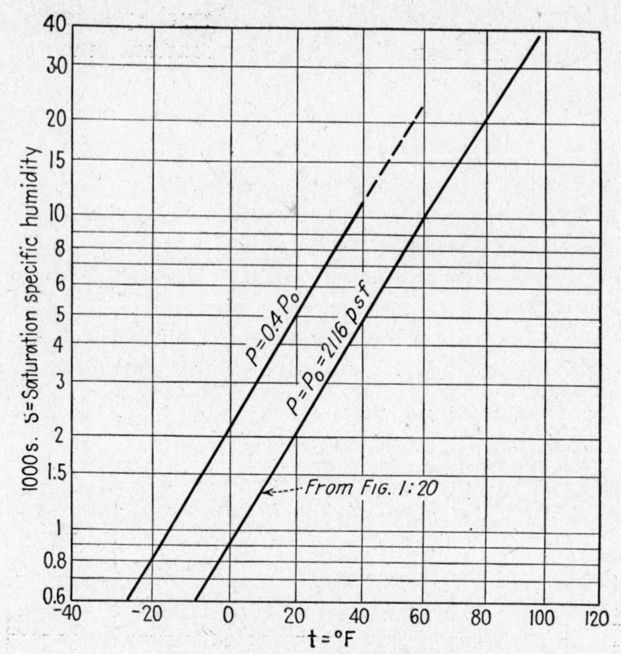

FIG. 1:22.—Effect of pressure on saturation specific humidity. (*Data from Byers, Synoptic and Aeronautical Meteorology.*)

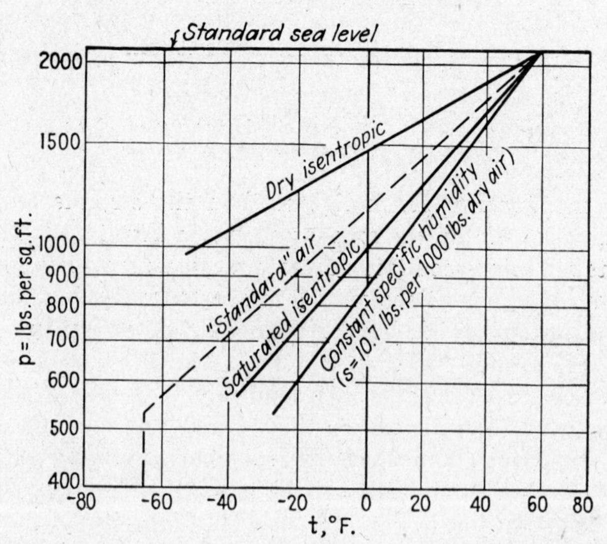

FIG. 1:23.—Comparison of dry-isentropic and constant-specific-humidity lines of P *vs.* T with assumed standard-air variation ($\approx$ mean at latitude 40°N).

moisture, the isentropic condition would be more nearly fulfilled if the temperature variation with altitude were that indicated by the line labeled "saturated air." The actual variation of temperature with altitude lies between these two extremes and usually is not a smooth or straight line because, with different relative humidities and temperatures at the ground, condensation will occur at different levels. The various possibilities are too numerous to be discussed in detail here and are left to the special field of meteorology. For most aerodynamic calculations, the correction for the effect of atmospheric moisture on density is neglected, and the air is treated as a perfect gas of known linear temperature distribution. The fact that the moisture was the cause of the temperature distribution then becomes of only academic importance.

If air containing even a very small amount of moisture (compared with normal atmospheric humidities) is used in a high-speed wind tunnel (at speeds near or above the speed of sound), the moisture is likely to form a cloud in the test section and prevent the taking of photographs of the flow.

The conditions necessary for the formation or avoidance of a fog in a high-speed wind tunnel may be calculated on the basis of Fig. 1:20 and the assumption (used in plotting Fig. 1:22) that saturation specific humidity s varies inversely with absolute pressure for a given temperature (or that the *saturation moisture content per cubic foot* is independent of pressure). Fog cannot, however, be assumed to form or disappear when the 100 per cent saturation condition is reached, as *time* is required for the associated heat transfer; under some conditions of humidity and air velocity a supersaturation of the order of 300 per cent ($s = 4s_{sat}$) has been found necessary for fog formation.[1]

1:8. Problems

1. With a dry-bulb temperature of 90°F and a wet-bulb temperature of 80°F find (*a*) relative humidity, (*b*) specific humidity, (*c*) the specific weight of dry air at 90°F and $P = 2{,}116$ lb per sq ft, (*d*) the humidity correction factor for density, and (*e*) the specific weight of the moist air.

2. With a dry-bulb temperature of 60°F and a wet-bulb temperature of 40°F, find (*a*) the relative humidity and (*b*) the humidity correction factor for density.

[1] OSWATITSCH, K., Condensation Phenomena in Supersonic Nozzles, *Z.A.M.M.*, 1–14 (February, 1942); issued by British Ministry of Aircraft Production as *R.T.P. Trans.* 1905, distributed by the Durand Reprinting Committee, California Institute of Technology, Pasadena, Calif. HERMANN, R., Condensation Shock Waves in Supersonic Wind Tunnel Nozzles, *Luftfahrt-Forsch.*, **19**, No. 6, 201–209 (June 20, 1942); issued by British Ministry of Aircraft Production as *R.T.P. Trans.* 1581, distributed by the Durand Reprinting Committee, California Institute of Technology, Pasadena, Calif.

1:9. Variation of Air with Altitude: Standard Air.—The performance of an airplane depends on the physical characteristics of the air in which it flies. The most important physical characteristics are density (ρ) and viscosity (μ). These factors in turn depend on the pressure (P), the temperature (T), and specific humidity (s), though humidity has a minor effect on ρ and μ. A general picture of the interrelationship of the physical factors involved must consider the following well-known facts.

1. The earth consists of bodies of water (frozen near the poles) and land (with mountains) on the surface of a sphere that rotates daily about its axis and revolves yearly about the sun.

2. The earth is surrounded by a mass of gases (air), chiefly nitrogen and oxygen near the earth's surface, that are held by gravitational attraction.

3. The sun is hot and radiates heat to the earth, heating the bodies of land quickly and the bodies of water slowly. The earth in turn radiates heat out into space, probably radiating a little more or a little less heat than it absorbs from the sun. However, the difference between total heat radiation and total heat absorption is small, and the mean temperature of the earth changes very little from century to century.

4. In the daytime the air over the land is heated by the land (by radiation and by transfer through contact) more than the air over the water is heated (the water evaporating into the air). The air over land becomes less dense and rises, and the moisture-laden sea air rushes in horizontally over the land, where it is deflected upward by mountains. As the air rises, it expands and becomes cooler, the moisture condenses as rain or snow, the condensation produces further warming of the air, and parts of the remaining moisture-laden air rise to heights of 7 to 10 miles.

5. The pressure gradient in the air is determined by the gravitational attraction of the earth and by the air density, which in turn depends on the pressure and temperature gradients. The temperature gradient is largely determined by the isentropic expansion of the rising air currents, but the evaporation and condensation of the water vapor in the air are also major factors. At heights of 7 to 10 miles, the temperature-pressure relationships become such that all water vapor is frozen to snow or ice and falls back to the earth. This region of water vapor and vertical currents is known as the *troposphere*. Beyond this height, vertical air currents cease to exist, and the air temperature is determined by radiation from the earth and sun. This portion of the atmosphere was formerly thought to be stratified into

layers of separate gases and has therefore been called the *stratosphere.* For vertical distances in the stratosphere that are small compared with the diameter of the earth, the temperature changes only slightly; therefore, this region is sometimes called the *isothermal region.*

6. The mean annual temperature at any latitude at the surface of the earth depends chiefly on the amount of heat received by radiation from the sun, though local water and air currents are also a major factor. Hence, the air near the equator is hot [t (mean annual) $\approx$ 85°F, $\pm 5°$ from warmest to coldest month], and the air near the poles is

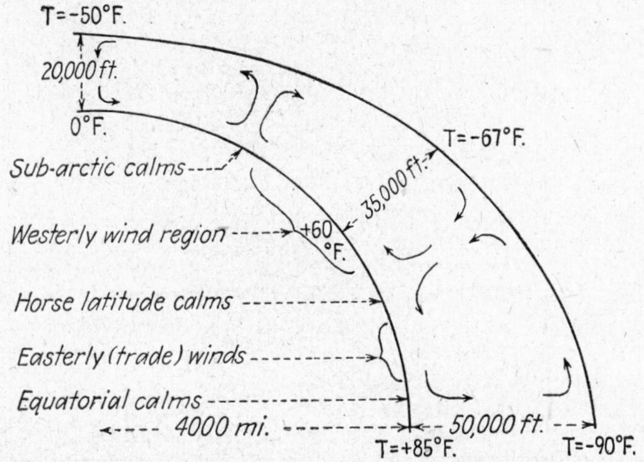

FIG. 1:24.—Relation between height of base of stratosphere and latitude. Approximate vertical and horizontal air circulations noted.

cold [t (mean annual) $\approx$ 0°F, $\pm 30°$ from warmest to coldest month]. This temperature difference causes a density difference and the general vertical circulations noted in Fig. 1:24, which react with the earth's rotation to give the prevailing surface winds noted (which in turn move the surface waters, forming ocean currents). The altitude at which the water vapor is all frozen out, and hence the upper limit of the troposphere, is thus a function of latitude, the coldest point in the troposphere being just above the equator, as noted in Fig. 1:24.

7. The temperature at any point in the stratosphere is determined by radiant heat received by a particle from the earth and sun. Its temperature must be such as to radiate all heat absorbed if it remains at constant temperature. The amount of heat received by a particle of gas from the sun or earth is proportional to the fourth power of the temperature of the radiating body and the solid angle subtended by the body. Calculations based on this principle indicate that the stratosphere temperature varies somewhat, as shown in Fig. 1:25, though the temperatures at higher altitudes are in doubt.

For aeronautical work, the troposphere and lower stratosphere are of chief significance. A more comprehensive picture of the conditions existing in the lower hundred miles of the atmosphere is shown in Fig. 1:26. The breaks in the density graph are due to changes of scale; the actual density variation is smooth. The cloud names are perhaps somewhat misleading. The names actually apply to types of cloud formation, and each type is found over a wide range of alti-

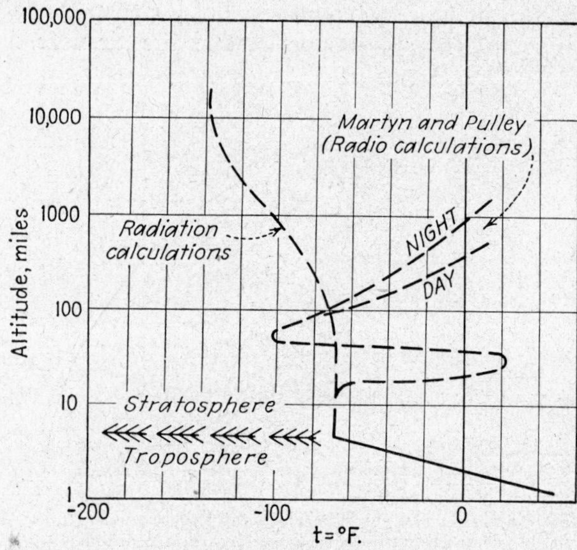

FIG. 1:25.—Relation between observed atmosphere temperatures and calculated temperatures and calculated temperatures in solar-system space.

tudes; only the median height of each type can be indicated on such a graph as this. The hypothetical existence of nearly pure hydrogen at altitudes in excess of 300,000 ft is noted as questionable. Military rockets have already reached this region. Exploratory sampling rockets are expected to give definite information on this matter within a few years.

In the isothermal region the pressure and density variation can be readily calculated by the use of equations (1:14) ($dP = -w dz$) and (1:17) ($P/w = 53.3T$) as follows: Combining these equations,

$$dP = \frac{-P dz}{53.3T} \tag{1:36}$$

which, for constant temperature, integrates between limits $(\quad)_1$ and $(\quad)_2$ to

$$\log_e \frac{P_1}{P_2} = \frac{z_1 - z_2}{53.3T} \tag{1:37}$$

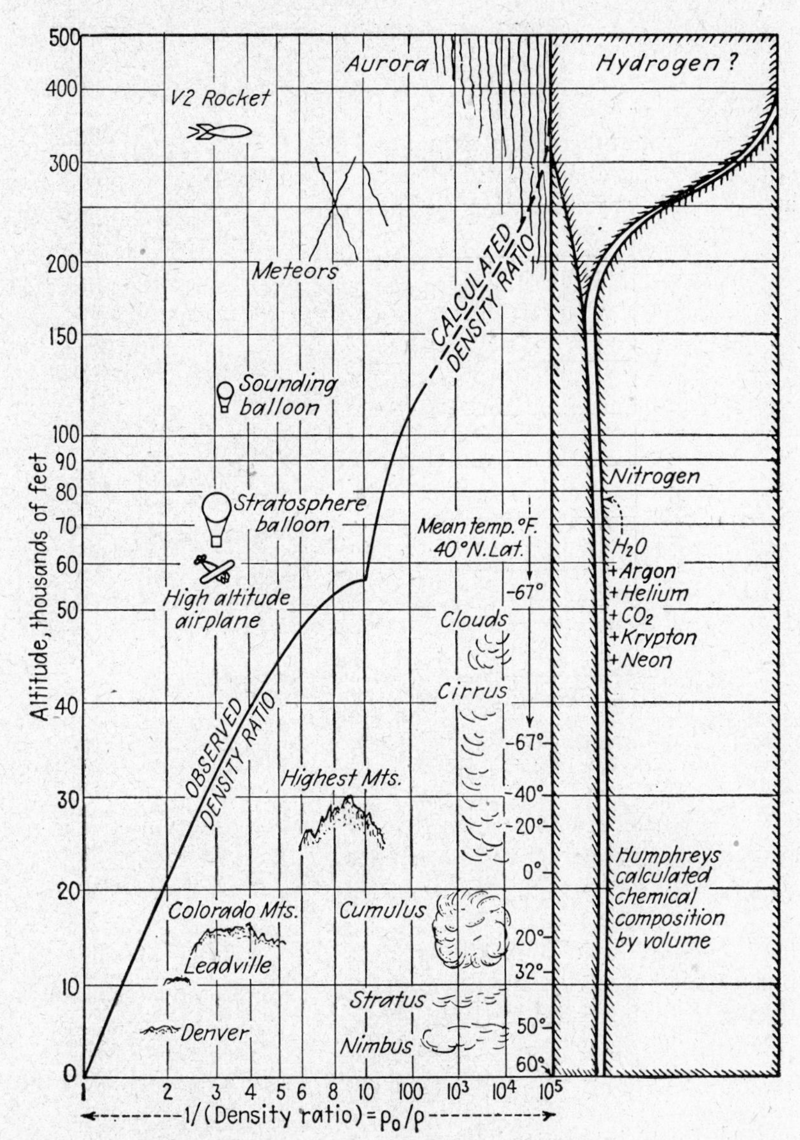

FIG. 1:26.—Properties of the lower 100 miles of the earth's atmosphere. (*From Smithsonian Tables and other sources.*)

Equation (1:37) is known as the *logarithmic barometric formula.* If the stratosphere temperature is assumed to be $-67°F$ ($T = 393$) and the pressure at its base is assumed to be 490 lb per sq ft, the pressure ratio at a height of 15,000 ft above the base of the stratosphere may be calculated from equation (1:37), which gives

$$\log_e \frac{490}{P_2} = \frac{15{,}000}{53.3 \times 393} = 0.717$$

Therefore $P_2 = 490/e^{0.717} = 239$ lb per sq ft.

In the troposphere, the actual conditions are variable and complicated by the presence of water vapor. To make a simple calculation that is a fair approximation to the average conditions at latitude

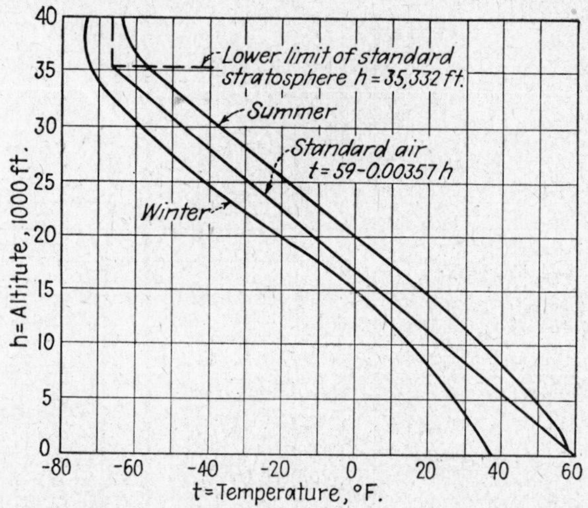

FIG. 1:27.—Comparison of temperature-altitude relations for standard air and average actual air at latitude 40°N. (*From NACA Rept.* 218, *and Humphrey's "Physics of the Air."*)

40°N it is customary to assume that the temperature varies linearly with altitude as given by the equation

$$T = T_0 - \lambda z \tag{1:38}$$

where $T_0 = 519$ and $\lambda = 0.00356$°F per ft for the "international standard air" used by British and United States engineers. Substituting equation (1:38) in (1:36) gives

$$\frac{dP}{P} = \frac{-1}{53.3} \frac{dz}{T_0 - \lambda z} = \frac{1}{53.3\lambda} \frac{d(T_0 - \lambda z)}{(T_0 - \lambda z)} \tag{1:39}$$

Equation (1:39) integrates between limits $(\ )_0$ and $(\ )_1$ to

$$\log_e \frac{P_1}{P_0} = \frac{1}{53.3\lambda} \log_e \frac{T_1}{T_0} \tag{1:40}$$

With $\lambda = 0.00356$, $1/53.3\lambda = 5.256$, and

$$\frac{P_1}{P_0} = \left(\frac{T_1}{T_0}\right)^{5.256} \tag{1:41}$$

Equation (1:41) is plotted in Fig. 1:23 as the line labeled "standard air." Properties of air calculated in this manner are given in Appendix 3. A comparison of standard air with mean summer and winter air conditions at latitude 40°N is shown in Fig. 1:27. Combining equation (1:41) with the equation of state (1:17) for dry air gives also

$$\frac{\rho_1}{\rho_0} = \left(\frac{T_1}{T_0}\right)^{5.256} \tag{1:41.1}$$

Other variations of temperature with altitude are equally justifiable on the basis of meteorological data, and suggested other standards for student solution in the above manner are found in Art. 1:10.

If the lapse rate λ is greater than the isentropic lapse rate, then air that rises rapidly becomes warmer and therefore lighter than the surrounding air and thus continues to rise. Such a lapse rate is called unstable. With a low lapse rate in the surrounding air, the rapidly rising air tends to settle down again. This condition is called stable. These relationships are shown in Fig. 1:28. The isentropic lapse rate of dry air may be found by combining equations (1:36) and the isentropic relation from Table 1:1,

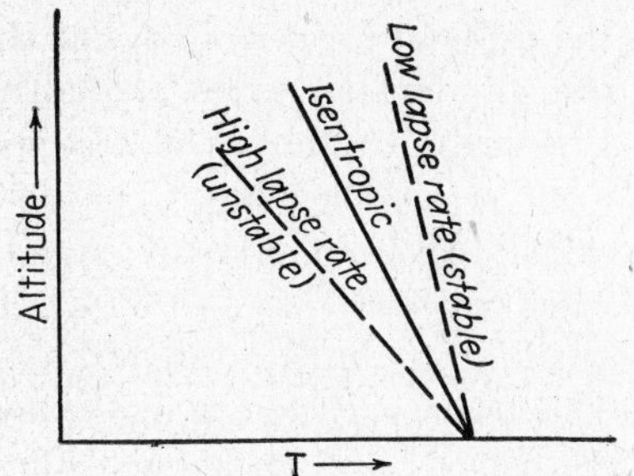

FIG. 1:28.—Stable and unstable lapse rates.

$$\frac{T}{P^{(k-1)/k}} = \frac{T}{P^{0.288}} = C = \frac{T_0}{P_0^{0.288}} \tag{1:42}$$

so that

$$dP = \frac{-Pdz}{53.3CP^{0.288}} \tag{1:43}$$

which may be readily integrated.

1:10. Problems

1. For a hypothetical "tropical desert standard air" that is assumed to be perfectly dry, to have a sea-level pressure of 2,116 lb per sq ft abs., a sea-level temperature of 540°F abs., and a temperature lapse rate of 4°F per 1,000 ft up to 50,000 ft, find (*a*) an equation for the variation of pressure with altitude and (*b*) the density ratio at 20,000 ft altitude and at 50,000 ft altitude.

2. For a hypothetical "polar standard air" that is assumed to be perfectly dry, to have a sea-level pressure of 2,116 lb per sq ft abs., a sea-level temperature of 460°F abs., and a temperature lapse rate of 2.5°F per 1,000 ft up to 20,000 ft and a temperature of −50°F from there on up, find (*a*) the pressure and density at 20.000 ft altitude and (*b*) the pressure and density at 50,000 ft altitude.

3. Using equation 1:42, find the variation of density with (*a*) temperature and (*b*) pressure for isentropic expansion of dry air from standard sea-level conditions. Is "standard air" stable or unstable?

1:11. Pressure and Density Altitudes; Use of Air Chart.—The temperature variation with altitude in standard air is that shown in Fig. 1:27, and the corresponding pressure and density ratios are given by equations (1:41) and (1:41.5). These pressure and density ratios are listed in Table XV, Appendix 3, which is known as the *standard-air table*.

In actual air at a given altitude the pressure and density may depart considerably from the standard-air values. If, in a flight test, the pressure is measured and the corresponding altitude looked up in the standard-air table, this altitude is known as the *pressure altitude*. Pressure altitude is the reading of an altimeter that has no instrument error. Similarly, the density in any given flight test may be calculated from pressure and temperature readings and divided by standard sea-level density. The altitude corresponding to this *density ratio* in the standard-air table is known as the *density altitude*. The actual altitude in feet above sea level will usually correspond to neither of these altitudes. For example, an airplane may be actually flying at an altitude of 10,000 ft above sea level, and its altimeter may read 12,000 ft (or it may carry a recording barometer that reads 19.03 in. Hg or 1,346 lb per sq ft). Suppose the air temperature is read as 40°F. Referring to Table XV (page 384), note that a pressure of 1,346 lb per sq ft corresponds to 12,000 ft altitude in standard air; accordingly, 12,000 ft is known as the *pressure altitude*. The density under the observed conditions may be calculated as

$$\rho = \frac{1{,}346}{53.3 \times 500 \times 32.2} = 0.001568$$

and the corresponding density ratio is

$$\sigma = \frac{\rho}{\rho_0} = \frac{0.001568}{0.002378} = 0.659$$

The altitude corresponding to this density ratio is found by interpolation in Table XV to be approximately 13,550 ft. This altitude is known as the *density altitude*.

The procedure involved in the above calculations can be greatly simplified by the use of a chart such as Fig. 1:29, which is sometimes also called a "density- and pressure-altitude conversion chart." An enlargement of this chart for more accurate readings is found in the pocket in the back of the book and is designated chart A. Uses of the chart are as follows: At the intersection of any given pressure-altitude line (= the corrected altimeter reading) and temperature line the density altitude in 1,000 ft may be read on the upper scale; on the lower scale is the density ratio, which is necessary for airplane-performance computations. An additional family of lines is provided on the chart for determining the kinematic viscosity at any pressure

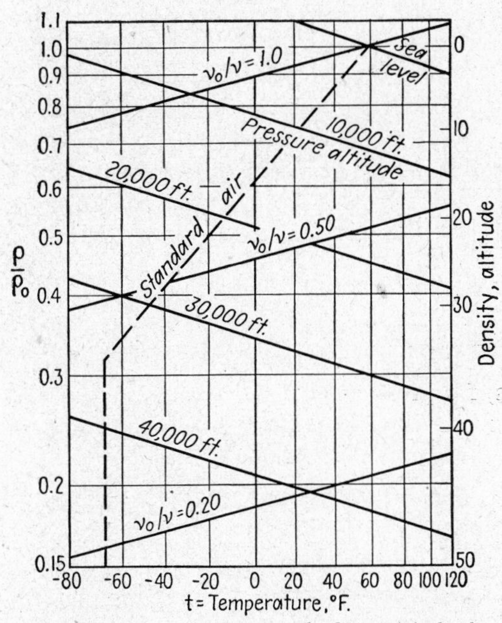

FIG. 1:29.—Air chart. (See large-scale Chart A in back of book.)

altitude and temperature. This is given in terms of the viscosity ratio ν_0/ν. The values of ρ and ν may then be calculated from the values of ρ_0 and ν_0 given under the title of the chart. Using the data in the above example, with a pressure altitude of 12,000 ft and a temperature of +40°F, read on the upper scale a density altitude of 13,600 ft and on the lower scale a density ratio of 0.66. Read also by interpolating in the viscosity scale a kinematic-viscosity ratio $\nu_0/\nu = 0.68$. The density and kinematic viscosity for the flight conditions can then be calculated as follows:

$$\rho = 0.002378 \times 0.66 = 0.00157$$

$$\nu = \frac{0.0001567}{0.68} = 0.000231$$

An additional example is given on the chart.

1:12. Problems

1. Find the air density ρ and the kinematic viscosity ν when the altimeter reads 40,000 ft and the temperature is $-40°F$.

2. An airplane is flying at a pressure altitude of 20,000 ft, and the temperature is $-10°F$. Find (*a*) the air density ρ, (*b*) the kinematic viscosity ν, (*c*) the density altitude, and (*d*) the density ratio.

3. At a point where the density ratio is 0.5, read on the air chart the pressure and density altitude and the kinematic ratio ν_0/ν for standard air.

4. An airplane is flying at 15,000 ft pressure altitude (indicated on a corrected altimeter), and the temperature is $-10°F$. Find (*a*) the density altitude, (*b*) the density ratio, and (*c*) the kinematic viscosity.

1:13. Pressure Waves; Velocity of Sound; Mach Number.—Air flowing at low speed around an object such as a wing streamlines itself, as shown in Fig. 1:30. The peculiar feature of this sort of flow is that the air at point O behaves as if it knew the wing was coming. From another point of view, it might be said that the wing telegraphs ahead to tell the air to get out of the way. This "telegraph system" actually exists, for pressure changes at point 1 can make themselves felt some short time later at point O. The maximum speed at which such a pressure wave can travel is shown later to be the velocity of sound. If the wing is traveling at a speed in excess of that at which

FIG. 1:30.—Air-flow pattern around wing at low speed.

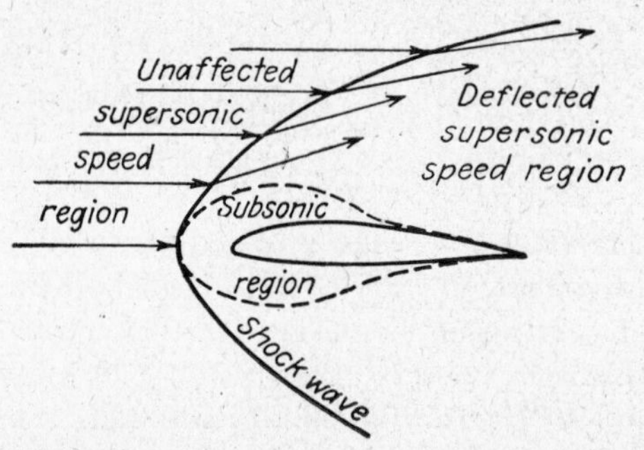

FIG. 1:31.—Idealized air-flow pattern around wing at supersonic speeds.

pressure can be transmitted through the air, then the air behaves as if it did not know the wing was coming, and when it hits the wing it splits sharply with a quite different flow pattern from that which is obtained at low speed. A typical high-speed flow pattern is shown in Fig. 1:31.

The mechanism by which pressure is transmitted in a compressible fluid is illustrated by the sketch in Fig. 1:32, which represents 1 cu ft of air with a pressure difference dP momentarily existing between its two sides. If the force dP is quickly applied, the air compresses isentropically a distance $dx = d\rho$. The force dP accelerates the mass ρ, and in a small amount of time dt the other end of the mass also moves a distance dx and the cubic foot of air is restored to its original size. The result of this process is that in a continuous compressible medium, the pressure change dP has been relocated 1 ft to the left in the time dt, and it therefore may be said that a pressure wave has gone through this cubic foot at a velocity equal to $1/dt$.

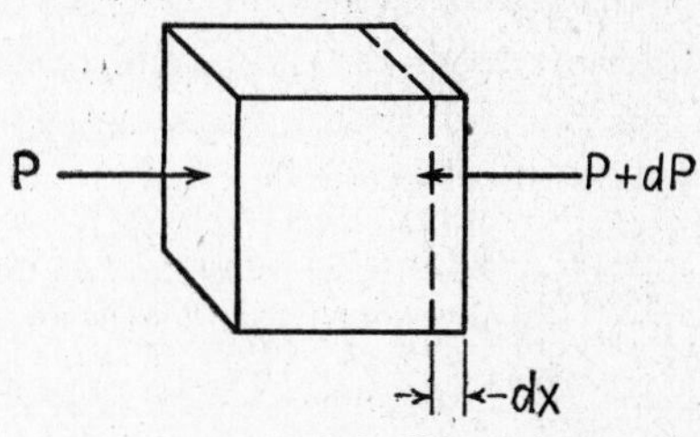

FIG. 1:32.—Sketch illustrating mechanism of pressure transmission in a compressible fluid.

A sound wave is a series of pressure waves of this sort of varying frequency and intensity. By applying Newton's second law and the equation for isentropic compression of a perfect gas it may be shown[1] that the velocity of propagation of a pressure wave is

$$c = \sqrt{kgRT} \tag{1:44}$$

For air with $k = 1.405$, $g = 32.2$, and $R = 53.3$, equation (1:44) may be rewritten

$$c = 1{,}120 \sqrt{\frac{T}{519}} \tag{1:45}$$

Equation (1:45) emphasizes the fact that the velocity of sound, or the velocity of pressure transmission, in air under standard sea-level conditions ($T = 519°$F abs.) is 1,120 ft per sec and the correction factor to other temperatures is $\sqrt{T/519}$.

Since it has been pointed out that the air-flow pattern around an object depends on the relative magnitude of the actual speed and the speed of sound, it is convenient to take the ratio V/c as a criterion of the changes in flow pattern due to compressibility of the air. This ratio

$$M = \frac{V}{c} \tag{1:46}$$

is known as the "Mach number." When air flows past an object at a speed equal to the speed of sound, the Mach number is said to be 1.00.

The local velocity around an object may be substantially greater than the general free-stream velocity; therefore, local changes in flow

[1] BINDER, R. C., "Fluid Mechanics," 1943 ed., p. 162.

pattern will occur when the *local Mach number* equals 1.00. In Fig. 1:30 the local Mach number would be $M_1 = V_1/c_1$, and the general free-stream Mach number of the flow would be $M_0 = V_0/c_0$. Since the process is usually isentropic rather than isothermal, c_1 is generally different from c_0; c_1 is usually less than c_0 because T_1 is usually less than T_0. Other important aspects of the meaning of the Mach number will be developed later.

1:14. Problems

1. Find the velocity of sound in the lower stratosphere where $T = 393°F$ abs.

2. Find the local velocity of sound in air near an object where the local temperature is $-90°F$.

3. Find the velocity of sound in a wind tunnel in which the temperature is $+120°F$.

4. Add to your air chart a graph of $c/1{,}000$ *vs.* Fahrenheit temperature, using the density ratio scale for the scale of $c/1{,}000$.

5. Using equation (1:44) and the perfect-gas law show that $c^2 = kP/\rho$.

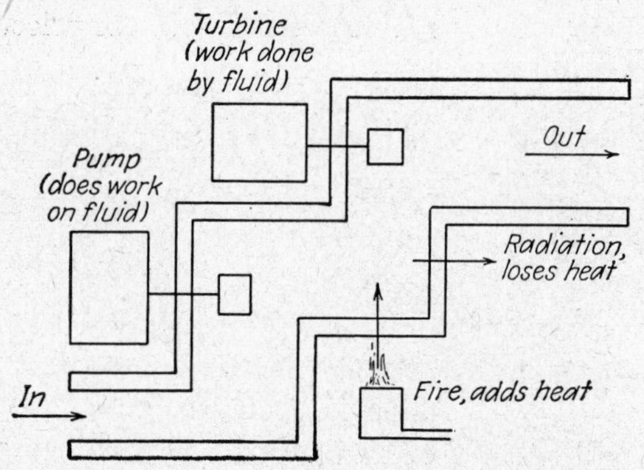

FIG. 1:33.—Fluid flow through a mechanical and thermodynamic system.

1:15. Fluid Flow: Continuity and Energy Equations.—When fluid flows into and out of a collection of apparatus that may include heaters, heat losses, pumps, and turbines, two basic equations are customarily written expressing the mechanical and thermodynamic relationships. They are (1) the equation of continuity and (2) the equation of energy.

The equation of continuity states that the mass of fluid flowing *into* the apparatus or system is equal to the mass of fluid flowing *out*. The equation of energy states that the energy flowing in plus the energy added in the form of heat and work minus the energy subtracted in the form of heat and work is equal to the energy flowing out. Such a mechanical and thermodynamic system is sketched diagrammatically in Fig. 1:33. In mechanics and thermodynamics (which includes aerodynamics) it is customary in writing such equations to neglect

(1) conversion of mass to energy by radioactivity and (2) chemical energy changes.

It should be particular y noted that the "general energy equation" used by the engineer is, from the point of view of the physicist or physical chemist, a very special case and that, particularly from the physicist's point of view, there are not *two* equations of continuity and energy, respectively, but only *one* equation of *conservation of mass and energy*. If two equations are to be written for convenience, it should be recognized that there may be a conversion from mass to energy, and possibly vice versa.

By indicating the inlet conditions by $(\ )_1$ and the outlet conditions by $(\ )_2$ and using the same notation as in preceding articles the *equation of continuity* may be written

$$\rho_1 A_1 V_1 = \rho_2 A_2 V_2 \text{ in slugs per sec} \tag{1:47}$$

and the *equation of energy* may be written

$$778U_1 + \frac{P_1}{1g} + \frac{V_1^2}{2g} + z_1 + 778\Delta Q_1^2 - [\text{work done } \textit{by} \text{ fluid}]_1^2$$
$$= 778U_2 + \frac{P_2}{\rho 2g} + \frac{V_2^2}{2g} + z_2 \text{ (in ft-lb per lb)} \tag{1:48}$$

For *isothermal flow* with no additions or losses of heat or work, equation (1:48) becomes

$$\frac{P_1}{\rho_1 g} + \frac{V_1^2}{2g} + z_1 = \frac{P_2}{\rho_2 g} + \frac{V_2^2}{2g} + z_2 \tag{1:49}$$

For *isothermal flow of an "incompressible" fluid* $\rho_1 g = \rho_2 g = w$, and

$$\frac{P_1}{w} + \frac{V_1^2}{2g} + z_1 = \frac{P_2}{w} + \frac{V_2^2}{2g} + z_2 \tag{1:50}$$

Equation (1:50) is the well-known *Bernoulli equation* widely used in hydraulic work. For work in aerodynamics the z terms become negligible, and the Bernoulli equation for incompressible flow of air with no additions or losses of heat or work [equation (1:50)] becomes

$$\frac{V_2^2 - V_1^2}{2g} = \frac{P_1 - P_2}{\rho g} \tag{1:51}$$

This may be called Bernoulli's equation for incompressible air and may be used only as long as the pressure change $P_1 - P_2$ is negligible compared with the original pressure P_1. For the flow of air around airplanes and other objects it is much more nearly correct to assume an isentropic compressible flow of air, in which case equation (1:48) becomes

$$\frac{V_2^2 - V_1^2}{2g} = \frac{P_1}{\rho 1g} - \frac{P_2}{\rho 2g} + 778(U_1 - U_2) = 778(H_1 - H_2)$$
$$= c_p(T_1 - T_2) \quad (1{:}52)$$

For air with $k = 1.405$ the equations developed in Art. 1:5 may be used to show that, for $V_2 < c$,

$$\frac{V_2^2 - V_1^2}{2} = 3.47 \frac{P_1}{\rho 1}\left[1 - \left(\frac{P_2}{P_1}\right)^{0.288}\right] \quad (1{:}53)$$

Equation (1:53) is commonly solved for the pressure ratio P_2/P_1 in terms of the velocity ratio and Mach number, using equations (1:44) and (1:46), to get

$$\frac{P_2}{P_1} = \left[1 - 0.2025M_1^2\left(\frac{V_2^2}{V_1^2} - 1\right)\right]^{3.47} \quad (1{:}54)$$

Equations (1:53) and (1:54) are the *energy equations for subsonic isentropic compressible flow of air.* The following air-flow examples and problems are chiefly illustrative of some of the many applications of equations (1:51) and (1:53) or (1:54), but it should not be overlooked that there are many problems to which these equations are inapplicable because the conditions assumed are not fulfilled. In such cases the general energy equation (1:48) must be used. The equation of continuity (1:47), however, is used for all problems involving airplane flight since it neglects only radioactivity.

For problems involving supersonic flow, equation (1:48) is inconvenient to apply, but a special useful form of equation (1:48) can be derived. Problems in the analysis of supersonic flow, while of great practical importance, are beyond the scope of this text.[1]

Example 1.—Given the duct shown in Fig. 1:34, with a pressure difference between points $(\ )_1$ and $(\ )_2$ of 12 in. Hg as shown. The air conditions at point $(\ )_1$ are those of standard sea-level air, namely, $P_1 = 2{,}116$ lb per sq ft, $T_1 = 519$°F abs., $w_1 = 0.0765$ lb per cu ft. Find (*a*) V_1 and V_2, assuming the air to be incompressible, and (*b*) V_1, V_2, w_2, and T_2, assuming the air to be compressible and to flow isentropically from $(\ )_1$ to $(\ )_2$.

Solution.—*a*. Incompressible flow. The *continuity equation* (1:47) with $\rho_1 = \rho_2$ gives

$$\frac{V_2}{V_1} = \frac{A_1}{A_2} = 2 \quad (1{:}55)$$

[1] See R. Sauer, "Introduction to Technical Gas Dynamics," translation published by J. W. Edwards, Ann Arbor, Mich., or A. Buzemann, Gas Dynamics, *R.T.P. Trans.* 2207, British Ministry of Aircraft Production, available from Durand Reprinting Committee, California Institute of Technology, Pasadena, Calif. See also H. Liepmann, and A. E. Puckett, "Introduction to Aerodynamics of a Corpressible Fluid," John Wiley & Sons, Inc., New York, 1947.

The *energy equation* (1:51) (Bernoulli's equation) gives, with $V_2 = 2V_1$ and $P_2 = 2{,}116 - 62.4 \times 13.56 = 2{,}116 - 846 = 1{,}270$ lb per sq ft,

$$\frac{4V_1^2 - V_1^2}{2g} = \frac{2{,}116 - 1{,}270}{0.0765} \tag{1:56}$$

Equation (1:56) may be solved for $V_1 = 487$ ft per sec. Hence, $V_2 = 974$ ft per sec. This solution is inaccurate because V_2 is nearly as great as the speed of sound [1,120 ft per sec at point $(\ )_1$] and because the pressure ratio $P_2/P_1 = 0.60$ indicates that the assumption $\rho_1 = \rho_2$ is far from a fact.

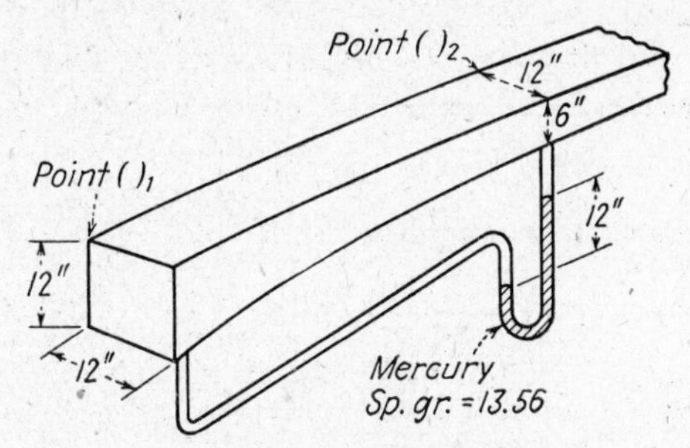

FIG. 1:34.—Air duct.

b. Compressible flow. The *continuity equation* (1:47) gives

$$\frac{V_2}{V_1} = \frac{A_1}{A_2}\frac{\rho_1}{\rho_2} = 2\frac{\rho_1}{\rho_2} \tag{1:57}$$

The *energy equation* (1:53) for isentropic compressible flow ot air gives, with $P_1 = 2{,}116$, $\rho_1 = 0.00238$, $P_2/P_1 = 0.60$, and $V_2 = 2(\rho_1/\rho_2)V_1$,

$$4\left(\frac{\rho_1}{\rho_2}\right)^2 V_1^2 - V_1^2 = 6.94\,\frac{2{,}116}{0.00238}\,(1 - 0.60^{0.288}) \tag{1:58}$$

Equation (1:58) may be readily solved if the isentropic-process equation

$$\frac{P_2}{P_1} = \left(\frac{\rho_2}{\rho_1}\right)^{1.405}$$

is combined with it. With $P_2/P_1 = 0.60$, solve for $(\rho_2/\rho_1) = 0.60^{0.712} = 0.695$ and $w_2 = 0.695 \times 0.0765 = 0.0531$ lb per cu ft. Since $4(\rho_1/\rho_2)^2 = 4/0.695^2 = 8.29$, equation (1:59) gives $V_1 = 340$ ft per sec, $V_2 = 2V_1/0.695 = 980$ ft per sec. From the isentropic-process equations in Table 1:1, calculate

$$\frac{T_2}{T_1} = \left(\frac{P_2}{P_1}\right)^{(k-1)/k} = 0.60^{0.288} = 0.863 \tag{1:59}$$

which gives $T_2 = 0.863 \times 519 = 448$, or $t = -12°$F. These are the answers called for.

In the compressible-flow solution, note the large density change and large temperature drop. If the air was moist, ice formation might be expected in the duct.

Since the above compressible-flow solution is simple and accurate, the question might be raised as to why the incompressible-flow solution was considered at all. The compressible-flow solution is simple, however, *only* for problems in which the pressures are given and the velocities to be found. For the more usual problem in which the velocities are given and the pressures are to be found [and equation (1:54) must be used], the solution must be by trial and is laborious and the simpler incompressible-flow solution may be used as a guide to the trial or graphical solution of the compressible-flow problem.

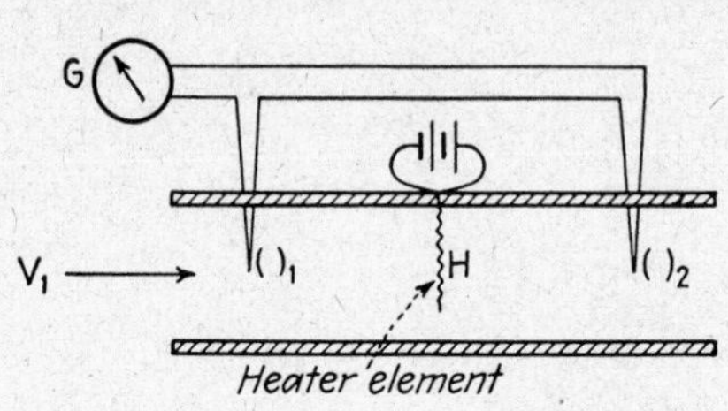

FIG. 1:35.—Thomas meter for air flow.

Example 2.—Given a duct of 2 sq ft cross section through which air flows at P = 2,116 lb per sq ft = const., as shown in Fig. 1:35. Thermocouples are located at points $(\ )_1$ and $(\ )_2$ and measure a temperature rise of 10°F from T_1 = 519 to T_2 = 529 when heat is supplied to the air stream at a rate of 500 watts. Find the rate of air flow through the duct.

Solution.—The continuity equation (1:47), with $A_1 = A_2$, gives, for P = const.

$$\frac{V_2}{V_1} = \frac{\rho_1}{\rho_2} = \frac{T_2}{T_1} = \frac{529}{519} = 1.02 \tag{1:60}$$

The *energy equation* (1:48), neglecting z terms and work done by the air, becomes (for each pound of air flowing)

$$778H_1 + \frac{V_1^2}{2g} = 778\Delta Q_1^2 = 778H_2 + \frac{V_2^2}{2g} \tag{1:61}$$

which may be rewritten

$$H_2 - H_1 = c_p(T_2 - T_1) = \Delta Q_1^2 + \frac{V_1^2}{2g \times 778}\left(1 - \frac{V_2^2}{V_1^2}\right) \tag{1:62}$$

Substitute $c_p = 0.24$, $T_2 - T_1 = 10$°F, and since 500 watts = 0.5 × 3,415 Btu per hr = 0.5 × 3,415/3,600 Btu per sec and w = 0.0765 and the weight of air flowing per second is $w_1 = 0.0765 \times 2 \times V_1$ and

$$\Delta Q_1^2 = \frac{0.5 \times 3{,}415}{0.0765 \times 2V_1 \times 3{,}600} \tag{1:63}$$

$$2.4 = \frac{0.5 \times 3{,}415}{0.0765 \times 2 \times 3{,}600V_1} + \frac{V_1^2}{2g \times 778}(1 - 1.04) \tag{1:64}$$

While equation (1:64) is a cubic readily solvable only by trial, a first approximation may be obtained quickly by neglecting the kinetic-energy term, which gives V_1 = 1.29 ft per sec and shows the kinetic-energy term to be truly negligible. The apparatus described above is known as a "Thomas meter." The Thomas meter is used only for measuring relatively low velocities but is a good example of the type of problem in which neither isothermal nor isentropic flow may be assumed.

1:16. Problems

1. Air flows through the Venturi meter shown in Fig. 1:36. If $P_1 = 24$ in. Hg abs., $T_1 = 540$°F abs., $A_1 = \pi$ sq ft, $A_2 = \pi/4$ sq ft, find the weight of air flowing per second when the mercury manometer reads 6 in., (*a*) assuming incompressible flow and (*b*) assuming isentropic compressible flow.

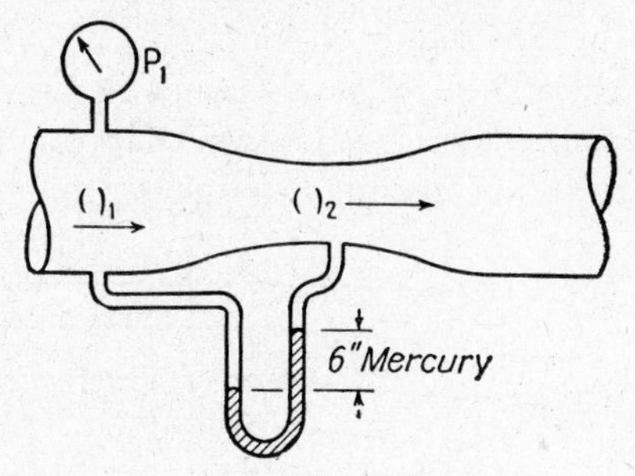

FIG. 1:36.—Venturi meter.

2. The pressure gauge in Fig. 1:37 reads 5 lb per sq in., $T_1 = 600$°F abs., $P_2 = 2{,}000$ lb per sq ft atmospheric pressure. Neglecting friction work, find the weight of air per second discharged by the nozzle, (*a*) assuming incompressible flow and (*b*) assuming isentropic compressible flow.

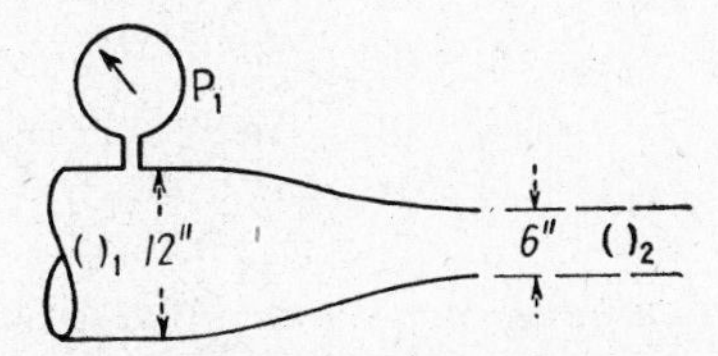

FIG. 1:37.—Air nozzle.

3. For the duct in Example 1 of Art. 1:15, assume $A_1 = 1.0$, $A_2 = 0.8$, and air conditions at point $(\ )_1$ to be standard sea level. For values of $P_2/P_1 = 0.9$ and 0.8, calculate V_2 and T_2 for compressible flow, and plot V_2 and c_2 *vs.* P_2/P_1. From the plot, find P_2/P_1, T_2, and V_2 for the condition that $V_2 = c_2$, or $M_2 = 1.0$.

4. Figure 1:38 represents the cowled coolant radiator of a pursuit airplane flying at 350 mph at 30,000 ft standard altitude. The engine of the airplane

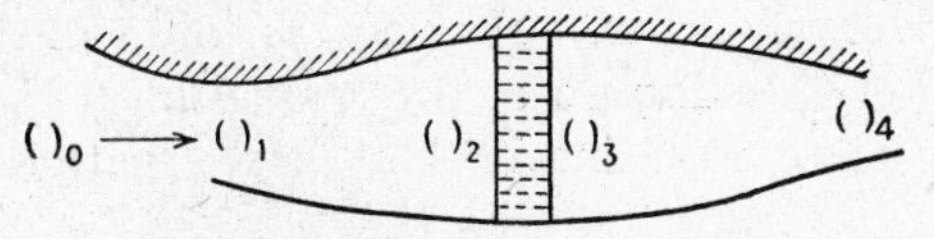

FIG. 1:38.—Cowled airplane radiator.

develops 1,500 hp, and an equal amount of heat is dissipated by the radiator. The cowl-entrance area $(\ )_1$ is 2 sq ft, and the discharge area $(\ )_4$ is 1.5 sq ft. The duct area at $(\ )_2$ and $(\ )_3$ is 6 sq ft, and the air flow through the radiator tubes is approximately at constant pressure. The temperature rise across the radiator is 20°F. Find (*a*) the mass flow of cooling air necessary, (*b*) the entrance velocity V_1, and (*c*) the outlet temperature T_4.

1:17. Fluid Friction in the Flow near an Object; Reynolds Number.—When a fluid flows near a solid body, the layers of fluid immediately adjacent to the body are retarded by friction, which does work on the fluid resulting in a slight rise in temperature. Such a process is called *adiabatic* if no heat is transferred to the fluid; it is neither isentropic nor isothermal. For a simplified picture, however, it is customary unless there is a large difference in temperature between the solid body and the fluid to assume that the temperature, and therefore the viscosity, is constant throughout the fluid.

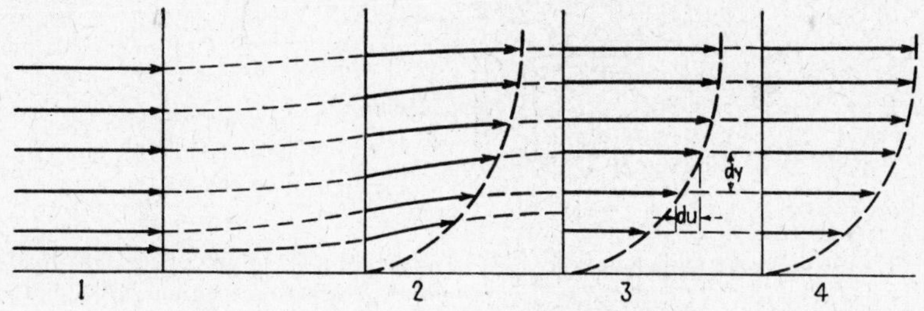

FIG. 1:39.—Transition from uniform to laminar flow as straight-parallel ("smooth") streams start to flow by a thin, smooth plate.

A fluid flow pattern in the vicinity of an object is greatly affected by small oscillations in magnitude and direction of the fluid velocity in the approaching air stream and by the surface roughness of the object. The geometry of the flow may well, in the interests of simplicity, be first described for a perfect uniform flow (consisting of straight parallel streamlines) as it starts to move past an infinitely thin and perfectly smooth flat plate. Such a flow is shown in Fig. 1:39. The air streams near the plate are retarded by the friction; the condition of continuity requires that the streams spread apart as they slow down, as shown at station 1 in Fig. 1:39. When the fluid has moved far enough back on the plate, it establishes a pattern like that shown at station 2 in Fig. 1:39, which is repeated at station 3 and at subsequent stations and involves a continuous sliding of one layer of fluid over the other. This flow is said to be *laminar*. The reverse process of speeding up of the central layers occurs when the fluid leaves the plate, resulting in the "wake" pattern shown in Fig. 1:40.

If there is a difference in velocity du between two layers a distance dy apart as shown in Fig. 1:39, the unit friction force between the layers, from the definition of viscosity given in Art. 1:1, is

$$\tau = \mu \frac{du}{dy} \qquad (1:65)$$

where τ is the unit shearing stress between layers.

The thickness of a laminar boundary layer increases as the fluid proceeds down the plate approximately as shown in Fig. 1:41. The local shearing force per unit area on the plate also decreases. For a

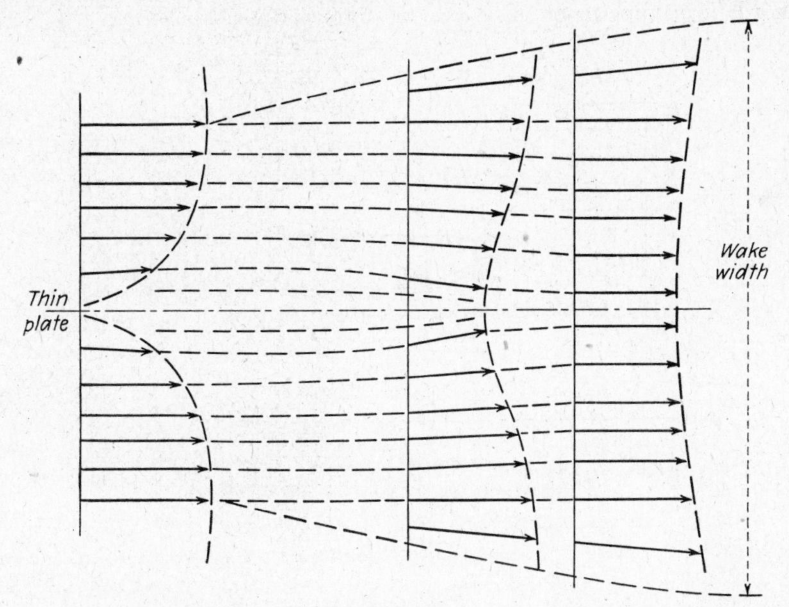

FIG. 1:40.—Flow pattern in the wake of a thin, smooth plate with laminar flow.

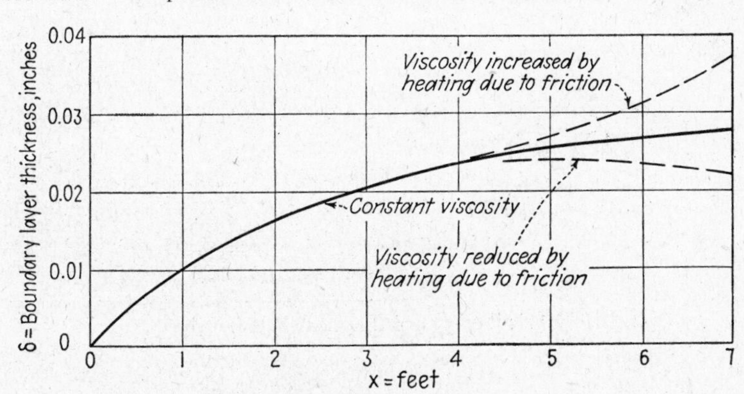

FIG. 1:41.—Approximate laminar boundary-layer thickness for flow of standard air past a thin, smooth plate.

given product of velocity and distance divided by kinematic viscosity, the unit shearing force is found to have a given value regardless of the fluid. This ratio

$$Re = \frac{Vx}{\nu} = \frac{Vx\rho}{\mu} \tag{1:66}$$

is known as Reynolds number and is widely used for plotting the results of experiments with fluid friction, as in Figs. 1:45 and 1:46. For an airplane wing, Re is calculated as Vc/ν, where c is the wing chord; for a pipe or circular duct of diameter d, $Re = Vd/\nu$.

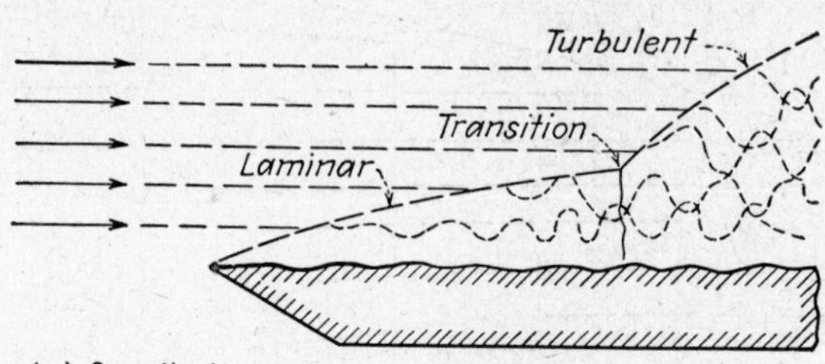

(a)- Smooth air at low velocity, slightly rough plate

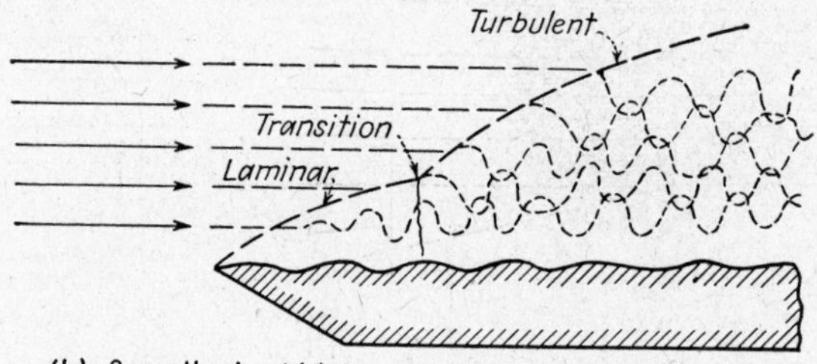

(b)- Smooth air at higher velocity, slightly rough plate

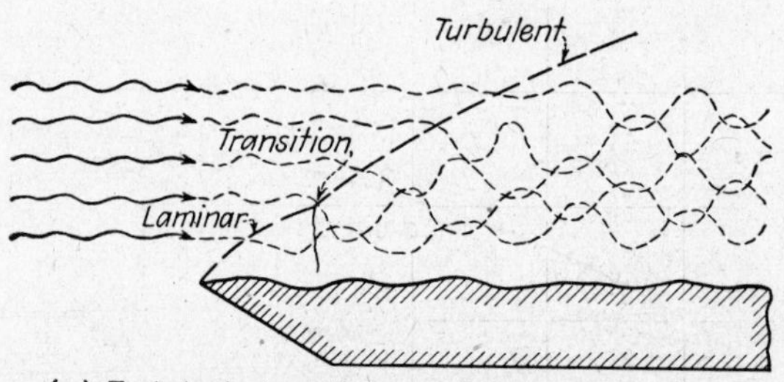

(c)- Turbulent air at higher velocity, slightly rough plate

FIG. 1:42.—Changes in air-flow patterns as smooth and slightly turbulent air starts to flow past a slightly rough plate.

Values of ν for computing Reynolds number for air flow at various pressures and temperatures can be read conveniently from the air chart in the back of the book.

The foregoing picture of ideal laminar flow never actually exists, however; for no actual plate is perfectly smooth when viewed under a microscope, and the air flow approaching the plate is never perfectly smooth (though a very close approximation to perfectly smooth air flow is obtained when an airplane wing flies through still air). The effects of air turbulence and surface roughness are shown in Fig. 1:42. The effect of the surface roughness is to make waves near the lower portion of the boundary layer, which are transmitted to adjacent layers of the fluid. In a region where the velocity is decreasing, these waves are magnified as they progress down the plate until a point is reached where the layers mix with each other (indicated by the crossing of the streamlines in Fig. 1:42). A boundary layer with this sort of interchange of energy between layers is known as a "turbulent boundary layer." It is more complex than the laminar flow, but still susceptible to mathematical analysis if reasonable assumptions can be made of the distance over which mixing occurs. Note in Fig. 1:42 that increasing either the velocity or the turbulence of the initial air stream causes a more rapid development of the turbulent boundary layer.

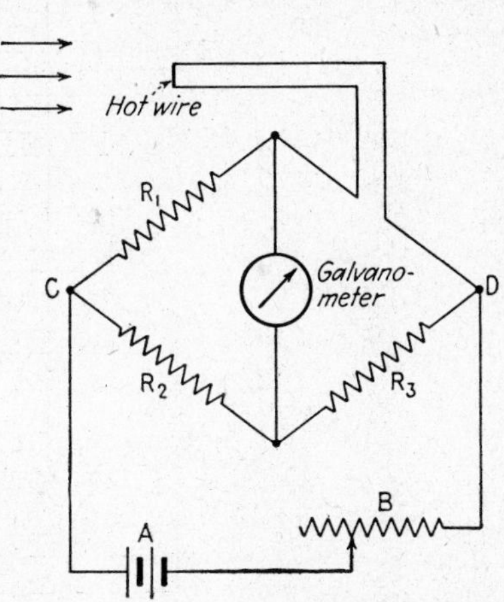

FIG. 1:43.—Constant-voltage hot-wire anemometer for measurement of turbulence. (*From Binder, "Fluid Mechanics."*)

A quantitative measure of the turbulence of an air stream is usually taken as the ratio of the velocity change ΔV to the velocity V. The ratio $\Delta V/V$ sometimes runs as high as 5 per cent in turbulent wind tunnels. For measuring turbulence, a "hot-wire" anemometer, shown in Fig. 1:43, is ordinarily used. In this instrument a very thin heated platinum wire is used as the detecting element. Small velocity fluctuations cause changes in the temperature of the wire that can be detected, and their frequency determined, by suitable electron-tube amplification and lag compensation.

By making suitable assumptions as to the mixing length in a turbulent flow, Kármán has developed the equation shown in Fig. 1:44 for velocity distribution in the turbulent boundary layer. Note in Fig. 1:44 that even with a turbulent boundary layer there is a very thin laminar sublayer which in turn continues to grow as it moves down the plate and becomes eventually turbulent.

The skin friction on a smooth flat plate is shown as a function of Reynolds number in Fig. 1:45, two different solid lines being shown for laminar and turbulent skin friction. Beyond a Reynolds number of about 20,000, note that the flow may be either laminar flow or turbulent. The transition from laminar to turbulent flow depends on the air-stream turbulence and surface roughness in a manner as

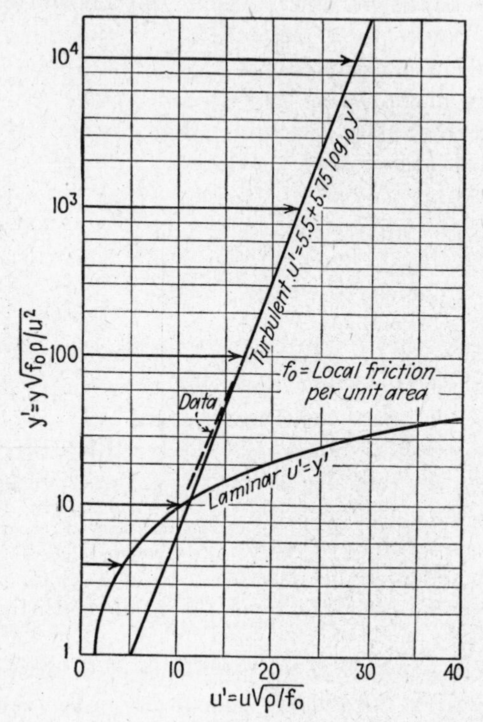

FIG. 1:44.—Velocity distribution for turbulent isothermal flow near a smooth flat plate. (*See von Kármán, J. Aeronaut. Sci.*, January, 1934.)

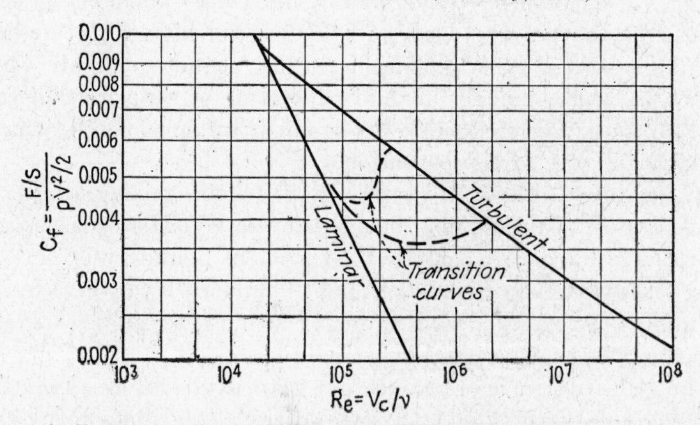

FIG. 1:45.—Skin-friction coefficient on a smooth flat plate.

yet difficult to predict. Major reductions in the skin friction of airplane wings have recently been obtained by so shaping the cross section, or profile, of the wing as to maintain laminar flow as far aft along the chord of the airfoil as possible, but in any actual wing design the flow must become turbulent before it reaches the trailing edge of the wing. A major factor in determining the transition from laminar to turbulent flow is the pressure and velocity gradient. As long as the velocity is increasing, the flow tends to remain laminar. Laminar-flow wings are so designed as to keep the surface velocity on the increase as far aft as is possible.

The skin-friction coefficient C_f plotted in Fig. 1:45 is defined by the equation

$$C_f = \frac{F/S}{\rho(V^2/2)} \tag{1:67}$$

where F/S is the skin-friction force per unit of wetted surface. An example of its use follows:

Example.—Air flows in a wind tunnel over a sheet of metal 3 ft wide and 15 ft long at a speed of 100 mph (146.7 ft per sec). The air is standard sea-level air, for which $1/\nu = 6{,}380$. Find the friction force on the sheet of metal.

Solution.—Calculate Reynolds number for the entire sheet as follows:

$$R_e = 146.7 \times 15 \times 6{,}380 = 14{,}020{,}000$$

In Fig. 1:45 read $C_f = 0.0029$. Using equation (1:67) with $S = 3 \times 15 = 45$, and using $\rho/2 = 0.00119$, calculate

$$F = C_f \rho \frac{V^2}{2} S = 0.0029 \times 0.00119 \times 146.7^2 \times 45 = 3.33 \text{ lb}$$

In analyzing the flow through Venturi meters, orifices, nozzles, and pipe lines it is customary to make an initial analysis neglecting fluid friction and then to inset a coefficient or friction factor that is a function of Reynolds number to take account of the energy loss due to fluid friction. Such coefficients are shown in Fig. 1:46. Figure 1:46*a*, for example, provides a correction factor for the solution of such problems as Prob. 1, Art. 1:16.

1:18. Problems

1. Solve Prob. 1, Art. 1:16, taking account of fluid friction by means of Fig. 1:46*a*.

2. An airplane with a wing of chord 5 ft is flying at 200 mph at 8,000 ft altitude in standard air. Find the Reynolds number of the wing.

3. An airplane with wing of 10 ft mean chord is flying at 300 mph at 2,000 ft altitude. Find the mean Reynolds number of the wing.

4. A small airplane wing of 3 ft mean chord is flying 60 mph at 8,000 ft altitude in standard air. The wing area is 150 sq ft. Calculate the skin friction on the wing surface, assuming that the factor C_f in Fig. 1:45 applies to both upper and lower surfaces of the wing and assuming turbulent flow.

5. Air flows through the orifice meter shown in Fig. 1:46*b*; $D_1 = 12$ in., $D_2 = 6$ in., $T_2 = 492$°F abs., $P_1 = 2{,}000$ lb per sq ft, and $P_2 = 1{,}900$ lb per sq ft. Assume incompressible flow with $w = w_1$, and find (*a*) V_2, assuming $K = 1.0$, and (*b*) V_2 including friction-loss effect.

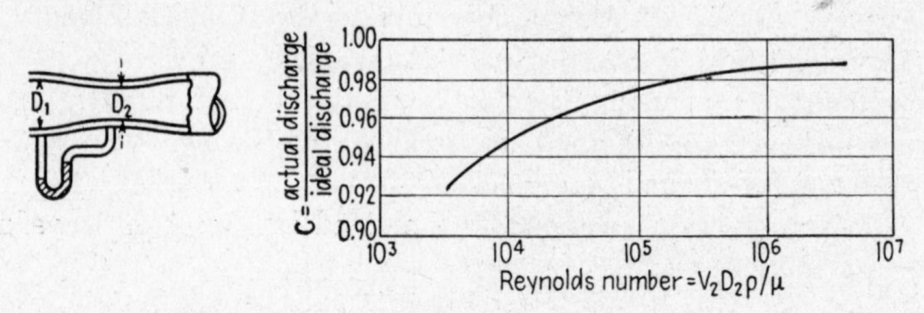

a. Venturi-meter discharge coefficient (incompressible flow).

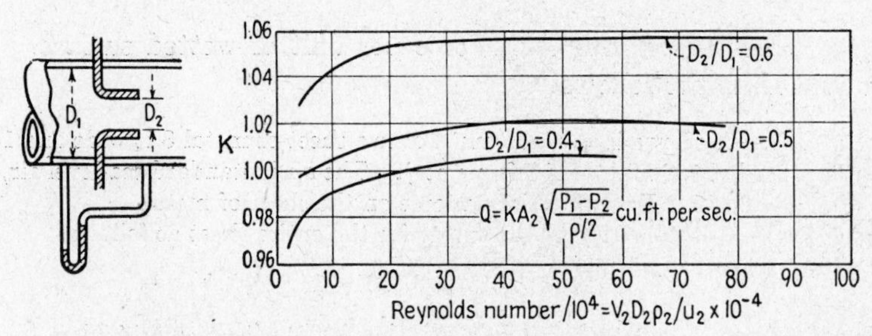

b. Flow coefficient K for ASME standard nozzles (incompressible flow).

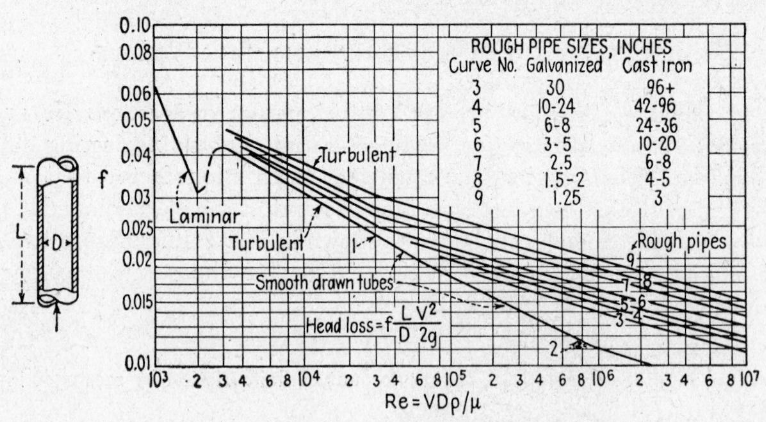

c. Friction-loss factor for flow in circular pipes.

FIG. 1:46.—Effect of Reynolds number on friction losses in Venturi meters, nozzles, and pipes. (*Replotted from Binder, "Fluid Mechanics."*)

1:19. Transfer of Heat between a Fluid and a Solid: Nusselt and Grashof Numbers.—Heat is transferred between objects in three distinct ways: (1) wave *radiation* of the infrared sort associated with light waves; (2) *conduction;* (3) *convection*, involving movement and mixing of fluid. Heat transfer from solid bodies to fluids, and vice versa, is usually chiefly by conduction and convection.

If a stationary fluid lies underneath a warmer solid body, as in Fig. 1:47*a*, the heat transferred from the object to the fluid is chiefly by *conduction*. Experiments show that conduction through a fluid is determined by the equation

$$\frac{\Delta Q \text{ conduction}}{\Delta \text{ time}} = k_c S \frac{\Delta T}{\Delta y} \qquad (1:68)$$

where S is the surface area in square feet, Δy is the distance in feet perpendicular to the surface, and ΔT is the temperature difference across the distance Δy. The usual units of conductivity k_c are Btu per hour-square foot-Fahrenheit degree per foot. Values of k_c for common liquids and gases are given in Appendix 2. The thermal conductivity of a fluid is almost exactly proportional to its dynamic viscosity; a dimensionless ratio including these two factors and specific heat is the Prandtl number given by equation (1:13). ($1/Pr$ is sometimes known as the Stanton number, designated by *St.*) Note in the table of gas properties in Table XIV, Appendix 2 that the Prandtl number for all the diatomic gases listed is within a 2 per cent range of 0.77.

If the fluid is located *above* the warmer body, as in Fig. 1:47*b*, the

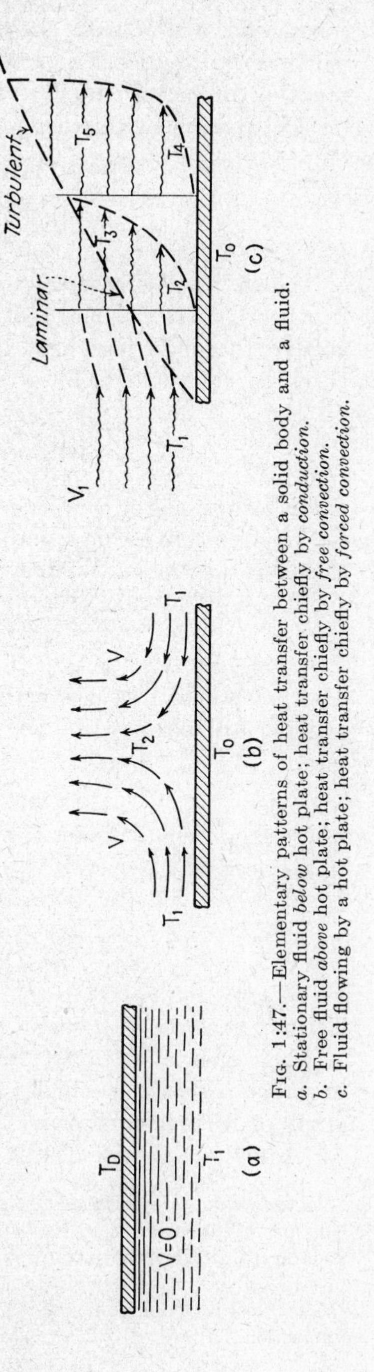

Fig. 1:47.—Elementary patterns of heat transfer between a solid body and a fluid.
a. Stationary fluid *below* hot plate; heat transfer chiefly by *conduction*.
b. Free fluid *above* hot plate; heat transfer chiefly by *free convection*.
c. Fluid flowing by a hot plate; heat transfer chiefly by *forced convection*.

conduction of heat from the body to the fluid soon results in a local reduction in the density of the fluid and a free *convective* flow starts, resulting in a more rapid rate of heat transfer. The rate of heat transfer is in this case usually expressed in the form of

$$\frac{\Delta Q \text{ convection}}{\Delta \text{ time}} = hS\Delta T \tag{1:69}$$

If S is the surface in square feet and $T = T_0 - T_1$, then the coefficient h, known as the *convective-heat-transfer coefficient,* is expressed in Btu per hour per square foot Fahrenheit degree. The ratio of convective to conductive heat transfer is found by dividing equation (1:69) by equation (1:68), giving

$$Nu = \frac{h\Delta y}{k_c} \tag{1:70}$$

and is known as the *Nusselt number.*

For free convection from a pipe of diameter D it is customary to calculate the Nusselt number as

$$Nu = \frac{hD}{k_c} \tag{1:71}$$

The pattern of free convective circulation about a circular pipe or cylinder is determined by the ratio

$$Gr = \frac{D^3 g}{\nu^2} \frac{\Delta T}{T_{\text{gas}}} \tag{1:72}$$

where D = pipe diameter
g = 32.2 ft per sec²
ν = kinematic viscosity at mean temperature
$T_m = (T_0 + T_1)/2$
$\Delta T = T_0 - T_1$
$T_{\text{gas}} = T_1$

This is known as the *Grashof number.*

Experimental data for free convection from hot pipes or wires to surrounding gases (chiefly air) are usually plotted in the form of a graph of Nusselt number *vs.* the product $GrPr$, as shown in Fig. 1:48. An example of the use of this graph follows:

Example 1.—A cylindrical airplane passenger compartment of 10-ft diameter is held at a temperature of 70°F (T_0 = 530°). The airplane is standing still out-of-doors in still air when the outside temperature is 20°F (T_1 = 480°). The barometric pressure of the air corresponds to 6,000-ft pressure altitude. Using Fig 1:48, find the heat loss per hour from a 30-ft length of the passenger compartment due to free convection.

Solution.—The mean air film temperature is $T_m = (530 + 480)/2 = 505$ ($t = 45°F$). For a pressure altitude of 6,000 ft and a temperature of 45°F, read on the air chart in the back of the book $\nu_0/\nu = 0.845$ and calculate

$$1/\nu = 0.845 \times 6{,}380 = 5{,}450.$$

Then, using $\Delta T = 530 - 480 = 50$ and $T_{\text{gas}} = 480$, calculate

$$Gr = 10^3 \times 32.2 \times 5{,}450^2\,{}^{50}\!/_{480} = 10 \times 10^{10}$$

$$GrPr = 0.77Gr = 7.7 \times 10^{10}$$

Using the curve labeled 10 in Fig. 1:48 because 10 is to the tenth power in the calculated value of $GrPr$, read in Fig. 1:48

$$Nu = 600 = \frac{hD}{k_c}$$

With $D = 10$ ft, and $k_c = 0.0131$ by interpolation on page 382, calculate

$$h = \frac{600 \times 0.0131}{10} = 0.786 \text{ Btu/(hr)(sq ft)(deg F)}$$

substituting this value of h in equation (1:69) and using $S = 10\pi \times 15 = 471$ sq ft.

$$\frac{\Delta Q}{\text{Hr}} = 0.786 \times 471 \times 50 = 18{,}500 \text{ Btu per hr}$$

This is the answer called for.

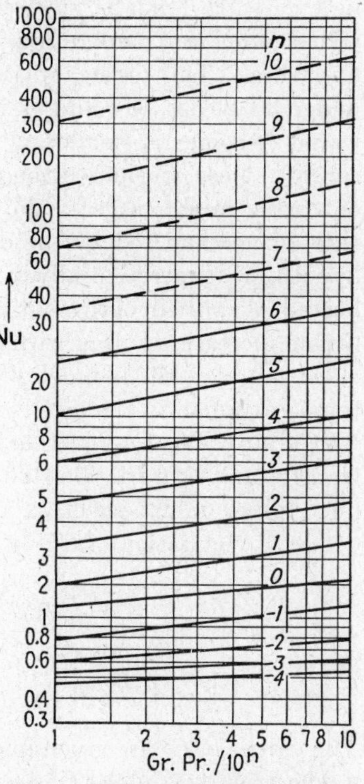

FIG. 1:48.—Mean of data on free convection about horizontal cylinders plotted by W. J. King. Cylinder diameters from 0.0016 to 4.5 in. Physical constants evaluated at arithmetic mean temperatures. Most data lie within 20 per cent of above line. Wall temperature 180 to 1900°F; fluid temperatures 50 to 80°F. (*Copied from replot in Boelter, Cherry, and Johnson, Heat Transfer Notes, University of California Press, Berkeley, April*, 1940.)

For turbulent air flowing by a hot, flat plate, the boundary layer develops as described in Art. 1:17, but because of the transfer of heat from the hot plate to the fluid, the fluid, of initial temperature T_1, has a temperature gradient from T_2 to T_3 in the laminar boundary layer and from T_4 to T_5 in the turbulent boundary layer, as shown in Fig. 1:47*c*. This change in temperature results in marked changes in viscosity and density of the fluid, particularly if it is a gas. Satisfactory solutions to this complicated but important problem do not appear to have been published at the present time, though Lees[1]

[1] LEES, LESTER, unpublished thesis, Massachusetts Institute of Technology, 1940.

has found that increasing the temperature of the plate for the case shown in Fig. 1:47c because it superimposes a tendency like that shown in Fig. 1:47b tends to destabilize the boundary layer and move the transition point from laminar to turbulent flow a considerable distance upstream. This effect was observed, however, only at velocities under 30 ft per sec, and it is reasonable to suppose that the effect would become of smaller if not of negligible importance at higher speeds. Lees considered the possibility that heating the lower surface of a wing might increase the length of the region of laminar flow on this surface and reduce the drag but did not find time to verify this hypothesis experimentally. Wind-tunnel tests on wings that are heated over their entire surface, top and bottom, have shown measurable increases in drag with increase in surface temperature, but this effect may be due as much to the increase in viscosity of the air with temperature as to changes in the flow pattern.

Colburn[1] has found, from a study of the relationship between heat transfer and skin friction, that the mean heat-transfer coefficient for a duct, pipe, or flat sheet h_m is related to the skin-friction coefficient defined by equation (1:67) by the equation

$$Nu = \frac{h_m L}{k_c} = \frac{C_f}{2} Re(Pr)^{1/3} \qquad (1:73)$$

or

$$Nu = 0.46 C_f Re \text{ for air with } Pr = 0.77 \qquad (1:73.1)$$

The values of C_f are given in Fig. 1:45. This variation of Nu with Pr is checked by Tifford.[2] An example of the use of equation (1:73) follows;

Example 2.—Air at a temperature of 28°F and barometric pressure of 2,116 lb per sq ft abs. flows at 60 mph (88 ft per sec) through a wind tunnel over a hot plate of temperature of 212°, the plate being 3 ft wide and 15 ft long. (*a*) Calculate Reynolds number for the plate, assuming a mean boundary-layer temperature equal to the arithmetic mean between the initial air temperature and the plate temperature, and find the corresponding coefficient of skin friction from Fig. 1:45; (*b*) find the mean heat-transfer coefficient from equation (1:73); (*c*) find the rate of heat transfer from the hot plate to the air stream; (*d*) find the coefficient of skin friction from Fig. 1:45 if the plate were the same temperature as the air, that is, 28°F.

Solution.—*a.* On the air chart in the back of the book, for sea-level pressure altitude and $t_m = (28 + 212)/2 = 120$, read $\nu_0/\nu = 0.815$, and calculate

[1] COLBURN, A. P., A Method of Correlating Forced Convection Heat Transfer Data, and a Comparison with Fluid Friction, *Trans. A.I.C.E.*, **29,** 174 (1933).

[2] TIFFORD, ARTHUR N., Thermodynamics of the Laminar Boundary Layer of a Heated Body in a High Speed Gas Flow Field, *J. Aeronaut. Sci.*, 241–251 (April, 1945).

$1/\nu = 6{,}380 \times 0.815 = 5{,}200$. Calculate also

$$Re = 88 \times 15 \times 5{,}200 = 6{,}870{,}000,$$

and read, in Fig. 1:45, $C_f = 0.0033$. These are the answers to (*a*).

b. Using equation (1:73.1), which is the special form of equation (1:73) applicable to air flow, and using values of C_f and Re found in (*a*), calculate

$$Nu = 0.46 C_f Re = 0.46 \times 0.0033 \times 6{,}780{,}000 = 10{,}400$$

Since $Nu = h_m L/k_c$, $L = 15$ ft, and $k_c = 0.0147$ by interpolation to $t_m = 120°$ on page 382, calculate

$$h_m = \frac{Nuk_c}{L} = \frac{10{,}400 \times 0.0147}{15} = 10.2 \text{ Btu/(hr)(deg F)(sq ft)}$$

This is the answer called for in (*b*).

c. Substituting in equation (1:69) with $S = 3 \times 15 = 45$ and $T = 184°$F, calculate

$$\frac{\Delta Q}{\text{Hr}} = 10.2 \times 45 \times 184 = 84{,}300 \text{ Btu per hr}$$

This is the answer called for in (*c*).

d. To calculate Re for $t = 28°$F and sea-level pressure altitude, read on the air chart in the back of the book $\nu_0/\nu = 1.12$, and calculate $1/\nu = 1.12 \times 6{,}380 = 7{,}150$ and $Re = 88 \times 15 \times 7{,}150 = 9{,}300{,}000$. In Fig. 1:45 read $C_f = 0.0031$, and note that, according to this calculation, the hot plate has 6 per cent higher skin friction than the cold plate. This is the answer called for in (*d*).

The foregoing procedure must, however, be regarded as questionable, as it does not adequately take account of the variations in local skin friction, boundary-layer thickness, temperature or viscosity, and heat-transfer coefficient. It does have the advantage, however, of giving a definite answer and shows a change in the right direction due to heating of the plate. This calculation would be the same whether the plate were in the top or bottom of the wind tunnel. It seems likely that a proper analysis, using the data from Lees' thesis,[1] would show only a small increase in skin friction if the plate were on the top of the tunnel but a large increase in skin friction with the plate on the bottom of the tunnel, an increase of quite a different order of magnitude from that calculated above.

While the foregoing analysis takes account of the compressibility of the fluid, the effect of high Mach number is not specifically considered and may be of primary importance. At first glance, it might appear that a high Mach number, accompanied by a correspondingly high rate of heat transfer to the air, would involve an analysis not substantially different from the foregoing, as long as a shock wave was not formed. The major difference would be that in the general flow pattern at high Mach number there would be a different temperature

[1] *Op. cit.*

distribution in the air with marked reductions in temperature in regions of high velocity. Accordingly, for speeds in excess of 300 mph, the normal temperature distribution for isentropic flow should be used instead of the constant initial air temperature. For flight at very high altitudes, the lift coefficient of the wing must be high, and the velocity increase over the upper surface must be high, resulting in abnormally low temperatures at the surface of the wing. For high altitudes, therefore, the upper surface may be a very favorable location for a surface radiator. Further research on this matter is needed.

1:20. Problems

1. A steam pipe of nominal 4-in. diameter ($D = 0.375$ ft) has a surface temperature of 200°F and loses heat by free convection to the still air of a room in which the temperature is 70°F. Find the heat loss per hour per square foot of pipe from the pipe to the room.

2. Air at a temperature of −20°F and at a pressure altitude of 20,000 ft flows at 300 mph over a portion of the upper surface of a wing 10 ft wide and 6 ft long ($c = 6$ ft) that is used as a wing-surface radiator for engine cooling. The coolant and wing surface are at a temperature of 200°F. (*a*) Find the skin friction of the radiator, assuming that the mean boundary-layer temperature is the arithmetic mean of coolant and air temperatures. (*b*) Find the mean coefficient of heat transfer from equation (1:73). (*c*) Find the rate of heat dissipation of this wing-surface radiator in horsepower.

1:21. Flow Patterns around Infinite Cylinders of Various Shapes: Addition of Simple Flow Patterns.—When a fluid flows around an infinite cylinder of mathematically regular shape, such as a circular or elliptic cylinder, the flow pattern, except in the boundary layer, also has a mathematical regularity. Such flow patterns are shown in Fig. 1:49 for circular and elliptic cylinders. The lines shown are "streamlines," which are the paths of particles in a laminar flow. Since there is no flow across a streamline, the problem of flow between streamlines may be handled just like the problem of flow in a duct of variable cross section. While these particular shapes are of only incidental importance in the flow around complete aircraft and aircraft parts, the method of development of equations of streamlines from the equation of continuity and of determining the pressure distribution from the energy equation is of fundamental importance and merits a careful study. The actual flow of an incompressible fluid may be considered to be the composite of several simpler flows such as the first three items in Table 1:2. Such flows are called "two-dimensional" because they are strictly applicable only to infinite cylinders for which the flow may be considered the same at all cross sections.

The primary simple flow patterns that may be combined to get the flow patterns of Fig. 1:49 and many other shapes are, referring to

Table 1:2, (1) a *uniform flow*, (2) a *source*, or *sink*, and (3) a *vortex*. The equation of continuity may be used to write equations for the streamlines of these simple flow patterns. Other flow patterns may be found by adding algebraically the streamline equations of the component simple flows.

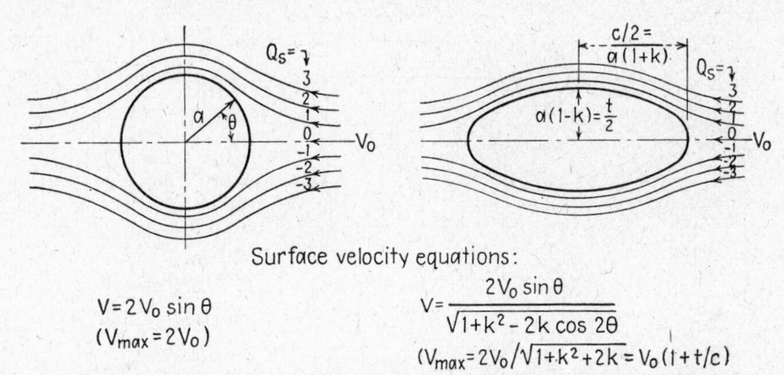

FIG. 1:49.—Comparison of ideal flows about circular and elliptic cylinders.

For example, the equation of the streamlines of a uniform flow, such as that shown in Fig. 1:50, may be calculated by writing the equation of continuity for the flow between any two streamlines a distance dy apart. If dQ_s represents the quantity of fluid flowing between two such streamlines in cubic feet per second and V_0 represents the velocity in feet per second in the $+x$ direction, then for a flow of 1 ft depth (perpendicular to the paper)

$$dQ_s = +V_0 dy \qquad (1:74)$$

Integrating equation (1:74) and suitably choosing the constant of integration gives

$$Q_s = +V_0 y \qquad (1:75)$$

Letting $y = 0$ gives the streamline $Q_s = 0$; and, for $V_0 = 100$ and $y = 1$, the streamline constant is $Q_s = 100$. Other values of Q_s are shown in Fig. 1:50. The meaning of the term Q_s (more usually designated by ψ) is thus seen to be the quantity flowing between the zero streamline (which is arbitrarily chosen) and the specified streamline. In equation (1:75) a streamline (Q_s = const.) is a function of y, but, in general, it will be a function of x and y (or r and θ).

For flow from a source (radially outward from a point), as in Fig. 1:51, the streamline equations are more conveniently developed in terms of polar coordinates. Thus, in Fig. 1:51, if the radial velocity

TABLE 1:2.—STREAMLINE EQUATIONS OF SIMPLE AND COMPOSITE FLOW PATTERNS IN AN INCOMPRESSIBLE FLUID

Item No.	Description	Sketch	Streamline equation $Q_s = C =$
1	Uniform flow	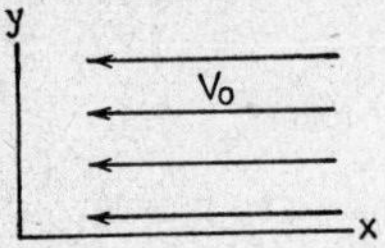 y, V_0, x	$-V_0 y$
2	Source (*a*) or sink (*b*)	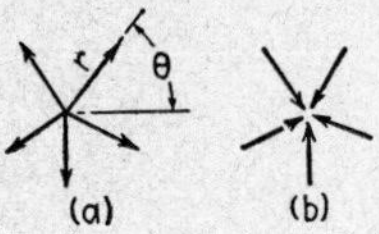 r, θ, (a), (b)	$\pm \frac{Q_0}{2\pi}\theta$ Q_0 = quantity flowing
3	Vortex		$\frac{\Gamma}{2\pi}\log_e r$ Γ = circulation
4	Uniform flow + source	 Streamlined nose	$-V_0 y + \frac{Q_0}{2\pi}\theta$
5	Uniform flow + source + sink dist. $2b$ apart	 "Rankine oval"	$-V_0 y + \frac{Q_0}{a\pi}\tan^{-1}\left(\frac{2b}{x^2 + y^2 - b^2}\right)$
6	Doublet = inf. source + inf. sink inf. close	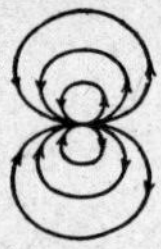	$\frac{By}{x^2 + y^2}$ where $B = Q_0 dx/2\pi$
7	Uniform flow + doublet	 Circle, radius *a*	$-V_0 y + \frac{V_0 a^2 y}{x^2 + y^2}$
8	Uniform flow + doublet + vortex	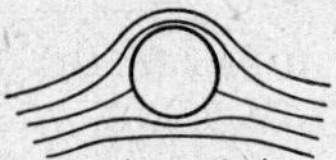 Rotating cylinder	$-V_0 r\left(1 + \frac{a^2}{r^2}\right)\sin\theta$ $-\frac{\Gamma}{2\pi}\log_e\frac{r}{a}$
9	Transformed No. 7 at surface, $y' = y(1 - k)$, $x' = x(1 + k)$	Ellipse, with axes 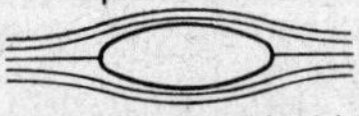 $a(1-k)$ and $a(1+k)$	

outward at radius r is V, the quantity flowing through an area 1 ft deep and $rd\theta$ ft wide is

$$dQ_s = Vrd\theta \tag{1:76}$$

Integrating completely around the circle and designating the total quantity flowing from the source by Q_0, equation (1:76) integrates to

$$Q_s = \frac{Q_0}{2\pi}\theta \tag{1:77}$$

For a vortex flow such as that shown in Fig. 1:52, with the tangential velocity distributed along the radius according to the equation $V_{\text{tangential}} = k/r$ (which is necessary for the vortex, like the source and uniform flow above, to be irrotational), the elementary flow through an area dr is

$$dQ_s = \frac{k}{r}\,dr \tag{1:78}$$

Equation (1:78), with suitably chosen constant of integration, becomes

$$Q_s = k \log_e r \tag{1:79}$$

k being known as the "circulation constant" of the vortex (the more usual notation is to call $k = \Gamma/2\pi$ and call Γ the "circulation").

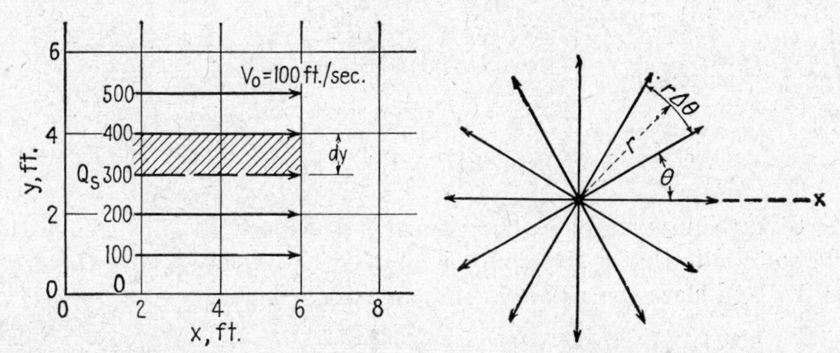

FIG. 1:50.—Elementary filament of uniform flow.

FIG. 1:51.—Elementary filament of source flow.

The combination of a uniform flow with a source and with a source and sink yields the flow patterns and streamline equations shown as items 4 and 5 of Table 1:2.

As a source and sink of equal strength are moved closer together until their locations coincide, it would appear at first glance that they would completely neutralize each other; but if the source and sink strengths Q_0 are increased to infinity as they get to an infinitesimal distance dx apart, so that the product Qdx is constant, a finite flow results. This flow is known as a *doublet*, sketched as item 6 in Table

1:2. To develop the streamline equation for a doublet, refer to Fig. 1:53, which shows a source and sink of equal strength Q_0 located a distance dx apart. At any point $y = r \sin \theta$ the radii r and $r + dr$ from the source and sink, respectively, are separated by an angle $d\theta = \theta' - \theta$. From the geometry of Fig. 1:53,

$$Q_s = \frac{Q_0}{2\pi} d\theta = \frac{Q_0}{2\pi} \frac{dx \sin \theta}{r} \tag{1:80}$$

If the product $Q_0 dx/2\pi$ is considered to have a constant value B, equation (1:80) may be written

$$Q_s = \frac{B \sin \theta}{r} = \frac{Br \sin \theta}{r^2} = \frac{By}{x^2 + y^2} \tag{1:81}$$

which is the doublet streamline equation given in Table 1:2.

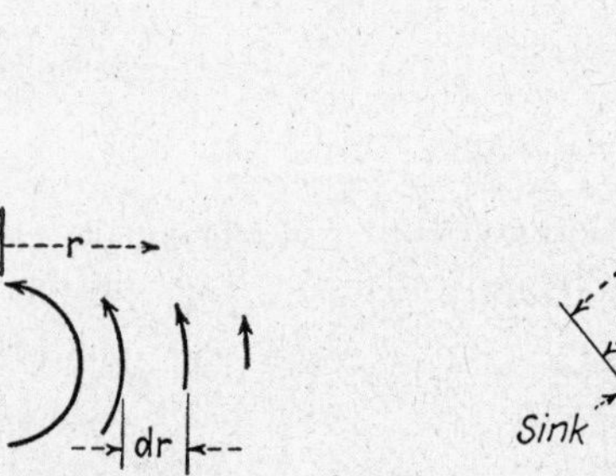

FIG. 1:52.—Elementary filament of vortex flow.

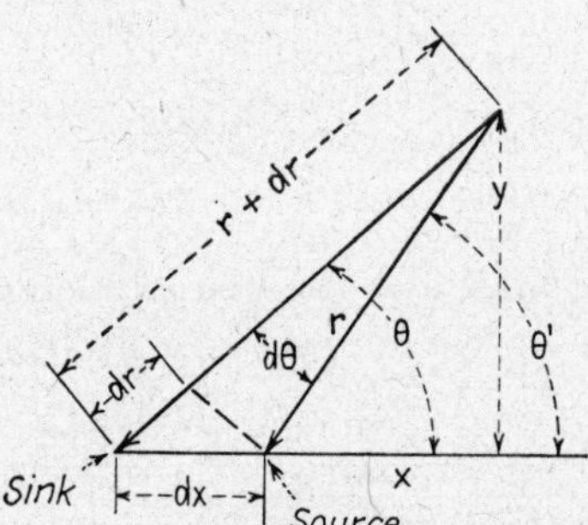

FIG. 1:53.—Geometry of source-and-sink relationships for a doublet.

Streamline equations (Q_s = const.) developed as above have the characteristic that a streamline is always in the direction of the flow, or if u and v are the x and y components of velocity

$$\frac{dy}{dx} = \frac{v}{u} \qquad \text{or} \qquad u\,dy - v\,dx = 0 \tag{1:82}$$

or if they are put in the form Q_s = const. $= f(x, y)$, then, from the definition of a partial derivative, $dQ_s = (\partial Q_s/\partial y)dy + (\partial Q_s/\partial x)dx$, and if $dQ_s = 0$

$$\frac{\partial Q_s}{\partial y} = u \qquad \text{and} \qquad \frac{\partial Q_s}{\partial x} = -v \tag{1:83}$$

Using equation (1:83), the x and y components of velocity at any point (x, y) of a flow pattern may be found by taking the proper partial derivatives of the streamline equations.

A combination of a doublet with a uniform flow gives a close approximation of the flow pattern around a circular cylinder, as shown in Table 1:2, item 7. To find the velocity at any point in this flow pattern, use equation (1:83). Using equation (1:83) on the streamline equation given in Table 1:2 gives the surface-velocity equations shown in Fig. 1:49.

When a circle is transformed into an ellipse by flattening it vertically and extending it horizontally and a similar transformation is applied to the flow pattern around a circular cylinder, the resulting flow pattern closely duplicates the actual flow pattern around an elliptic cylinder. The mathematics of this transformation is beyond the scope of this text, but the resulting velocity distributions at the surface of the circular and elliptic cylinders, including the maximum velocity, which occurs at the widest point, are given in Fig. 1:49. Note particularly that the maximum velocity at the widest point of the circular cylinder is *twice* the free-stream velocity.

The foregoing relationships were developed for incompressible flow. The regions of high velocity must, from consideration of the energy equation, be regions of low pressure. As the velocity increases to Mach numbers in excess of about 0.3 for air flow, the low-pressure regions become regions of appreciably lower density (and greater specific volume) and this effect serves to increase the velocity in the low-pressure regions still further. The relationships involved in *compressible* flow about thin elliptic cylinders have been summarized by Kármán[1] in the statement that the effect of compressibility can be approximately correctly treated by assuming an effective width of the body equal to the actual width times the factor $1/\sqrt{1 - M_0^2}$, where M_0 is the Mach number of the original flow, or

$$\frac{\text{Effective } (t/c)}{\text{Actual } (t/c)} = \frac{1}{\sqrt{1 - M_0^2}} \tag{1:84}$$

The use of this simple estimate of compressibility effect will be seen in the pressure-distribution calculations in Art. 1:23.

1:22. Problems

1. Using the results shown in Table 1:2, find the streamline equations for a uniform flow with velocity components of $+u$ in the x direction and $-v$ in the y direction.

2. Sketch a source with 12 streamlines from which the total quantity flowing is $Q_0 = 2{,}400\pi$, and assign numerical values of Q_s to each streamline.

3. For the flow around a streamlined nose that is the composite of a source of

[1] KÁRMÁN, TH. VON, Compressibility Effects in Aerodynamics, *J. Aeronaut. Sci.*, 337 (July, 1941).

$Q_0 = 2{,}400\pi$ cu ft per sec and a uniform flow of $V_0 = -100$ ft per sec, plot the streamlines for $Q_s = 0$, 100, 200, 300, 400, and 500 cu ft per sec.

4. For numerical values of $B/Q_s = 1$ ft, 2 ft, and 3 ft plot the doublet streamlines given by equation (1:81).

5. Find the ratio of maximum to free-stream velocity for an ellipitic cylinder for which the thickness is 30 per cent of the chord for incompressible flow.

6. Using equation (1:84), calculate the ratio of maximum to free-stream velocity about a 30 per cent thick elliptic cylinder for compressible flow, assuming a Mach number of 0.6 for the free stream.

7. Using equation (1:84) and the equation for V_{max}/V_0 for an elliptic cylinder as given in Fig. 1:49, find by trial the value of $M_0 = V_0/c_0$ to give $V_{\text{max}}/c_0 = 1.00$ for a 30 per cent thick elliptic cylinder. This is one approximation of the critical Mach number of the cylinder.

1:23. Flow between Streamlines; Pressure on Objects; Pitot Tubes.—Since there is no flow *across* a streamline, the flow between streamlines can be handled mathematically like the flow in a duct without friction, and the general energy equation (1:48) applies to such flow. Since such flow of an air stream may be regarded as incompressible at low speed, or isentropic at high speed, the special forms of the energy equation (1:51) (the Bernoulli equation for incompressible flow) and (1:54) (the Bernoulli equation for subsonic isentropic compressible flow of air) may also be applied to the problem of finding the *pressure distribution* around objects corresponding to such velocity distributions as were developed in Art. 1:21. Since the compressible-flow solution must often be a trial solution, the simpler incompressible-flow solution may often be used as the first approximation to the more nearly correct compressible-flow solution.

For example, in the incompressible flow around a circular cylinder developed in Art. 1:21, the flow between streamlines immediately adjacent to the cylinder sketched in Fig. 1:54 may be considered as the flow in a duct, the area of which contracts from 1 sq ft at point $(\ )_0$ to 0.5 sq ft at point $(\ )_2$, since, as shown in Fig. 1:49, $V_2 = 2V_0$. Consider that the air at point $(\ )_0$ has a pressure P_0 and a density ρ_0 (and for incompressible flow $\rho_0 = \rho =$ const.); then, from equation (1:51),

$$\frac{4V_0^2 - V_0^2}{2} = \frac{P_0 - P_2}{\rho} \qquad \text{or} \qquad P_2 - P_0 = -3\,\frac{\rho V_0^2}{2}$$

Likewise, if the velocity at point $(\ )_1$ may be considered zero (a "stagnation point"), which follows from the equations in Fig. 1:49, equation (1:51) gives

$$\frac{0 - V_0^2}{2} = \frac{P_0 - P_1}{\rho} \qquad \text{or} \qquad P_1 - P_0 = \frac{\rho V_0^2}{2}$$

The quantity $P_1 - P_0$ is known as the *impact pressure* and is designated by q. Note from this analysis that the pressure reduction at the side of a circular cylinder is three times as great as the pressure increase at the front or $(P_2 - P_0)/q = 3$. The pressure distribution around a cylinder or other object is commonly plotted as a radial graph of $\Delta P/q = (P - P_0)/q$, as shown in Fig. 1:55.

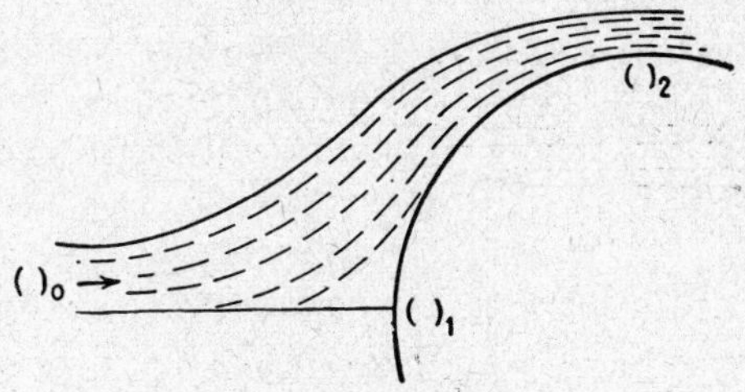

FIG. 1:54.—Flow between streamlines adjacent to a circular cylinder.

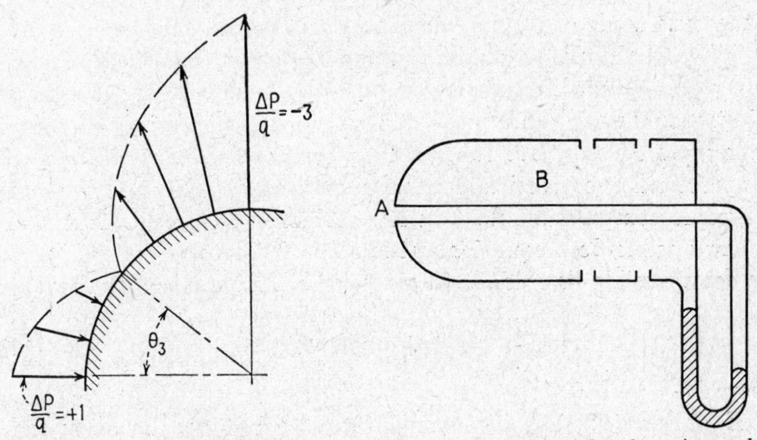

FIG. 1:55.—Diagram of pressure distribution around a circular cylinder for incompressible flow.

FIG. 1:56.—Pitot tube for air-speed measurement.

If a small hole is drilled in the cylinder at any point and connected to a manometer, the pressure at that point can be read on the manometer (or sensitive pressure gauge). For measurement of air speed, the most widely used instrument is the *pitot tube*, sketched in Fig. 1:56, in which an impact opening A, located at a stagnation point, and static pressure opening B, located well aft of the nose of a cylindrical tube, are connected to opposite sides of a manometer, or pressure gauge, which can be graduated in terms of air speed. Note that the pressure gauge measures ρV^2, so that the graduation in terms of V can be correct only for one particular value of ρ. The value of ρ usually taken for graduating air-speed meters is that of standard sea-level air. An air-speed meter so graduated is said to read "indicated air speed," which is $V\sqrt{\rho/\rho_0} = V\sqrt{\sigma}$.

If a manometer is connected to two openings on the surface of a cylinder located at the angle θ_3 shown on Fig. 1:55 where the pressure increase is zero, this arrangement, sketched in Fig. 1:57, will give zero manometer reading only when the air approaches the cylinder symmetrically with respect to the two openings. For other angles θ of approach of the air stream, the manometer can be graduated in terms of θ. This arrangement can thus be used to measure air-stream direction; since it is sometimes used to measure angle of yaw on airplanes, it is known as a *yawmeter*.

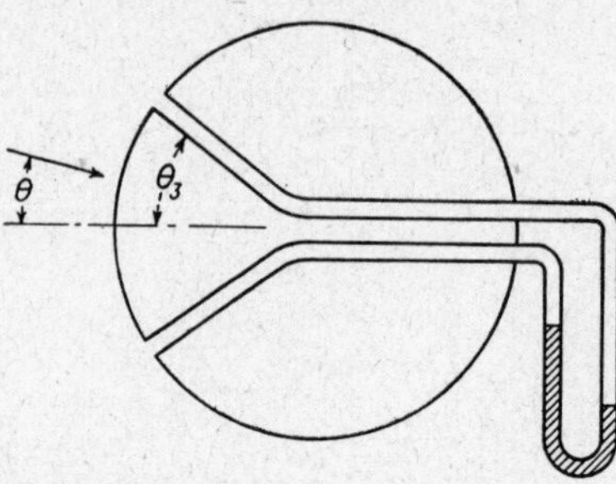

FIG. 1:57.—Yawmeter connections.

When the pressure changes become so great that the flow can no longer be regarded as incompressible, the velocity and pressure distributions change, and pitot tubes and yawmeters graduated for incompressible flow are subject to a *compressibility correction*. The compressibility correction can be calculated accurately by assuming isentropic compressible flow, as in equations (1:53) and (1:54). The incompressible-flow equation, with $V_1 = 0$, gives $(P_1 - P_0)/q_0 = 1$; the compressible-flow equation gives for air, from equation (1:52),

$$\frac{P_1}{P_0} = (1 + 0.2025M_0^2)^{3.47} \tag{1:85}$$

where $M_0 = V_0/c_0$.

Equation (1:85) is inconvenient to use but can be expanded in terms of a convergent power series to give, for air,

$$\frac{P_1 - P_0}{q_0} = 1 + \frac{M_0^2}{4} - \frac{M_0^4}{40.3} \tag{1:86}$$

and if $M_0^4/40.3$ is small compared with 1, as it is, within 1 per cent, if $M_0 \leq 0.80$ ($v_0 \leq 612$ mph at sea level), the compressibility correction factor for air is approximately

$$\frac{\Delta P \text{ comp}}{\Delta P \text{ incomp}} = 1 + \frac{M_0^2}{4} \tag{1:87}$$

Air-speed meters graduated for incompressible flow thus give a reading higher than the true air speed by the amount shown in Fig. 1:58.

Since compressible flow about a cylinder is isentropic and not isothermal, a temperature pattern can be calculated to correspond to the velocity pattern. At high speeds, the temperature at the side of a circular cylinder is markedly less than the temperature at the front; thus a thermocouple device such as that sketched in Fig. 1:59 can be used as an air-speed meter at high air speeds.

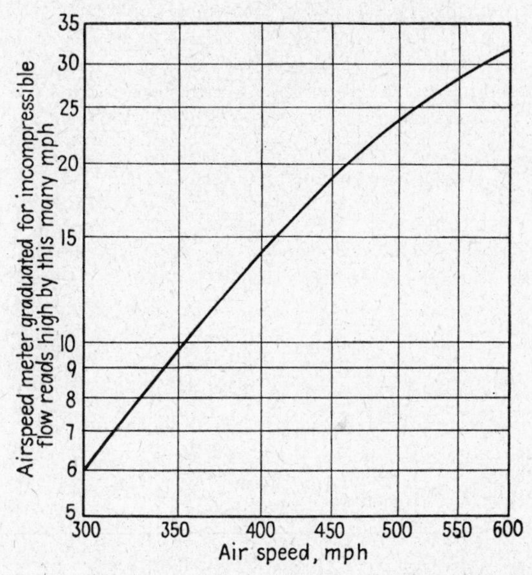

FIG. 1:58.—Compressibility correction at sea level for Pitot-tube air-speed meters.

For compressible flow around a cylinder, it is of particular interest to calculate the minimum temperature, which corresponds to the minimum velocity of sound, and to calculate the free-stream velocity that will give a maximum velocity [at the side of the cylinder, point $(\ )_2$ in Fig. 1:54] equal to the local velocity of sound at that point. The calculated value of $M_0 = V_0/c_0$ for this condition is known as the *lower critical Mach number* because a shock wave *may* form under these conditions. The Mach number which will give zero absolute pressure at point $(\ )_2$ is one below which a shock wave *must* have formed; the condition for infinite pressure gradient is sometimes known as the *upper critical Mach number*. The calculation of upper critical Mach number is beyond the scope of this text. An example of the calculation of the lower critical Mach number for a circular cylinder follows:

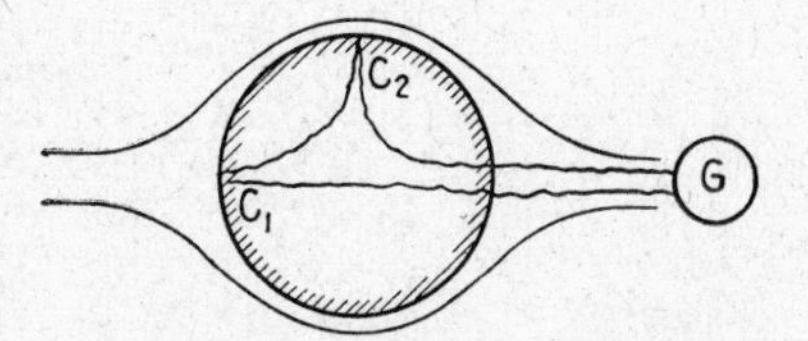

FIG. 1:59.—Possible use of thermocouples in a cylinder for measurement of high air velocities.

Example.—To calculate the lower critical Mach number of a circular cylinder.

Solution.—(Notation as in Fig. 1:54.) First approximation. For incompressible flow, $V_2 = 2V_0$, from Fig. 1:49. If this flow was isothermal, $c_2 = c_0$; and when $V_2/c_2 = M_2 = 1$, $V_0 = V_2/2$, $c_0 = c_2$, and $V_0/c_0 = M_{0\,cr} = 0.50$. The actual $M_{0\,cr}$ must be considerably less than this.

Second approximation. Assume velocity pattern as for incompressible flow ($V_2 = 2V_0$) and calculate P_2, T_2, and c_2 for compressible flow. Find by trial the value of V_0 that will give $V_2 = c_2$. Then $V_0/c_0 = M_{0\,cr}$. This problem is identical with the air-duct problem in Art. 1:15 except that the velocity is known and the pressure to be found instead of vice versa. For this case, with $V_2 = 2V_0$, equation (1:54) becomes

$$\frac{P_2}{P_0} = [1 - 0.2025M_0^2(2^2 - 1)]^{3.47} = \left(\frac{T_2}{T_0}\right)^{3.47}$$

Assume a series of values of M_0, calculate $c_2/c_0 = \sqrt{T_2/T_0}$ and $M_2 = 2M_0/(c_0/c_2)$, and find by trial the value of M_0 that gives $M_2 = 1.00$. A series of such calculations follows:

M_0	M_0^2	$0.6075M_0^2$	$(1 - 0.6075M_0^2) = \frac{T_2}{T_0}$	$\frac{c_2}{c_0}$	M_2
0.50	0.25	0.152	0.848	0.921	1.084
0.45	0.2025	0.123	0.877	0.936	0.960
0.40	0.16	0.097	0.903	0.951	0.84

Plot M_2 *vs.* M_0, and read $M_0 = 0.466$ for $M_2 = 1.00$.

Third approximation. Repeat the above calculation, assuming that equation (1:84) determines the ratio V_2/V_0 for compressible flow. (This is a good approximation for relatively thin ellipses, but it is not intended to apply accurately to the circular cylinder.) Using the same values of M_0 as above for the trial solution:

(1) M_0	(2) M_0^2	(3) $\frac{1}{\sqrt{1 - M_0^2}}$	(4) $\frac{V_2}{V_0}$	(5) $0.2025\left(\frac{V_2^2}{V_0^2} - 1\right)$	(6) Col. 5 $\times M_0^2$	(7) 1 − col. 6	(8) $\frac{c_2}{c_0} = \sqrt{\text{Col. 7}}$	(9) $M_2 = \frac{\text{col. 4} \times M_0}{\text{col. 8}}$
0.50	0.25	1.153	2.153	0.735	0.184	0.816	0.904	1.19
0.45	0.2025	1.12	2.12	0.704	0.142	0.858	0.927	1.03
0.40	0.16	1.09	2.09	0.681	0.109	0.891	0.945	0.885

The above table solves the equation

$$M_2 = 1 = M_0\left(1 + \frac{t/c}{\sqrt{1 - M_0^2}}\right)\sqrt{1 - 0.2025M_0^2\left(1 + \frac{t/c}{\sqrt{1 - M_0^2}} - 1\right)} \qquad (1:87.1)$$

Plot M_2 *vs.* M_0, and read $M_0 = 0.44$ for $M_2 = 1.00$. Because of the error of approximation of equation (1:84), this is still not the true value of $M_{0\,cr}$ for a circular cylinder, which actually comes out about 0.42[1] ($v_{0\,cr}$ = 321 mph). This same method can however be applied to elliptic cylinders with excellent accuracy for $t/c \leq 0.3$.

1:24. Problems

1. Using the equation for velocity distribution on the surface of a circular cylinder given in Fig. 1:49 and the Bernoulli equation for incompressible flow, find the angle θ_3 in Fig. 1:55 where the pressure on the surface of the cylinder is equal to the free-stream pressure. (For actual flow with a boundary layer, this angle is measured at about 39.2 deg for the average turbulent flow.)

2. Using equation (1:84) to find the velocity at the side of a 30 per cent thick elliptic cylinder, find the pressure and temperature at the side of the cylinder when standard sea-level air flows by the cylinder at a speed of 459 mph (M_0 = 0.6).

3. Calculate the critical Mach number of a 30 per cent thick elliptic cylinder.

4. In the third approximation for the compressible flow about a circular cylinder given in Art. 1:23, find the temperature (*a*) at the front of the cylinder and (*b*) at the side of the cylinder, for the critical condition of M_0 = 0.44 if the air is initially at the standard sea-level condition.

1:25. Effect of Velocity Gradient on Boundary-layer Flow: Drag of Cylinders and Spheres; Effective Reynolds Number.—The velocity- and pressure-distribution calculations of Arts. 1:21 and 1:23 neglect boundary-layer-flow considerations and therefore fail to explain some of the most important aspects of the flow around bodies, though they must be considered before the combined effect can be adequately portrayed and useful results obtained. The laminar and turbulent boundary layers discussed in Art. 1:17 are compared in Fig. 1:60. The effect of the turbulence is to accelerate the inner layers. In a region of *increasing* stream velocity, as on the upstream side of a cylinder, the laminar boundary layer resists transition to turbulent flow; in fact, a turbulent flow may become more nearly laminar. In a region of *decreasing* stream velocity, not only is transition from laminar to turbulent boundary layer promoted, but reducing all velocities an equal amount may give *negative* velocities near the surface, as shown in Fig. 1:61*b*. The point at which the surface velocity changes from positive to negative is known as the *separation point.* At this point, the velocity-distribution diagram is perpendicular to the surface, as shown in Fig. 1:61*a*.

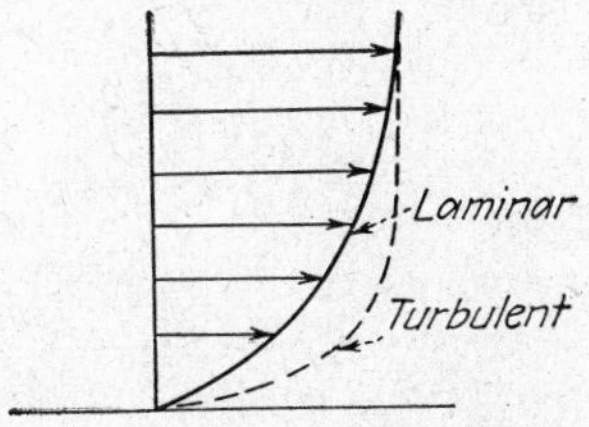

FIG. 1:60.—Comparison of laminar and turbulent boundary layers.

Typical boundary-layer velocity distributions (but exaggerated in boundary-layer thickness) for the flow around a cylinder are shown

[1] KAPLAN, CARL, Two-dimensional Subsonic Compressible Flow past Elliptic Cylinders, *NACA Tech. Rept.* 624 (1938).

in Fig. 1:62. The location of the separation point will be determined chiefly by the nature of the boundary layer in the region of decreasing external velocity. If the general air stream is smooth and the bound-

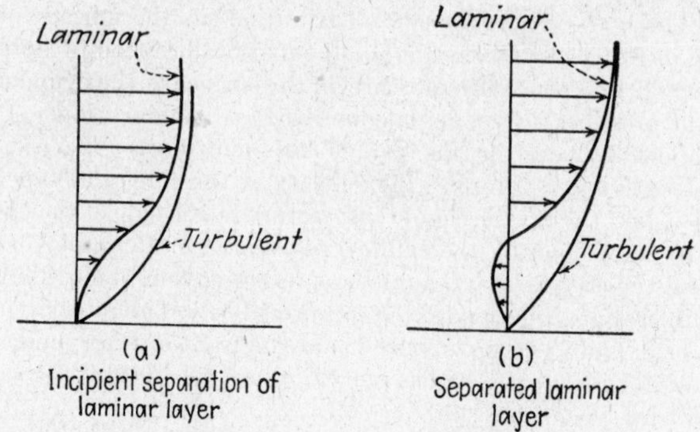

FIG. 1:61.—Laminar and turbulent boundary layers after a reduction in velocity. Note that laminar boundary layer has separated in sketch (*b*).

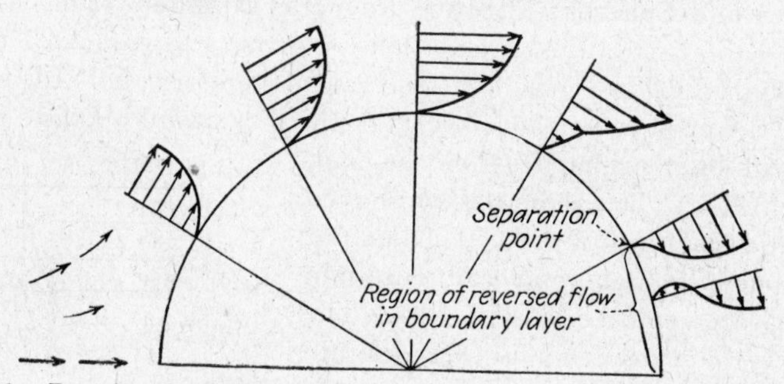

FIG. 1:62.—Boundary-layer-flow distribution around a circular cylinder, showing separation point.

FIG. 1:63.—Flow around cylinder at low *Re* or low turbulence. Smooth and laminar flow promote early separation and high drag.

FIG. 1:64.—Flow around cylinder at high *Re* or high turbulence. Turbulent boundary layer resists separation and permits a small wake and low drag.

ary layer laminar, separation will come early, as shown in Fig. 1:63, a wide wake will be formed, and the resistance of the cylinder to the flow of the fluid (drag) will be high. If the boundary layer is turbulent in the region of decreasing velocity, separation is delayed and the wake can be narrow and the drag low, as shown in Fig. 1:64. Note that this effect of turbulence is just the opposite from its effect of the skin friction. Turbulent skin friction is high because of high velocity gradients in the laminar sublayer, but in the flow around a bluff body like a cylinder, the turbulent boundary layer resists separation and causes a more streamlined flow. These facts are witnessed by the experimental data on drag of infinite cylinders shown in Fig. 1:65. The drag coefficient plotted in Fig. 1:65 is

$$C_D = \frac{\text{drag}}{qS} \tag{1:88}$$

where $q = \rho V^2/2$ and S is the frontal area in square feet for the length of cylinder on which the drag is measured.

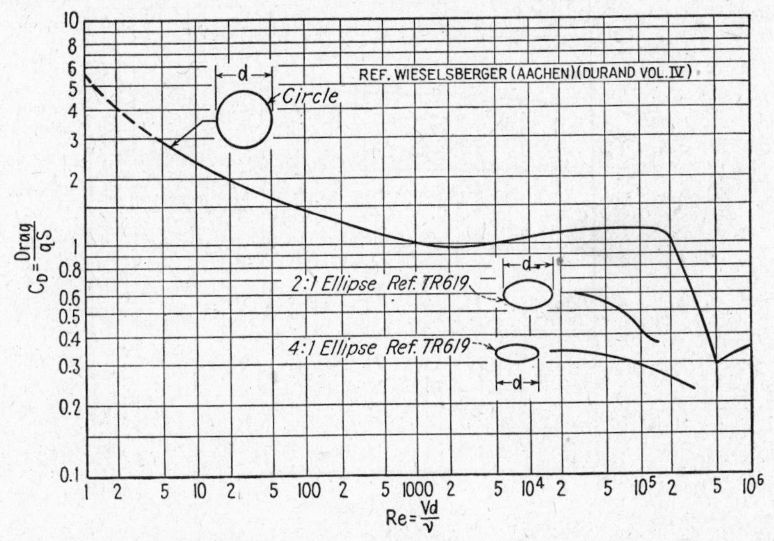

FIG. 1:65.—Drag coefficient of infinite cylinders as a function of Reynolds number. Mach number low ($M < 0.4$), free-stream turbulence not specified.

Note in Fig. 1:65 that the cylinder-drag coefficient is high in the region of low Re usually associated with laminar flow. At a high Re of about 3×10^5, the turbulence in the boundary layer becomes sufficiently well developed to resist separation, and with a small increase in Re, the drag is divided by about 4, meaning that there is an entirely different flow pattern with a much narrower wake.

The initial, or free-stream, turbulence was unfortunately not measured for the cylinder data in Fig. 1:65. Turbulence was measured, however, in connection with drag tests on spheres in the region of Re between 10^5 and 10^6 where the flow pattern changes markedly, and such test results are shown in Fig. 1:66. The flow around a sphere is more complicated than that around a cylinder because it is three-dimensional, but the transition and separation phenomena described above are the same.

Note in Fig. 1:66 that the higher free-stream turbulence promotes an earlier drop in drag as *Re* is increased. The intersections of the lines in Fig. 1:66 with the line of $C_D = 0.30$ for the sphere are some-

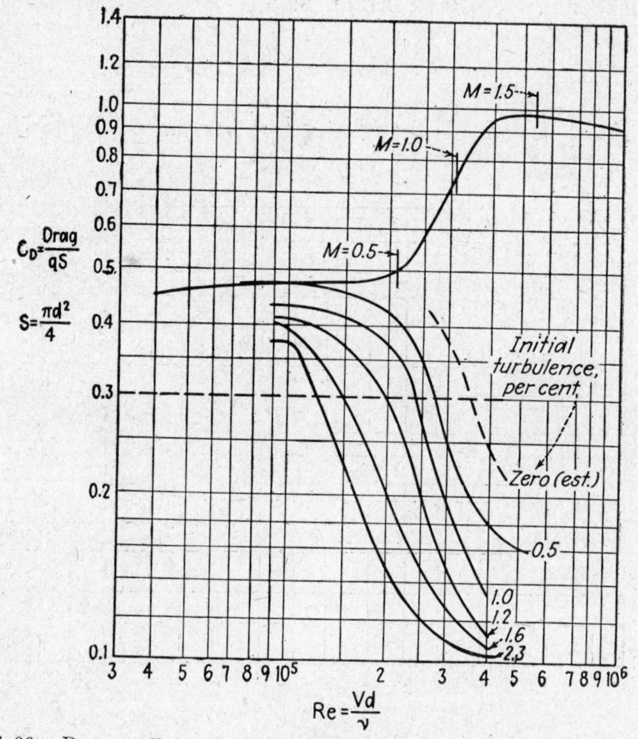

FIG. 1:66.—Drag coefficient of spheres as a function of *Re* for various values of free-stream turbulence. (*Replotted from NACA Tech. Rept.* 342, *Figs.* 6 *and* 7.) Mach number low ($M < 0.3$).

times taken as a measure of the free-stream turbulence. These intersections are plotted against the per cent turbulence in Fig. 1:68, which can be used to infer the turbulence from sphere-drag measurements and avoid elaborate hot-wire measurements. The pressure difference between the front and back of the sphere can similarly be used as a secondary standard of turbulence. The essential similarity in shapes of curves in Fig. 1:66 for various values of turbulence was noted by Jacobs,[1] who found that the curves could be reduced to a

[1] JACOBS, EASTMAN N., and ALBERT SHERMAN, Airfoil Section Characteristics as Affected by Variations in the Reynolds Number, *NACA Tech. Rept.* 586 (1939).

single curve by multiplying the *Re* for each curve by a turbulence factor F_t so chosen as to make the intersections at $C_D = 0.3$ coincide.

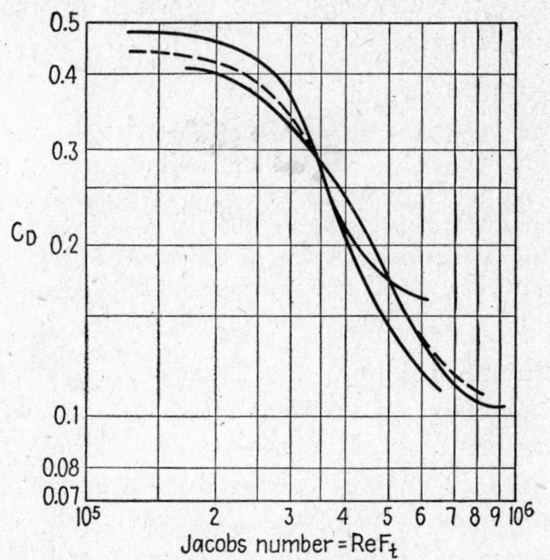

FIG. 1:67.—Adjustment of Fig. 1:66 to make lines for different turbulence nearly coincide.

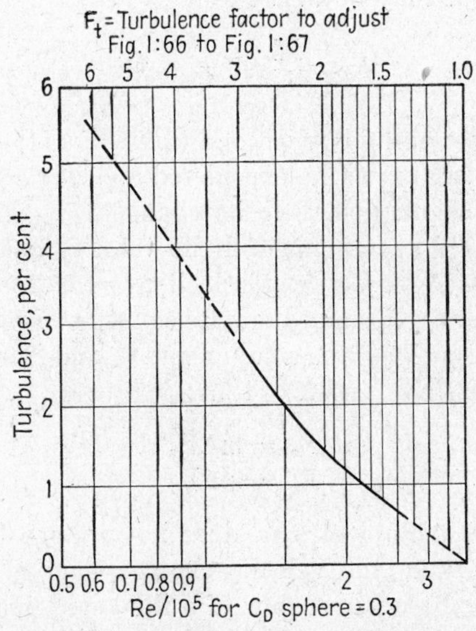

FIG. 1:68.—Relation between *Re* (for $C_D = 0.30$ for a sphere) and free-stream turbulence. Turbulence factor to adjust Fig. 1:66 to Fig. 1:67, also shown.

This factor F_t is shown in Fig. 1:68. The product F_tRe was called by Jacobs the effective Reynolds number but is here, in the interests of simplicity and to give proper credit to its inventor, called the *Jacobs number*. The substantial agreement of the curves of Fig. 1:66 when thus corrected is shown in Fig. 1:67. The Jacobs number is widely used in estimating the characteristics of wings in free flight on the basis of wind-tunnel tests.

1:26. Problems

1. Using Fig. 1:65, find the drag per foot of length in standard sea-level air of a 2-in.-diameter circular cylinder (*a*) at 180 mph and (*b*) at 360 mph.

2. Using Fig. 1:66, find the drag of a 2-in.-diameter sphere at 160 mph, in a wind tunnel with a standard sea-level air and a turbulence of 1 per cent.

3. For a wind tunnel in which the drag coefficient of a sphere is found to be 0.30 at a Reynolds number of 210,000, find (*a*) the wind-tunnel turbulence and (*b*) the Jacobs number.

1:27. Momentum Relations for Steady Flow of Fluids.—For a stream of fluid to change its velocity, either in magnitude or in direction, a force must be exerted on the stream. From Newton's laws, an equal and opposite force is exerted by the stream on the object that causes the change of velocity. Newton's law states that force F = rate of change of momentum MV, or $F = d(MV)/dt$, or, for constant M, $F = M\Delta V/\Delta t = Ma$. For the problem of a flowing stream of fluid, this may be written

$$F = \frac{M}{\Delta t}\Delta V = m\Delta V \tag{1:89}$$

where m is the mass of fluid per second that suffers the velocity change ΔV. Equation (1:89) must be considered a vector equation, with the force F in the direction of the velocity change ΔV. In many problems it is convenient, after having found the velocity change ΔV by subtracting the initial from the final velocity vector, to analyze ΔV into components ΔV_x and ΔV_y and to rewrite equation (1:88) in terms of the relationship between the force components F_x and F_y and the velocity-change components ΔV_x and ΔV_y thus:

$$F_x = m\Delta V_x \tag{1:90}$$

$$F_y = m\Delta V_y \tag{1:91}$$

If the velocity of a fluid stream does not change in direction but changes in magnitude, the velocity-change diagram is as shown in Fig. 1:69. If the direction of flow of a fluid stream changes, but the speed does not change, the velocity-change diagram is as shown in Fig. 1:70. In each figure, V_0 is the original velocity and V_1 is a new velocity. In the general case, there may of course be increases or decreases in *both* magnitude and direction, and equations (1:90) and (1:91) are applicable, but the cases sketched in Fig. 1:69 and Fig. 1:70

are the only ones that will be considered here. Examples of the use of equations (1:90) and (1:91) follow:

Example 1.—A rocket, similar to the German V-2 rocket (sketched in Fig. 1:71) used for bombing England in 1945, has an initial gross weight of 24,000 lb and a

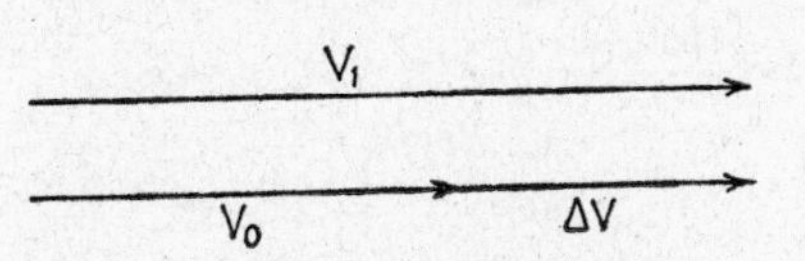

FIG. 1:69.—Velocity change with no change in direction.

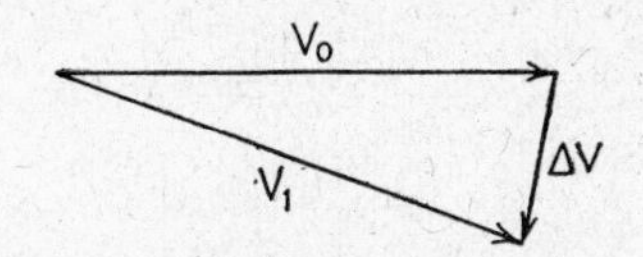

FIG. 1:70.—Velocity change with no change in speed.

final gross weight of 4,000 lb after propelling gases are discharged. It discharges its gases at a rate of 1,000 lb per sec for 20 sec. The relative discharge velocity is 3,000 ft per sec. (*a*) Find the thrust exerted by the discharged gases. (*b*) Neglect-

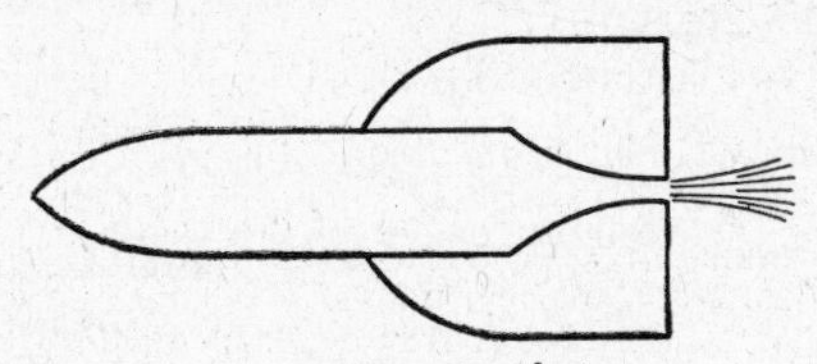
FIG. 1:71.—Rocket.

ing gravitational forces, which are negligible compared with the thrust, find the velocity of the rocket at the end of 20 sec.

Solution.—To substitute in equation (1:90) calculate as follows:

$$m = 1{,}000/32.2 = 31.05 \text{ slugs per sec}$$

and with $\Delta V_x = 3{,}000$ ft per sec.

$$F_x = m\Delta V_x = 31.05 \times 3{,}000 = 93{,}200 \text{ lb}$$

This is the answer required by (*a*).

To find the acceleration of the rocket from $F = Ma = Wa/g$ note that

$$W = 24{,}000 - 1{,}000t$$

where t is the time after starting in seconds. Then

$$a = \frac{93{,}200 \times 32.2}{24{,}000 - 1{,}000t}$$

Using $a = dV/dt$, solve for V at $t = 20$ by integrating thus:

$$\int_0^{V_1} dV = 93.2 \times 32.2 \int_0^{20} \frac{dt}{24 - t} = 3{,}000 \log_e \frac{24}{4}$$

$$V_1 = 3{,}000 \log_e 6 = 3{,}000 \times 1.79 = 5{,}360 \text{ ft per sec}$$

This is the answer required by (*b*).

Example 2.—An airplane propeller of diameter $D_1 = 10$ ft exerts a thrust of 500 lb when standard sea-level air approaches it at a velocity $V_0 = 100$ ft per sec as shown in Fig. 1:72. Find the slip-stream velocity V_2.

Solution.—It is customary to assume, for reasons demonstrated later (Chap. 4) that the velocity V_1 through the propeller disk is the arithmetic mean of the velocity of approach V_0 and the slip-stream velocity V_2. Hence, for this case,

$$V_1 = \frac{100 + V_2}{2}$$

and

$$m = \rho A_1 V_1 = 0.00238 \frac{100\pi}{4} \frac{100 + V_2}{2}$$

and

$$\Delta V = V_2 - 100$$

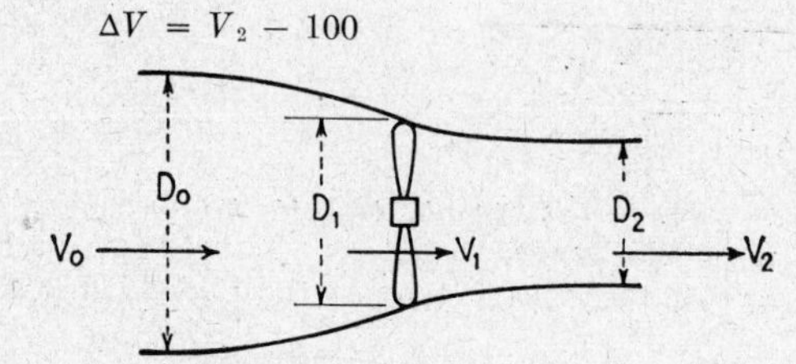

FIG. 1:72.—Air flow through an airplane propeller.

Substitute these quantities in equation (1:90), and get

$$T = 500 = \frac{0.00238}{2} \frac{100\pi}{4} (V_2 + 100)(V_2 - 100)$$

Expanding,

$$\frac{1{,}000}{0.00238 \times 78.54} = V_2^2 - 10{,}000$$

Solve for $V_2 = 124$ ft per sec. This is the answer required.

Example 3.—A jet of standard sea-level air flows through a duct of 1-sq-ft cross-sectional area and is deflected through an angle of 30 deg from its original direction, as shown in Fig. 1:73. Find the x and y components of force exerted on the duct.

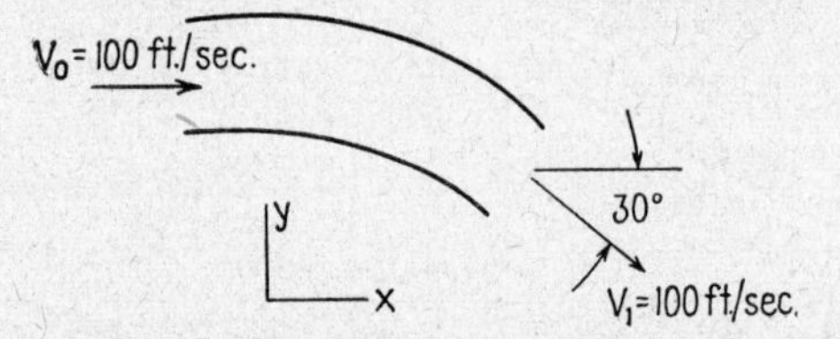

FIG. 1:73.—Duct deflecting an air stream.

Solution.—With x and y axes, as in Fig. 1:73, the velocity diagram of Fig. 1:74 permits calculating, by geometry, $\Delta V_y = -50$ ft per sec, $\Delta V_x = -13.4$ ft per sec. To substitute in equations (1:90) and (1:91), calculate

$$m = \rho A_0 V_0 = 0.00238 \times 1 \times 100 = 0.238 \text{ slugs per sec}$$

and get

$$F_y = -0.238 \times 50 = -11.9 \text{ lb}$$
$$F_x = -0.238 \times 13.4 = -3.19 \text{ lb}$$

These are the answers required.

Example 4.—The air flow in the wake of an infinite cylinder has the velocity distribution sketched in Fig. 1:75. The original velocity V_0 was 100 ft per sec.

The wake velocities in feet per second at various distances y in feet from the wake center line are given by the following table:

y, ft..................	0	+1	+2	+3	+4	+5	+6
V, ft per sec..........	60	65	70	80	90	95	98

Find the drag of the cylinder per foot of length.

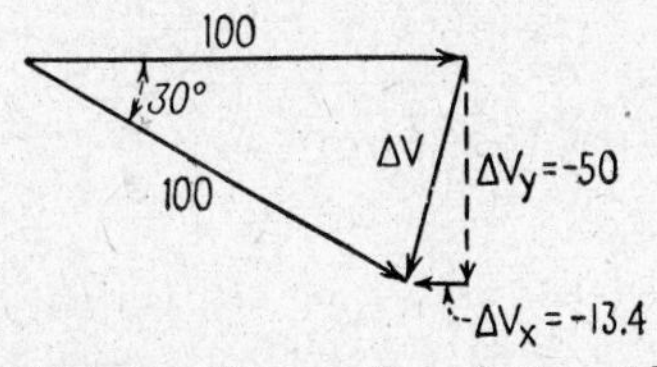

FIG. 1:74.—Velocity diagram for solution of Example 3.

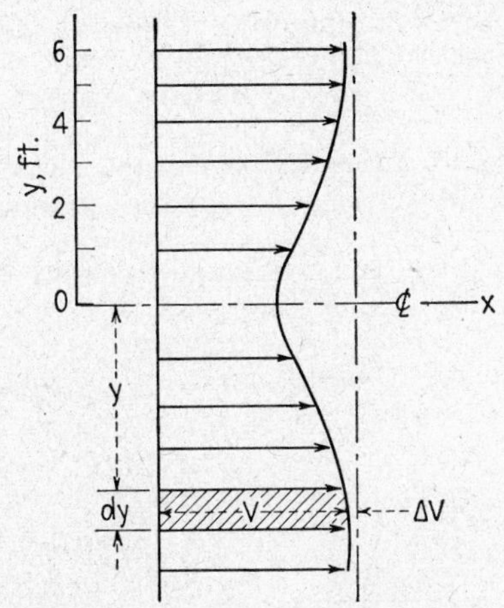

FIG. 1:75.—Velocity distribution in the wake of a cylinder.

Solution.—At any distance y from the wake center line the velocity is V as shown, and the velocity reduction is $\Delta V = 100 - V$. The rate of loss of momentum is $m\Delta V$, where $m = \rho AV = \rho V dy$. The total force that has been exerted on the air is the sum of the forces necessary to produce the velocity changes ΔV, or

$$\text{Drag} = \int \rho V \Delta V dy = \rho \int V \Delta V dy$$

This integral may be evaluated by Simpson's rule (or other rule for approximate integration).

Simpson's rule states, for six intervals Δy,

$$\int u dy = \frac{\Delta y}{3} [u_0 + u_6 + 4(u_1 + u_3 + u_5) + 2(u_2 + u_4)]$$

In this case the integration will be performed from the center line of the wake to the outer limits of the data and the result multiplied by 2 because of the specified symmetry. For a Δy increment of 1 ft and $\rho = 0.00238$, values of $u = V\Delta V$ are calculated in groups as specified by Simpson's rule as shown in the table below:

y, ft	0	1	2	3	4	5	6	Sums	Factors	Sums × factors
V, ft per sec	60	65	70	80	90	95	98			
ΔV, ft per sec	40	35	30	20	10	5	2			
$V\Delta V$ end	2,400						196	2,596	1	2,596
$V\Delta V$ odd		2,265		1,600		475		4,340	4	17,360
$V\Delta V$ even			2,100		900			3,000	2	6,000
Total										25,956

Hence, $\rho \int V\Delta V dy = 2 \frac{0.00238}{3} 25{,}956 = 41.2$ lb. This is the answer required.

1:28. Problems

1. A skyrocket has an initial gross weight of 2.5 lb and a weight empty of 0.5 lb. Its gases are discharged at a speed of 1,000 ft per sec at a uniform rate in a total time of 3 sec. Find the velocity of the rocket at the end of 3 sec.

2. An airplane propeller disk has an area of 100 sq ft. The velocity of the air before it strikes the propeller is 100 ft per sec; the velocity of the air leaving the propeller is 120 ft per sec. Assuming the air to be standard sea-level air, find the thrust of the propeller.

3. A jet of standard sea-level air of diameter 30 ft and velocity 100 ft per sec is deflected by a vane on which a component of a force perpendicular to the initial jet direction of 1,000 lb is exerted. Find (*a*) the component of force on the vane parallel to the direction of the jet and (*b*) the angle through which the jet is deflected.

4. Assume the following data for the velocity in the wake of a thin flat plate over which there has been laminar flow with viscous friction, and calculate (using Simpson's rule) the total skin friction per foot of width of the plate. Assume the original velocity to have been 10 ft per sec and the original air condition to have been standard sea level.

y, hundredths of a foot	0	1	2	3	4	5	6
V, ft per sec	6.0	6.4	6.9	7.5	8.4	9.0	9.5

1:29. Dimensional Analysis Applied to Aerodynamic Problems.—In all engineering problems, the scientific laws on which the engineering analysis is based may be expressed in the form of equations such that the dimensions are the same on both sides of the equation. By suitably rearranging terms in such equations they can always be put in such a form that the units cancel and the equation consists of nothing but terms without dimensions, known as "dimensionless ratios." For example, the equation $F = Ma = Wa/g$ may be written in the form $F/W = a/g$ or $(F/W) - (a/g) = 0$.

For aerodynamic problems in which the basic physical laws are incompletely understood or expressed, it is convenient and useful to generalize the foregoing statement by the supplementary statement that any dimensionless ratio of the quantities known to be involved in a particular problem *may be* a function of any other dimensionless ratio of the quantities involved. The dimensions of most of the factors involved in this chapter are listed in Table 1:3 in terms of force F, length L, and time t. For quantities involving heat and temperature, F, L, and t dimensions are calculated by assuming (1) that the Btu is a unit of energy and hence has dimensions FL and (2) that specific heat is dimensionless, from which it may be inferred that temperature has the dimension of length L.

The so-called Buckingham π theorem states that if $\pi_1, \pi_2, \pi_3, \ldots,$ represent dimensionless combinations of powers or roots of the quantities involved, then the physical law can be expressed in the form

$$f(\pi_1, \pi_2, \pi_3, \cdots) = 0 \qquad (1:91.1)$$

With m quantities involved in a problem involving three dimensions, it can be shown that $(m - 3)$ dimensionless ratios (π's) may be found. The procedure is to write the π's as functions of the variables to unknown powers and solve for the unknown powers from the known conditions that the π's have no dimensions. This procedure is illustrated by the following example:

Example.—The force per unit surface F/S on an airplane wing is judged to be a function of the following variables: velocity V, air density ρ, kinematic viscosity of air μ, and the chord of the wing c. Find two dimensionless ratios involving these five quantities for a three-dimensional system involving F, L, and t.

Solution.—Write expressions for the two π's in terms of unknown exponents, using the following procedure: Select three variables (for a three-dimensional system) to be written with unknown exponents, and combine these with each of the other variables in turn to form the π's, thus:

$$\pi_1 = \left(\frac{F}{S}\right)^{x_1} V^{y_1} c^{z_1} \nu \qquad (1:92)$$

$$\pi_2 = \left(\frac{F}{S}\right)^{x_2} V^{y_2} c^{z_2} \rho \qquad (1:93)$$

Write the condition that the dimensions of the π's shall be zero, thus: If, from the π_1 equation and the dimensions in Table 1:3, $(F/L^2)^{x_1}(L/t)^{y_1}L^{z_1}L^2/t$ has no dimensions, then

$$\left.\begin{array}{ll} \text{For no dimensions of } F, & x_1 = 0 \\ \text{For no dimensions of } L, & -2x_1 + y_1 + z_1 + 2 = 0 \\ \text{For no dimensions of } t, & -y_1 - 1 = 0 \end{array}\right\} \qquad (1:94)$$

Solve for $x_1 = 0$, $y_1 = -1$, $z_1 = -1$, and

$$\pi_1 = \frac{\nu}{Vc} \qquad (1:95)$$

Similarly, from the π_2 equation, if $(F/L^2)^{x_2}(L/t)^{y_2}LFt^2/L^4$ has no dimensions, then

$$\left.\begin{array}{ll} \text{For no dimensions of } F, & x_2 + 1 = 0 \\ \text{For no dimensions of } L, & -2x_2 + y_2 + z_2 - 4 = 0 \\ \text{For no dimensions of } t, & -y_2 + 2 = 0 \end{array}\right\} \qquad (1:96)$$

Solve for $x_2 = -1$, $y_2 = 2$, $z = 0$, and

$$\pi_2 = \frac{\rho v^2}{(F/S)} \qquad (1:97)$$

Note that $1/\pi_1 = Re$; $1/\pi_2 = (F/S)/\rho V^2$ is commonly called a force coefficient; $2/\pi = (F/S)/(\rho V^2/2)$ is usually designated by the symbol C_F.

The foregoing procedure has thus determined that if the quantities listed in the statement of the example are the only ones involved, the forces on an airplane wing may be expressed in the form $f(C_F, Re) = 0$,

TABLE 1:3.—UNITS AND DIMENSIONS OF SOME QUANTITIES IN THIS CHAPTER

Quantity	Symbols	Defining equation	Usual engineering units	F, L, t dimensions
Force, weight	F, W	......	Lb	F
Length, distance	L, d, c, x, y	......	Ft	L
Time	t	......	Sec	t
Area, surface	A, S	......	Sq ft	L^2
Velocity, speed	V	......	Ft per sec	$\frac{L}{t}$
Acceleration	a, g	$\frac{dv}{dt}$	Ft per sec²	$\frac{L}{t^2}$
Angular velocity	ω, n	......	Radians per sec, rps	$\frac{1}{t}$
Angular acceleration	......	$\frac{d\omega}{dt}$	Radians per sec²	$\frac{1}{t^2}$
Volume	Vol.	......	Cu ft	L^3
Quantity rate of flow	Q	$\frac{d(\text{vol.})}{dt}$	Cu ft per sec	$\frac{L^3}{t}$
Unit pressure or force	P, T	$\frac{F}{S}$	Lb per sq ft	$\frac{F}{L^2}$
Specific weight	w	$\frac{W}{\text{vol.}}$	Lb per cu ft	$\frac{F}{L^3}$
Specific volume	$\bar{V}$	$\frac{\text{vol.}}{W}$	Cu ft per lb	$\frac{L^3}{F}$
Mass	M	$\frac{W}{g}$	Slugs/(lb)(sec²)(ft)	$\frac{Ft^2}{L}$
Density	ρ	$\frac{w}{g}; \frac{M}{\text{vol.}}$	Slugs per cu ft	$\frac{Ft^2}{L^4}$
Torque, moment	Q	......	Lb ft	FL
Work, energy, heat	Work, Q	......	Ft-lb	FL
Dynamic viscosity	μ	$\frac{\tau}{(dV/dy)}$	Lb-sec per ft²	$\frac{Ft}{L^2}$
Kinematic viscosity	ν	$\frac{\mu}{\rho}$	Sq ft per sec	$\frac{L^2}{t}$
Temperature	T	......	Deg F	L
Specific heat	c_p, c_v	......	None	None
Thermal conductivity	k_c	$\frac{\Delta Qx}{S\Delta T\Delta t}$	Btu/(ft)(deg F)(hr)	$\frac{F}{Lt}$
Convective-heat-transfer coefficient	h	$\frac{\Delta Q}{S\Delta T\Delta t}$	Btu/(sq ft)(deg F)(hr)	$\frac{F}{L^2t}$

or

$$C_F = f(Re) \qquad (1{:}98)$$

Dimensionless ratios are commonly designated as *coefficients* [for example, drag coefficient $= C_D = (D/S)/(\rho V^2/2)$] or *numbers* (for example, Reynolds number $= Re = Vc/\nu$). The names associated with the numbers usually have some relation to the history of the science. The principal coefficients and numbers referred to in this chapter and a few others that will be discussed later are summarized in Table 1:4 for reference.

TABLE 1:4.—SOME DIMENSIONLESS RATIOS OF IMPORTANCE IN AERODYNAMICS

Name	Symbol	Defining equation	Of importance in
Mach number	M	$V/c = V/\sqrt{kgRT}$	Compressible flow
Reynolds number	Re	VL/ν	Surface friction
Prandtl number	Pr	$3{,}600\mu c_p g/k_c$	Heat transfer
Stanton number	St	$1/Pr$	Heat transfer
Peclet number	Pe	$RePr = Re/St$	Heat transfer
Nusselt number	Nu	hD/k_c	Heat transfer
Grashof number	Gr	$\frac{D^3 g}{\nu^2}\frac{\Delta T}{T}$ (for gas)	Heat transfer
Froude number	Fr	V^2/gb	Waves in liquid
Euler number	Eu	$\frac{\Delta P}{\Delta y}\frac{d}{V^2\rho}$	Airfoils, propellers
Entropy, specific	ΔS	$\Delta Q/WT$	Compressible flow
Advance ratio	J	V/nD	Propellers
Velocity ratio	λ	$V/\pi nD$	Helicopters

1:30. Problems

1. The characteristics of an airplane propeller are judged to involve the following variables:

Variable	Symbol	Usual units	F, L, t dimensions
Thrust	T	Lb	F
Diameter	D	Ft	L
Forward velocity	V	Ft per sec	L/t
Rotative speed	n	Rps	$1/t$
Fluid density	ρ	Slugs per cu ft	Ft^2/L^4

Find two dimensionless combinations of these variables that may be used in a study of the experimental data.

2. Find the Froude number for a ship of 100-ft beam b traveling at a velocity of 50 ft per sec, using the beam of the ship as the standard linear dimension. For the same Froude number, what should be the speed of a model of the ship of 10-ft beam?

CHAPTER 2

AIRFOIL CHARACTERISTICS

2:1. Forces on Airfoils; Airfoil Coefficients.—An airfoil is defined in general as any body shaped so as to get a useful reaction from an air stream that moves relative to it, but the term is most often used to describe a body of cross section similar to Fig. 2:1, which is acted on by a large force perpendicular to the air-stream direction (lift) and a small force parallel to that direction (drag). The wings and tail surfaces of airplanes, and some airplane fuselages, are airfoils. This chapter is devoted to (1) the presentation of the laws of force action on airfoils as derived from experimental data on airfoils (wind-tunnel and free-

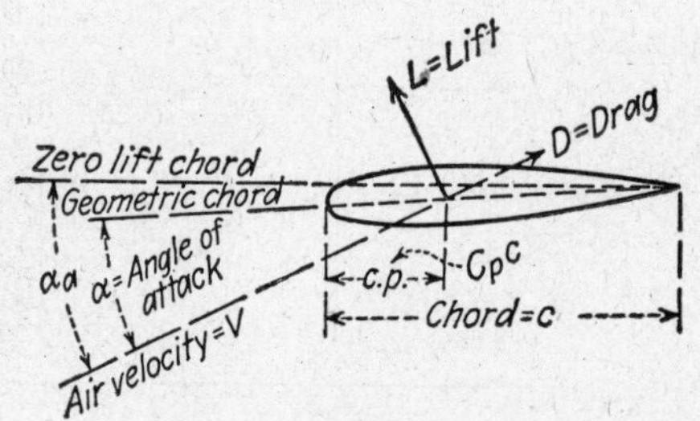

FIG. 2:1.—Forces on airfoil in an air stream.

flight tests) and from general physical experimentation (resulting in Newton's laws and Bernoulli's theorem) and (2) the use of such laws in mathematical form to calculate the forces acting on airplane wings and tail surfaces.

A force is completely specified by specifying its *magnitude*, *direction*, and *line of action*. Forces on airfoils are commonly specified, as in Fig. 2:1, by specifying lift (L), drag (D), and center-of-pressure location (c.p.) from the leading edge (L.E.) of the airfoil. Experiments on airfoils show that lift and drag are proportional to air density (ρ), airfoil surface (S), and the square of the relative air velocity (V^2) for a given angle of attack (α) between the airfoil chord (c) and the air-velocity vector, provided that other factors remain constant. The effects of density, surface, and velocity are usually eliminated from the specification of airfoil forces, by specifying lift and drag *coefficients* (C_L and C_D) defined by

$$C_L = \frac{L}{qS} \tag{2:1}$$

$$C_D = \frac{D}{qS} \tag{2:2}$$

where $q = \rho V^2/2$ and L and D are the total lift and drag forces of the airfoil. The *location* of the lift and drag forces on the airfoil is often specified by the coefficient

$$C_p = \frac{c.p.}{c} \tag{2:3}$$

An alternate means of specifying the line of action of the force on the airfoil is arbitrarily to locate the L and D forces at some definite point, such as 25 per cent of the chord from the leading edge, and add a pitching couple or moment $M_{c/4}$ to produce the same result, as shown in Fig. 2:2. The moment $M_{c/4}$ is then specified by the equation

$$C_{Mc/4} = \frac{M_{c/4}}{cqS} \tag{2:4}$$

The point $c/4$ is commonly selected as a center of moments (and location of L and D) because the pitching moment on most airfoils is approximately constant about this point. The results of tests on airfoils of a definite span (b) and surface (S), and hence of a definite aspect ratio ($\text{Æ} = b^2/S$), are usually plotted as shown in Fig. 2:3. The curves in Fig. 2:3 are determined partly by the aspect ratio and partly by the cross section of profile of the airfoil. To eliminate the effect of aspect ratio, tests are often made on airfoils running completely across the test section of a wind tunnel, so that all sections of the airfoil have the same characteristics. The *section characteristics* are usually designated by small letters thus:

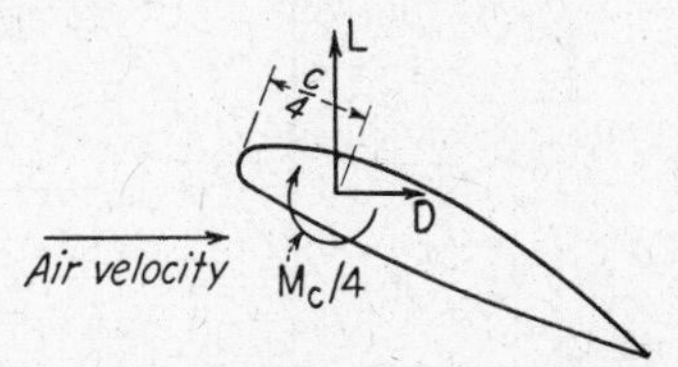

FIG. 2:2.—Force system equivalent to Fig. 2:1.

$$c_l = \frac{dL}{qdS} \tag{2:5}$$

$$c_{d0} = \frac{dD}{qdS} \tag{2:6}$$

$$c_{m\,a.c.} = \frac{dM}{cqdS} \tag{2:7}$$

where dL, dD, and dM are the lift, drag, and pitching moment, respectively, on the elementary area $dS = cdy$, c being the chord and dy being an elementary spanwise distance. A plot of the section coefficients, with c_l as the abscissa, is shown in Fig. 2:4. The section- or profile-drag coefficient is designated c_{d0} for reasons discussed later; the moment coefficient is designated $c_{m\,a.c.}$, the subscript *a.c.* referring to the aerodynamic center of the wing, which is defined as the point about which the pitching moment is constant as the angle at which the

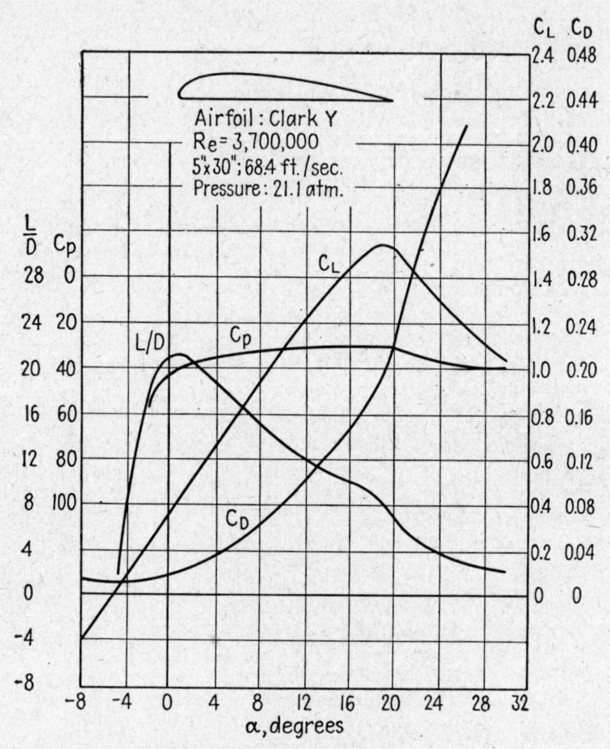

FIG. 2:3.—Airfoil characteristics of Æ = 6.

air strikes the airfoil is varied. The aerodynamic center is approximately at 0.25*c* but is different for different airfoil sections and is usually determined experimentally for each section. The range of values usually found is:

$$a.c. = 0.25c - (0.005 \text{ to } 0.025)c \qquad (2:8)$$

The results shown in Fig. 2:3 are typical of many airfoils. There is always some angle at which the wind can strike an airfoil so as to give no force perpendicular to the wind direction (no lift). Under these conditions the resultant air force is parallel to the wind-velocity vector and is drag. The line drawn through the trailing edge of the airfoil in this direction is known as the *zero-lift chord*. The zero-lift chord bears no necessary relationship to the *geometric chord*, which is an arbitrary line selected by the designer for making a drawing of the airfoil section. The angle that the wind-velocity vector makes with the geometric chord is known as the *angle of attack* (α); angles of attack measured from the zero-lift chord are known as *aerodynamic* or

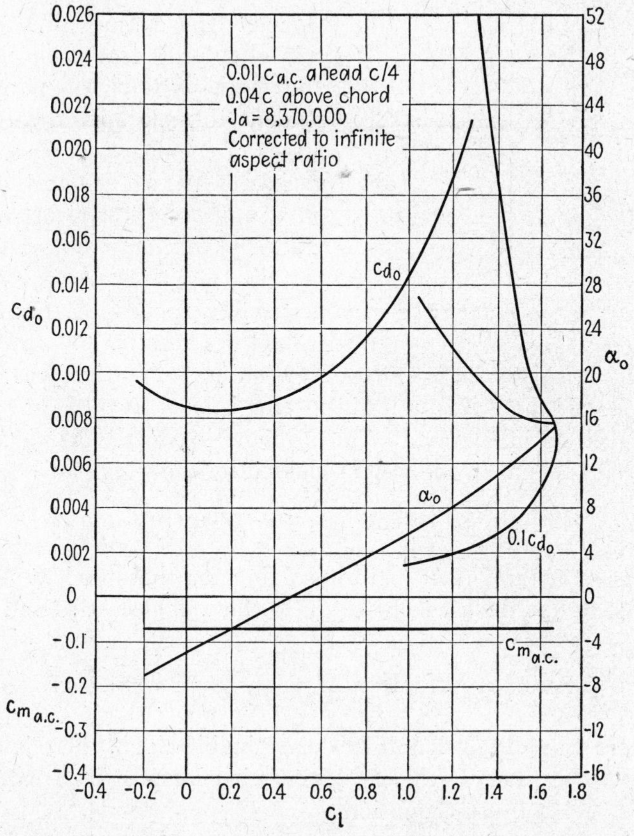

FIG. 2:4.—Characteristics of portion of airfoil of infinite span.

absolute angles of attack and are usually designated by α_a. As α_a is increased from zero, Fig. 2:3 shows that the lift increases linearly with the angle, the drag increases at a higher rate, and the center of pressure changes. The limit beyond which the lift does not increase with the angle of attack is known as the *stall*. The *stalling angle* and maximum lift coefficient ($C_{L\,\max}$) are determined by the separation of the boundary layer, which in turn, as in the flow around a cylinder, depends on the scale (*Re*) of the airfoil test and the initial turbulence (dV/V) of the air stream. The *minimum drag coefficient* ($C_{d\,\min}$) is determined by skin friction (like a flat plate) and by the flow pattern in the wake (like a cylinder) both of which are determined chiefly by the Reynolds number (*Re*). Both lift and drag curves are markedly affected by changes in the flow pattern associated with compressibility of the air. The curves given in Figs. 2:3 and 2:4 are for low Mach number ($M < 0.3$). One of the major objectives of this chapter is to outline the data and methods that will permit the student to make quantitative estimates of the effects of these major variables (Æ, *Re*, *M*) on the forces on airfoils and their distribution, with the ultimate object of predicting flight characteristics as accurately as possible from wind-tunnel test results.

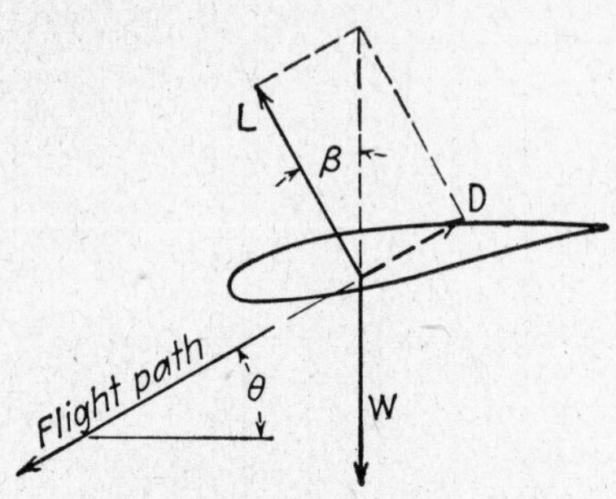

FIG. 2:5.—Balance of forces on a wing in steady glide.

A wing in steady flight in free air is subjected to the forces shown in Fig. 2:5. If the flight path of the wing is level ($\theta = 0$) (or approximately level, as in the case of an airplane in gliding flight), the lift of the wing is equal to the weight carried by the wing and

$$L = W \cos \theta \approx W \tag{2:9}$$

Equations (2:9) and (2:1) permit solving for the speed at which a wing must fly for the lift to be equal to the weight carried and give

$$V = \sqrt{\frac{W/S}{\rho C_L/2}} \tag{2:10}$$

Since every wing has a definitely determinable $C_{L\,\max}$, there is a minimum speed $V_{\min}$ below which a given wing loading W/S cannot be supported, given by the equation

$$V_{\min} = \sqrt{\frac{W/S}{\rho C_{L\,\max}/2}} \tag{2:11}$$

This is also known as the *stalling speed* of the wing. Converting equation (2:11) from feet per second to miles per hour and using $\rho = \rho_0 = 0.00238$ for sea level gives for sea-level stalling speed

$$v_{s0} = \sqrt{\frac{W/S}{0.00256 C_{L\,\max}}} = 19.75 \sqrt{\frac{W/S}{C_{L\,\max}}} \tag{2:12}$$

At higher speeds, C_L and α will be smaller. At three times the stalling speed, which is a common high speed for airplanes, C_L will be $\frac{1}{3}^2 = \frac{1}{9}$ of $C_{L\,\max}$.

2:2. Problems

1. A model wing is tested in a wind tunnel in which the pressure is 24 in. Hg and the temperature 100°F. The wing model is rectangular and has a span of 30 in. and a chord of 5 in. When the air speed is 100 ft per sec, the forces measured on the model are $L = 5$ lb and $D = 1$ lb. The pitching moment about the $c/4$ point is -10 in.-lb. Find (*a*) C_L, (*b*) C_D, (*c*) $C_{Mc}/4$, and (*d*) C_p.

2. A wing of 180-sq ft planform surface S carries a weight of 1,200 lb in level flight in standard sea-level air. (*a*) Find the lift coefficient for speeds of 120, 100, 80, 70, 60, and 50 mph. (*b*) Find the angle of attack from Fig. 2:3. (*c*) Find the stalling speed.

3. An airplane wing model extends completely across the throat of a wind tunnel in which standard sea-level air flows at 100 mph. The wing characteristics are given by Fig. 2:4. The chord of the wing is 18 in. When the angle of attack is 10 deg, find the lift per foot of span of the wing model.

2:3. Measurement of Airfoil Characteristics; Wind Tunnels.— The object of tests on airfoils is to obtain data that will permit calculating the forces acting on airplanes in flight. Some data on airfoils can be obtained and some measurements made on an airplane while it is flying. Such tests are known as "flight tests."

Flight-test measurements of airfoil characteristics on airplanes are of four principal types: (1) *pressure-distribution tests*, in which the wings are fitted with numerous small openings connected by tubes to sensitive pressure gauges, or manometers (these tests being correlated with wind-tunnel tests involving similarly located openings); (2) *wake-survey tests*, in which a rake of Pitot tubes is located behind the wing and measures the momentum loss, from which the drag can be calculated, as in Art. 1:27; (3) *boundary-layer-survey tests*, in which a small Pitot tube is located a short distance from the wing surface and rigged so that it can be moved up and down and back and forth on the wind to measure velocity distribution in the boundary layer; and (4) *glide tests*, in which the speed of steady glide for various angles of flight path is measured. Glide tests permit determining the lift and drag of the complete airplane with dead propeller; the propeller can be operated at zero thrust to eliminate its effect; or, for small airplanes, the propeller can be removed, and the airplane flown as a glider. Accurate flight-test measurements are difficult to obtain in spite of careful instrumentation, chiefly because of the difficulty of obtaining steady air conditions for running the tests. Since much steadier conditions can be obtained in laboratory wind tunnels, the most accurate measurements on airfoil characteristics are obtained from *wind-tunnel tests*.

Most wind tunnels are closed-circuit air ducts such as that shown in Fig. 2:6. The model to be tested is mounted in the *throat*, and the air is kept moving around the circuit by means of the motor and fan. The circuit consists of a long expanding portion followed by a short contraction cone; there are *vanes* in the corners to minimize the energy losses in the flow around the circuit. The model is usually mounted on balances in the throat and may be equipped with orifices connected to manometers for measurement of surface pressures at various points. Orifices in the throat walls may be used instead of balances.

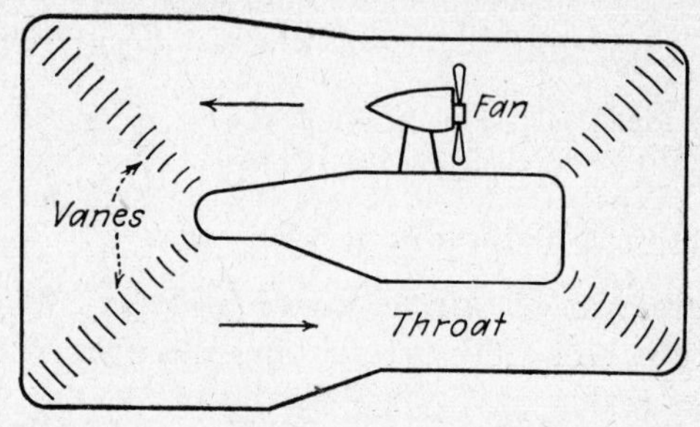

FIG. 2:6.—Typical single-return closed-circuit wind tunnel.

The major aerodynamic feature of a closed-circuit wind tunnel is the friction loss in total head $[= P + (\rho V^2/2)]$ around the closed circuit, which is made up by a rise in pressure ΔP across the fan disk. The head loss in each part of the tunnel is proportional to V^2 in that part; with fixed area ratios, it is also true that

$$\Delta P = kq_t \tag{2:13}$$

where $q_t = \rho V_t^2/2$ = impact head at throat
V_t = velocity at throat
k = pressure-loss coefficient

Typical values of k are shown in Table 2:1.

The over-all performance of a wind tunnel and its propeller is also commonly described by the energy ratio (E.R.) defined by

$$\text{E.R.} = \frac{\rho A_t V_t^3}{1{,}100 \text{ Bhp}} \tag{2:14}$$

The fan efficiency is defined by

$$\eta = \frac{Q\Delta P}{550 \text{ Bhp}} \tag{2:15}$$

where Q = quantity of air flowing around the circuit, cu ft per sec.

Combining equations (2:13), (2:14), and (2:15) gives

$$\text{E.R.} = \frac{\eta}{k} \tag{2:16}$$

With a properly designed fan, η can usually be made about 0.8. (The design of wind-tunnel fans is discussed in Chap. 4.) Energy ratios of typical wind tunnels, as well as pressure-drop coefficients, are shown in Table 2:1.

Table 2:1.—Typical Energy Ratios and Pressure-drop Coefficients for Wind Tunnels

	Energy ratio E.R.	Pressure-drop coefficient $= \frac{\Delta P}{q_t} = k$
Low-loss tunnel (*e.g.*, GALCIT 10 ft)	5.7	0.14
Medium-loss tunnel	3.5	0 23
High-loss tunnel (*e.g.*, University of Colorado, 22 by 39 in.)	1.2	0.66

Some of the wind tunnels in operation in the United States in 1946 are listed in Table 2:2; photographs and drawings of some of these wind tunnels are shown in Figs. 2:7 to 2:10.

Only a few wind tunnels have been built large enough to accommodate even the smaller full-sized airplanes because of the excessive first cost and operating cost of such wind tunnels. The original NACA full-scale tunnel is shown in Fig. 2:7*a*. It has an open jet 60 ft wide and 30 ft high, capable of accommodating airplanes up to about 50 ft span, but the maximum air speed of the tunnel (118 mph) is considerably less than the high speed of the faster airplanes of this size so that this tunnel actually falls far short of giving full-scale Reynolds number. Even the newer full-scale tunnel under construction at Moffet Field for the NACA, with an 80-ft-wide throat, will accommodate only what are, in 1947, the smaller transport and bomber airplanes, although the air speed (not yet announced) may be comparable with the cruising speed of such bombers and transport airplanes.

In the interests of economy, most wind tunnels are used only to test scale models of airplanes and airplane parts. Wind tunnels with a throat (or jet if open) as small as 4 ft in minimum dimension have given results of technical importance; but, in general, the smaller the tunnel, the larger the corrections for scale that must be made for the results to be applicable to full-sized airplanes. The model-test results differ from the full-scale test results for two principal reasons: (1) The Reynolds number is much lower than that of the full-scale airplane. (2) The Mach number is much lower than that of the full-scale airplane. To save time and money, an attempt has been made in the newer tunnels to get high Reynolds number by increasing the air density in the tunnel and to get high speed and high Mach number

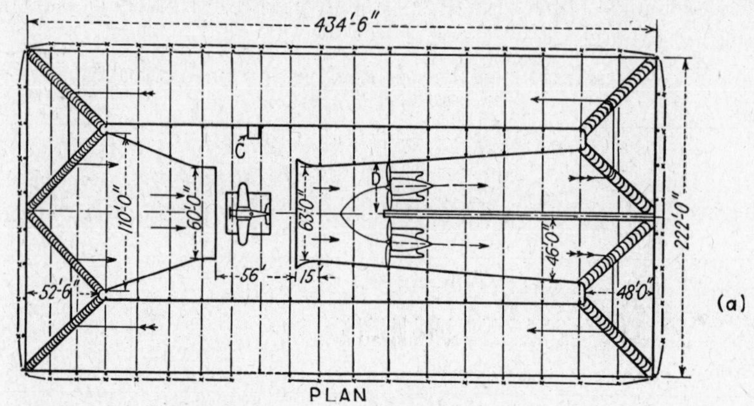

a. Sectional elevation and plan of full-scale tunnel. (*From NACA Tech. Rept.* 459.

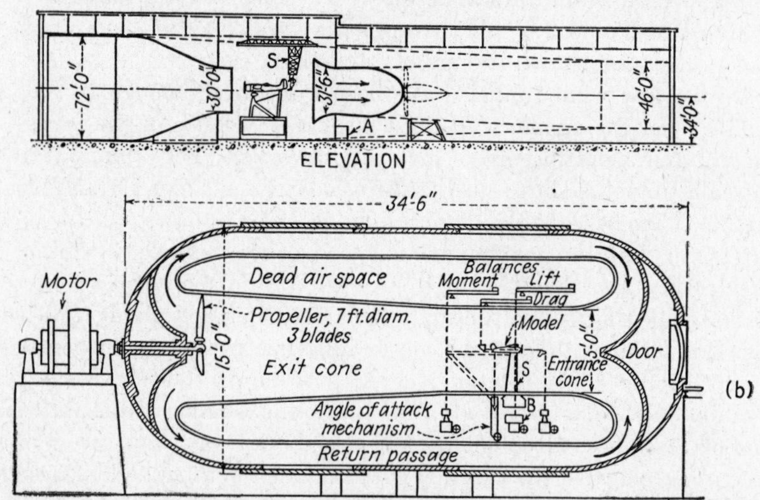

b. Sectional elevation of variable-density tunnel. (*From NACA Tech. Rept.* 385.)

FIG. 2:7.—Some Federal government wind tunnels at Langley Memorial Aeronautical Laboratories, Langley Field, Va.

by decreasing the air density in the wind tunnel so that a given amount of power will produce a much higher speed. The high Reynolds and Mach numbers are thus not obtained simultaneously, but some light is thrown on the Reynolds- and Mach-number corrections.

The original variable-density tunnel (VDT) of the NACA, shown

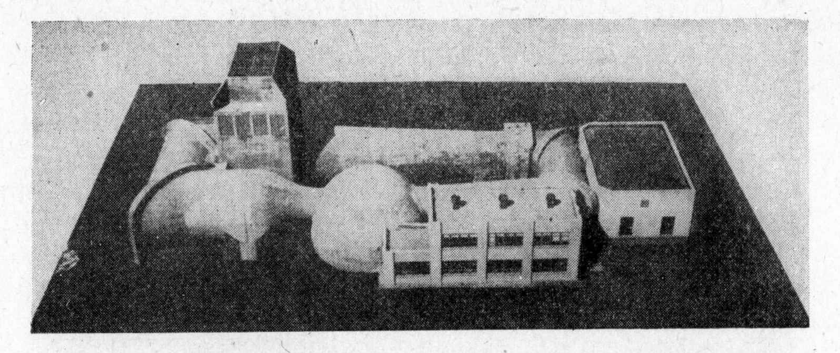

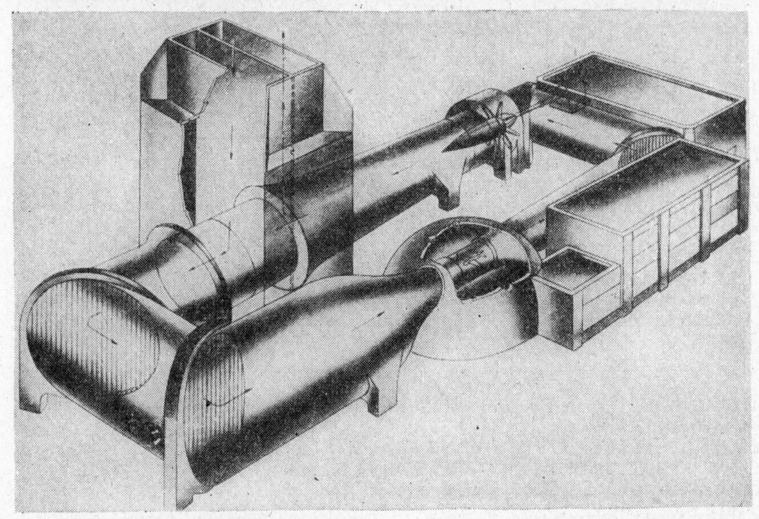

c. Photograph of 8-ft high-speed tunnel. (*From Stack, J. Aeronaut. Sci., April,* 1945.)

d. Schematic diagram of 16-ft high-speed tunnel. (*From Stack, J. Aeronaut. Sci., April,* 1945.)

FIG. 2:7.—*Continued.*

in Fig. 2:7*b*, has been in fairly continuous operation since 1926 and is the principal source of test data on airfoils published by the NACA. The Mach number of such tests is low; an attempt has been made by the NACA to get the Mach-number effect by tests in the two high-speed tunnels shown in Fig. 2:7*c* and *d*. High Reynolds number is obtained in the variable-density tunnel by increasing the air pressure to about twenty times standard atmospheric pressure.

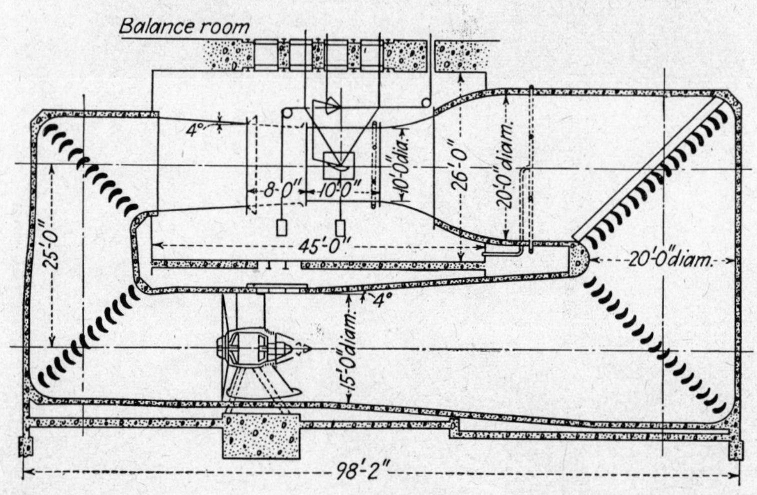

FIG. 2:8.—Sectional elevation of the 10-ft-throat wind tunnel at the Guggenheim Aeronautical Laboratory of the California Institute of Technology (known as the GALCIT 10-ft tunnel). *(From C. B. Millikan, "Aerodynamics of the Airplane," John Wiley & Sons, Inc., New York. Reproduced with permission.)*

The most extensive testing of airplane models for manufacturers in the period from 1930 to 1940 was done in the GALCIT (Guggenheim Aeronautical Laboratory, California Institute of Technology) wind tunnel shown in Fig. 2:8. The original balances of the GALCIT tunnel are shown in Fig. 2:9. These balances provided for the simultaneous measurement of three components of force and three components of moment as a function of angle of attack on the airplane wing but were limited in their usefulness by the fact that the angle of yaw could not also be conveniently varied. The balances shown in Fig. 2:9 have since been replaced by a set of six-component balances in which yaw as well as angle of attack is conveniently varied and in which the model is supported by struts rather than by wires.

A simple type of three-component balance without wires (used in the Purdue University 2- by 4-ft wind tunnel) is shown in Fig. 2:11. The sketch shows provision for measuring three components and for varying only the angle of attack, but this system can be conveniently modified to vary the angle of yaw and to measure the three additional components. The essential feature is an A frame with the $c/4$ point of the model wing chord mounted at the vertex of the A. Drag forces move only the vertical links L_1 and L_2 and can be read directly on the D balance; pitching moments distort the A frame but do not move

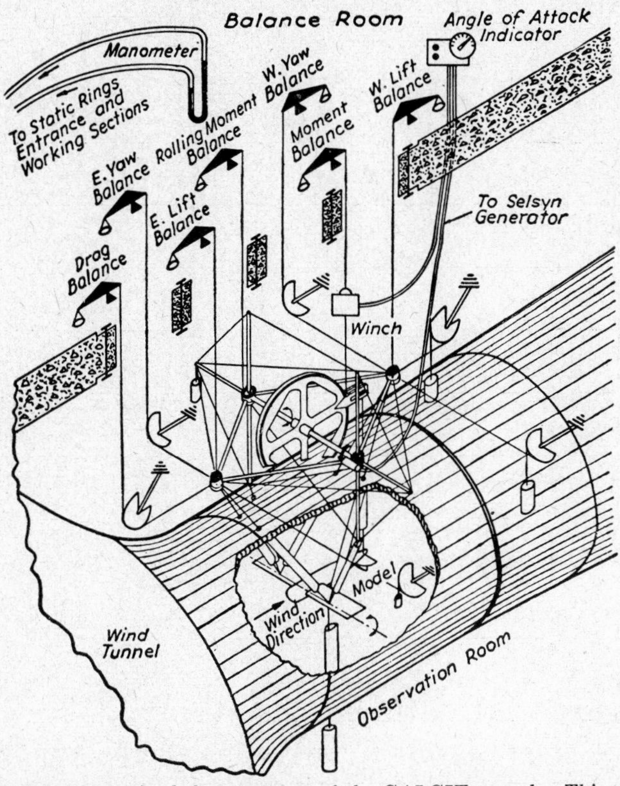

FIG. 2:9.—Original wire balance system of the GALCIT tunnel. This rigging has since been superseded by an improved system. It is reproduced here because it shows more clearly the essential features of the force resolution than the more complicated system. (*From C. B. Millikan, "Aerodynamics of the Airplane," John Wiley & Sons, Inc., New York. Reproduced with permission.*)

the drag links and thus can be read independently of drag forces. The lift can be measured in the vertical links or by a lift balance L as shown. Angles of yaw and yawing moments are also measured by rotating the supporting struts about a vertical axis. Addition of rolling-moment and cross-wind-force balances does not complicate this arrangement excessively; many of the newer wind tunnels use six-component balances similar in principle to that sketched in the figure.

TABLE 2:2.—DATA ON SOME UNITED STATES WIND TUNNELS IN OPERATION IN 1945

Agency and tunnel	Date of start	Throat size, ft	Shape	Area, sq ft	Max. vel. mph	Pressure, atm		$\frac{Re}{10^6}$ Max.	Min. turb., %	Max. hp	E.R.	Fan D, ft	No. of bl.	Init. cost $1,000
						Min.	Max.							
United States government:														
NACA Langley Field:														
Var. density	1928	5	Round	19.6	45	1	20	4	2.5	200	2.3	7.0	3	
Propeller research	1927	20	Round	314	110	1	1	3.1	...	2,000	1.6	28	8	
7- by 10-ft	1930	7 by 10	Rectangular	70	80	1	1	1.1	...	200	1.41	10.5	6	
Full-scale	1931	30 by 60	Rectangular	1,800	118	1	1	8	0+	8,000	2.84	35	4 by 2	
8-ft high-speed	1936	8	Round											
16-ft high-speed	1942	16	Round											
NACA Moffet Field:														
Full-scale	1945	40 by 80	Rectangular	3,200		Data not available				36,000				
American Air Force Wright Field:														
5-ft	1920	5	Round	19.6	300	1	1	2.1						
20-ft	1944	20	Round	314	400	1	1	...	...	40,000	....	40	16 by 2	2,500
Universities; Technical Institutions:														
California Institute of Technology	1930	10	Round	78.5	260	1	1	4	0.2	800	5.7	15	3	100
University of Colorado	1942	2 by 4	Rectangular	.....	150	1	1	...	...	100	1.1	....	......	1
Massachusetts Institute of Technology	1937	10	Elliptic	63	400	0.25	4	6						
University of Michigan	1925	8	Octagonal	.....	100	1	1							
New York University	1925	9	Square	81	100	1	1	...	1.5					
Stanford University	1919	6	Round	.....	90	1	1							
Industrial laboratories:														
Boeing Aircraft (Seattle)	1944	8 by 12	Rectangular	96	610	0.8	1	11	...	18,000	....	24	16	750
Curtiss-Wright (Buffalo)	1944	8 by 12	Rectangular	96	700	0.25	0.4	9	...	9,000	....	....	......	500
Southern California Cooperative (Pasadena)	1945	8 by 12	Rectangular	96	700	0.25	0.4	9	...	9,000	....	....	......	500
Consolidated-Vultee Aircraft (San Diego)	1945	8 by 12	Rectangular	96	350	1	1+	5.5	...	2,250	....	....	......	520
Lockheed Aircraft (Burbank)														
North American (Los Angeles)		Not published												
Northrop (Los Angeles)	1940	10	Circular	78.5	160	1	1+	2.5	...	1,200	4	15	4	50

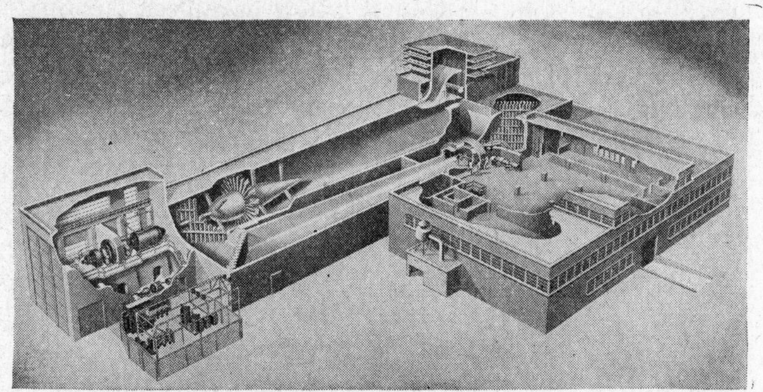

a. Principal parts. Power unit is at left. Air-interchange tower at right.

b. External view of laboratory building and wind tunnel. Building in foreground houses shops, offices, and operations rooms.

c. Test section of tunnel and control room. Test-section enclosure slides on tracks. Models are brought in by overhead track from shop. Easel at left has 100 manometer tubes; controls and instrument panel are at right.

FIG. 2:10.—Boeing Aircraft Company Edmund T. Allen wind tunnel, which started operation in 1944. (*Courtesy Aviation, August,* 1944.)

Since 1943 most airplane manufacturers have been building their own wind tunnels. Figure 2:10, showing the Boeing Aircraft Company wind tunnel at Seattle, is typical of the newer industrial wind tunnels. This is not a pressurized tunnel, but fairly high values of Reynolds number and Mach number are obtained with a throat and model of convenient size for construction and installation of the model.

Many universities now have tunnels that will accommodate models of about 3-ft span with speeds up to 150 mph, such as the University of Colorado wind tunnel shown in Fig. 2:11.1. Such wind tunnels

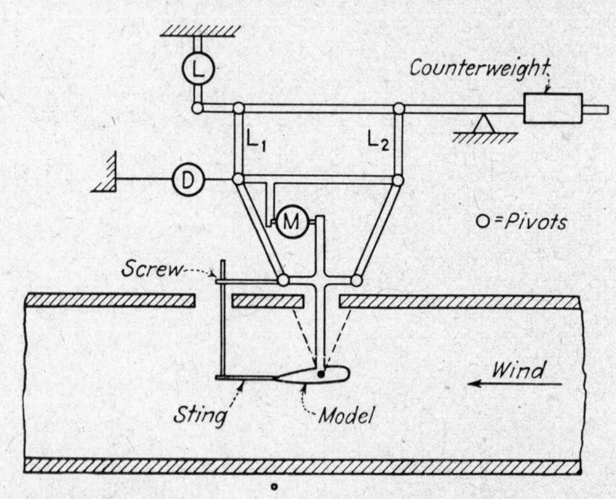

FIG. 2:11.—Simple type of wind-tunnel balance using struts to support model.

are inexpensive to construct and operate but cannot be considered of great technical importance. Wind tunnels must be expensive to give accurate results. A study of the cost of the wind tunnels listed in Table 2:2 shows that the tunnel cost per square foot of throat area (including housing, balances, and controls) is about $\$(150 + 0.04v^2)$, where v is the maximum throat speed in mph. The error in correcting the results to full scale is large if the scale of the tests (which is proportional to $v\sqrt{A_t}$) is small. Small error ($v\sqrt{A_t}$ large) requires large expense; wind-tunnel apparatus of technical importance is rarely if ever obtainable on tuition fees.

Minimum energy losses in a closed-circuit wind tunnel, such as that shown in Fig. 2:6, are obtainable only with some type of vanes in the corners as shown. While such vanes minimize losses, they result in eddies in the air stream that introduce a turbulence into the wind tunnel. Turbulence is thus easy to add; it is also difficult to remove, and particular care must be taken in the design of the wind tunnel if it is desired to have the turbulence low. Values of turbulence for some of the wind tunnels in Table 2:2 are listed in the table.

While high values of turbulence give a high Jacobs number (effective Reynolds number), it is usually considered desirable to have the turbulence as low as possible, for a high turbulence adds another uncertain correction to the already uncertain corrections for Reynolds number and Mach number.

FIG. 2:11.1.—Portion of the University of Colorado 22- by 39-in.-throat wind tunnel. W. L. Hull, who constructed the tunnel, is shown reading the air-speed manometer.

During the Second World War, German developments in the field of rockets (like the V-2) and supersonic aircraft (see, for example, Fig. 4:13) were based on data from a number of supersonic wind tunnels. A number of supersonic wind tunnels were under construction or in the early stages of operation at the close of the war. One of the most adequately publicized of these tunnels is that of the U.S. Army Ordnance Department at the Aberdeen Proving Ground, described by Barnes.[1]

A supersonic wind tunnel is essentially a converging-diverging nozzle as sketched in Fig. 2:11.3. With P_2/P_0 less than the critical value of (0.53 for dry air), $M_1 = V_1/a_1 = 1.00$ and $M_2 = V_2/a_2 > 1.00$

[1] BARNES, MAJ. GEN. G. M., Supersonic Wind Tunnel Laboratory, *Mech. Eng.*, 827–835. (December, 1945).

because of the expansion of the air between points ($)_1$ and ($)_2$. The pressure ratio P_0/P_3 necessary to get a given Mach number M_2 as calculated by Crocco[1] and the throat pressure ratio P_0/P_2 accompanying the Mach number M_2 as calculated by various authors, are shown in Fig. 2:11.2. While the highest Mach numbers reported by

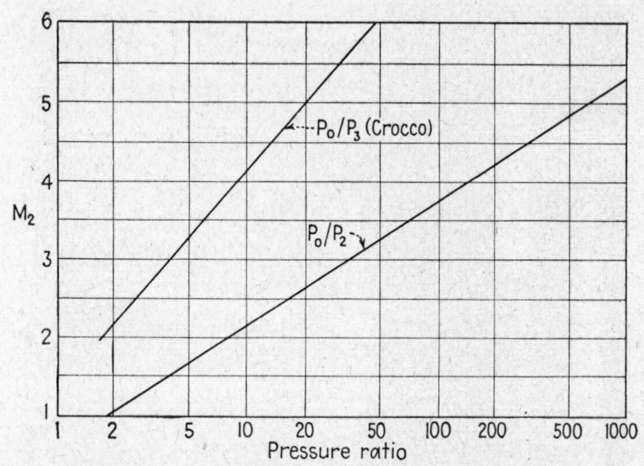

FIG. 2:11.2.—Pressure ratio accompanying a given supersonic Mach number.

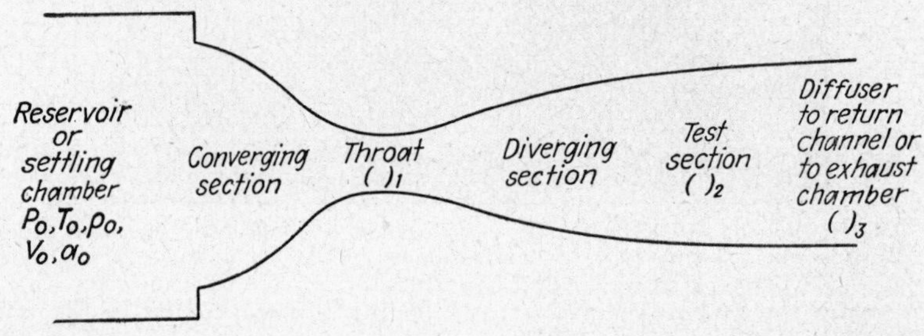

FIG. 2:11.3.—Sketch of portion of supersonic wind tunnel (all sections rectangular).

Barnes[2] in European tunnels are less than 5, it is evident from Fig. 2:11.2 that Mach numbers of 10 or greater are obtainable with materials available; data at $M \approx 40$ in rarified air are necessary to understand the performance of meteors entering the outer atmosphere of the earth.

For a given nozzle length, it is necessary in practice to have a different nozzle shape for each value of M_2 desired. In the Aberdeen

[1] CROCCO, L., Design Manual for High Speed Wind Tunnels, *L'Aerotecnica*, March, 1935; translated by British Ministry of Aircraft Production as 1915 *Ae. Techl.* 962.

[2] *Op. cit.*

wind tunnel the various nozzle shapes necessary are obtained by means of a flexible nozzle arrangement.

Model forces are measured in the Aberdeen tunnel by means of electric strain gauges mounted on the supporting strut, and photographs of the shock-wave pattern in the air flow are usually taken for each force reading. The Aberdeen tunnel uses "schlieren"

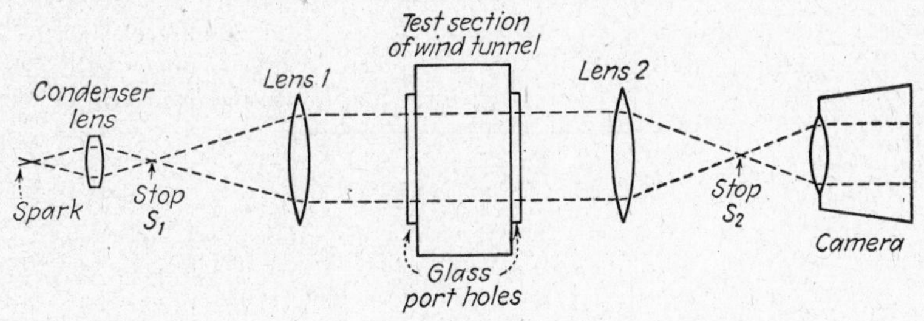

FIG. 2:11.4.—Diagram of schlieren equipment for photographing supersonic flow.

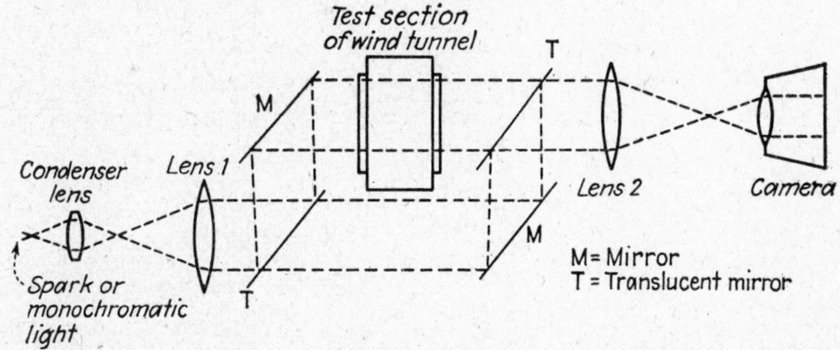

FIG. 2:11.5.—Diagram of Mach interference refractometer equipment for photographing supersonic flow.

photographic equipment. This is one of three common types of equipment used in photographic study of supersonic flow. The three types are described by Buzemann[1] as follows:

1. The *shadow* method of V. Dvorak uses a point source of light (usually a spark of short duration to avoid blurring) and a screen on the opposite side of the wind tunnel. Differences in optical density of the air cause shadows on the photographic plate, which show shock-wave locations but do not permit much quantitative analysis.

2. The *schlieren* (striation, or streak) method of Toepler also uses a spark but has lenses or mirrors to make the light rays parallel and to focus them after passing through the wind tunnel. This arrangement is sketched in Fig. 2:11.4. The stop s_1 provides a sharp edge to the light beam, and the stop s_2 masks

[1] BUZEMANN, A., Gas Dynamics; issued by British Ministry of Aircraft Production as *R.T.P. Transl.* 2207; translated by M. Flint from the *Handb. Experimentalphysik* (Wien-Harms), **4**, 343–460 (1931).

various amounts of light depending on the refraction. The light intensity on the film is proportional to $d\rho/dy_1$, where ρ is density and y is distance perpendicular to the edge of the stops. The resulting photograph is like a plaster model of the density distribution illuminated from one side.

3. The *interference* method of Mach sends a monochromatic light to the film by two different paths, one through the air jet and the other by means of a detour as sketched in Fig. 2:11.5. The interference pattern appearing on the film is a contour system, in wave lengths of light, proportional to the optical density. Accurate studies of density distribution in the vicinity of the shock waves around an object are possible with the Mach interference refractometer.

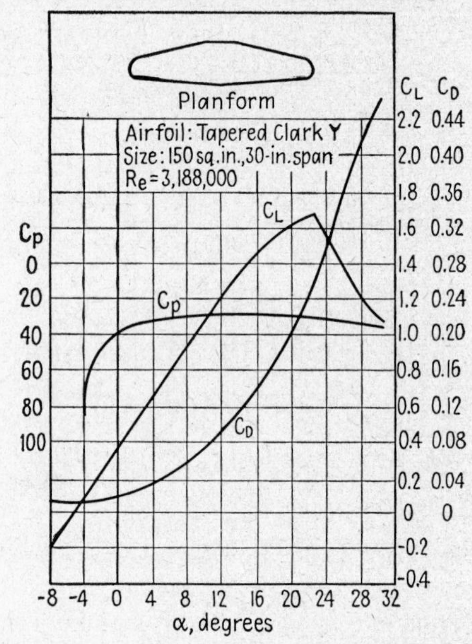

FIG. 2:12.—Conventional plot of characteristics of tapered Clark Y wing.

2:4. Problems

1. The University of Colorado 22- by 38-in.-throat wind tunnel gets a throat velocity of 150 mph with air of density of 0.0019 slug per cu ft with 100 hp. Find the energy ratio.

2. In the NACA variable-density tunnel, a test is run at an air pressure of 21 atm and an air speed of 80 ft per sec. If the air temperature is 100°F and the chord of the model is 5 in., find the Reynolds number of the test.

3. A wind tunnel like that of Fig. 2:6 has a throat velocity of 150 mph and a pressure-drop coefficient $k = \Delta P/q_t = 0.20$. For an air density $\rho = 0.0020$ slug per cu ft, find the pressure rise across the wind-tunnel fan.

2:5. Straight-line Plotting of Airfoil Test Data.—The airfoil characteristics shown in Fig. 2:3 are for a rectangular airfoil of Clark Y section of aspect ratio 6. Similar test data for a tapered Clark Y of aspect ratio 6 but with rounded tips and a 2:1 taper in planform and a taper in thickness ratio are shown in Fig. 2:12. In each case the wing characteristics are completely specified by graphs C_L, C_D, and C_n *vs.* angle of attack α. Of these three graphs only the graph of C_L *vs.* α is a straight line. The equation of this straight line, from analytic geometry, is

$$C_L = a(\alpha - \alpha_{L0}) \tag{2:17}$$

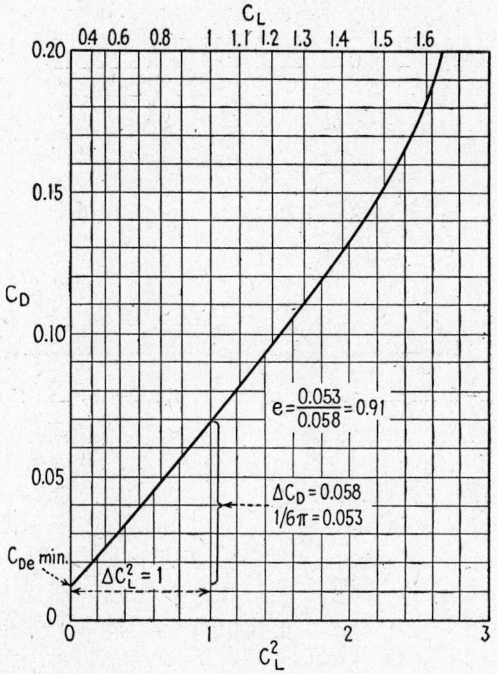

FIG. 2:13.—Straight-line plotting of C_D for tapered Clark Y wing.

where a is the lift-curve slope and α_{L0} is the angle of attack of zero lift or the intercept of the graph on the α axis. The graph of C_D *vs.* α can be straightened by replotting C_D *vs.* C_L^2, as shown in Fig. 2:13. The intercept of this graph on the C_D axis is known as the effective minimum drag coefficient of the wing and is designated $C_{De\,\min}$, and its slope, theoretically equal to $1/\pi A\!\!R$ for reasons to be discussed later, may be designated $1/\pi e A\!\!R$, so that the equation of the plot of C_D *vs.* C_L^2 may be written

$$C_D = C_{De\,\min} + \frac{C_L^2}{\pi e A\!\!R} \tag{2:18}$$

The graph of C_p *vs.* α may be straightened by plotting C_p *vs.* $1/C_L$ as in Fig. 2:14, for which the equation is

$$C_p = a.c. - \frac{C_{M\,a.c.}}{C_L} \tag{2:19}$$

the quantities *a.c.* and $C_{M\,a.c.}$ being the intercept on the C_p axis and the slope, respectively.

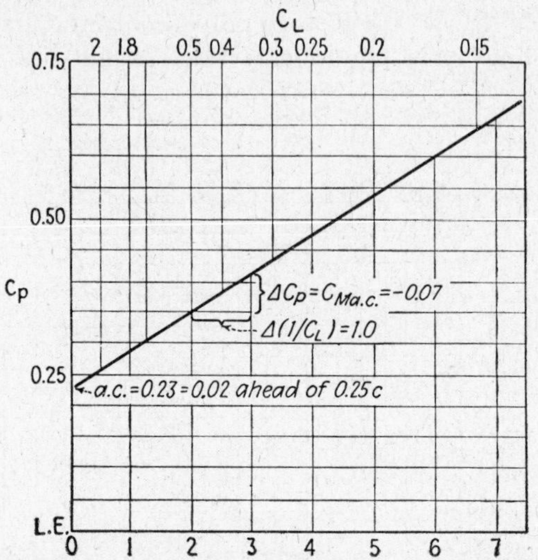

FIG. 2:14.—Straight-line plotting of C_p for tapered Clark Y wing.

The three linear equations (2:17), (2:18), and (2:19) are seen to specify completely the airfoil characteristics shown in Fig. 2:12 below the stall. Three intercepts and three slopes, plus the stalling-lift coefficient, thus completely specify the airfoil characteristics plotted in 2:12. In studying a large number of airfoil sections or wing characteristics it is simpler, briefer, and more illuminating to calculate and study these aerodynamic constants of the airfoils than to deal directly with the plotted graphs similar to Fig. 2:12. Such a tabulation for a number of tapered wings is given on page 393. The aerodynamic constants for the tapered Clark Y wing plotted in Fig. 2:12 are there tabulated as follows:

$$C_{L\,\max} = 1.67 \text{ (stalling-lift coefficient)}$$

$$\left.\begin{aligned} \alpha_{L0} &= -5.2^\circ \\ a &= 0.071 \text{ per deg} \end{aligned}\right\} \text{intercept and slope of lift curve}$$

$$\left.\begin{aligned} C_{De\,\min} &= 0.0076 \\ \frac{1}{\pi Æe} &= 0.058 \\ e &= 0.91 \end{aligned}\right\} \text{intercept and slope of graph of } C_D \ vs.\ C_L^2$$

$$\left.\begin{aligned} a.c. &= 0.25 - 0.02 \\ &= 0.23 \\ C_{M\,a.c.} &= -0.071 \end{aligned}\right\} \text{intercept and slope of graph } C_p \ vs.\ \frac{1}{C_L}$$

These seven aerodynamic constants of this tapered wing may also be read from the graphs plotted in Figs. 2:12 to 2:14. Conversely, the constants may be read from the table and the graphs plotted.

The aspect ratio Æ appears explicitly in equation (2:18), but the lift-curve slope (a) and the wing efficiency (e) are also functions of aspect ratio. The effect of aspect ratio, leading to an "aspect-ratio correction," is developed theoretically and experimentally in the next few articles. Equation (2:19) is practically independent of aspect ratio. A correction to "infinite aspect ratio" gives what is called the true "section characteristics" and eliminates the effects of wing-tip shape and planform-taper ratio included in the table on page 393. The procedure in estimating or calculating the characteristics of a particular tapered wing from the section characteristics is thus to correct the section characteristics for the primary effects of Reynolds number and Mach number and to correct the results to the actual aspect ratio, taper ratio, and wing-tip shape. A rational procedure for doing this requires further study of fundamental wing theory developed in the next few articles.

2:6. Problems

1. Using the wing constants listed on page 393, write and plot equations for C_L *vs.* α, C_D *vs.* C_L, and C_p *vs.* C_L for the wing of 2:1 taper ratio and Æ $= 6$ there designated M6(18) − (09); 0 − 0.

2. Repeat Prob 1 for the elliptical wing of Æ $= 6$ designated as 4412 − 4412; 0 − 0.

2:7. Momentum Theory of Airfoils.—The following analysis of the forces exerted on an airfoil by a fluid stream that moves relative to the airfoil involves the major assumption that the airfoil deflects a cylindrical stream of diameter equal to the span of the airfoil. A more rational heading for the article might therefore be *the cylindrical air-stream analysis of airfoil action.* This method is elementary, being based on the momentum relationships developed in Art. 1:27, but it gives several of the results that are usually ascribed to the more elaborate classical treatment ordinarily described as the *circulation* theory. The rudiments of the circulation theory of this same problem are given in Art. 2:10.

As applied to a deflected stream of fluid, Newton's law may be stated, as in equation (1:89),

$$F = m\Delta V \tag{2:20}$$

where F is the resultant force exerted on the airfoil by the deflecting stream of fluid, m is the mass of fluid deflected per unit time, and ΔV is the vector change of velocity of the fluid stream. If ΔV is in feet per second and m is in slugs per second, F is in pounds.

Let Fig. 2:15 represent the flow of air past an airfoil the cross section of which is shown. The air velocity relative to the airfoil a short distance in front of the airfoil is represented by the vector V_0; a

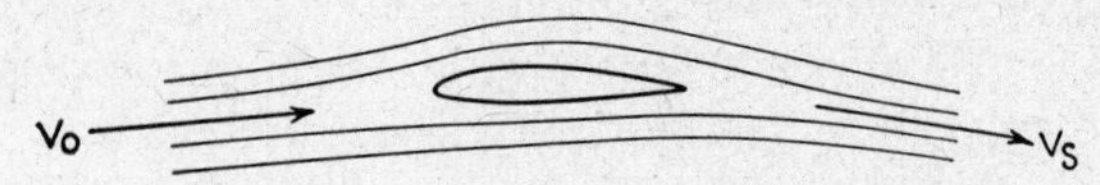

FIG. 2:15.—Streamline flow past an airfoil.

short distance behind the airfoil the velocity is V_s, which is numerically equal to V_0 but differs from V_0 in direction in that it is deflected downward through an angle ϵ_r (called the *angle of down-wash*), the subscript r denoting that the angle is in radians. The change of velocity ΔV is determined, as shown in Fig. 2:16, from the difference between the two velocity vectors. The magnitude of ΔV for small angles ϵ_r is, from geometry,

$$V = V_0\epsilon_r \tag{2:21}$$

and, according to Newton's laws, the force on the air stream necessary to produce this velocity change is in the direction of ΔV. The force

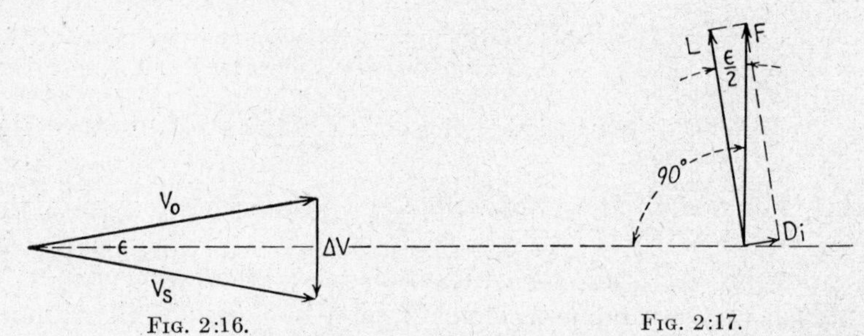

FIG. 2:16. FIG. 2:17.
FIG. 2:16.—Change of velocity of air stream.
FIG. 2:17.—Resolution of force exerted on airfoil by the deflecting stream of air.

exerted on the airfoil is in the opposite direction and is designated by F in Fig. 2:17. In this figure, F is shown analyzed into lift and drag components in the usual manner; the lift L is perpendicular to the original velocity V_0. The drag is labeled D_i to indicate *induced drag;* the actual total drag is greater than D_i because there is actually fluid friction on the airfoil surface (no matter how smooth) and eddies in the air stream behind the airfoil (no matter how thin). The friction and eddy drag depend on the shape of the airfoil cross section (or profile) and are called *profile drag* (D_p). The total drag (D_{total}) is the sum of D_i and D_p, thus:

$$D_{total} = D_i + D_p \tag{2:22}$$

The term induced drag may be considered to mean the drag *induced* by the lift.

The mass of air per second deflected by the airfoil may be calculated by assuming that the airfoil deflects a cylindrical stream of air of diameter equal to the span of the airfoil. (This is usually stated as a corollary to other assumptions but can just as well be a major assumption.) For an airfoil of span b, the area of this air stream is $\pi b^2/4$, as shown in Fig. 2:18, and the mass of air flowing through the area per second is

$$M = \frac{\rho \pi b^2}{4} V_0 \qquad (2:23)$$

Substituting equations (2:23) and (2:21) in equation (2:20),

$$F = \frac{\rho \pi b^2}{4} V_0^2 \epsilon_r \qquad (2:24)$$

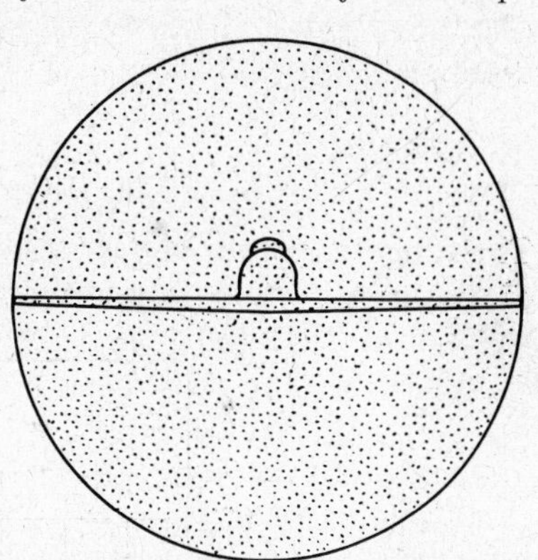

FIG. 2:18.—Front view of airplane wing, showing area of air stream assumed to be deflected by wing.

For small angles ϵ_r, the resultant force F is approximately equal to the lift; and, upon writing $L = C_L S V_0^2/2$, it follows from equation (2:24) that

$$C_L = \frac{\pi b^2}{2S} r \qquad (2:25)$$

Also, in Fig. 2:17, note that $D_i = L(\epsilon_r/2)$.

$$C_{Di} = \frac{\pi b^2}{2S} \frac{\epsilon_r^2}{2} \qquad (2:26)$$

Eliminating ϵ_r from equations (2:25) and (2:26) it follows that

$$C_{Di} = \frac{C_L^2}{\pi A\!\!R} \qquad (2:27)$$

where $A\!\!R$ is the aspect ratio of the airfoil. The total drag coefficient from equation (2:22) is

$$C_D = C_{De} + \frac{C_L^2}{\pi A\!\!R} \qquad (2:28)$$

where C_{De} is the effective profile-drag coefficient. If C_{De} were independent of C_L, then differentiating equation (2:28) would give

$$\frac{dC_D}{dC_L^2} = \frac{1}{A\!\!R} = 0.053 \qquad \text{for } A\!\!R = 6 \qquad (2:29)$$

Experimental values of dC_D/dC_L^2 for aspect ratio 6 are usually 0.055 to

0.066, depending on the planform-taper ratio and wing-tip shape. The ratio of the ideal to the actual value of dC_D/dC_L^2, determined from a plot of C_D *vs.* C_L^2, is usually designated by e and is commonly known as the "airfoil efficiency factor" but is here designated the *induced-drag efficiency factor* to avoid confusion with the lift-curve-slope efficiency discussed later. Hence,

$$e = \frac{1/\pi AR}{dC_D/dC_L^2} \tag{2:30}$$

The range of values of e corresponding to the above-mentioned range of values dC_D/dC_L^2 is 0.8 to 0.96. This means that the effective

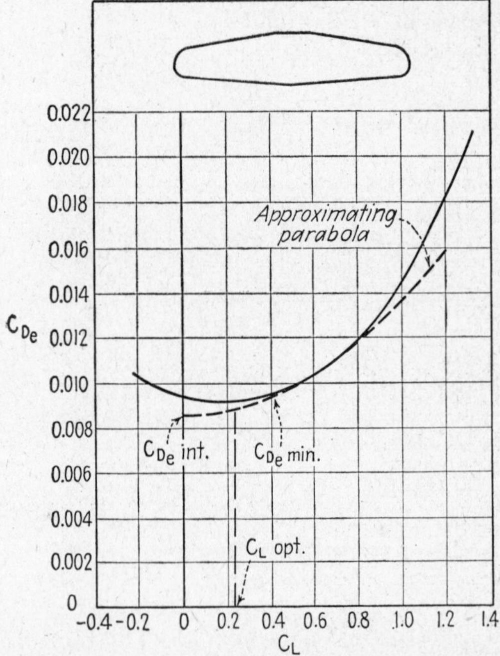

FIG. 2:19.—Plot of C_{De} *vs.* C_L, showing the meaning of the optimum lift coefficient CL_{opt}.

profile-drag coefficient $C_{De} = C_{De\,int} + KC_L^2$ where $C_{De\,int}$ is the intercept of the approximating parabola on the C_{De} axis, and K is a different constant for each wing.

The variation of C_{De} with C_L corresponding to Fig. 2:12 is shown in Fig. 2:19 along with the approximation parabola. In some NACA reports the value of C_L at which C_{De} is the minimum is called the "optimum lift coefficient" and is designated by $C_{L\,opt}$. (This term is somewhat misleading because this lift coefficient is actually "optimum" only if it is desired to fly at minimum C_{De}, and this is not usually an important criterion for airplane flight, for it does not correspond to minimum drag, to minimum power, or to maximum range or endurance.) Values of the optimum lift coefficient for the wing tests reported in *NACA Tech. Rept.* 627 are listed on page 393, Table XX, Appendix 4 along with the other aerodynamic constants for the wing tests there reported. Note in Fig. 2:19 that the intercept for the approximating parabola ($C_{De\,\text{int}}$) is a few per cent less than the actual effective minimum profile-drag coefficient ($C_{De\,\text{min}}$). This difference is disregarded in writing equation (2:18) (which should read $C_{De\,\text{int}}$ instead of $C_{De\,\text{min}}$) because the Reynolds- and Mach-number corrections are large compared with this difference.

To return to Figs. 2:16 and 2:17, the mean direction of the velocity is seen to make an angle $\epsilon_r/2$ with the original velocity. The effective angle of attack of the wing chord may thus be said to be reduced by the angle $\epsilon_r/2$, which is called the *induced angle of attack.* From equation (2:25),

$$\alpha_{ir} = \frac{C_L}{\pi A\!\!R}$$

Since equation (2:27) shows that the induced drag is zero for aspect ratio $A\!\!R = \infty$, the profile drag may be spoken of as the *drag for infinite aspect ratio.* Since no induced drag implies no induced angle of attack, the angle

$$\alpha_{0r} = \alpha_r - \frac{C_L}{\pi A\!\!R} \qquad (2:31)$$

may be spoken of as the *angle of attack for infinite aspect ratio.* In some NACA reports α_0 is plotted against C_L in presenting the results of airfoil tests, with corrections for the effect of rectangular tips and wind-tunnel walls to be described later.

The above simple analysis says nothing about the absolute angle of attack and hence does not give a numerical value for the slope of the lift curve for infinite aspect ratio. To determine this, the more elaborate method that follows appears to be necessary.

2:8. Problems

1. For a particular tapered wing of $A\!\!R = 6$ (wing 2218-09; 0 − 0 on page 393), the following test data are reported: $\alpha = 12.48°$, $C_L = 1.00$, $C_D = 0.068$. Calculate C_{Di}, C_{De}, and α_0.

2. Given the following data on the test of a particular wing of $A\!\!R = 10$ and taper ratio 3:1, calculate and plot C_{De} and α_0 as ordinates *vs.* C_L as abscissa. (*a*) From these graphs, find $C_{De\,\text{min}}$, $C_{L\,\text{opt}}$, and $dC_L/d\alpha_0$. (*b*) Also plot C_{De} *vs.* C_L^2, and find $C_{De\,\text{int}}$ and e.

α	−1.2	0	2	4	8	12	16	18	20
C_L	0	0.1	0.27	0.43	0.77	1.09	1.38	1.50	1.42
$10^4 C_D$	82	85	111	156	318	555	873	1,100	1,640

The above data are from *NACA Tech. Rept.* 627, Fig. 13, without corrections. Check these results with data on the airfoil on page 393 designated 23018-09; 0-0. (The data on page 393 have been corrected as specified in a later report, *NACA Tech. Rept.* 669.)

2:9. Circulation Theory of Airfoils.—This theory follows the assumption and methods of Art. 1:21 and assumes that the flow patterns of nonviscous incompressible fluids about cylinders of various

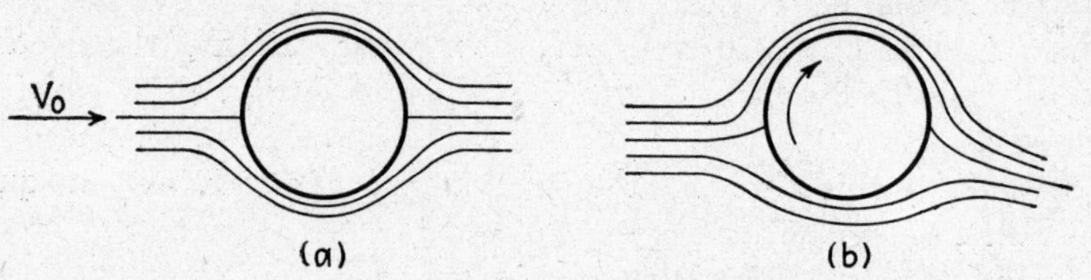

FIG. 2:20.—Ideal flow patterns (neglecting fluid viscosity) around (*a*) stationary and (*b*) rotating circular cylinders.

profiles may be closely duplicated by the vector combination in space of a uniform flow pattern with suitably located sources, sinks, and vortices, all of which can be handled with fairly simple mathematics. It may be shown by this method, combined with Bernoulli's equation, that the lift L of a portion of length b of an infinite rotating cylinder in a fluid stream of density ρ flowing with velocity V_0 is given in the equation[1]

$$L = \rho V_0 \Gamma b \qquad (2:32)$$

where Γ is the circulation of the vortex determined by the speed of rotation of the cylinder. The flow patterns with and without rotation are shown in Fig. 2:20.

It may likewise be shown that the flow pattern around an elliptic cylinder (determined by flattening and extending the circle) inclined at an angle α to the direction of free-stream velocity may be approximately reproduced mathematically by a similar flattening of the flow pattern around a rotating cylinder, the lift being given by equation (2:31). The flow patterns around such elliptic cylinders are shown in Fig. 2:21. If the circulation Γ and the angle of attack α are properly related, the flow pattern around the elliptic cylinder closely approximates actual flow patterns. The necessary relationship between the

[1] The "Kutta-Joukowsky equation."

angle of attack and the circulation is a function of the thickness ratio of the elliptic cylinder; as the thickness ratio approaches zero, it may be shown that the lift-curve slope $dc_l/d\alpha_0$ is

$$a_0' = \frac{dc_l}{d\alpha_0} = 2\pi \text{ per radian} = 0.1096 \text{ per deg} \qquad (2:33)$$

The actual lift-curve slope of infinite elliptic cylinders of finite thickness and of airfoils as tested in wind tunnels is usually found to be somewhat less than 2π per radian, and it is accordingly stated that

$$a_0 = \eta' a_0' \qquad (2:34)$$

where η' is sometimes called the "airfoil efficiency factor" but is here designated the *lift-curve-slope efficiency factor*. Applications of Ber-

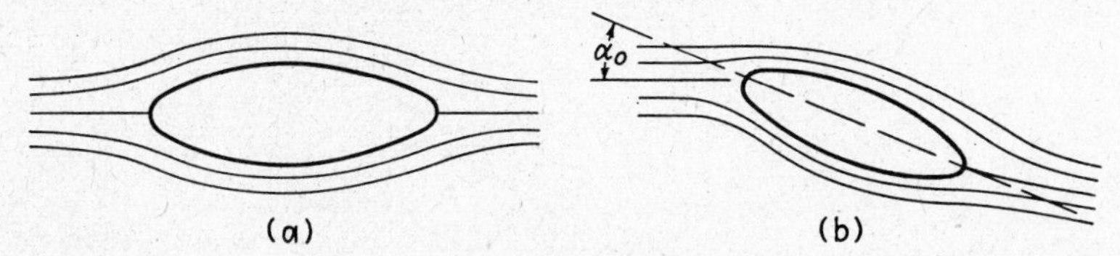

FIG. 2:21.—Ideal flow patterns around elliptic cylinders with cylinder axis at angles to the air stream of zero (a) and α (b).

noulli's equation to Fig. 2:21*b* also shows that the resultant lift on an elliptical airfoil is at 25 per cent of the chord or

$$(a.c.)' = 0.25 \qquad (2:35)$$

Because of these relationships it is sometimes considered that an infinite elliptic cylinder behaves like a "lifting-line" vortex located at 25 per cent of the chord of the ellipse from the leading edge. For an elliptic cylinder of finite length or for a finite airplane wing, the lifting line must have an end; and according to the Prandtl wing theory[1] the condition of continuity is made consistent with having a finite lifting line by assuming that the three-dimensional flow pattern around an actual wing consists of a horseshoe-shaped vortex system, as shown in Fig. 2:22. The down-wash pattern behind the horseshoe system is shown in Fig. 2:23; this also corresponds to the lift distribu-

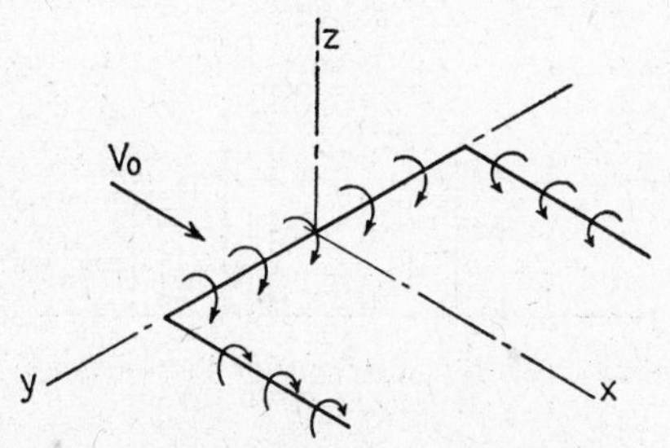

FIG. 2:22.—Horseshoe vortex pattern.

[1] PRANDTL, L., *NACA Tech. Rept.* 116.

tion along the span of the wing. To take account of actual wing-lift distributions Prandtl conceived of the wing lift being due to a combination of a group of horseshoe vortices such as that shown in Fig. 2:24,

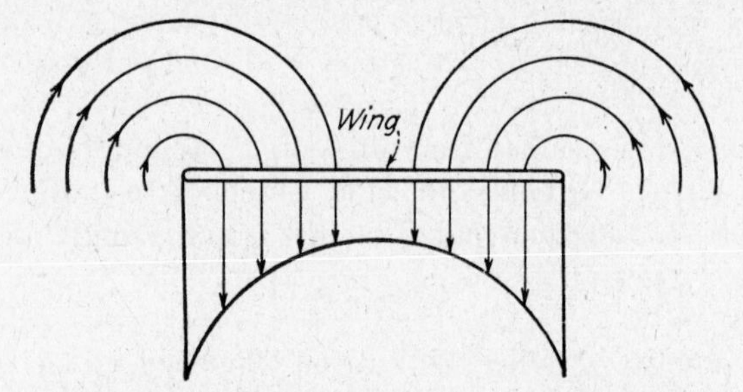

FIG. 2:23.—Down-wash system for horseshoe vortex.

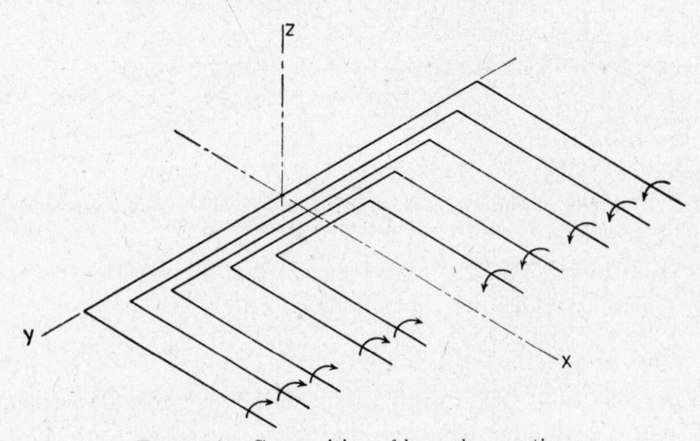

FIG. 2:24.—Composition of horseshoe vortices.

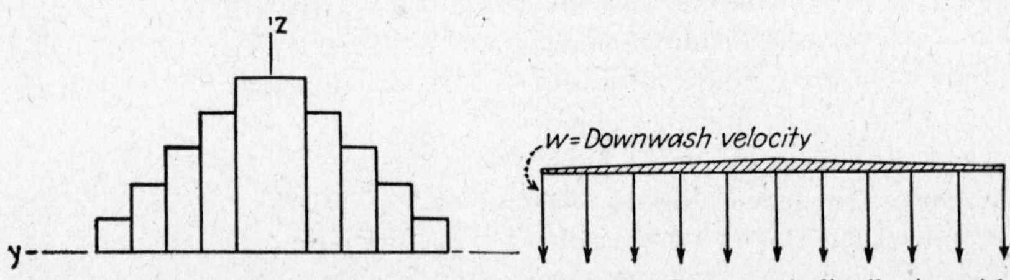

FIG. 2:25.—Lift distribution due to several horseshoe vortices.

FIG. 2:26.—Down-wash distribution with elliptic lift distribution.

giving a lift distribution as shown in Fig. 2:25. Note in Fig. 2:24 that at various points on the span of the wing there are various numbers of vortices contributing to the lift at that point, but there is considered to be only one lifting line for the wing. Using the calculus conception of an infinite number of infinitesimal vortices combined in this manner, Prandtl shows that for a uniform spanwise distribution of down-wash velocity behind a wing, as in Fig. 2:26, the necessary lift distribution is elliptic, as shown in Fig. 2:27. He concluded also that this elliptic lift distribution is the condition for minimum induced drag and that it occurs with an untwisted elliptic planform

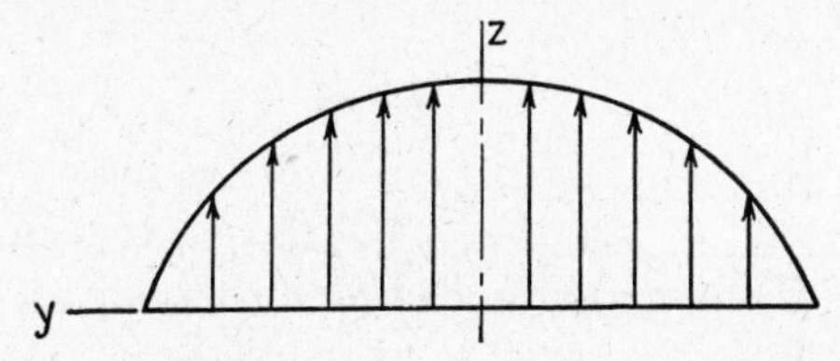

FIG. 2:27.—Elliptic lift distribution due to infinite number of infinitesimal vortices.

(closely approximated by trapezoidal wings of 2:1 or 3:1 taper). These assumptions were shown by Prandtl to result in equations (2:27) and (2:30) previously developed in the momentum theory of airfoils.

Prandtl found experimentally good agreement between the theory and experiments for airfoils of aspect ratio 1:7, but later tests on airfoils of aspect ratio 1:3 showed major discrepancies between theory and experiment, particularly in the lift-curve slope, indicating that this theory was inadequate for low-aspect-ratio wings and for tail surfaces. More recent studies have shown[1] that a chordwise distribution of lifting lines, as shown in Fig. 2:28, is necessary to account for the aspect-ratio effect of low-aspect-ratio wings.

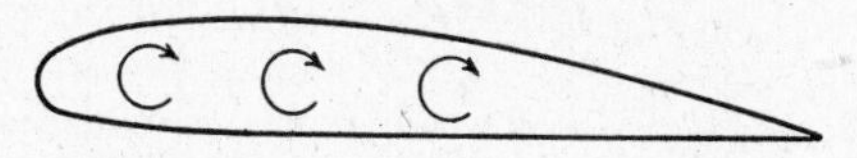

FIG. 2:28.—Chordwise distribution of lifting lines necessary to account for low-aspect-ratio wing characteristics.

2:10. Problems

1. The lift per foot of span of an airfoil extending completely across a wind tunnel in which standard sea-level air flows at a speed of 100 mph is 50 lb. Using equation (2:31), find the circulation necessary to produce this lift.

2. For the NACA 0006 wing listed on page 387, use equation (2:33) and find the lift-curve-slope efficiency factor η'.

3. Using equation (2:31), find the relationship between the lift coefficient c_l at any point on the span of the wing of chord c and the circulation Γ around the lifting line of the wing at that point.

2:11. Aspect-ratio Corrections.—Of the six aerodynamic constants (α_{L0}, a, $C_{De\ \mathrm{int}}$, e, *a.c.*, $C_{M\ a.c.}$) needed for straight-line plotting of characteristics of a particular airfoil, four (α_{L0}, $C_{De\ \mathrm{int}}$, *a.c.*, and $C_{M\ \mathrm{a.c.}}$) are substantially independent of aspect ratio. Aspect-ratio corrections are needed for the induced drag C_{Di} and the lift-curve slope a. To a lesser extent $C_{L\ \max}$ is also a function of aspect ratio, but it is also a

[1] WOOD, K. D., Aspect Ratio Corrections, *J. Aeronaut. Sci.*, October, 1943, pp. 270–272.

function of a number of other factors, chiefly spanwise lift distribution, which are discussed later.

The theory of elliptic wings developed in Art. 2:9 confirmed equations (2:28) and (2:31), which, for the elliptic wings, are written

$$C_D = C_{D0} + \frac{C_L^2}{\pi A\!\!R} \tag{2:36}$$

$$\alpha_r = \alpha_{0r} + \frac{C_L}{\pi A\!\!R} \tag{2:37}$$

Equation (2:37) is commonly divided by C_L to give as an equation for the lift-curve slope

$$\frac{1}{a} = \frac{1}{a_0'} + \frac{57.3}{\pi A\!\!R} \tag{2:38}$$

The above equations are intended to be applicable only to wings of elliptic planform.

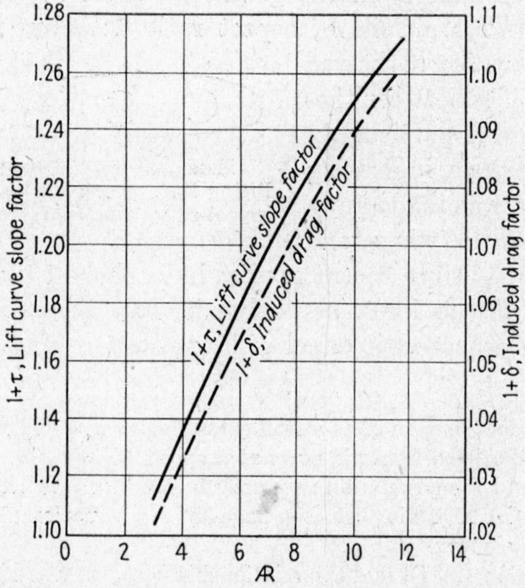

FIG. 2:29.—Aspect-ratio correction factors for rectangular wings, based on lifting theory. (*From NACA Tech. Rept.* 416.)

The lifting-line theory has been applied to rectangular and trapezoidal wings by Glauert,[1] yielding the following modifications of equations (2:36) and (2:38):

$$C_D = C_{D0} + \frac{(1+\delta)C_L^2}{\pi A\!\!R} \tag{2:39}$$

$$\frac{1}{a} = \frac{1}{a_0'} + \frac{(1+\tau)57.3}{\pi A\!\!R} \tag{2:40}$$

[1] GLAUERT, H., "The Elements of Aerofoil and Airscrew Theory," Cambridge University Press, London, 1942.

The factors $(1 + \delta)$ and $(1 + \tau)$ are given by Fig. 2:29 for rectangular wings. For trapezoidal or "straight-tapered" wings, see page 416, where, in Fig. A 13, $u = e = 1/(1 + \delta)$ is plotted against taper ratio c_t/c_r for lines of constant AR from 4 to 20 and, in Fig. A 12, $J = f(1 + \delta)$ is also plotted against taper ratio and aspect ratio.

To get the profile-drag coefficients and lift-curve slopes tabulated in *NACA Tech. Rept.* 669 (Tables XVI, XVII and XVIII in Appendix 4, pages 387 to 391) and subsequent reports, however, it was judged that this airfoil theory of rectangular wings was inadequate to get the true section characteristics, and new section characteristics using lower-case lift- and drag-coefficient symbols were calculated from the equations (in which t = thickness ratio of the airfoil section in per cent of chord)

$$c_{d0} = C_{D0} + 0.0016C_L^2 - \frac{0.0002(t - 6)}{3} \tag{2:41}$$

$$a_0 = 0.96a_0' \tag{2:42}$$

Equations (2:41) and (2:42) combined with equations (2:39) and (2:40) can be used to get finite-aspect-ratio wing characteristics from published NACA data, as illustrated by an example later in this article.

If airfoil test data of aspect ratio 6 are available, the recommended practice of the Civil Aeronautics Administration in making aspect-ratio corrections[1] is given by

$$C_D = C_{D6} - \frac{C_L^2}{6\pi} + \frac{C_L^2}{\pi AR} \tag{2:43}$$

$$m = \frac{(4m_6/3)AR}{AR + 2} \tag{2:44}$$

where m is the lift-curve slope per radian ($m = 57.3a$) and $(\ \ )_6$ refers to test results at $AR = 6$. This practice may be noted to be an application of elliptic-wing theory. Equation (2:44) follows from equation (2:37) if the lift-curve slope $a_0' = 2\pi/57.3$.

Equation (2:39) can also be put in the form

$$C_D = C_{De} + \frac{C_L^2}{\pi e AR} \tag{2:45}$$

and e may be plotted against aspect ratio as in Fig. 2:30 for comparison of theory and experiments. Note that the experimental data in Fig. 2:30 are not in very good agreement with the theory. For best estimates of experimental results the recommended practice is to use the broken lines in Fig. 2:30.

[1] Civil Aeronautics Administration, Air Commerce Manual 04.129B2.

An improved theory of lift-curve-slope correction has been developed by Jones,[1] who concludes that the Prandtl theory should be corrected to give

$$m = 2\pi A\!\!R(EA\!\!R + 2) \approx \frac{2\pi A\!\!R}{A\!\!R + 2.5} \tag{2:46}$$

where E is the ratio of the semiperimeter to the span of the ellipse and

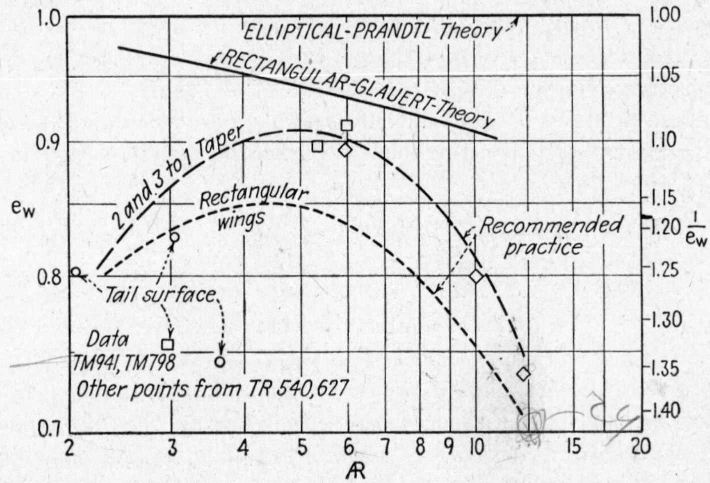

FIG. 2:30.—Theoretical and experimental variation of e for wings with aspect ratio.

is therefore a function of the aspect ratio. Experiments on rectangular wings show that the lift-curve slope is approximately

$$m = \frac{2\pi\ A\!\!R}{A\!\!R + 3} \tag{2:47}$$

The recommended practice, if data at $A\!\!R = 6$ are available, in making lift-curve-slope corrections for aspect ratio on rectangular wings or airfoils is therefore

$$m = \frac{(3m_6/2)\,A\!\!R}{A\!\!R + 3} \tag{2:48}$$

A comparison of various sources of theoretical and experimental data on aspect-ratio correction of lift-curve slope is shown in Fig. 2:31, an enlarged copy of which is in Fig. A10, for making graphical aspect-ratio corrections.

A suitable procedure for using published NACA data to estimate the characteristics of a particular wing is illustrated by the following example.

[1] JONES, ROBERT T., Theoretical Correction for the Lift of Elliptical Wings, *J. Aeronaut. Sci.*, **9**, No. 1, 8 (November, 1941).

Example.—Given the NACA 4412 wing-section data on page 387. Find (*a*) equations for C_L in terms of α, C_D in terms of C_L, and C_p in terms of C_L for a rectangular wing of $Æ = 6$; (*b*) equations for a rectangular wing of $Æ = 9$; (*c*) equations for an elliptic wing of $Æ = 3$.

Solution.—Read on page 387 for the 4412 wing the following data: $\alpha_{l0} = -4.0°$, $a_0 = 0.098$, $c_{d0\,\min} = 0.0071$, $a.c. = 0.8\%$ ahead of $c/4$, $c_{m\,a.c.} = -0.088$, $m_6 = 4.28$, $C_{D\,\min} = 0.0072$ for $Æ = 6$.

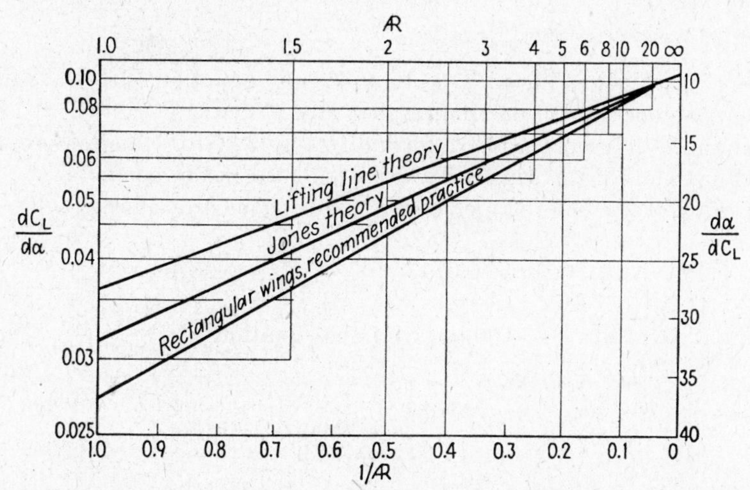

FIG. 2:31.—Lift-curve-slope correction for aspect ratio. Enlarged copy of this chart for graphical solutions on page 415.

a. *For a rectangular wing of* $Æ = 6$, use the data uncorrected for the lift curve thus: Calculate $a = m_6/573 = 4.28/57.3 = 0.0745$, and with $\alpha_{L0} = \alpha_{l0} = -4.0°$ write $C_L = 0.0745(\alpha + 4.0)$. For the drag curve use the value of $C_{D\,\min}$ given as the intercept drag coefficient, and read $e = e_w$ from Fig. 2:30. In Fig. 2:30, for a rectangular wing of $Æ = 6$ read $e_w = -0.84$, and calculate

$$C_{Di} = \frac{C_L^2}{6\pi e} = 0.063C_L^2$$

The desired drag-curve equation is then

$$C_D = 0.0072 + 0.063C_L^2$$

The C_p equation requires no $Æ$ correction and is

$$C_p = 0.242 + \frac{0.088}{C_L}$$

b. *For a rectangular wing of aspect ratio* 9, use equation (2:48) to get for the lift-curve slope

$$a = \frac{3}{2}\,0.0746\,\frac{9}{9+3} = 0.084$$

To estimate the induced drag for a rectangular wing of aspect ratio 9 refer to Fig. 2:30, and read on the line of recommended practice for rectangular wings e for the wing = e_w = 0.77. The estimated equations for the rectangular wings of aspect ratio 9 are then

$$C_L = 0.084(\alpha + 4.0)$$
$$C_D = 0.0075 + \frac{C_L^2}{9\pi e_w} = 0.0075 + 0.046C_L^2$$
$$C_P = 0.242 + \frac{0.088}{C_L}$$

These are the answers called for in (*b*).

For an elliptic wing of aspect ratio 3 use equation (2:46) for the lift-curve-slope correction from aspect ratio 6 and equation (2:45) for the induced-drag correction, referring to Fig. 2:30 for e and assuming that an actual elliptic wing will approximate the recommended practice for a wing of 2:1 or 3:1 taper in Fig. 2:30. This procedure gives

$$a = \frac{8.5}{6} \times 0.0746 \times \frac{3}{3 + 2.5} = 0.0576$$

In Fig. 2:30 read e_w = 0.86, and get the equations

$$C_L = 0.0576(\alpha + 4.0)$$
$$C_D = 0.0075 + \frac{C_L^2}{3\pi e_w} = 0.0075 + 0.123C_L^2$$

It is quite possible that the NACA will soon inaugurate a new program of airfoil testing, possibly abandoning the practice of trying to infer infinite-aspect-ratio characteristics from tests on rectangular wing models of aspect ratio 6 and using instead pressure-distribution measurements on airfoils extending completely across the wind tunnel.

2:12. Problems

1. A wing model of rectangular planform, 30-in. span, and 5-in. chord was tested in a wind tunnel, and the results of the tests, when corrected for the effect of the wind-tunnel walls, were expressible by the equations

$$C_L = 0.070(\alpha + 0.8°)$$
$$C_D = 0.0077 + 0.0734C_L^2$$

Using equations (2:43) and (2:48), write the equations for a rectangular wing of Æ = 3, and check with Fig. 2:30.

2. Using the section characteristics of the NACA M6 wing on page 591, follow the method given in the example in Art. 2:11, and write equations for the characteristics of a rectangular NACA M6 wing of Æ = 10.

3. Using the characteristics of NACA 0009 wing on page 387, follow the method of the example in Art. 2:11, and write equations for the characteristics of an elliptic-tail plane of NACA 0009 section of Æ = 4.

2:13. Scale and Turbulence Corrections.—Of the seven aerodynamic constants of an airfoil mentioned in Art. 2:5 as necessary to specify completely the airfoil characteristics below the stall, only two ($C_{D\ min}$ and $C_{L\ max}$) are appreciably affected by Reynolds number and turbulence. Three minor effects are shown on page 413, Figs. A5, A6, and A7. Here it is seen that the lift-curve slope a_0, the angle of zero lift α_{l0}, and the pitching-moment coefficient about the aerodynamic center $c_{m\ a.c.}$ show slight variations with Jacobs number (effective Reynolds number) values below 1,000,000. These variations are presumably due to departures from normal flow pattern at angles of

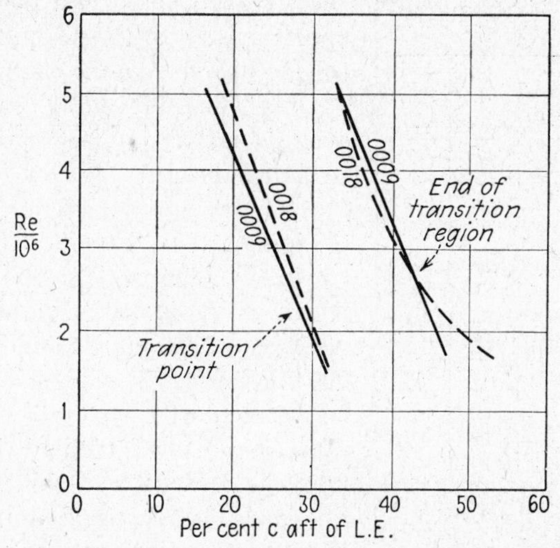

FIG. 2:32.—Variation with *Re* of transition point and end of transition region for symmetrical airfoils at $c_l = 0$. (*From NACA Tech. Rept.* 637.)

attack near the zero-lift condition caused by separation on the lower surface with certain nose shapes. It is common practice, however, to neglect the Reynolds-number effect on all section characteristics except $c_{l\ max}$ and $c_{d0\ min}$, partly because values of effective Reynolds number less than 1,000,000 rarely occur in free flight of full-scale airplanes.

The effects of laminar and turbulent flow on skin friction and on eddy drag behind a sphere were described in Arts. 1:17 and 1:25. It was there pointed out that *laminar skin friction is low* because of the low velocity gradient and that after some distance along the plate, which depends on the speed and therefore on *Re*, the laminar flow undergoes a transition to turbulent flow, resulting in higher skin friction, whereas *laminar flow around a sphere or other bluff body permits early separation and causes higher drag than with turbulent flow*, which, because of its higher velocity gradient, resists separation. The drag of an airfoil section consists of both skin friction and eddy drag, and the flow is usually partly laminar and partly turbulent, as is seen in

Figs. 2:32 and 2:33, which show the variation of the transition point, and of the end of the *transition region*, with *Re* for symmetrical airfoils 0009 and 0018 and for section-lift coefficients of 0 and 0.33. Note in Fig. 2:32 that, on the symmetrical sections at zero lift, the flow is laminar for the first 18 to 30 per cent of the chord depending on the Reynolds number and that the turbulent flow is fully developed at 35 to 45 per cent of the chord. Note in Fig. 2:33 that, with an appreciable lift of $c_l = 0.33$, the transition point moves sharply forward on the thinner- and sharper-nosed airfoils like the 0009 but stays approximately at the zero-lift position for thicker airfoils like the 0018.

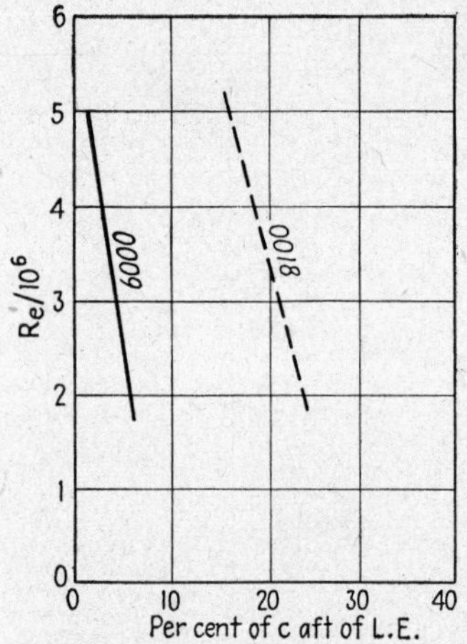

FIG. 2:33.—Variation with *Re* of transition point for 0009 and 0018 airfoils at $c_l = 0.33$. (*From NACA Tech. Rept.* 637.)

The minimum drag coefficient for symmetrical airfoils is determined chiefly by skin friction. Note in Fig. 2:32 that at a Reynolds number of about 1,000,000 the laminar flow extends all the way back to the maximum thickness of the airfoil, which is at 30 per cent of the chord, whereas at a Reynolds number of 5,000,000 the laminar flow extends to less than 20 per cent of the chord. With a fixed ratio of areas of laminar to turbulent flow, the variation of skin friction with *Re* would be determined by the skin-friction variation shown in Fig. 1:45. But with a change in transition point with changes in *Re* this variation is reduced. Accordingly, for the region above an effective Reynolds number of 1,000,000 the reduction in minimum profile-drag coefficient of most good airfoils with Reynolds number is *less* than the skin-friction relationships alone would indicate, as shown in Fig. A3 in Appendixes. At values of *Re* above 8,000,000 the flow is almost entirely turbulent; therefore, the minimum drag coefficient follows closely the turbulent skin-friction variation, although it is somewhat higher because a small eddy drag is also involved.

Figure A3 in Appendixes can be used to estimate the drag coefficient of any airfoil listed in the variable-density-wind-tunnel test results in Tables XVI to XX in Appendix 4 for values of Jacobs number (effective Reynolds number) different from those of the variable-density-tunnel tests, by the following procedure: (1) Plot the variable-density-tunnel test result on Fig. A3 in Appendixes. (2) Draw a line through the plotted point similar to the lines there plotted for other airfoils. (3) Read the corrected value on the line just plotted at the desired *Re*.

Example 1.—Find $c_{d0\ min}$ for the B-103 airfoil section listed on line 1 of page 390 at $Re = 3{,}000{,}000$.

Solution.—Read $c_{d0\ min}$ on Table XIX as 0.0075. Plot 0.0075 at $Re = 8{,}000{,}000$ on Fig. A3. Note that it lies slightly above the line labeled "NACA 2412." To find the value of $c_{d0\ min}$ at an effective Reynolds number of 3,000,000 follow this line back to the 3,000,000 effective Reynolds-number line, and read $c_{d0\ min} = 0.0085$.

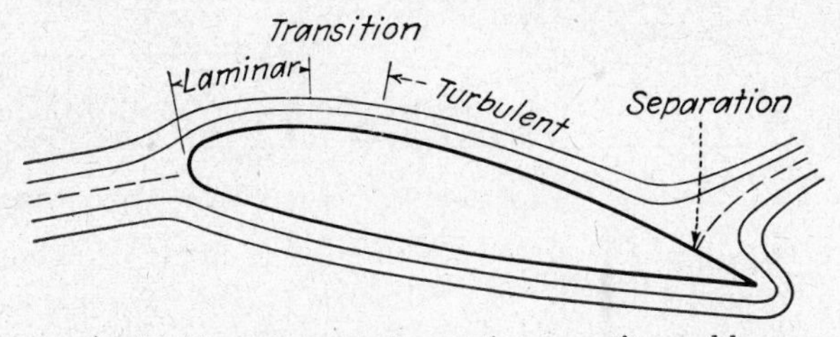

FIG. 2:34.—Laminar flow on wing: early separation and low $c_{l\ max}$.

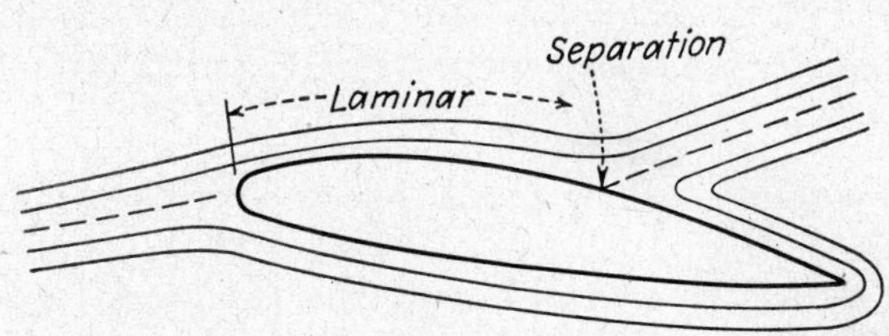

FIG. 2:35.—Early transition from laminar to turbulent flow; separation delayed, high $c_{l\ max}$.

The effect of Reynolds number on $c_{l\ max}$ is explained physically in terms of the relationship between transition and separation in the region of decreasing velocity above the airfoil. Stall of a wing begins when the flow separates; a laminar boundary layer is more likely to separate than a turbulent boundary layer, as was seen in the case of flow around a sphere described in Art. 1:25. The velocities of the edge of the boundary layer are determined by the thickness of the airfoil and the shape of its nose; a well-rounded nose and a moderately thick airfoil (12 to 20 per cent thick) are favorable to the formation of smooth streamlines at high angles of attack by permitting a gradual reduction of velocities near the upper surface, whereas the thin airfoil at high angle of attack requires a marked reduction in velocity for smooth flow around its relatively sharp nose. The thin airfoil therefore stalls at a relatively low angle of attack and the $c_{l\ max}$ is relatively independent of Reynolds number. For airfoils of moderate thickness the effect of increasing Reynolds number, as seen in Fig. 2:32, is to move the transition point forward, giving more turbulent flow in the possible separation region; this tends to increase $c_{l\,max}$ with Reynolds number. These relationships are pictured in Figs. 2:34 and 2:35.

The stall of a wing is determined, however, not only by the airfoil section, but also by the planform shape. The $C_{L\,max}$ for a complete wing differs from that of the wing section because of the distribution of the stall along the span, the point of initial stall being markedly different for a tapered wing and for a rectangular wing, as shown in Fig. 2:36. The more heavily shaded areas indicate the areas of first

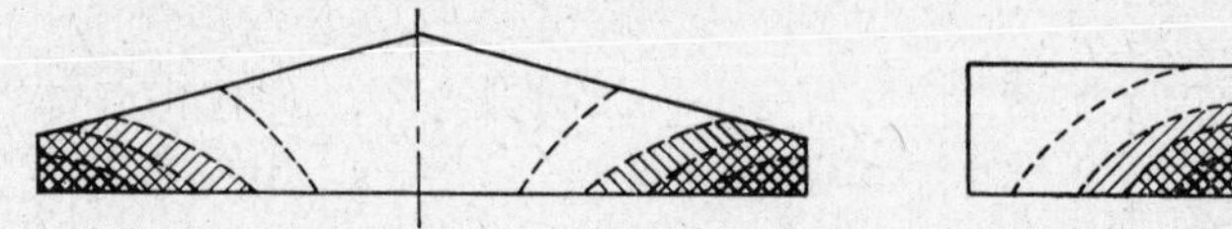

FIG. 2:36.—Comparison of stall distribution for tapered and rectangular wings.

stall; the progress of the stall with increasing angle of attack is indicated by successive lighter shaded areas. The estimation of $C_{L\,max}$ for a tapered wing requires a special study presented later in the chapter. For rectangular wings of moderate aspect ratio, it is customary to assume, for the usual type on the lift curve, that

$$c_{l\,max} = 1.07C_{L\,max} \tag{2:49}$$

although this ratio is as low as 1.04 for airfoil sections having rather flat peaks.

Typical variations of $c_{l\,max}$ with Reynolds number for zero turbulence (or with effective Reynolds number) are shown on Fig. A2, the curves being numbered to correspond to the number in the second column of Table XVI to Table XVIII. An example of the use of figure A2 follows:

Example 2.—Estimate $c_{l\,max}$ for the B-103 airfoil listed on the first line of page 390, and estimate the value of $C_{L\,max}$ for a rectangular wing of $Æ = 6$ using this section, at a free-flight Reynolds number of 3,000,000.

Solution.—On Table XVIII, line 2, read $c_{l\,max} = 1.76$; note in column 2 that the $c_{l\,max}$ scale effect is classified C4. Refer to Fig. A2, page 411, and on curve 4 in the group type C (the lower left-hand of the four groups) for a Reynolds number of 3,000,000 read $\Delta c_{l\,max} = -0.17$; then calculate $c_{l\,max} = 1.76 - 0.17 = 1.59$; calculate $C_{L\,max} = 1.48$, from equation (2:49). This is the answer called for.

2:14. Problems

1. A Piper Cub airplane has a rectangular wing of $S = 180$ sq ft and $Æ = 7$ and USA-35B section (see Table XVIII, line 21, for data). Its stalling speed at sea level (determined by $C_{L\,max}$) is 40 mph, and its level high speed at sea level (determined chiefly by $C_{D\,min}$) is 100 mph with a particular engine and propeller. Using the correction methods in Art. 2:13, estimate the proper values of $C_{L\,max}$ and $C_{D\,min}$ to use for stalling-speed and high-speed flight calculations.

2. The root section of a large airplane has a chord of 15 ft and a 23021 section. Using the data on Table XVII, line 15, estimate, for flight in sea-level air, $c_{l\,max}$ at a speed of 60 mph and $c_{d0\,min}$ at 240 mph.

2:15. Compressibility Corrections and High-speed Airfoils.—For Mach numbers greater than 0.3 or 0.4 (230 to 300 mph at sea level) major compressibility corrections may be necessary to get accurate estimates of airplane performance. These corrections are in three categories, which involve (1) subsonic-compressible-flow effects, below the critical Mach number ($M_{0\,cr}$), which is defined as the Mach number of the free stream at which the local Mach number at some point of the airfoil equals 1.00, (2) determination of the critical Mach number, and (3) supersonic compressible-flow effects, which may occur without serious losses and which are commonly involved in the flow around propeller-blade tips and in jet-propelled airplanes.

The subsonic compressible-flow effects are chiefly on the lift-curve slope a_0. The physical explanation of this presented by Prandtl[1] and

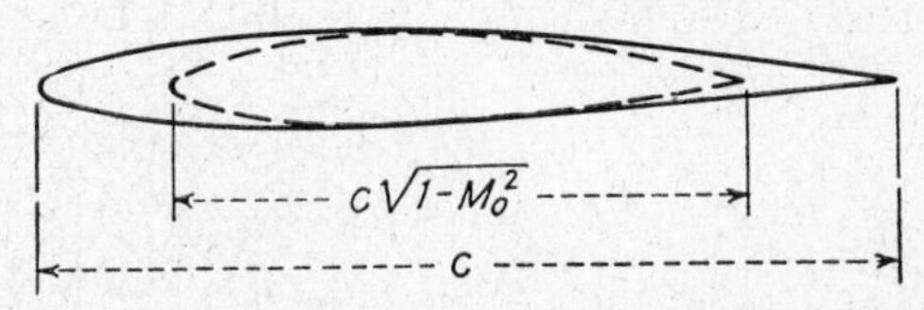

FIG. 2:37.—Simulation of effect of compressibility.

implied in equation (1:84) is that the compressible flow about a thin airfoil is similar to the incompressible flow about a thicker airfoil. Stack[2] prefers to consider that the analogous airfoil for incompressible flow is one of the same thickness but shorter chord, as shown in Fig. 2:37. With this shorter chord it is evident from the definition $c_l = L/bcq$ that the lift-curve slope is proportional to $1/\sqrt{1 - M_0^2}$. This relationship is plotted in straight-line form in Fig. 2:38, which also shows some substantiating experimental data. The effect of subsonic compressible flow on $c_{l\,max}$ and $c_{d0\,min}$, as measured in high-speed wind tunnels, is complicated by the fact that, as the tests are usually run, the Reynolds number as well as the Mach number is varied, and the boundary-layer flow pattern as well as the general flow pattern is involved. Kármán[3] finds that the variation of $c_{d0\,min}$ with Mach number can often be calculated with good accuracy by using equation (1:84) to calculate the effective-thickness ratio of the airfoil and, taking account of the increased Reynolds number as well as the higher Mach number, in estimating the variation of drag with

[1] PRANDTL, L., General Considerations on Flow of Compressible Fluids, *NACA Tech. Note* 805 (1936).

[2] STACK, JOHN, Compressible Flows in Aeronatucis, *J. Aeronaut. Sci.* (April, 1945).

[3] KÁRMÁN, TH. VON, Compressibility Effects in Aeronautics, *J. Aeronaut. Sci.* (July, 1941).

speed. In some cases, as in Fig. 2:39, the Reynolds- and Mach-number effects offset each other, and the minimum drag coefficient

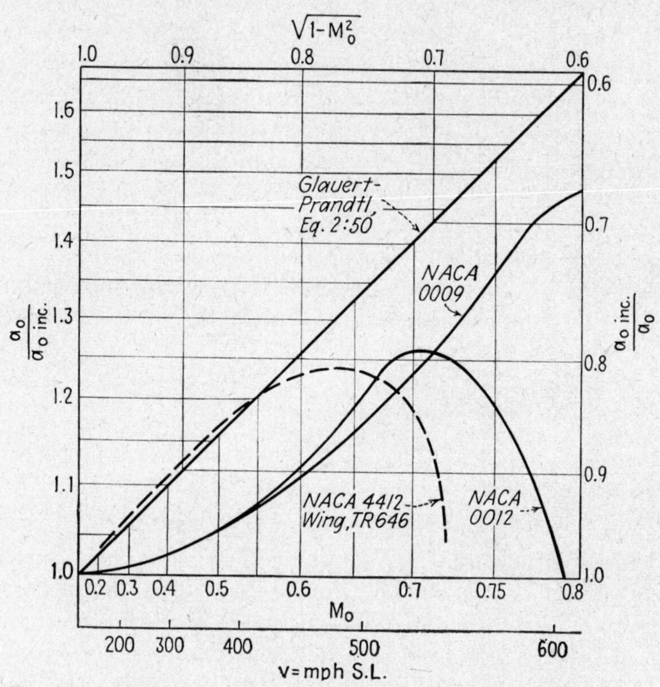

FIG. 2:38.—Subsonic compressible-flow correction to lift-curve slope.

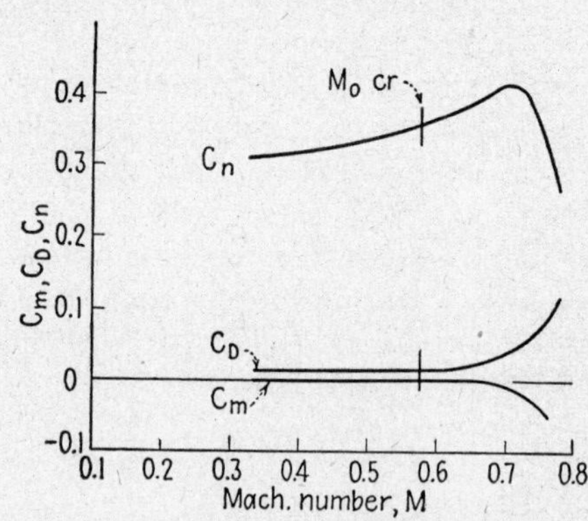

FIG. 2:39.—Force- and moment-coefficient variation with Mach number. NACA 23015 airfoil, $\alpha = 0$ deg. NACA rectangular high-speed wind tunnel.

shows no appreciable increase up to and even beyond the critical Mach number. In the absence of special test results on a particular airfoil it is considered a good approximation to assume that the lift-curve slope is related to the Mach number by

$$\frac{a_0}{a_0 \text{ incomp}} = \frac{1}{\sqrt{1 - M_0^2}} \tag{2:50}$$

This simple theory for subsonic compressible flow unfortunately results in the conclusion that the forces are infinite when the Mach number attains a value of 1.0. Since it is not reasonable to postulate infinite forces, it must be concluded that the assumption of an isen-

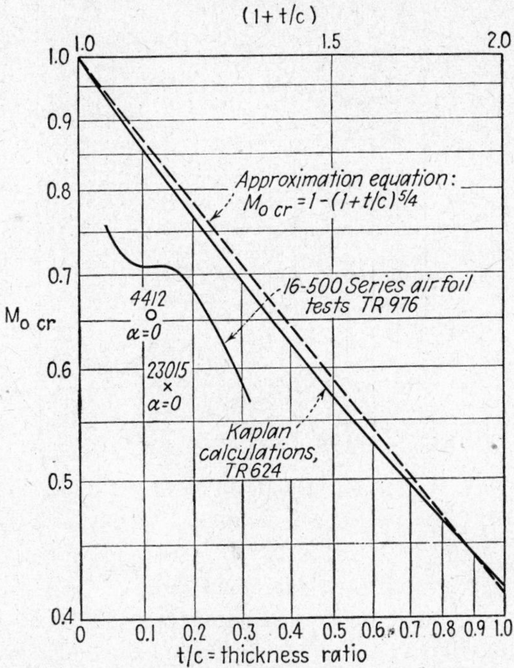

FIG. 2:40.—Critical Mach number of elliptic cylinders and wings as a function of thickness.

tropic process is not justifiable and that a different type of flow, possibly with discontinuities, occurs when some local velocity reaches the speed of sound. The calculation of the critical Mach number for airfoils is of considerable technical importance, for a shock wave may begin to form at that speed. The results of the critical-speed calculations in Arts. 1:23 and 1:24 for elliptic cylinders taking into account the actual subsonic-compressible-flow velocity are plotted in Fig. 2:40 along with the experimental data on some typical NACA wing sections. Note that the elliptic cylinders are far superior to conventional airfoils in the matter of critical Mach number. This suggests that good high-speed airfoils could be constructed by making the front portion of such airfoils elliptic cylinders.

The basic procedure used in Art. 1:23, involving the calculation of velocity and pressure distribution first for the case of incompressible flow, suggests that the maximum velocity of incompressible flow or the minimum pressure coefficient for incompressible flow is a major

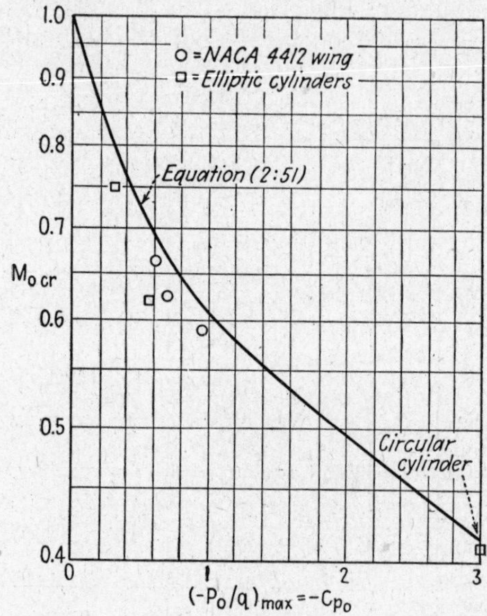

FIG. 2:41.—Critical Mach number as a function of maximum negative-pressure coefficient.

determining factor in the critical Mach number, and Fig. 2:41 shows this to be true. Using the fundamental thermodynamic relationships for compressible flow of air, Jacobs[1] derived the equation

$$C_{p0}M_{0\text{ cr}}^2 = 1.42\sqrt{1 - M_{0\text{ cr}}^2}\left[1 - \left(\frac{2 + 0.405M_{0\text{ cr}}^2}{2.405}\right)^{3.47}\right] \quad (2{:}51)$$

and this equation is plotted in Fig. 2:41 and is seen to be in fair agreement with measured critical speed. Using the relationships in Fig. 2:41, the NACA developed the family of high-critical-speed airfoils shown in Fig. 2:42. The optimum median line of this series was determined so as to give a uniform chord load at $C_L = 1.0$. The last two numbers designating the airfoils of this series are the thickness ratios in per cent. The middle number or numbers designate the design lift coefficient in tenths.

[1] *Ibid.*

Stack[1] points out that the first attainment of the critical Mach number usually involves only numerous small shocks of insignificant intensities without extensive flow separation and that pronounced separation and consequent flow changes occur only when the smaller shocks combine to form a steep front. Stack illustrates this by Fig. 2:43. He points out that the loss of total head in Fig. 2:43 required to produce separation and large changes in the force on the wing depends on the boundary-layer thickness, the airfoil shape and surface condition ahead of the shock, the pressure gradients ahead

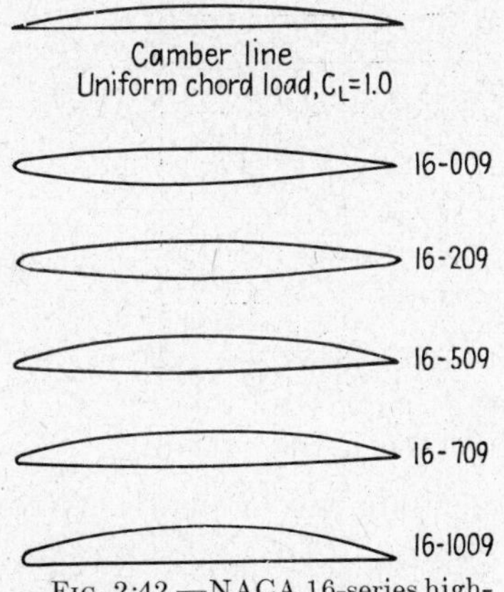

FIG. 2:42.—NACA 16-series high-critical-speed airfoils. (*From Stack, J. Aeronaut. Sci., April*, 1945.)

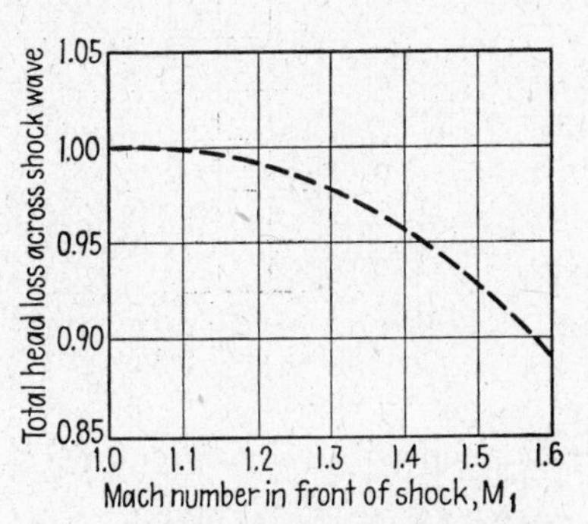

FIG. 2:43.—Ratio of total pressure across shock as a function of the Mach number in front of shock.

of the shock, and the Reynolds number. These relationships account for the marked discrepancy between the location of the defined critical Mach number shown in Fig. 2:39 and the point of rapid dropping off of the normal force coefficient.

Figure 2:43 makes it evident that the definition of the critical Mach number $M_{0\,cr}$ as the free-stream Mach number at which the local Mach number at some point equals 1.0 might well be replaced with some other definition of critical Mach number of greater significance for the high-speed performance of the airfoil.

Typical high-speed-airfoil test data are shown in Fig. 2:44 and are characterized, when the shock wave has reached considerable proportions, by a peak in the lift curves and a rapid rise in the curves of profile-drag coefficient. The critical Mach number *could*, for instance, be defined as the Mach number at which the drag coefficient has increased 100 per cent, and the critical Mach number so defined is plotted for NACA symmetrical airfoils in Fig. 2:45, which also shows a

[1] *Op. cit.*

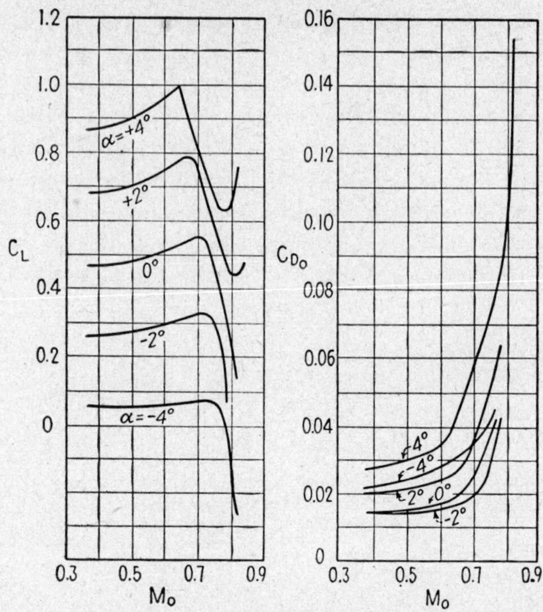

FIG. 2:44.—High-speed-test results of NACA 4409-34 airfoil.

comparison with calculated critical Mach numbers of elliptic cylinders from Fig. 2:40.

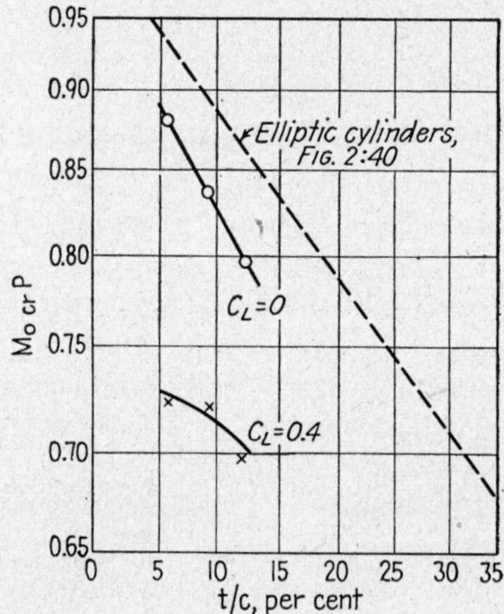

FIG. 2:45.—Critical Mach number based on 100 per cent drag increase as a function of thickness of NACA symmetrical airfoils. (*Data from NACA Tech. Rept.* 592.)

A critical Mach number might also be based on the peaks of the lift curves of Fig. 2:44; such critical Mach numbers are plotted in Fig. 2:46 for several NACA airfoils. Figures 2:45 and 2:46 taken together provide a basis for estimating the onset of severe adverse effects on an airplane wing because of independent variations of thickness and lift coefficient. This procedure is necessary because both thickness and lift coefficient combine to produce high speed over the upper surface of the airfoil. In Fig. 2:45, for instance, it might be estimated by extrapolation that the critical Mach number of a symmetrical NACA wing of 15 per cent thickness would be about 0.73 at $C_L = 0$, and from

Fig. 2:46 it might be estimated that at a lift coefficient of 0.8 the critical Mach Number would be reduced from 0.73 to 0.65.

At *supersonic* speeds, Taylor[1] has shown that for thin airfoils as in Fig. 2:46.1

$$a_{0\ \text{supersonic}} = \frac{4}{\sqrt{M_0^2 - 1}} \text{ per radian} \qquad (2{:}51.1)$$

$$C_{p\ \text{supersonic}} = 0.50 \qquad (2{:}51.2)$$

$$C_{D0\ \text{supersonic}} = \frac{16t^{2/3}}{\sqrt{M_0^2 - 1}} + \frac{\sqrt{M_0^2 - 1}}{4} C_L^2 \qquad (2{:}51.3)$$

These equations neglect viscosity effects; the calculated values of a_0 and C_{D0} are in good agreement with some experimental data, but C_p has often been found to be as far forward as 0.35. Note in equation (2:51.3) that a term analogous to induced drag appears even with infinite aspect ratio. With finite-aspect-ratio wings, sweepback has a major effect on drag,[2] as the supersonic airplane design shown in Fig. 4:13 would imply.

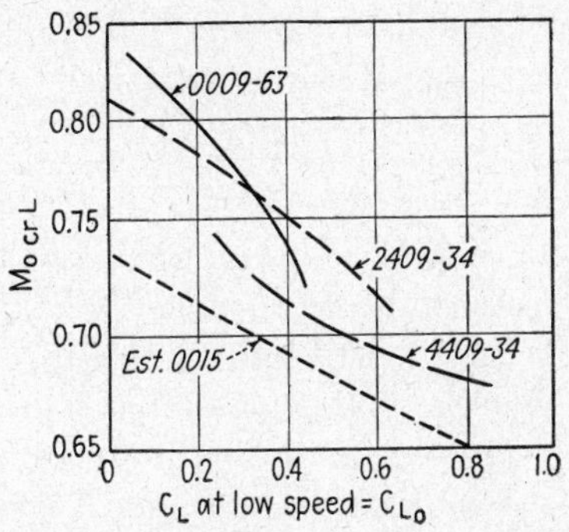

FIG. 2:46.—Critical Mach number based on peaks of lift curves (as in Fig. 2:44) as a function of C_L at low speed. (*Data from NACA Tech. Rept.* 492.)

2:16. Problems

1. Using the Clark Y (CY) airfoil data in Table XVIII, page 390, lines 15 and 22 to 26, estimate a_0 and $c_{d0\ \text{min}}$ for a Clark Y wing section of 7-ft chord, flying at 450 mph in standard sea-level air.

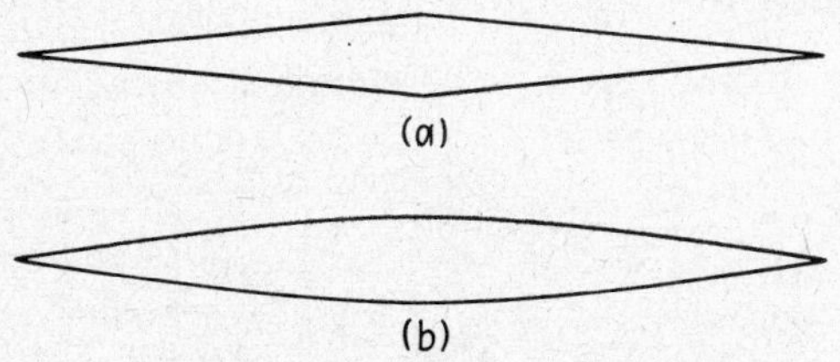

FIG. 2:46.1.—Supersonic airfoil sections.

2. An airfoil is tested at low speed and found to have a maximum negative pressure coefficient on the upper surface of 1.0. Using Fig. 2:41, find the critical Mach number and the critical speed at 40,000 ft standard altitude. Can this

[1] TAYLOR, G. I., Applications to Aeronautics of Ackert's Theory of Aerofoils Moving at Speeds Greater than That of Sound, *Brit. Aeronaut. Research Comm. Rept. Mem.* 1467.

[2] LIEPMANN, H. W., and A. E. PUCKETT, "Introduction to Aerodynamics of a Compressible Fluid," John Wiley & Sons, Inc., New York, 1947.

speed be exceeded without getting a large increase in drag coefficient? Why or why not?

3. Using Figs. 2:45 and 2:46, estimate the critical Mach number and critical sea-level speed for an 18 per cent thick NACA symmetrical airfoil on an airplane flying at a wing loading of 50 lb per sq ft. A trial solution is recommended; get first trial ($C_L = 0$) from Fig. 2:45, and then calculate C_L and repeat, using Fig. 2:46.

2:17. Systematic Investigation of Airfoils.—Pressure-distribution measurements over the upper and lower surfaces of airfoils led to the

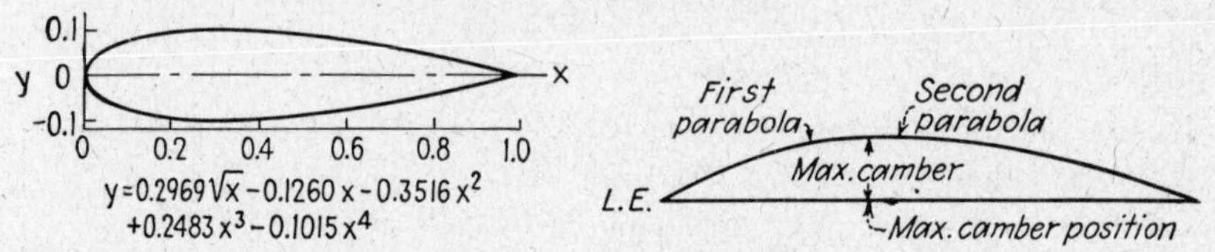

FIG. 2:47.—NACA basic thickness distribution.

FIG. 2:48.—Mean camber shape for four-digit series of airfoils.

concept of investigating independently the geometrical variation of upper and lower surfaces, but this procedure was found unsatisfactory because modifications of either upper or lower surface were found to alter the flow characteristics over the entire airfoil.

Studies in the hydrodynamic theory of airfoils led to a concept of systematic investigation of airfoils based on changing first the shape of the median line and then the thickness distribution about the median line. A good thickness distribution determined by tests on symmetrical airfoils at low speed is that shown in Fig. 2:47, and this thickness distribution was adopted in the testing of two large families of airfoils known as the four-digit and five-digit series.

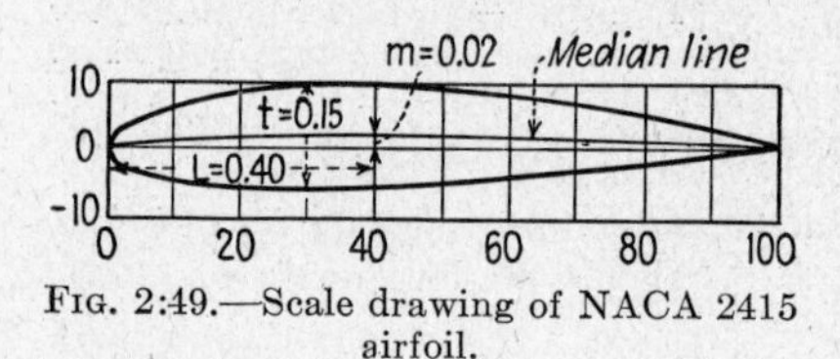

FIG. 2:49.—Scale drawing of NACA 2415 airfoil.

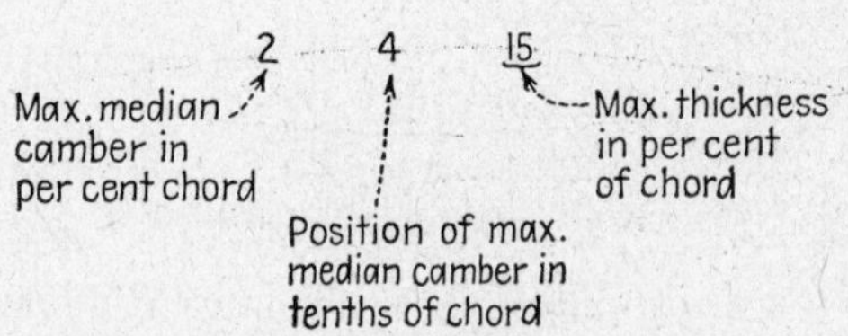

FIG. 2:50.—Diagram showing meaning of digits of four-digit airfoil series.

For the four-digit series, a mean camber line consisting of two parabolas, as shown in Fig. 2:48, was used. A typical airfoil of the NACA four-digit series is drawn to scale in Fig. 2:49. This is the NACA 2415 airfoil. A diagram showing the meaning of the four digits used to designate the airfoil is presented in Fig. 2:50, and a sketch showing the complete NACA four-digit series as tested in the variable-density tunnel and reported in *NACA Tech. Rept.* 460 is

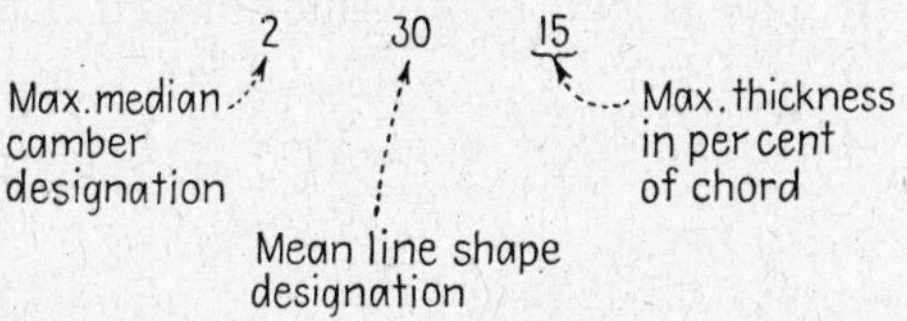

Fig. 2:51.—Diagram showing meaning of digits of five-digit airfoil series.

shown in Fig. 2:53. The meaning of the digits of the five-digit series of airfoils is shown in Fig. 2:51 and further explained in Table 2:3. The mean lines of the five-digit series are of two types shown in Fig.

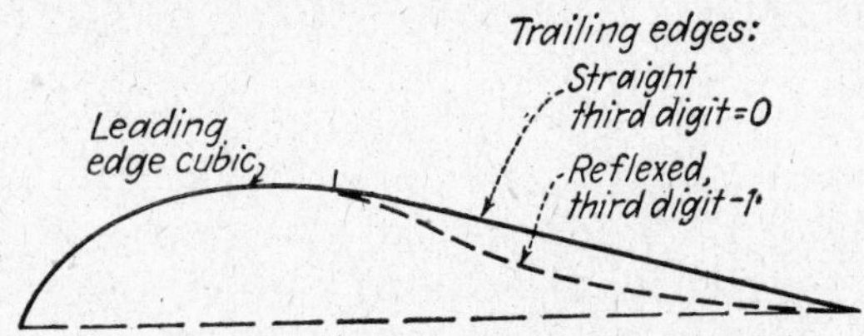

Fig. 2:52.—Mean camber lines for NACA five-digit series.

2:52, those with a straight trailing edge having a third digit of 0 and those with a reflex trailing edge having a third digit of 1.

Table 2:3

Camber designation (first digit)	Mean-line shape designation (second and third digits):					
	Straight	10	20	30	40	50
	Reflexed	11	21	31	41	51
	Position of max. median-line camber, % of chord	5	10	15	20	25
		(actual camber, % of chord)				
2		1.1	1.5	1.8	2.1	2.3
3		...	2.3	2.8	3.1	
4		...	3.1	3.7	4.2	
6		...	4.6	5.5	6.2	

Modifications of both these four-digit and five-digit series involving changed nose radius and changed location of the point of maximum thickness are designated by two supplementary digits preceded by a dash, the *first digit after the dash* designating the *leading-edge radius* and the *second digit after the dash* designating the *maximum-thickness location* according to the scheme shown in Table 2:4. The dash number -63 is usually not written because it represents the normal leading-edge radius and thickness locations shown in Fig. 2:47. For

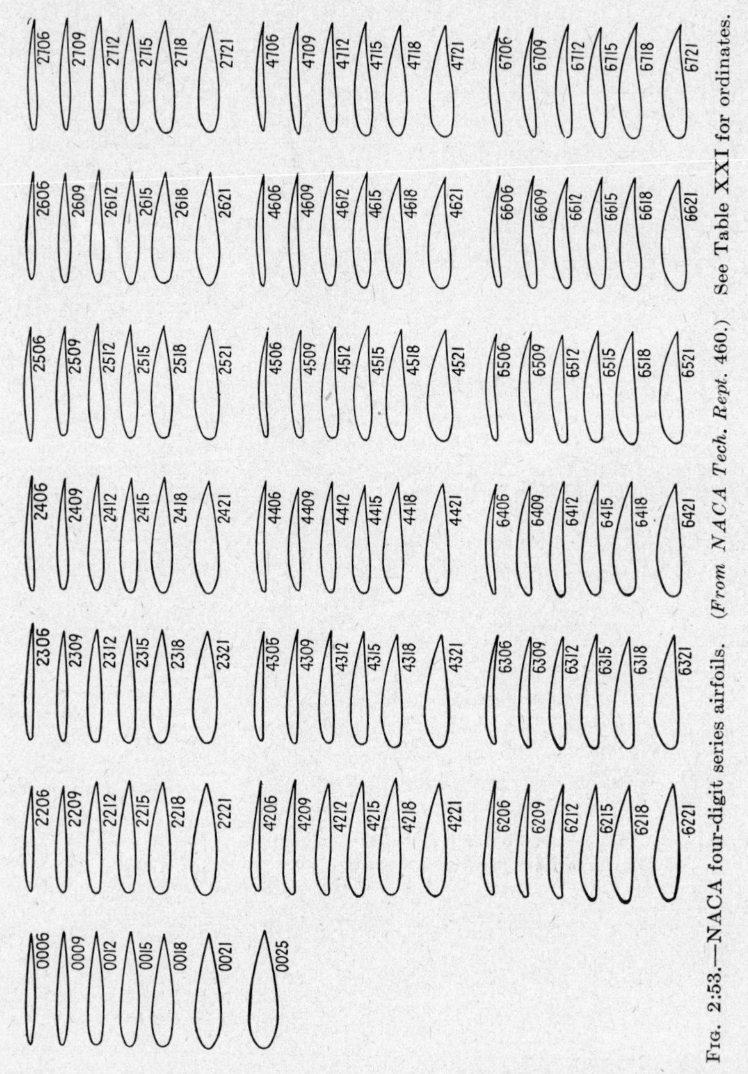

FIG. 2:53.—NACA four-digit series airfoils. (*From NACA Tech. Rept.* 460.) See Table XXI for ordinates.

example, 2415-63 is the same as 2415. Modified 0009 airfoils are shown in Figs. 2:55 and 2:56; the modified four-digit-series airfoils reported in *NACA Tech. Rept.* 492 are shown in Fig. 2:54. The complete set of five-digit airfoils reported in *NACA Tech. Rept.* 610 is shown in Fig. 2:57.

Table 2:4.—Meaning of Two Digits after Dash Indicating Nonstandard Leading-edge Radius and Nonstandard Maximum-thickness Location

First digit	L.E. radius	Second digit	Max.-thickness location, tenths
0	Sharp	2	2
3	¼ normal	3 (standard)	3
6 (standard)	Normal	4	4
9	3 × normal	5	5
		6	6

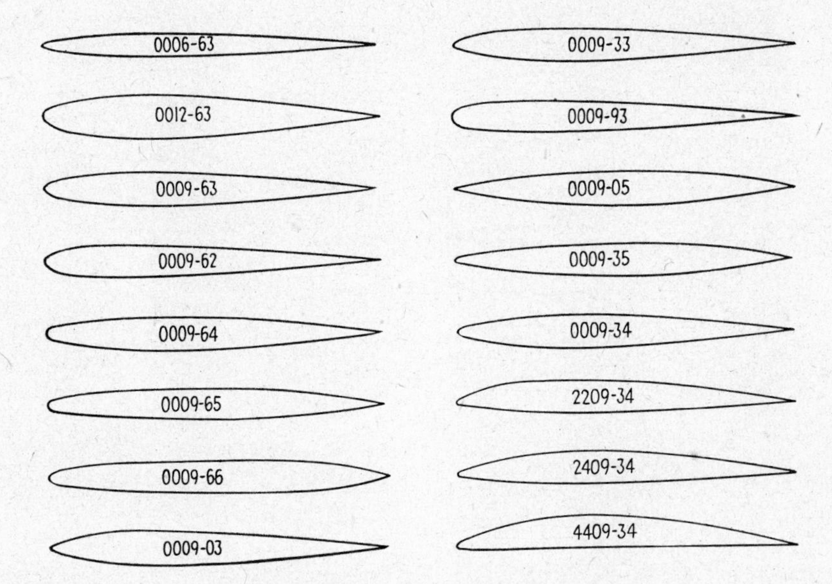

Fig. 2:54.—NACA four-digit airfoils with modified thickness distribution and nose shape. (*From NACA Tech. Rept.* 492.)

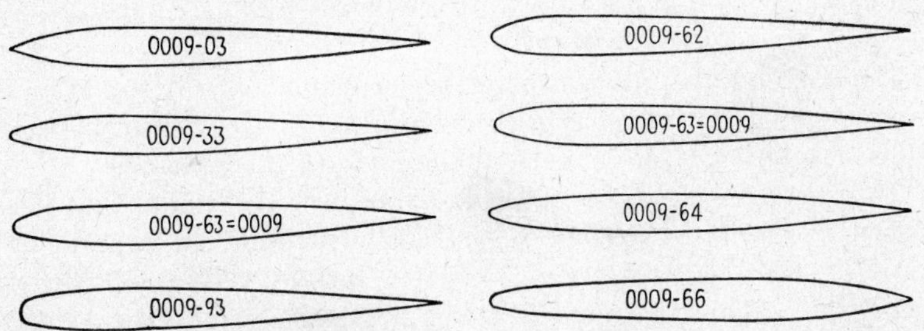

Fig. 2:55.—Comparison of airfoils with modified nose radii.

Fig. 2:56.—Comparison of airfoils with modified location of point of maximum thickness.

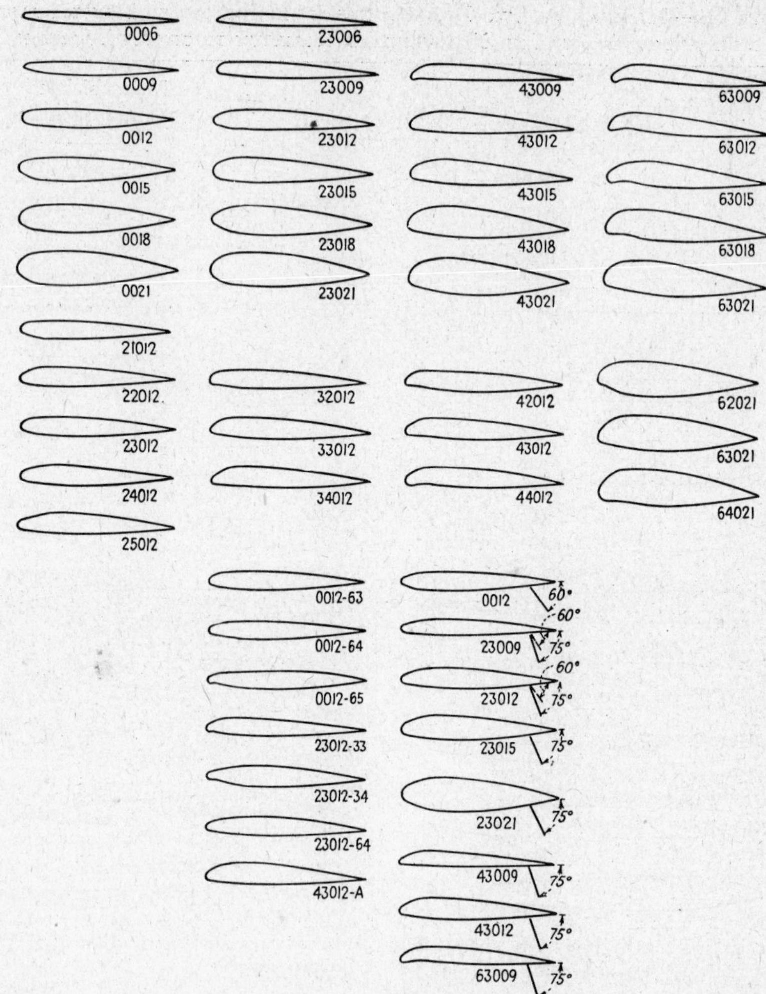

FIG. 2:57.—NACA five-digit series of airfoils and other airfoils reported in *NACA Tech. Rept.* 610. See pp. 407 to 410 for ordinates.

The dash number -45 was found to correspond closely to the special shapes developed for high speed shown in Fig. 2:42. Thus the 16-009 airfoil may be considered nearly identical with the 0009-45.

This NACA system of airfoil designation is so flexible that it can be used to specify almost any useful airfoil, whether it is part of the four-digit or five-digit series or not. For example, consider the Goettingen 593 airfoil sketched in Fig. 2:58, specified by the ordinates listed in Table 2:5. The *problem* is to find the equivalent NACA four-digit airfoil. The *solution* follows:

TABLE 2:5.—ORDINATES OF GOETTINGEN 593 AIRFOIL

% c	0	5	10	20	30	40	50	60	70	80	90	95	100
Upper.....	3.00	7.85	9.75	11.50	12.00	11.70	10.85	9.45	7.65	5.50	3.00	1.65	0
Lower.....	3.00	0.85	0.40	0.15	0.10	0	0	0	0	0	0	0	0

1. Find the maximum thickness and the maximum-thickness location. Inspection of Table 2:5 shows that the maximum thickness is 11.9 per cent and is located at 30 per cent of the chord from the leading edge. This means that the Goettingen 593 airfoil is of normal thickness distribution (maximum thickness at 30 per cent) and is approximately 12 per cent thick.

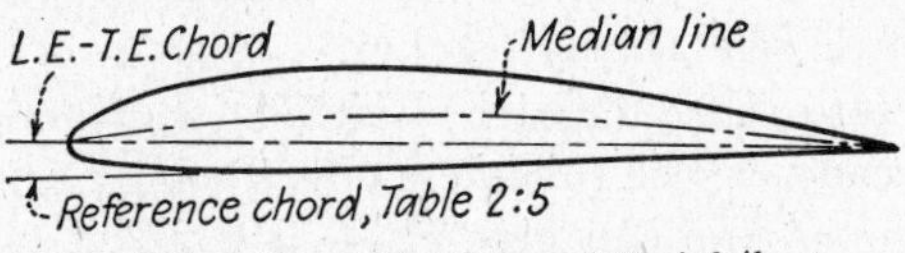

FIG. 2:58.—Goettingen 593 airfoil.

2. Find the maximum median camber m and the maximum-median-camber location L. For the Goettingen airfoil these items are calculated as in Table 2:6. The second line of Table 2:6 represents

TABLE 2:6.—CALCULATION OF MAXIMUM MEDIAN CAMBER m AND MAXIMUM-CAMBER LOCATION L OF GOETTINGEN 593 AIRFOIL

Location, % c	20	30	40	50	60
L.E.-T.E. chord ordinate, % c	2.40	2.10	1.80	1.50	1.20
Median-camber ordinate, % c	5.82	6.05	5.85	5.42	4.72
Camber from L.E.-T.E. chord, % c	3.42	4.05	3.95	3.92	3.52

the ordinate of a line through the leading and trailing edges, calculated by similar triangles. This line is used as a reference line for the median camber as in the NACA four-digit and five-digit system. Inspection of Table 2:6 shows that the maximum median camber m is 4.05 per cent and that it is located between 30 and 40 per cent of the chord from the leading edge. The NACA airfoil approximately equivalent to the Goettingen 593 therefore has a value of $m = 0.04$ and $L = 0.3$ or 0.4. The equivalent NACA airfoil is therefore the 4312 or the 4412. Characteristics of the NACA 4412 may be read in Table XVI and may be assumed to correspond closely to the characteristics of the Goettingen 593 airfoil.

The effects of the airfoil dimensions on the aerodynamic characteristics may be seen by inspecting the tables of four-digit data in Table XVI. The following effects may be noted in these data.

1. *Lift curve.* (*a*) α_{l0} is zero for symmetrical wings and increases negatively with increased camber, the thickness effect being negligible.

(*b*) a_0 decreases slightly with increasing thickness beyond 12 per cent thickness but is practically unaffected by camber.

2. *Drag curve.* (*a*) $c_{d0\,\min}$ increases fairly rapidly with thickness and more slowly with camber. A graph of $c_{d0\,\min}$ plotted against thickness gives as an intercept at zero thickness approximately the skin-friction coefficient.

(*b*) The induced-drag efficiency factor e while chiefly a function of aspect ratio, as shown in Fig. 2:30, is also slightly reduced for abnormally thick airfoils.

3. *Pitching-moment curve.* (*a*) *a.c.* is close to 0.24 for thicknesses up to about 15 per cent; with larger thicknesses it moves forward slightly but is little affected by camber.

(*b*) $c_{m\,a.c.}$ is zero for symmetrical airfoils and increases negatively with increasing camber, the thickness effect being negligible. A reflex or S-shaped camber line can give $c_{m\,a.c.} = 0$, $c_{m\,a.c.}$ being determined chiefly by the angle between the camber line at the trailing edge and the chord through the leading and trailing edges. It is increasingly negative with increases in this angle.

4. *Maximum lift coefficient.* $c_{l\,\max}$ increases rapidly with increasing camber. It also increases with thickness up to 12 to 15 per cent. Beyond 15 per cent it drops off, first slowly and then more rapidly.

If it is known what aerodynamic characteristics of an airfoil are principally desired, an airfoil can be selected from the series to give the best complete characteristics. Compromises are necessary, for the requirements are usually conflicting, for example, thin airfoils are desired because they have low drag, but thick airfoils are desired because a lighter structure can be built within them to carry a given weight. For the unusual cases in which the airfoil is to be used without high-lift devices (described later), $c_{m\,a.c.}$ should be small to reduce the twisting moment on the wing structure, and $c_{l\,\max}$ should be large to permit a small wing area for a given landing speed. Since, however, high-lift devices are used on practically all airplanes, the $c_{m\,a.c.}$ and $c_{l\max}$ for the original wing section are of little importance and the principal design problem is to determine the best thickness for a compromise between drag and structural weight. The details of a procedure for making a reasonable compromise between weight and drag are beyond the scope of this text but are usually covered by texts on airplane design.[1]

[1] WOOD, K. D., "Airplane Design," 8th ed., 1947; distributed by University Bookstore, Boulder, Colo.

2:18. Problems

1. Describe the airfoil designated 23115-35.

2. Coordinates of the upper and lower surfaces of a Clark X airfoil are given in the following table. Find the constants for straight-line plotting of the variable-density-tunnel characteristics of this airfoil for a rectangular wing of Æ = 6.

% c	0	5	10	20	30	40	50	60	70	80	90	95	100
Upper	4.00	7.96	9.68	11.28	11.70	11.40	10.52	9.15	7.35	5.22	2.80	1.49	0.12
Lower	4.00	1.14	0.50	0.03	0	0	0	0	0	0	0	0	0

3. An airplane wing is measured and found to have the following dimensions: span 40 ft, chord 50 in., maximum thickness 6 in., location of maximum thickness at 30 per cent chord, lower surface flat aft of 25 per cent chord, height of leading edge above plane of rear lower surface 2.0 in. Assuming $L = 0.3$, what is the equivalent NACA four-digit-series airfoil?

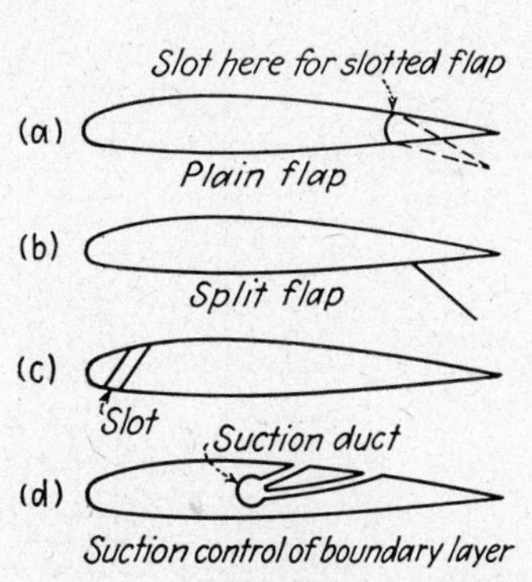

Fig. 2:59.—Types of high-lift devices. *a*. Plain flap. *b*. Split flap. *c*. Slot. *d*. Suction control of boundary layer.

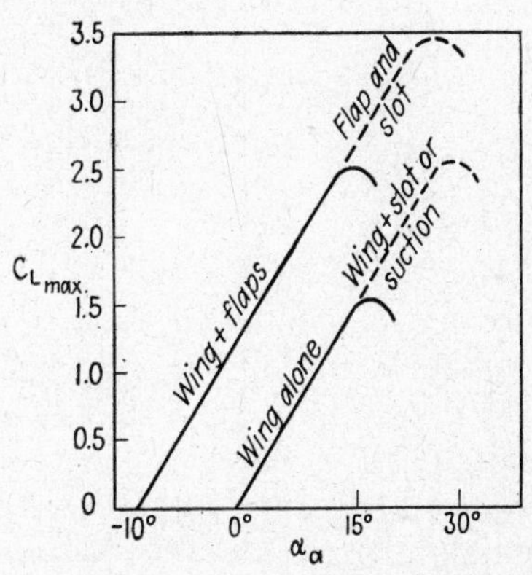

Fig. 2:60.—Effects of high-lift devices on lift curve.

2:19. High-lift Devices.—Four types of devices used to increase $C_{L\,max}$ of a wing are shown in Fig. 2:59, and their aerodynamic effects on the lift curves are shown in Fig. 2:60. The effect of the flaps (Fig. 2:59*a* and *b*) are seen in Fig. 2:60 to be equivalent to increasing the camber of the wing, which simultaneously increases the $c_{l\,max}$ and changes the angle of zero lift, while the stalling angle of the wing is changed only slightly. The effect of the leading-edge slot (Fig. 2:59*c*) or of suction (or blowing) control of the boundary layer (Fig. 2:59*d*) is quite different and is shown in Fig. 2:60 to result in extending the lift curve without change in the zero-lift angle. In most airplanes the increased stalling angle is a disadvantage because the wing is at a fixed angle relative to the plane of the wheels and it does not make for a soft landing to have the airplane tilted up at a high angle when the rear wheel or wheels touch the ground. Hence, the increased lift of slot or boundary-layer-control device can usually not be used effectively. Part-span slots, however, are frequently used to delay the stall of tips of a wing that has an unfortunate tendency to stall first at the tips. Boundary-layer suction-control devices have rarely been

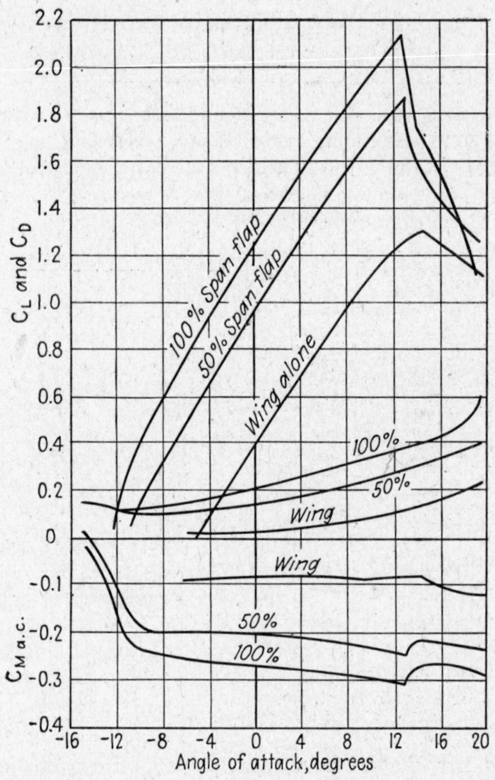

FIG. 2:61.—Effect of 0.15*c* split flaps deflected 60 deg on aerodynamic characteristics of a 5:3 tapered wing. (*From NACA Tech. Rept.* 611.)

used because of the cumbersome blower machinery necessary to provide the suction control.

Most airplane wings, however, are equipped with flaps of one sort or another for one of two purposes, (1) to assist in take-off or (2) (the chief purpose) to permit slower landings and steeper glides. The effects of half-span, and full-span flaps on a particular 5:3 tapered wing are shown in Fig. 2:61, compared with the characteristics of the wing alone. The large increase in $C_{L\,\max}$ permits a large reduction in wing area for a given landing speed, but the full maximum lift is rarely used because, as may be noted in Fig. 2:61, the stall is much sharper with flaps than without, and the airplane tends to drop without warning when the stalling angle is only slightly exceeded. The most important effect of the flap is usually considered to be the effect on the angle of glide, which is determined by the L/D ratio. The

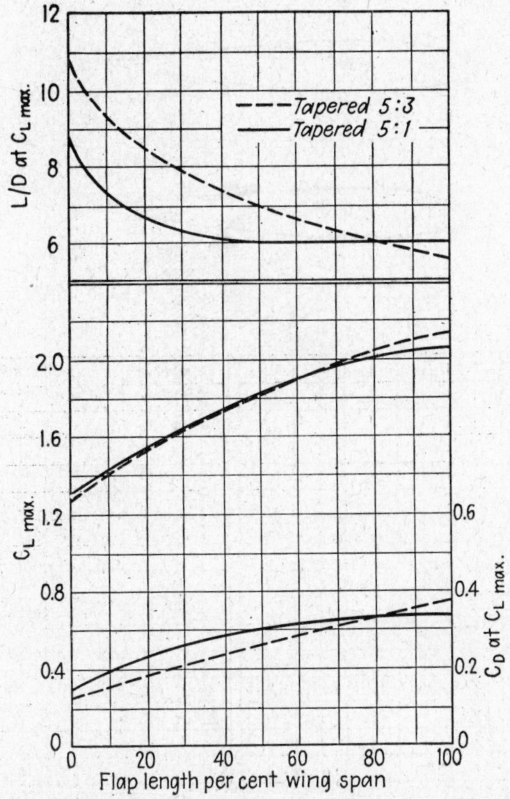

FIG. 2:62.—Effect of slap span on tapered-wing characteristics, 0.15c split flaps deflected 60 deg. (*From NACA Tech. Rept.* 611.)

effect of flap span on L/D is shown in Fig. 2:62 for two particular tapered wings. Since D/L is the tangent of the angle of glide (from Fig. 2:5), it may be noted in Fig. 2:62 that an airplane wing alone, of the shape reported in Fig. 2:62, would glide nearly twice as steeply with flaps as without in approaching a landing; this is considered a major safety feature in facilitating the entry to small fields surrounded by obstructions.

Flaps are usually made to cover the inner 30 to 70 per cent of the span of the wing, the outer portion being devoted to ailerons, although in some recent designs flaps of over 90 per cent span have been used, with aileron control provided by ailerons retractable into the upper surface of the wing (*e.g.*, on the Northrop Black Widow).

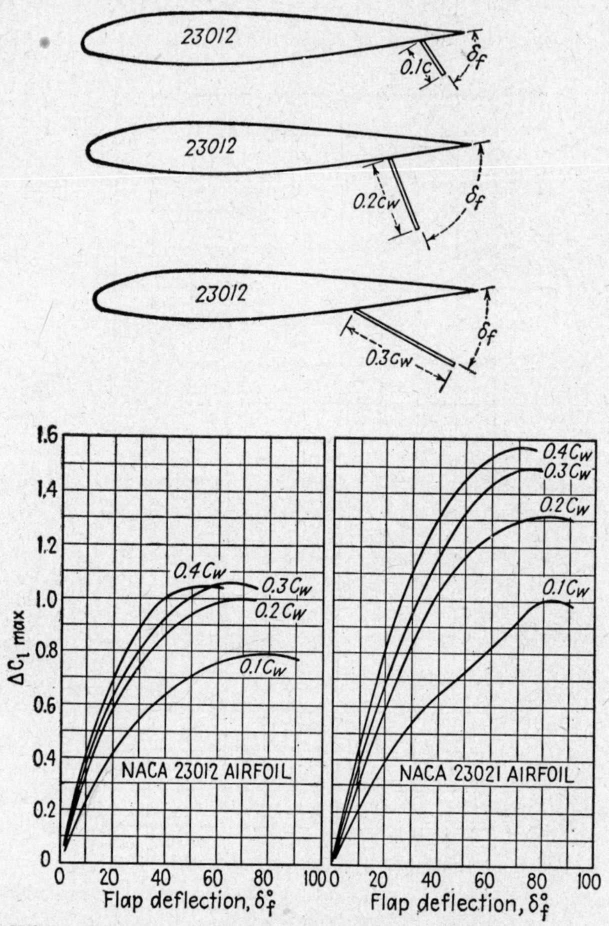

FIG. 2:63.—Effects of flap chord and flap angle on $\Delta c_{l\,max}$ for split flaps. (*From NACA Tech. Rept.* 668.)

The effects of flap chord and a flap angle on the increase in $c_{l\,max}$ for split flaps is shown in Fig. 2:63. Note that larger flaps and larger angles, up to about 75 deg, give greater increases in $c_{l\,max}$ on either a medium thickness section like the 23012 (typical of the outer portions of cantilever monoplane wings) or a thick section like the 23021 (typical of the inboard sections of cantilever monoplane wings). A greater increment $\Delta c_{l\,max}$, however, is always accompanied by a greater diving-moment coefficient $c_{m\,a.c.}$, as seen in Fig. 2:61, which puts heavier structural loads on the wing beams and sometimes requires a change in elevator-control force. A type of flap that gives increased drag without appreciable pitching moment is shown in Fig. 2:64. This flap is sometimes used to reduce the diving speed on airplanes built for dive bombing.

A comparison of the aerodynamic characteristics of several types of full-span flaps on 23000 airfoils, as tested in the NACA 7- by 10-ft wind tunnel, is shown in Table 2:7. The comparison is on the common basis of 20 per cent flap chord (except where otherwise noted) and with the flap at such an angle as to get maximum increase in $c_{l\,max}$.

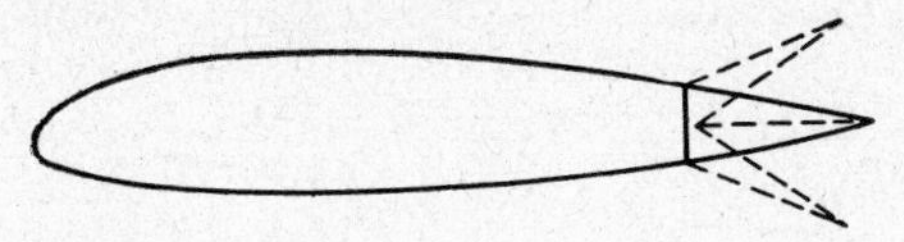

FIG. 2:64.—Dive-retarding flaps used on some dive bombers.

The Reynolds number of these tests was about 2,200,000 and the Jacobs number about 3,500,000. For some wings, variable-density-tunnel test results at a Jacobs number of about 8,000,000 are also given; the variable-density-tunnel test results are not always in good agreement with the 7- by 10-ft-tunnel test results. Some, but not all, tests show negligible scale corrections for $\Delta c_{l\,max}$, so that the data in Table 2:7 should be used with caution for design calculations on large airplanes.

Since *high drag at maximum lift* and *a high value of* $c_{l\,max}$ are usually the principal criteria for the selection of flap type, the split flap is the type most commonly used, particularly because it is also light and inexpensive. Where improvement in take-off is a major consideration, as it is in some long-range ships, especially flying boats, a type of flap that will give *low drag* with high maximum lift is sometimes selected instead. This criterion usually leads to the selection of the Fowler flap (item 6 in Table 2:7) or the multiple-slotted flap (item 5 in Table 2:7). The Fowler flap is reported quite satisfactory on some recent Lockheed airplanes, though it is the most expensive and complicated type to build of those listed in Table 2:7.

The characteristics given in Table 2:7 are *section* characteristics and require correction before they can be considered to apply to a wing of a particular aspect ratio and taper ratio, although with flaps of greater than 90 per cent span, the value of $C_{L\,max}$ will usually differ by less than 10 per cent from those of $c_{l\,max}$. A procedure for estimating $C_{L\,max}$ in terms of $c_{l\,max}$ must take account of the spanwise distribution of lift on the wings and is discussed later in the chapter.

Data on high-speed sections (like the NACA 16 series shown in

TABLE 2:7.—COMPARISON OF FULL-SPAN FLAPS TESTED IN THE NACA 7- BY 10-FT TUNNEL*

Item No.	Sketch reference	δ_{f_1}	$c_{l\,max}$	$\Delta c_{l\,max}$	$c_{m\,a.c.}$	c_{d0} at $c_{l\,max}$
1	 1 TR 679		1.55		−0.015	0.049
	TR 669 (VDT, Ja = 8 million)		1.74			
2	 2 TR 664	75°	2.4	0.85	−0.20	0.20
	TR 661 (VDT, Ja = 8.4 million)	75°	2.39	0.65	−0.26	0.22
3	 3 TR 668	75°	2.6	1.05	−0.20	
	TR 661 (VDT, Ja = 8.1 million) δ_{f_1}	75°	2.54	0.80	−0.27	0.21
4	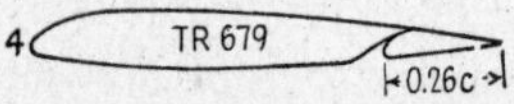 4 TR 679 0.26c	40°	2.73	1.18	−0.370	0.13
5	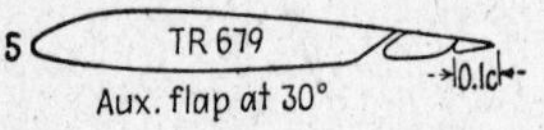 5 TR 679 0.1c Aux. flap at 30°	40°	3.00	1.45	−0.520	0.17
6	 6 TR 664 Fowler flap 0.27c	30°	2.9	1.35	−0.58	0.11
		40°	2.65	1.10	−0.44	0.20
7	 7 23021 TR 668		1.35		0	0.048
8	 8 23021 TR 668 δ_{f_1}	75°	2.6	1.25	0.34	0.18
9	 9 23021 TR 677 2b	40°	2.76	1.41	−0.405	0.095
		50°	2.82	1.47		0.13

*Section 23012 unless otherwise specified. Flap chord = $0.2c_w$ unless otherwise specified R_e = 2,200,000. Ja = 3,500,000.

Fig. 2:42) with flaps and slots have not been released at the present time; such combinations might prove the best for some airplanes. The NACA 16 series of wings has low $c_{l\,max}$ because the relatively sharp nose stalls at a relatively small angle of attack. However, this effect can be corrected by means of a leading-edge slot, and high lift can probably be obtained by the addition of a multiple-slotted flap.

Infinite-aspect-ratio data on some wings with split flaps are given in the customary form in Table XVII and can be used to write the equations for aerodynamic characteristics of such wings with flaps deflected.

2:20. Problems

1. Using data in Tables XVI and XVII, compare the equations for C_L and C_p of an NACA 0012 wing with and without 20 per cent chord split flaps deflected 60 deg. Assume a rectangular wing of aspect ratio 6 with full-span flaps.

2. Using data in Table XVII and in Fig. 2:63, estimate $c_{l\,max}$ for a 23012 wing section with a 40 per cent chord split flap at 45 deg.

3. Referring to Fig. 2:62, find the angle with the horizontal of a steady glide of the 5:3 tapered wing of characteristics there shown with 50 per cent span, 15 per cent chord split flaps deflected 60 deg.

4. A light airplane weighing 1,400 lb and having a rectangular wing of 35 ft span and 180 sq ft area is equipped with full-span multiple-slotted flaps as shown in item 5 in Table 2:7. Assuming $C_{l\,max} = c_{l\,max}/1.07$, calculate the stalling speed of the airplane in standard sea-level air.

2:21. Chordwise Load Distribution.—The chordwise distribution of air loads on a wing section is of primary importance for two reasons: (1) It is necessary for structural analysis of the chordwise wing members. (2) It determines or is determined by the velocity distribution along the wing surface, which in turn determines the Mach number of the free stream at which some local velocity will equal the velocity of sound. This is known as the "critical Mach number" and is designated by $M_{0\,cr}$.

The chordwise pressure distribution is, from Bernoulli's equation [equation (1:50)] a function of the velocity distribution as long as the Mach number is small (say less than 0.3). For symmetrical sections (as the NACA 00 series or an elliptic cylinder), the pressure is equal on the upper and lower surfaces when there is no lift on the wing section because of the symmetrical velocity patterns such as those shown in Fig. 1:49. For unsymmetrical sections the flow pattern is not symmetrical on the top and bottom, and even at zero lift there is an unsymmetrical and irregular pressure distribution depending on the shape of the airfoil.

The distribution at zero lift, which is a function of the airfoil shape, depends chiefly on what is known as the *basic lift distribution.* For symmetrical airfoil sections, the basic lift distribution is zero. For other airfoil sections, the basic lift distribution depends only on the pitching-moment coefficient $c_{m\,a.c.}$ and the maximum camber of the median line z_c expressed as a fraction of the chord. Two effects are additive, as expressed by the equation

$$P_b = -c_{m\,a.c.}P_{bm} + z_cP_{bc} \tag{2:52}$$

in which P designates the ratio p/q at any point on the chord (where p = local unit pressure in pounds per square foot and $q = pV^2/2$) and the subscripts designate the appropriate components. The function P_{bm} is the same for all airfoils listed in Appendix 4 and is designated as class 1 of P_{bm} and is given in Table XXVIII on page 427. The function P_{bc} has been found to be either zero or one of the two functions designated as class 1 or class 2 of P_{bc}; these functions are also given in Table XVIII on page 427. The numbers of these classes are commonly combined to form a classification number for the basic pressure distribution. These classification numbers are given in Table XXIX for all airfoils listed in Appendix 4. Such airfoils are designated classified airfoils. The classifications in Table XXIX also include a letter designation for the additional pressure distribution due to lift as explained below.

The pressure distribution at zero lift, designated P_0, is related to the basic lift distribution by the equation

$$P_0 = P_b - c_{nb}P_{a1} \tag{2:53}$$

where c_{nb} is the normal force coefficient (approximately c_l) at which the basic lift coefficient is calculated (simply the value of c_n that gives a stagnation point for the theoretical flow at the leading edge of the median line) and P_{a1} is the additional lift function explained below. To find c_{nb} for classified airfoils, use the equation

$$c_{nb} = -6.30c_{m\,a.c.} + z_cc_{nbc} \tag{2:54}$$

and read c_{nbc} in Table XXVIII on page 472 under the designated classification.

As the angle of attack is increased from the zero-lift angle, the lift is distributed along the chord of the airfoil in a manner that depends on the aerodynamic-center location $x_{a.c.}$, the maximum thickness ratio (t/c), and the thickness distribution. The additional lift P_a is proportional to increase in lift or normal force coefficient as indicated in the equation

$$P = P_0 + P_a = P_0 + c_nP_{a1} \tag{2:55}$$

in which P_{a1} is the lift distribution at $c_n \approx c_1 = 1.00$. The effects of thickness and aerodynamic-center location are given by the equation

$$P_{a1} = P_{at} + x_{a.c.}P_{ac1} \tag{2:56}$$

The function P_{ac1} is the same for all classified airfoils and is given in Table XXX. The function P_{at} depends on the thickness distribution and maximum thickness ratio. For all airfoils listed on pages 387 to 391 the thickness distribution is the same, and P_{at} functions, corresponding to classifications lettered from A to F corresponding to thickness ratios from 6 to 21 per cent, are given in Table XXX, page 429. A method of interpolating for other thickness ratios is given in ANC-1(2) (entitled Chordwise Air-load Distribution),[1] which also explains a method for calculating P_{a1} for unclassified airfoils and nonstandard thickness distributions. Major improvements in airfoils have been made by using nonstandard thickness distributions (such as the 16 series of high-speed airfoils in Fig. 2:42) designated to avoid high negative pressures on the upper surface.

A chart showing the distribution of the pressure P between an upper surface pressure P_u and a lower surface pressure P_l is given in Fig. A22. Use is made in this chart of the surface-pressure coefficient P_f on the base profile at zero angle of attack, but the chart is so constructed that P_f need not be read to get P_u and P_l for a given value of $P = -P_u + P_l$ (designating upward forces as positive).

For positive angles of attack, the maximum upper surface pressure $-P_{u\,\max}$ determines the critical Mach number, as shown in Fig. A23 page 431, which also provides a compressibility correction for all points on a pressure-distribution calculation for subsonic compressible flow. The use of these charts and tables is illustrated in the following examples.

Example 1.—Given a 23015 airfoil section. Find the basic pressure distribution P_b.

Solution.—To use equation (2:52) for P_b, note that $c_{m\,a.c.}$ and z_c are necessary. In Table XVII, read $c_{m\,a.c.} = -0.008$ and

$$z_c \text{ (maximum camber, per cent)} = 1.8 \text{ per cent} = 0.018.$$

Hence, equation (2:52) becomes for this airfoil

$$P_b = 0.008P_{bm} + 0.018P_{bc} \tag{2:57}$$

To find the classification of this airfoil, read on Table XXIX page 428, a classification D12. Hence, copy the P_{bm} class 1 data and the P_{bc} class 2 data from Table XXVIII, and substitute in equation (2:57). This is done in Table 2:8 below (omitting alternate chord stations to abbreviate the table).

[1] ANC stands for Army-Navy-Commerce. These publications are obtainable from Civil Aeronautics Authority, Washington, D.C.

TABLE 2:8.—CALCULATION OF BASIC PRESSURE DISTRIBUTION FOR 23015 AIRFOIL

1	Chord station...	0	2.5	7.5	15	30	50	70	90	100
2	P_{bm} class 1......	0	4.25	7.10	8.80	9.50	7.75	5.30	2.05	0
3	P_{bc} class 2......	0	47.0	59.0	47.5	24.5	13.0	5.5	1.5	0
4	$0.008P_{bm}$........	0	0.03	0.06	0.07	0.07	0.06	0.04	0.02	0
5	$0.018P_{bc}$.........	0	0.85	1.06	0.86	0.44	0.23	0.10	0.03	0
6	P_b..............	0	0.88	1.12	0.93	0.51	0.29	0.14	0.05	0

Example 2.—Given a 23015 airfoil section (as in Example 1). Find the pressure distribution at zero lift P_0.

Solution.—To use equation (2:53), note that both c_{nb} and P_{a1} must be calculated. Calculate c_{nb} from equation (2:54), using $c_{m\,a.c.} = -0.008$ and $z_c = 0.018$ as in Example 1, taking c_{nbc} as 18.75 for class 2 airfoils in Table XXVIII, page 427, thus:

$$c_{nb} = -6.30(-0.008) + 0.018 \times 18.75 = +0.05 + 0.34 = +0.39$$

To get P_{a1}, use equation (2:56), reading P_{at} from Table XXX, page 429, and P_{ac1} from page 426, class D, and tabulate as in Table 2:9 below. Use $x_{a.c.} = 0.011$ from Table XVII, page 389.

TABLE 2:9.—CALCULATION OF PRESSURE DISTRIBUTION AT ZERO LIFT FOR 23015 AIRFOIL

1	Chord station...	0	2.5	7.5	15	30	50	70	90	100
2	P_{ac1} p. 426......	0	4.5	5.9	5.0	2.9	0	−2.9	−5.7	0
3	$0.011P_{ac1}$........	0	0.05	0.06	0.06	0.03	0	−0.03	−0.06	0
4	P_{at} (p. 426).....	0	4.02	2.76	1.90	1.16	0.68	0.37	0.12	0
5	$3 + 4 = P_{a1}$.....	0	4.07	2.82	1.96	1.19	0.68	0.33	0.06	0
6	$0.39P_{a1}$..........	0	1.59	1.10	0.77	0.46	0.27	0.13	0.02	0
7	P_b, Table 2:8....	0	0.88	1.12	0.93	0.51	0.29	0.14	0.05	0
8	$7 - 6 = P_0$.....	0	−0.71	0.02	0.16	0.05	0.02	0.01	0.03	0

Example 3.—Given a 23015 airfoil section (as in above examples). Find the chordwise pressure distribution P and the upper- and lower-surface pressure distribution P_u and P when the normal force coefficient is $c_n = 1.24$.

Solution.—Use equation (2:55) to find P, taking the values of P_0 and P_{a1} from Tables 2:8 and 2:9 respectively. Read values of P_u and P_l from the chart on page 430 (Fig. *A*22). The results are listed in Table 2:10 below.

TABLE 2:10.—CALCULATION UPPER-SURFACE, LOWER-SURFACE, AND TOTAL CHORDWISE PRESSURE DISTRIBUTION ON A 23015 AIRFOIL WITH $c_n = 1.24$

1	Chord station...	0	2.5	7.5	15	30	50	70	90	100
2	P_{al}, Table 2:9...	0	4.07	2.82	1.96	1.19	0.68	0.33	0.06	0
3	$1.24P_{al} = P_a$....	0	5.05	3.50	2.43	1.47	0.84	0.42	0.07	0
4	P_0, Table 2:9....	0	−0.71	0.02	0.16	0.05	0.02	0.01	0.03	0
5	$3 + 4 = P$......	0	4.34	3.52	2.59	1.49	0.86	0.43	0.10	0
6	P_u (p. 430)......	0	0.98	0.74	0.49	0.22	0.12	0.06	0.08	0
7	P_n (p. 430)......	0	−3.36	−2.78	−2.10	−1.27	−0.74	−0.37	0.02	0

Example 4.—Given the results shown in Table 2:10 above. Find the critical Mach number and critical speed at sea level for the 23015 airfoil at $c_n = 1.24$.

Solution.—In Table 2:10, note that the maximum negative pressure on the upper surface, which is the region of maximum velocity, is $3.36q$. Consider 3.36 as $(P)_0$ in the chart on page 431, (Fig. A23) and read $M_c = 0.365$. The critical speed at sea level where the speed of sound is 765 mph is then

$$v_c = 0.365 \times 765 = 280 \text{ mph}$$

The NACA 23015 airfoil is not suited to high-speed flight.

2:22. Problems

1. Calculate the basic chordwise pressure distribution P_b for an NACA 2418 airfoil at the same chordwise stations as in Table 2:8.

2. Calculate the chordwise pressure distribution at zero lift P_0 for a 2418 airfoil at the same chordwise stations as in Table 2:9.

3. Calculate the upper- and lower-surface pressure distribution P_u and P_l for a 2418 airfoil at $c_n = 1.00$ at the same chordwise stations as in Table 2:10.

4. Find the critical Mach number and critical speed at the base of the stratosphere ($t = -67°F$) for a 2418 airfoil at $c_n = 1.00$.

2:23 Spanwise Load Distribution.—The spanwise distribution of air loads (lift, drag, and pitching moment) on a wing must be known for structural analysis of the wing. The spanwise distribution of *lift* is also a factor determining the critical Mach number of the wing.

Wings are often constructed with the zero-lift chords of all spanwise sections parallel; such wings are said to have *zero aerodynamic twist.* An equally common method of construction, however, is to have the geometric chords parallel, in which case the wing is said to have *zero geometric twist;* it will then have, however, a definite aerodynamic twist corresponding to the difference in values of α_{l0} between the root and tip sections.

Tapered wings are wings in which the chord at the tip c_t is different from the chord at the root c_r. The ratio c_t/c_r (or its reciprocal c_r/c_t) is known as the "taper ratio." The wing section at the tip is often made different from the wing section at the root. Tapered wings with $c_t/c_r < 0.5$ usually stall first at the tips, as sketched in Fig. 2:36. This tip stall is usually considered disadvantageous. The angle of incidence at the tips is sometimes made less than that at the root in order to reduce the tendency to stall first at the tips. This kind of twist is known as "washout" of incidence and is arbitrarily designated by the negative sign; the reverse twist, a "washin" of incidence, is called positive. The twist in degrees is commonly designated by the symbol ϵ. A twisted wing has a different spanwise load distribution from an untwisted wing.

When a wing with a positive angle of twist has *zero total lift,* the lift is not zero at all points; the zero lift is a result of a negative lift near the middle and a positive lift near the tips, as sketched in Fig. 2:65. A wing without twist has a spanwise lift distribution similar to that sketched in Fig. 2:66, with a maximum at the middle and a reduced lift near the tips, the lift distribution depending chiefly on the planform of the wing, the air velocities resulting in this lift distribution usually being considered to be a composite of a number of horseshoe-shaped vortices, as sketched in Figs. 2:24 and 2:25. The Prandtl wing theory

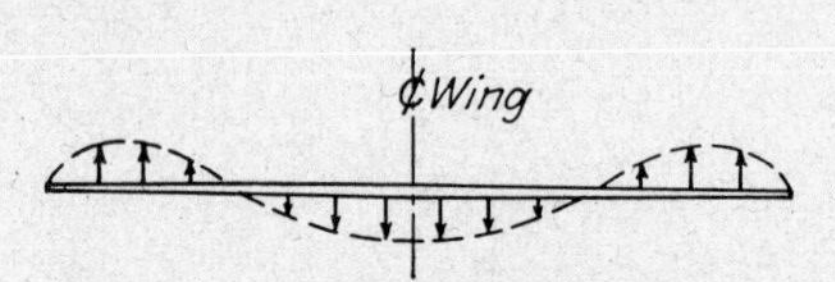

FIG. 2:65.—Basic lift distribution due to positive twist.

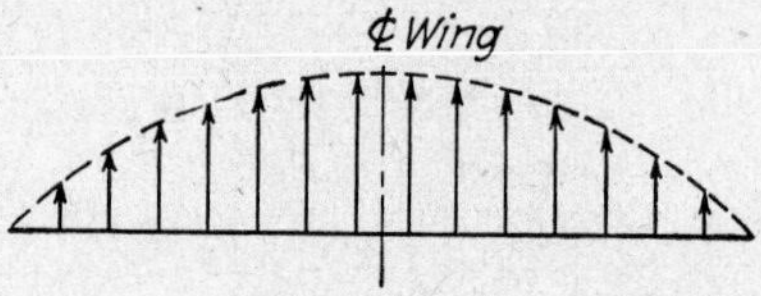

FIG. 2:66.—Additional lift distribution due to angle of attack.

(Art. 2:9) concludes that minimum drag is obtained with an elliptic planform and an elliptic lift distribution. The lift components due to twist and angle of attack are usually considered additive, as sketched in Fig. 2:67 and as represented by the equation.

$$c_l = c_{lb} + c_{la} = c_{lb} + c_{la1}C_L \tag{2:58}$$

in which c_{lb} is the basic lift coefficient at any spanwise section and c_{la} is additional lift coefficient. Since c_{la} is proportional to angle of attack, it is also proportional to the average lift coefficient on the wing C_L. The constant of proportionality is designated c_{la1} and may be considered to represent the local additional lift coefficient when the average lift coefficient C_L is 1.00.

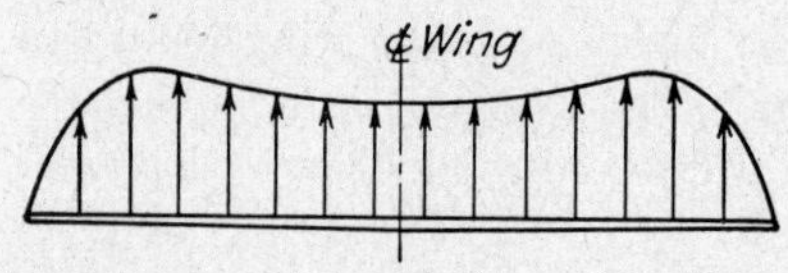

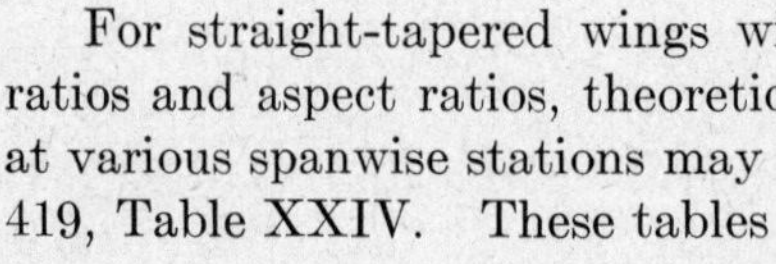

FIG. 2:67.—Resultant lift distribution on wing with positive twist at positive angle of attack.

For straight-tapered wings with rounded tips and various taper ratios and aspect ratios, theoretically calculated values of c_{la1} and c_{lb} at various spanwise stations may be obtained from the tables on page 419, Table XXIV. These tables give values of

$$L_a = c_{la1} \frac{c}{c_{mg}} \tag{2:59}$$

$$L_b = \frac{c_{lb}}{a_0 \epsilon} \frac{c}{c_{mg}} \tag{2:60}$$

where $c_{mg} = S/b =$ geometric mean chord, c is the local chord, a_0 is the infinite-aspect-ratio lift-curve slope, and ϵ is the total aerodynamic twist between the root and tip sections. Use of the functions L_a and

L_b in calculating the spanwise lift distribution is illustrated by the following example:

Example 1.—Given a straight-tapered wing of taper ratio 0.333, aspect ratio 10, and −5° twist between the root section (23018) and the tip section (23009). Find the spanwise distribution of c_l for an average lift coefficient $C_L = 0.5$.

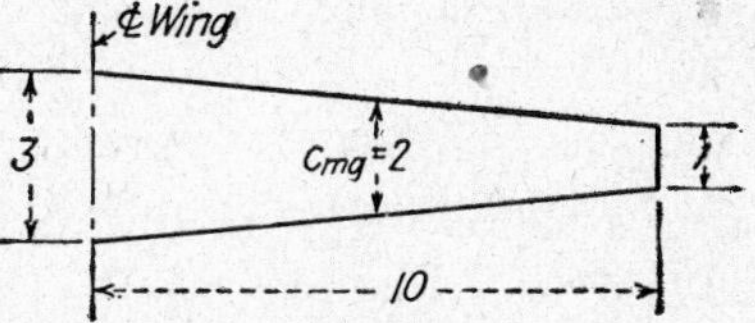

FIG. 2:68.—Proportions of wing planform for Example 1.

Solution.—The proportions of the planform of the wing are shown in Fig. 2:68. List the spanwise stations at the points on page 425, as in line 1 of Table 2:11. Calculate values of c and c_{mg}/c from the geometry of Fig. 2:68, and list as in lines 2 and 3 of Table 2:11. Read values of L_a and L_b from page 425, interpolating between $c_t/c_r = 0.3$ and 0.4 to get values for $c_t/c_r = 0.333$, and list as in lines 4 and 5 of Table 2:11. Calculate $c_{la1} = (c_{mg}/c)L_a$ from equation (2:59) as in line 6. Calculate $c_{lb} = (c_{mg}/c)a_0\epsilon L_b$ from equation (2:60) as in line 7, using $a_0 = 0.098$ as a mean value for the 23018- and 23009-airfoil data in Table XVIII on page 390 [a more refined calculation taking account of the variation of a_0 with thickness is given in ANC-1(1), Spanwise Air-load Distribution, but this refinement is here considered not justified]. Calculate $C_Lc_{la1} = 0.5c_{la1}$ and list as in line 8. Add lines 7 and 8 to get c_l from equation (2:58) as in line 9 of the table. This is the answer called for.

TABLE 2:11.—CALCULATION OF SPANWISE LIFT DISTRIBUTION FOR EXAMPLE 1

		Root							Tip
1	Span station..	0	0.2	0.4	0.6	0.8	0.9	0.95	1.00
2	Relative chord	3.0	2.6	2.2	1.8	1.4	1.2	1.1	1.0
3	c_{mg}/c	0.67	0.77	0.91	1.11	1.43	1.67	1.82	2.0
4	L_a (p. 425)...	1.39	1.29	1.14	0.952	0.719	0.557	0.427	0
5	L_b (p. 425)...	−0.322	−0.224	−0.012	+0.123	+0.190	+0.188	+0.155	0
6	c_{la1}..........	0.922	0.985	1.03	1.05	1.02	0.92	0.775	0
7	c_{lb}...........	+0.104	+0.084	+0.005	−0.071	−0.132	−0.152	−0.138	0
8	$C_Lc_{la1} = 0.5c_{la1}$......	0.461	0.492	0.515	0.525	0.510	0.460	0.388	0
9	c_l [equation (2:58)]......	0.565	0.576	0.520	0.454	0.378	0.308	0.250	0

The spanwise lift distribution calculated above takes no account of fuselage or nacelle interference with the wing, which is seen in Fig. 2:69 to be a major effect. Accordingly, an equivalent approximate method developed by Schrenk[1] is becoming widely used. The simple and reasonable assumptions of the Schrenk method (admittedly approximate) are as follows: (1) The additional lift distribution is proportional to the arithmetic mean between the actual wing chord and the chord of an ellipse having the same area as the wing. (2) The basic lift distribution at any point is equal to the angle of twist measured

[1] *NACA Tech. Mem.* 948.

from the mean zero-lift chord multiplied by *one-half* the infinite-aspect-ratio lift-curve slope. The factor of ½ is difficult to justify theoretically but works out fairly well in practice. While this method is not as simple to apply as the solution of Example 1 above, it is of more general application and much simpler than the general method of ANC-1(1).

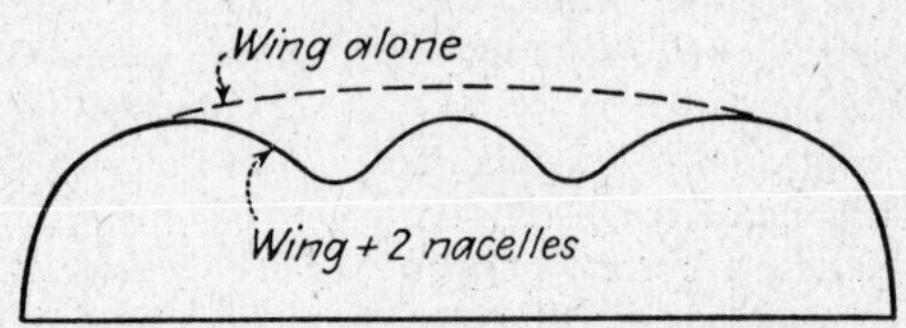

FIG. 2:69.—Effect of nacelles on spanwise lift distribution. (*From Durand, Vol.* IV, *p.* 161.)

For the complete structural-analysis problem, drag and moment distribution must be calculated as well as lift and these forces analyzed into chord and beam components. A systematic but elaborate method of doing this is provided in ANC-1(1).

When the spanwise distribution of lift is known, a comparison with the spanwise variation of $c_{l\,max}$ along the span permits the determination of $C_{L\,max}$ for the wing. For a straight-tapered wing, $C_{L\,max}$ can be very simply determined by means of the transparent Chart B in the back of the book, as illustrated in the following example:

Example 2.—An untwisted straight-tapered wing of aspect ratio Æ = 6 and taper ratio $c_r/c_t = 2$ has an NACA 2418 root section and an NACA 2409 tip section. Find $C_{L\,max}$ for the wing at a Jacobs number based on the mean wing chord of 8,000,000 Test result listed in Table XX on page 393 for a similar 2200-series wing was 1.60.

Solution.—Calculate $c_{l\,max}$ at a series of spanwise stations as in Table 2:12 below, and plot as in Fig. 2:71 below to the same semilogarithmic scales as on Chart B in the back of the book.

TABLE 2:12.—CALCULATION OF $c_{l\,max}$ DISTRIBUTION FOR EXAMPLE 2

	Root							Tip
1 Span station	0	0.2	0.4	0.6	0.8	0.9	0.95	1.00
2 $\frac{c}{c_{mg}}$	1.33	1 20	1.07	0.93	0.80	0.733	0.70	0.67
3 $\frac{Ja}{10^6}$	10.6	9.6	8.6	7.4	6.4	5 9	5.6	5.4
4 t, relative	0.72	0.61	0.50	0.40	0.29	0.23	0.21	0.18
5 $\frac{t}{c}$	0.18	0 170	0.156	0.143	0.121	0.105	0.10	0.09
6 $c_{l\,max}$ (p. 387)	1.53	1.57	1.63	1.67	1.72	1.67	1.65	1.62
7 S.E. (p. 387)	E2	D2	D2	D2	C2	C2	B2	B2
8 $\Delta c_{l\,max}$	0	+0.01	0	−0 22	−0.03	−0.05	−0.11	−0.12
9 $c_{l\,max}$, corr	1 53	1.58	1.63	1.65	1.69	1.62	1.54	1.50

Steps in the calculation of 2:12 follow:

Line 1. Arbitrary span stations.

Line 2. Use Fig. 2:70 to find c/c_{mg} at each station.

Line 3. Local Jacobs number $= c/c_{mg}$ times Ja based on c_{mg}.

Line 4. Use Fig. 2:70 to find relative wing thickness at each station, assuming linear variation of wing thickness with span.

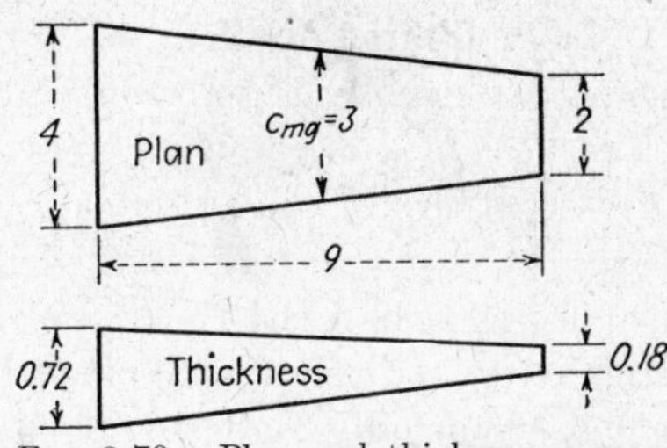

FIG. 2:70.—Plan and thickness proportions for Example 2.

Line 5. Calculate from Fig. 2:70.

Lines 6 to 9. Follow the procedure in Art. 2:13.

Superimposing Chart D on Fig. 2:71 with the $c_{l\,max}$ line tangent to the c_{lal} line for the specified aspect and taper ratios permits reading $C_{L\,max} = 1.52$. The point of tangency, indicating first stall, is found to be at about 20 per cent of the semispan from the center. At $C_L = 1.60$ the stall may be seen to have spread over the middle 60 per cent of the wing. This corresponds to the observed peak in the variable-density-tunnel test on a similar wing.

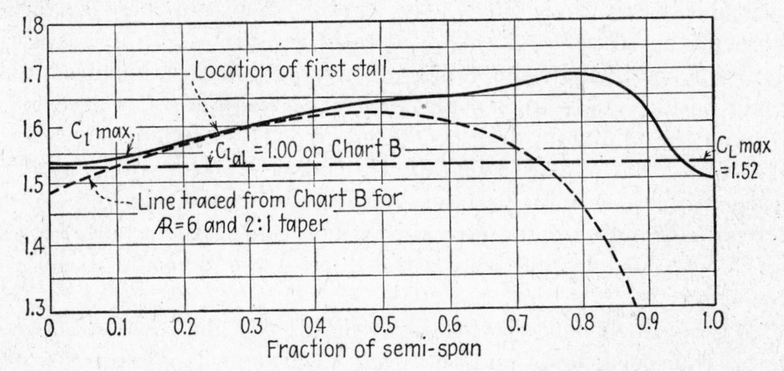

FIG 2:71.—Semilog plot of $c_{l\,max}$ to same scales as Chart B.

2:24. Problems

1. For a straight tapered wing of aspect ratio Æ = 6, taper ratio $c_r/c_t = 2$, and twist $\epsilon = -10$ deg, use equation (2:60) and find c_{lb} at ribs at $y/(b/2) = 0.2$ and 0.9. Assume $a_0 = 0.097$ per deg.

2. For the wing in Prob. 1, use equation (2:59), and find c_{lal} at the same spanwise stations.

3. For the wing of Probs. 1 and 2, find c_l at the same spanwise stations for $C_L = 0.3$.

4. For a straight-tapered wing of aspect ratio Æ = 10, taper ratio $c_r/c_t = 3$, and no twist, calculate and plot on semilogarithmic graph paper like Chart B a graph of c_{lal} *vs.* per cent semispan.

5. Using the graph calculated in Prob. 4 to apply to a wing of $S = 202.5$ sq ft, root section NACA 0018, tip section NACA 0012, and linear variation of thickness (not t/c) with span, calculate Ja at the spanwise stations listed on page 425, and estimate and plot a graph of $c_{l\,max}$ *vs.* per cent semispan to the same semilogarithmic scales as in Prob. 4. Assume $v = 60$ mph.

6. Superimpose the graphs of Probs. 4 and 5 to find $C_{L\,max}$ for this wing, and specify the point at which stalling first occurs.

2:25. Characteristics of Straight-tapered Wings.—Monoplane wings are usually tapered in planform so as to approximate the ideal elliptic planform, the usual taper ratios being 2:1, 3:1, or 5:1. It is also structurally advantageous to have a taper in thickness greater than the taper in planform; hence, the thickness ratio at the tip is usually less than the thickness ratio at the root. In the interests of simplicity of design and construction, the plan and front-elevation views are usually made to consist of straight lines except for a rounding off at the tip. The linear variation of thickness t and chord c with distance from the plane of symmetry y corresponds to a nonlinear variation of t/c with y. The calculation of the thickness ratio at any spanwise location y is illustrated in Table 2:11 in Art. 2:23.

The aerodynamic characteristics of a tapered wing do not correspond to those of any simple weighted mean airfoil section. Thus, for the tapered wing on Table XX, page 393 designated 2415-09, 0-0, the mean thickness ratio is $(15 + 9)/2 = 12$ per cent; but there is a larger chord at the 15 per cent thickness ratio because of the 2:1 taper in planform specified in the table. A weighted mean thickness ratio would be $(2 \times 15 + 9)/3 = 13$ per cent. There is a fair agreement between the minimum drag coefficient of a 2413 rectangular wing of $AR = 6$ and that of a 2415–09 tapered wing of 2:1 taper ratio, perhaps sufficiently accurate for practical purposes in view of the uncertainty of Reynolds and Mach number corrections, but a more accurate result can be obtained by integrating the drag of the elements to get the total drag.

If dS is an element of wing area equal to cdy, the relation between the section coefficients and the wing coefficients is specified by the equations

$$C_L S = \int c_l dS \qquad (2:61)$$

$$C_D S = \int c_d dS \qquad (2:62)$$

$$C_M c_{ma} S = \int c_m c dS \qquad (2:63)$$

Equation (2:63) may be considered to define c_{ma}, which is called the *mean aerodynamic chord* of the wing. Diehl[1] has shown that the *mean geometric chord* $c_{mg} = S/b$ is the best available approximation to the mean aerodynamic chord c_{ma}.

To write equations (2:17) to (2:19) for a tapered wing, six wing constants (exclusive of $C_{L\,max}$, which can be found as in Art. 2:23) are necessary. They are

a and α_{L0} for the lift curve.

$C_{De\,min}$ and e for the drag curve.

x_{ac} and $C_{M\,a.c.}$ for the center-of-pressure curve.

[1] *NACA Tech. Rept.* 751.

The values of these constants may be determined as follows:

a. Use Fig. 2:31 or Fig. A10 page 415 and a correction intermediate between the Jones theory (elliptic wings) and the recommended practice for rectangular wings; check with the mean a_0 of the root and tip sections. Figure A13 on page 416 may be used as a check but is of questionable accuracy.

α_{L0}. For a wing without aerodynamic twist, the zero-lift chords are all parallel; hence, assume $\alpha_{L0} = \alpha_{l0}$ of root section for such a wing. If the wing is twisted, calculate the local angle of attack at each point; assume $c_l = a_0\alpha$, and plot a graph c_lc *vs.* y. Find by trial the value of root α that will give $\int c_lcdy = 0$. Figure A12 on page 416 may be used as a check.

$C_{De\ \min}$. For a first approximation of an untwisted wing, take

$$C_{De\ \min}S = \int c_{d0\ \min}cdy \tag{2:64}$$

For a twisted wing, calculate the spanwise lift distribution as in Art. 2:23, and use the proper value of c_{d0} for each local c_l in integrating equation (2:62).

e. Use Fig. 2:30. This is necessarily only a first-order approximation, for equation (2:18), which defines e, is only an approximation (but a very useful one). Figures A13 to A15 on page 416 may also be used to find C_{Di}, but the added complication is not believed justified by the accuracy of the theoretical assumptions on which they are based.

a.c. Locate a weighted mean quarter-chord point by the equation[1]

$$\bar{x}_{c/4}S = \int x_{c/4}dS \tag{2:65}$$

in which $x_{c/4}$ designates the fore-and-aft location of the quarter chord of the element $dS = cdy$ measured from some arbitrary y axis such as that through the root section $c/4$ and $\bar{x}_{c/4}$ is the corresponding mean effective quarter-chord location. Find $x_{a.c.}$ for an airfoil section of the weighted mean thickness ratio from the tables of aerodynamic data. Then $a.c. = \bar{x}_{c/4} + \bar{x}_{a.c.}$. If a wing is so tapered that $x_{c/4}$ is zero at all points, equation (2:65) gives $\bar{x}_{c/4} = 0$. A wing so designed is said to have zero sweepback on the quarter-chord line. Many wings are initially designed with zero sweepback, but the sweepback is often changed after the design has been started to balance the airplane better. Figure A18 on page 418 may be used as a check.

$C_{M\ a.c.}$. For a wing with angle of twist ϵ and angle of sweepback on the quarter-chord line β, both the section-moment coefficients and the basic lift distribution contribute to the wing pitching moment as

[1] From *NACA Tech. Rept.* 751.

indicated in the equation

$$C_{M\,a.c.} = C_{MS} + C_{Mb} \tag{2:66}$$

in which C_{MS} may be found by integration of

$$C_{MS}c_{mg}S = \int c_{m\,a.c.}c^2dy \tag{2:67}$$

and C_{Mb} may be found by integration of

$$C_{Mb}c_{mg}S = \int c_{lb}cx_{a.c.}dy \tag{2:68}$$

For straight-tapered wings with rounded tips and $c_{m\,a.c.}$ = const. along the span, the integrations specified in equation (2:67) and (2:68) can be avoided by reading the factors E and G in Figs. A16 and A17 on pages 417 and 418 and using the relationships

$$C_{Ms} = Ec_{ms} \tag{2:69}$$
$$C_{Mb} = G\epsilon a_0 AR \tan\beta \tag{2:70}$$

The foregoing procedure is illustrated by the following example. An additional example from *NACA Tech. Rept.* 572 is given on pages 423 to 427.

Example.—Given the third wing listed in Table XX on page 393 (planform as in Fig. 2:72), including the following data: root section 2415, tip section 2409, sweepback = 15 deg on the $c/4$ line, taper ratio = 2:1, AR = 6, geometric twist = 0. Use the section characteristics listed in Table XVI on page 387, find the wing characteristics listed in Table XX on page 393 (except $C_{L\,opt}$ and $C_{L\,max}$), and write equations for $C_L(\alpha)$, $C_D(C_L)$, and $C_p(C_L)$.

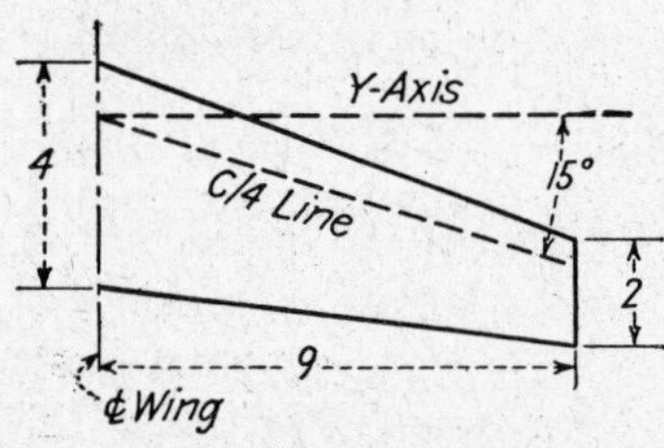

FIG. 2:72.—Wing planform in example.

Solution.

Lift curve.

a. On page 415 Fig. A10, read a = 0.076 for AR = 6 as a compromise between elliptic and rectangular wings. This is a good check with the experimental value of 0.075.

α_{L0}. On page 387, Table XVI, read $\alpha_{L0} = -1.7$ deg for both 2415 and 2409 sections. Hence α_{L0} = 1.7 is a good estimate, which checks well with the experimental value of $\alpha_{L0} = -1.9$ deg.

The desired lift coefficient equation is then $C_L = 0.076(\alpha + 1.70)$.

Drag curve.

e. In Fig. 2:30, for AR = 6 and 2:1 cr 3:1 taper, read e = 0.90; this checks the experimental value.

$C_{De\,min}$. On page 387, Table XVI, read $c_{d0\,min}$ = 0.0068 for a 2415 section and $c_{d0\,min}$ = 0.0060 for a 2409 section. With such a small range of values, $C_{d0\,min}$ for the weighted mean airfoil of $t/c = (2 \times 15 + 9)/3 = 13$ per cent is close enough. By interpolation $C_{D0\,min} = 0.0060 + \frac{2}{3}(0.0068 - 0.0060) = 0.0065$. This checks the experimental value $C_{De\,min}$. The desired drag-coefficient equation is then

$$C_D = 0.0065 + \frac{C_L^2}{0.9 \times 6\pi}$$

Center-of-pressure curve.

a.c. Find the weighted mean quarter-chord location by means of equation (2:65), using $dS = cdy$, $c = 4 - 2y/9$, $x_{c/4} = y \tan 15°$, and $S = 27$ with dimensions as in Fig. 2:72; integrate y from 0 to 9, thus,

$$\bar{x}_{c/4}27 = \int_0^9 y \tan 15°(4 - 2y/9)dy$$

and get

$$\bar{x}_{c/4} = 4 \tan 15° = 1.04 = 0.268 \times \text{root chord} = 0.358 \times c_{mg}$$

Since $x_{ac} = 0.007$ for the 2409 airfoil (page 387, Table XVI) and $x_{ac} = 0.014$ for the 2415 airfoil, interpolate and get $x_{a.c.} = 0.011$ for the weighted mean 2413 airfoil. Hence

$$\bar{x}_{ac} = 0.358 - 0.011 = 0.347$$

This is a fair check with the experimental value of 0.352 aft of the root $c/4$(-0.352 ahead of the root $c/4$ is listed).

$C_{Ma.c.}$. Since the root and tip values of α_{L0} are equal, the aerodynamic twist, as well as the geometric twist, is zero and $C_{Ma.c.}$ is given by equation (2:67). In this case, the root and tip values of $c_{m\,a.c.}$ are -0.040 and -0.044, respectively. Since these values differ by only 10 per cent, integration is hardly necessary, and the weighted mean of

$$C_{M\,a.c.} = -\frac{(2 \times 0.040 + 0.044)}{3} = -0.041$$

is in good agreement with the experimental value of -0.043 listed in Table XX on page 393. The desired C_p equation is then

$$C_p = 0.336 + \frac{0.041}{C_L}$$

For tapered wings using the high-speed sections listed in Table XIX on page 392 for which wing-section data are available but tapered-wing tests are not, the foregoing procedure must be applied with caution, for the various sections of a tapered wing operate at different values of Reynolds number, though at the same Mach number. The test data in Table XIX on page 392 do not give information on the effects of independent variations of *Re* and *M*. Hence, to estimate the drag of a high-speed tapered wing, a reasonable assumption must be made for the *Re* effect at a given *M*. A suggested conservative assumption for the $c_{d0\,min}$ variation is that it follows a line parallel to that in Fig. 1:45 (and in Fig. A3 on page 412) for turbulent skin friction or a line midway between that and the laminar-skin-friction line.

2:26. Problems

1. For the 23018-09 wing of 5:1 taper ratio, Æ = 10, and no twist or sweepback, listed in Table XX on page 393, use the characteristics of the 23000 series of airfoils in Table XVII on page 389 and calculate $C_{De\,\min}$ and $C_{Ma.c.}$ for the complete wing. Check with the experimental values listed in Table XX on page 393.

2. For a high-speed straight-tapered wing of root section 16-515, tip section 16-509, taper ratio 2:1, and $AR = 6$, use the high-speed wing-section data in Table XIX on page 392, and calculate $C_{De\,\min}$ and $C_{Ma.c.}$ at $M = 0.6$. Assume the wing has zero aerodynamic twist at this Mach number and zero sweepback on the $c/4$ line. Assume $c_{mg} = 6$ ft.

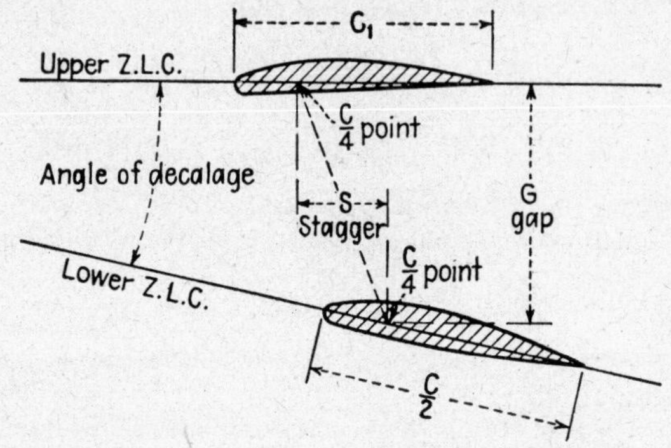

FIG. 2:73.—Side view of biplane cellule showing meaning of terms.

3. Using the results of Prob. 2 and the methods of Art. 2:25, write the equations for the characteristics $C_L(\alpha)$, $C_D(C_L)$, and $Cp(C_L)$ for the wing in Prob. 2. (Results can be only approximate, since data on independent variations of characteristics with *Re* and *M* are necessary for a particular airplane flying at a specified speed and altitude, and such data are not available in this text. Accurate solution of this type of problem is one of the major aims of current NACA research on high-speed wings.)

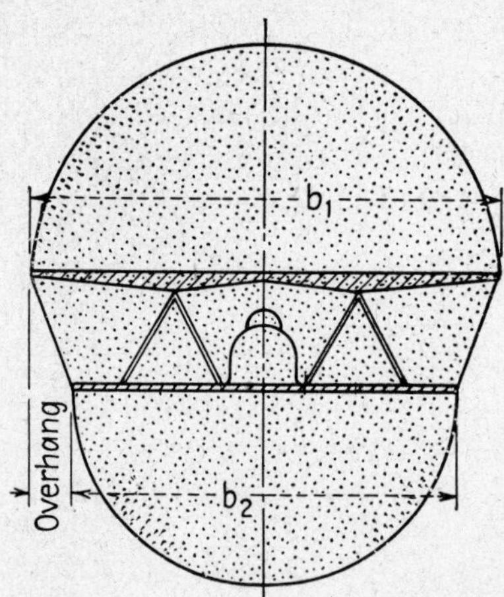

FIG. 2:74.—Front view of biplane cellule showing meaning of terms. Shaded area is air stream assumed deflected in momentum theory in calculating $AR_{eq.\,d}$.

2:27. Biplanes.—For a given stalling speed and gross weight, a biplane can usually be made lighter than a monoplane; it also can be housed in a smaller hangar; it has, however, more drag. Prior to 1930 most of the airplanes built were biplanes, but in 1946 only 1 of about 100 current-production airplanes (listed in Table A) was a biplane.

Geometric relationships between the two wings of a biplane and the terms used to describe them are shown in Figs. 2:73 and 2:74.

If two wings, each having an aspect ratio of 6, are made into a biplane, the area of air stream that can be assumed deflected by the wings (as in Art. 2:7 and as sketched in Fig. 2:74) is only slightly greater than for a monoplane wing. The induced drag is approximately the same as if the wings were located one behind another. Hence, the equivalent monoplane wing (having the same induced drag for a given lift) has an aspect ratio of approximately 3. The change from monoplane to biplane thus has a serious adverse effect on the L/D ratio and aerodynamic efficiency.

The monoplane aspect ratio that would give the same induced drag as a biplane is known as the *equivalent monoplane aspect ratio* and is here designated by $Æ_{eq.\,d}$. For equal-chord biplanes, $Æ_{eq.\,d}$, as calculated by the Prandtl wing theory, has been expressed by Munk[1] in the form

$$Æ_{eq.\,d} = \frac{(kb)^2}{S} \qquad (2:71)$$

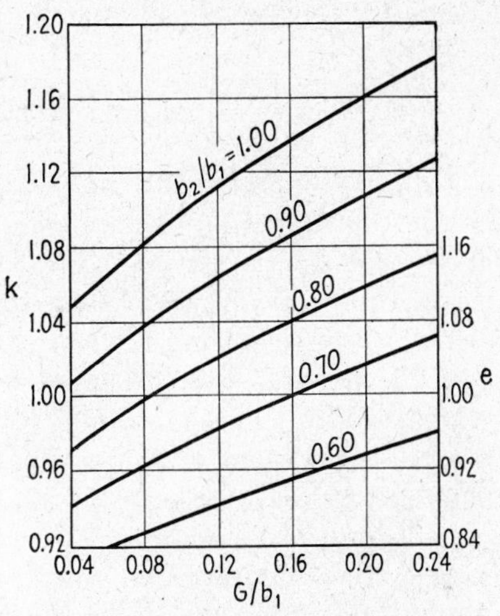

FIG. 2:75.—Munk span factor [equation (2:71)] for equal-chord biplanes.

in which k is known as the Munk span factor and can be read from Fig. 2:75 as a function of G/b and b_2/b_1. More comprehensive charts for biplanes of unequal chords as well as unequal spans can be found in Diehl's "Engineering Aerodynamics," revised edition.

The subscript *eq. d* on the term $Æ_{eq.\,d}$ should be especially noted, for it properly implies that the "equivalent" monoplane aspect ratio calculated by equation (2:71) and Fig. 2:75 is equivalent only in the sense that the induced drags are equal. It may not be used for calculating the lift-curve slope for a biplane. The lift-curve slope of a biplane is also a function of G/c ratio. For elliptic wings the Jones theory line of Fig. 2:31 and equation (2:46) as modified by Reid's[2] analysis, gives a lift-curve slope per radian of

$$m = \frac{2\pi Æ_{eq.\,d}}{Æ_{eq.\,d}[1 + (c/G)^2/8] + 2.5} \qquad (2:72)$$

Other effects of biplane arrangement on wing characteristics are as follows:

[1] MUNK, MAX, "Fluid Dynamics for Aircraft Designers."
[2] REID, E. G., "Applied Wing Theory."

α_{L0}. No effect reported. With decalage, α_{L0} must be a weighted mean.

$C_{De\,min}$. Higher velocities due to wing interference increase the monoplane value by 5 to 15 per cent.

$C_{M\,a.c.}$. No effect reported.

a.c. Wing interference moves the aerodynamic center forward. Effects of G/c (for equal-chord biplanes) and stagger s (degrees) are given by

$$\Delta x_{a.c.} = 0.03\left(\frac{G}{c}\right)^2 + \frac{s}{1{,}000} \qquad (2{:}73)$$

$C_{L\,max}$. Biplanes with no stagger or decalage usually show 5 to 10 per cent less than monoplanes for a given wing section. With 50 per cent positive stagger (upper wing forward) plus 3 deg negative decalage (lower wing steeper) a slotted-wing effect is obtained, giving a small *increase* in $C_{L\,max}$.

2:28. Ground Effect; Tunnel-wall Corrections.—An airplane wing flying less than one semispan from the ground (or water) has appreciably less drag than at higher altitudes. Below this height, the elementary momentum-theory sketch in Fig. 2:18 cannot apply, for the ground prevents a circular air stream from being freely deflected. Instead, the wing floats on a layer of compressed air, and high velocities over the upper surface are not necessary for high lift. The entire lower surface of the wing, moreover, is a region of increasing velocity, which favors laminar flow in the boundary layer. The Prandtl wing theory may be applied to this condition by assuming that the horseshoe-vortex system is matched by an "image" system of equal strength below the ground, as in Fig. 2:76, so that the obvious condition of no flow through the ground plane is fulfilled. The effects thus calculated are equivalent to an increase in aspect ratio. The equivalent aspect ratio for induced-drag calculation is shown in Fig. 2:77. The effect on lift-curve slope is shown in Fig. 2:78. Their use is illustrated by the following example:

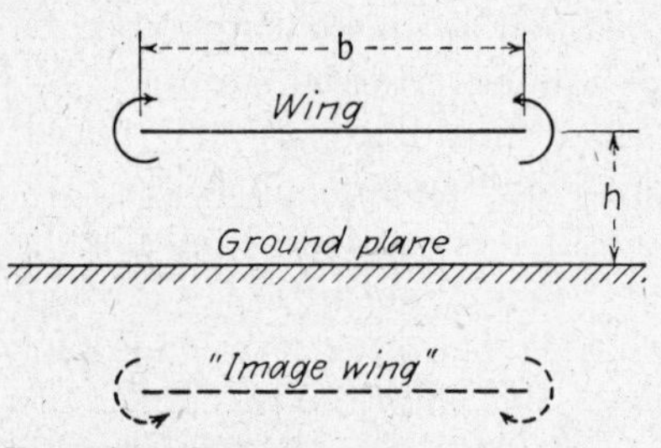

FIG. 2:76.—Vortex system used for calculating ground effect.

Example 1.—Given a 2:1 tapered wing of Æ = 6 and span = 60 ft, such as the first wing listed in Table XX on page 393, for which the lift and drag equations in free flight are $C_L = 0.075\alpha$, $C_D = 0.0065 + C_L^2/0.896\pi$. Find the lift and drag equations when the wing is flying 6 ft from the ground.

Solution.—Calculate $h/b = 6/60 = 0.10$. In Fig. 2:77, for $h/b = 0.10$, read $AR/AR_{gd} = 0.53$. Hence, $AR_{gd} = 6/0.53 = 11.3$ and

$$C_D = 0.0065 + \frac{C_L^2}{0.89 \times 11.3\pi}$$

In Fig. 2:78, for $h/b = 0.10$ and $AR = 6$, read $\alpha_{ag}/\alpha_a = 0.88$; hence,

$$C_L = \frac{0.075}{0.88}\alpha = 0.085\alpha$$

These are the answers called for.

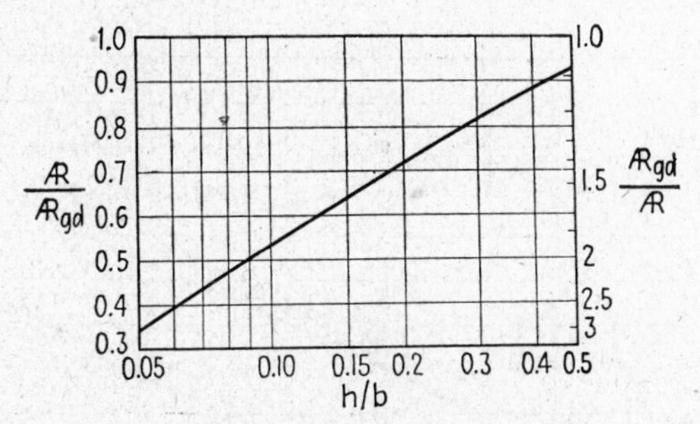

FIG. 2:77.—Effective aspect ratio of monoplane wing near the ground for induced-drag computation.

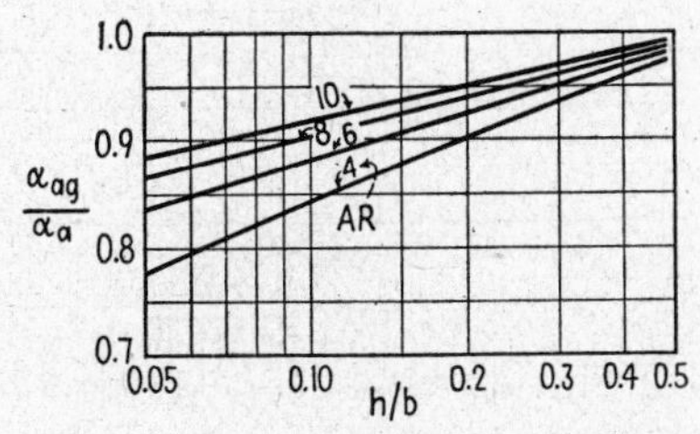

FIG. 2:78.—Effect of proximity to ground on lift-curve slope or on angle of attack for a given lift coefficient.

When a wing model is tested in a closed-throat wind tunnel, the same effect as that shown in Fig. 2:76 exists, plus a similar effect on the upper tunnel wall. For a wind tunnel with an open-jet test section (without walls), an opposite effect occurs because the air stream available is not sufficiently large to provide a normal stream deflection as in free flight. Wind-tunnel tests must therefore always be corrected for the tunnel-wall effect to get the free-flight characteristics. Since the tunnel-wall effect with a closed throat, like the ground effect, is to *increase* the effect aspect ratio, the correction to free air for such a tunnel involves a decrease in effective aspect ratio (an increase in induced drag, a decrease in lift-curve slope). Numerical values for such corrections are commonly put in the form

$$\Delta C_{Di} = \delta \frac{S}{A} C_L^2 \tag{2:74}$$

$$\Delta\alpha = \delta \frac{S}{A} C_L \text{ in radians} \tag{2:75}$$

in which S is the wing surface and A is the area of the tunnel throat (or area of the jet). For a circular throat or jet, the values of δ are $+0.125$ and -0.125, respectively. For rectangular throats and jets of various sorts, Theodorsen[1] developed the correction factors shown in Fig. 2:79.

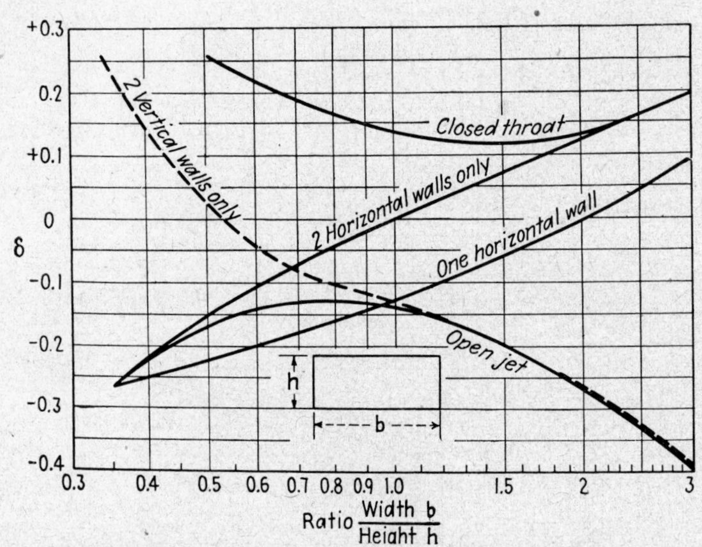

FIG. 2:79.—Tunnel-wall correction factors for subsonic flow in rectangular tunnels and jets.

For closed-throat tunnels, there is also a drag error due to the static-pressure gradient along the throat, which Diehl aptly describes as a "horizontal buoyancy" since it is proportional to the volume of the model; for variable-density-tunnel tests on airfoils, this correction is of the order of 2 per cent, though for tests on airship models it may run as high as 20 per cent of the drag measured on the tunnel balances.

For wind-tunnel tests in which the Mach number is high (say $M > 0.3$), there is an additional correction for compressibility, as yet unpublished. The use of equations (2:74) and (2:75) and Fig. 2:79 is illustrated by the following example:

Example 2.—Given a wing of 13.5 sq ft surface S is tested in a 7- by 10-ft closed-throat rectangular tunnel. The wind-tunnel test results on lift and drag

[1] *NACA Tech. Rept.* 410.

are $C_L = 0.080\alpha$, $C_D = 0.0070 + 0.040C_L^2$. Find the lift and drag equations in free air.

Solution.—Calculate $b/h = {}^{10}/_7 = 1.43$. In Fig. 2:79, for $b/h = 1.43$ read for closed-throat tunnels $\delta = +0.125$. Calculate $S/A = 13.5/70 = 0.193$ and

$$\delta(S/A) = 0.125 \times 0.193 = 0.024$$

Equations (2:74) and (2:75) then give

$$\Delta C_{Di} = +0.024C_L^2$$
$$\Delta\alpha = 0.024C_L \text{ radians} = 1.4C_L^\circ = 1.4^\circ \quad \text{when } C_L = 1.00$$

The corrected results in free air are calculated thus from the test:

$$\alpha = \frac{C_L}{0.080} = 12.5C_L = 12.5^\circ \qquad \text{at } C_L = 1.00$$
$$\alpha' = \alpha + \Delta\alpha = 12.5 + 1.4 = 13.9^\circ$$
$$a' = \frac{1}{13.9} = 0.072$$

Hence, the corrected results are

$$C_D = 0.0070 + 0.064C_L^2$$
$$C_L = 0.072\alpha$$

These are the answers called for.

2:29. Effects of Chordwise Slot in Wings; Interaction of Two Airplanes Flying Side by Side.—Wings are usually constructed in panels

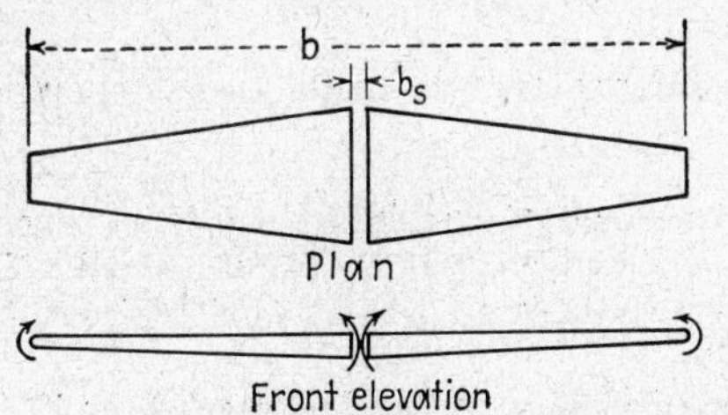

FIG. 2:80.—Wing with chordwise slot.

joined together by a chordwise joint, as sketched in Fig. 2:80. If the chordwise joint is not adequately sealed against air leakage through the joint, the two halves of the wing behave somewhat independently, with a large adverse effect on the drag and lift. The effect on the drag is equivalent to a large reduction in aspect ratio. The Munk span factor in equation (2:71) is a function of the ratio of slot width b_s to wing span b, as shown in Fig. 2:81. For a 40-ft-span wing ($b = 480$ in.) with a 1-in. slot, $b_s/b = 1/480 = 0.0021$ and $k = 0.85$. This corresponds to a reduction in effective Æ in the ratio $0.85^2 = 0.72$ and to increase in induced drag in the ratio $1/0.72 = 1.40$.

Two airplanes flying side by side have greatly *reduced* drag for the same reason, and the same graph (Fig. 2:81) can be used to calculate the effect with rectangular wings. For two wings of Æ = 6 flying separately, C_{Di} is $C_L^2/e6\pi$ for each. If they are flying side by side with the wing tips at a distance apart equal to 1/100 of the combined span, k can be read from Fig. 2:81 to be 0.82, and $C_{Di} = C_L^2/e12\pi$. This corresponds to a reduction of induced drag in the ratio

$$\frac{6}{0.82^2 \times 12} = 0.75$$

if the values of e are approximately the same. It is thus seen that two 50-ft-span airplanes flying with wing tips 1 ft apart have about 25 per cent less induced drag than if they keep a large distance apart. Millikan suggests this is of importance to migratory birds.

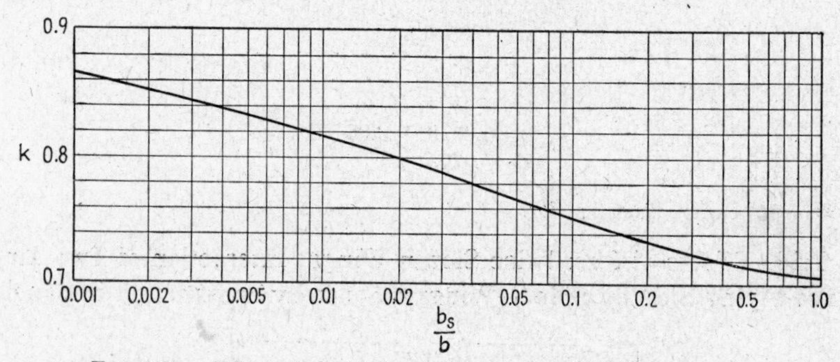

FIG. 2:81.—Effect of chordwise slot in wing on Munk span factor.

2:30. Problems

1. A biplane has two equal rectangular (rounded-tip) wings of Clark Y section, of span $b = 26.7$ ft, and chord $c = 3.2$ ft. The gap-chord ratio is $G/c = 1.33$, and the total surface of the two wings is 171 sq ft. Using Fig. 2:75, find the equivalent monoplane aspect ratio.

2. A 3:1 tapered wing of Æ = 10, listed on page 393 as 23018-09; 0-0 has a span of 48 ft. Using Figs. 2:77 and 2:78 and the data in Table XX on page 393, write equations for $C_L(\alpha)$ and $C_D(C_L)$ for this wing when it is flying 4 ft from the ground.

3. A wind model of 5 in. chord and 30 in. span is tested in a wind tunnel of closed throat 39 in. wide and 22 in. high. Equations for lift and drag characteristics as measured in the tunnel were $C_L = 0.083\alpha_a$ and $C_D = 0.0095 + 0.050C_L^2$. Using equations (2:74) and (2:75) and Fig. 2:79, find the lift- and drag-characteristic equations in free air.

4. Two rectangular wings of $e = 0.90$ and Æ = 6 each have a span of 48 ft. They fly side by side with their tips 4 ft apart. Use Fig. 2:81 and find the percentage saving in induced drag over flying separately a great distance apart.

CHAPTER 3

PARASITE DRAG; POWER REQUIRED FOR FLIGHT

3:1. Methods of Estimating Drag.—The drag coefficient of a complete airplane, like the drag coefficient for a wing alone, usually plots as a straight line when C_D is plotted against C_L^2. The intercept of this curve on the axis of $C_L = 0$ is commonly known as the "effective parasite-drag coefficient" and is defined by

$$C_{Dpe} = C_D - \frac{C_L^2}{\pi e \mathcal{R}} \qquad (3:1)$$

The relationship between the wing drag and the drag of the complete airplane is shown in Fig. 3:1. Parasite drag thus defined includes the effective minimum profile drag of the wing, although in some earlier definitions the minimum drag was not included. It is common practice to consider that the total parasite drag on airplanes consists of effective minimum profile drag of the wing plus the increments of drag ΔD due to the various parts such as fuselage, tail, etc. Hence

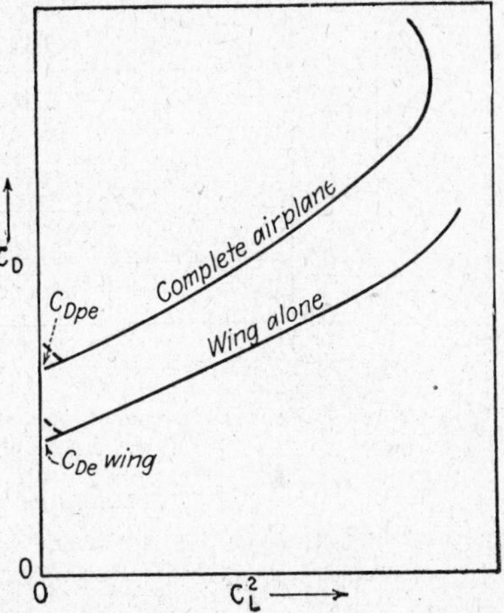

Fig. 3:1.—Drag of wing alone and of complete airplane.

$$C_{Dpe} = C_{De\ \text{wing}} + \Delta C_{De\ \text{fus}} + \Delta C_{De\ \text{tail}} + \Delta C_{De\ \text{other parts}} \qquad (3:2)$$

The increment of airplane drag coefficient due to a fuselage or other part is not necessarily equal to the drag of that part measured alone in the wind tunnel. Thus,

$$\Delta C_{De\ \text{fus}} = C_{De\ \text{fus}} + \Delta C_{De\ \text{interference}} \qquad (3:3)$$

where $C_{De\ \text{interference}}$ may be either positive or negative; for fuselages it is usually only a small per cent of $C_{De\ \text{fus}}$ and is often found to be zero.

The fact that the drag of a combination of two bodies is not equal to the sum of the drags of the two bodies is illustrated in Fig. 3:2, which shows that the drag of two wires, one behind another, depends on the spacing between the wires. While the drag of the two wires is usually less than twice the drag of one wire, as in the case of the cylindrical-wire data shown, it is sometimes greater than twice the drag of one wire, as is seen for the streamlined wires at a spacing greater than eight times the maximum dimension of the streamlined cross section. This condition could be described by saying that the interference drag of two cylindrical wires is negative, whereas the interference drag of two streamlined wires is sometimes positive.

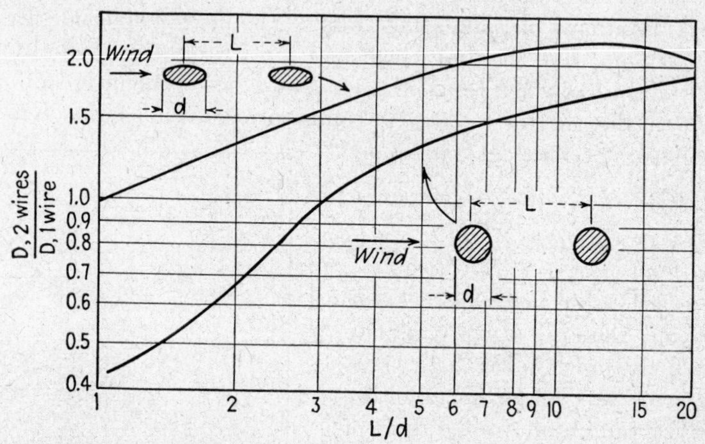

FIG. 3:2.—Effects of fore-and-aft spacing on the drag of a pair of wires. (*Replotted from Diehl, "Engineering Aerodynamics," rev. ed.*)

When the drag of a fuselage or other part is measured alone in the wind tunnel, there is no wing associated with it and an increment of drag coefficient $\Delta C_{De\ \mathrm{fus}}$ as in equation (3:2) cannot be calculated. It is customary to calculate instead a drag coefficient based on some area associated with the fuselage or other part. The area of the part used in calculating a coefficient for that part is known as the "proper area" and is designated by $S\pi$. Thus,

$$C_{D\pi} = \frac{D}{qS\pi} \tag{3:4}$$

When the fuselage or other part is combined with a wing, it is necessary to convert the drag coefficient based on the proper area $S\pi$ to a drag coefficient based on wing area by the equation

$$C_{De\ \mathrm{fus}} = C_{D\pi\ \mathrm{fus}} \frac{S_{\pi\ \mathrm{fus}}}{S} \tag{3:5}$$

The effective parasite-drag coefficient for the complete airplane is then given by

$$C_{Dpe} = C_{De\ \mathrm{wing}} + \Delta C_{D\pi 1} \frac{S_{\pi 1}}{S} + \Delta C_{D\pi 2} \times \frac{S_{\pi 2}}{S} + \Delta C_{D\pi 3} \frac{S_{\pi 3}}{S} + \cdots \tag{3:6}$$

It is common practice in describing the parasite drag of complete airplanes also to calculate an equivalent flat-plate area f_e defined by

$$f_e = \frac{D_{pe}}{q} = C_{Dpe}S \tag{3:7}$$

Equation (3:7) implies that the drag coefficient for a flat plate is 1.00, which is approximately true for small square or circular flat plates, as shown in Fig. 3:3. For rectangular flat plates of infinite aspect ratio, Fig. 3:2 shows that the proper drag coefficient $C_{D\pi}$ is more nearly equal to 2.0, depending slightly on the Reynolds number and the thickness of the plate.

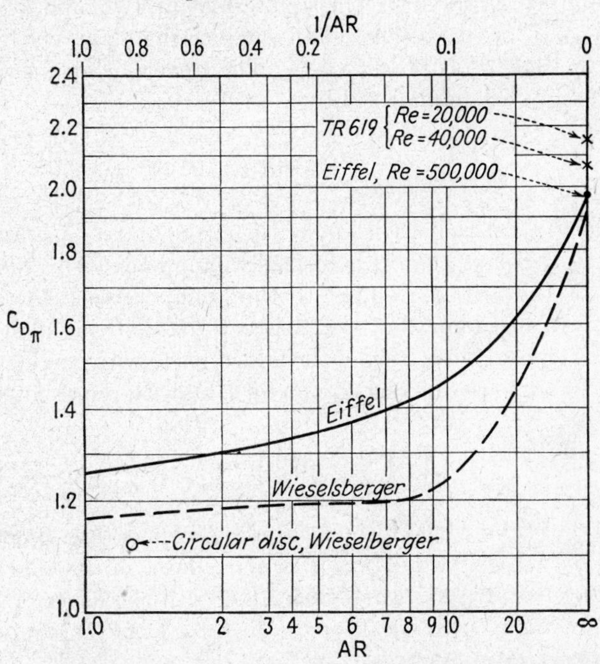

FIG. 3:3.—Low-speed data ($M_0 > 0.3$) on drag coefficient of rectangular flat plates as a function of aspect ratio. See Appendix 5 for drag data on other simple forms.

The drag of complete airplanes is difficult to estimate accurately because insufficient information is available. Adequate information would consist of abundant data as a function of Reynolds number and Mach number on all types of airplane components measured separately and in combination with other parts. With such data as are available, it is usually necessary to make estimates of Reynolds number corrections and to check these with the known parasite drag of complete airplanes already tested. An additional useful check is to calculate the total surface exposed to the air flow (the "wetted" area), to estimate from Fig. 1:45 or similar other data the total skin friction for the complete airplane, and to add various amounts for form and eddy drag depending on the size and shape of the principal exposed parts other than wing.

Many of the available parasite-drag data are summarized in this chapter, and an example is given showing how such data can be used to estimate the drag of a complete airplane.

Drag coefficients given in this chapter are usually in the form of proper drag coefficients $C_{D\pi}$ and must be converted to drag coefficients based on wing area by equation (3:5). Drag coefficients are sometimes also given as the drag per square foot at 100 mph at sea level $[(D/S)_{100 \text{ mph S.L.}}]$ or in terms of an engineering drag coefficient K_x which is $1/10{,}000x[(D/S)_{100 \text{ mph S.L.}}]$. The relationship between the coefficients may be summarized by

$$\left(\frac{D}{S}\right)_{100 \text{ mph S.L.}} = 10^4 K_x = 25.6 C_{D\pi} \qquad (3:8)$$

Note in Fig. 3:1 that the slope of the curve C_D *vs.* C_L^2 is greater for the complete airplane than it is for the wing alone. This means that the parts of the airplane added to the wing decrease the factor e, which was already somewhat less than 1.0 for the wing alone; this is due to the increase of the drag of the added parts with angle of attack. The effect of various parts on the factor e may be represented by the equation

$$\frac{1}{e} = \frac{1}{e_w} + \Delta\left(\frac{1}{e}\right)_{\text{fus}} + \Delta\left(\frac{1}{e}\right)_{\text{tail}} + \Delta\left(\frac{1}{e}\right)_{\text{other parts}} \qquad (3:9)$$

in which $1/e_w$ is the wing-efficiency factor shown in Fig. 2:30 and the increment $\Delta(1/e)$ is specified for other parts later in the chapter.

Since the factor e is always associated with the aspect ratio, it is sometimes customary to speak of the factor $e\text{Æ}$ as the equivalent or effective aspect ratio or Æ_e

$$e\text{Æ} = \text{Æ}_e \qquad (3:10)$$

3:2. Fuselage- and Nacelle-drag Data.—Data on the minimum proper drag coefficients $C_{D\pi}$ of a variety of fuselages are shown on pages 432 to 434. The information from the three wind tunnels (variable-density tunnel, GALCIT, Washington Navy Yard) are in surprisingly good agreement in view of the differences in Reynolds numbers. The Reynolds number based on fuselage length for full-scale airplanes in free flight range from 10,000,000 for a small two-seater to 100,000,000 for a large transport like the Lockheed Constellation, whereas the wind-tunnel data are at values of Re from 400,000 to 14,000,000. Since the fuselage drag is largely skin friction for well-designed fuselages, it is reasonable to suppose that the proper drag coefficients for fuselages given on pages 432 to 434 are subject to a large Reynolds number correction, but no full-scale fuselage-drag data appear to be available. Note in the NACA data on page 433 that there is a substantial negative-interference drag between wing and fuselage for most of the combinations there reported, in some cases exceeding 35 per cent of the fuselage drag. For wings with the less favorable wing-fuselage junctions, there is a small positive-interference

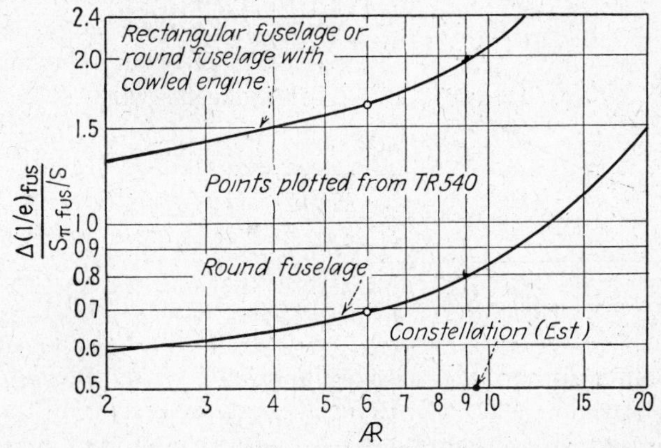

FIG. 3:4.—Chart for estimating effect of fuselage on airplane efficiency factor *e*. [$1/e = 1/e$ wing $- \Delta(1/e)$ fus.]

drag. The effect of the fuselage on the efficiency factor, as determined by extrapolation of the NACA data on wing-fuselage combinations on the assumption that the fuselage effect is proportional to S_π for the fuselage, is shown in Fig. 3:4 The fuselage effect is seen in Fig. 3:4 to depend on the aspect ratio of the wing. The use of Fig. 3:4 is illustrated by the following example:

Example.—Estimate the airplane efficiency factor *e* for a combination of a rectangular wing of aspect ratio 7 and 180-sq ft area with a rectangular fuselage of $S_{\pi \text{ fus}} = 15$ sq ft.

Solution.—In Fig. 2:30 read the $e_w = 0.82$, and calculate $1/e_w = 1.22$. In Fig. 3:4 read $\Delta(1/e)_f/(S_{\pi \text{ fus}}/S) = 1.75$. Using equation (3.9), calculate

$$1/\epsilon = 1.22 + 1.75 \times {}^{15}\!/_{180} = 1.37.$$

Hence, $e = 0.73$.

The drag of engine nacelles is shown on page 435. The nacelle-drag data are mostly data from the propeller-research tunnel of the NACA on full-scale nacelles so that the Reynolds number can be considered to correspond to low-speed free-flight conditions of full-scale airplanes. The data are all at $M_0 < 0.3$. Stack reports (footnote 2, page 151) that most of the older nacelles have a critical Mach number in the range of 0.45 to 0.5, that high-speed tests of conventional radial engine cowlings reported in *NACA Tech. Rept.* 745 led to a raising of the critical Mach number to 0.64, and that further research on the general problem of inlet openings in the nose of a streamlined body (not yet released) has resulted in air-cooled engine installations having critical Mach number over 0.8. Nacelles with a high critical speed were also found to have a low drag coefficient throughout the entire range of Reynolds numbers. GALCIT tests have shown in general that nacelles with a sharp leading-edge radius tend to have a higher drag than those with a large leading-edge radius that fairs in smoothly at the maximum diameter. For nacelles in which the drag has been thus greatly reduced by careful design, the additional drag due to the flow of cooling air through the nacelle becomes a major factor in the total drag of the nacelle. Data for accurate estimates on the cooling drag of low-drag nacelles are not released at the present time but are in the general form of Fig. 3:5. A major effect of the nacelles is to move the aerodynamic center forward from 2 to 5 per cent depending on the size of the nacelles relative to the wing, producing a major destabilizing effect and requiring a larger tail surface than without the nacelles.

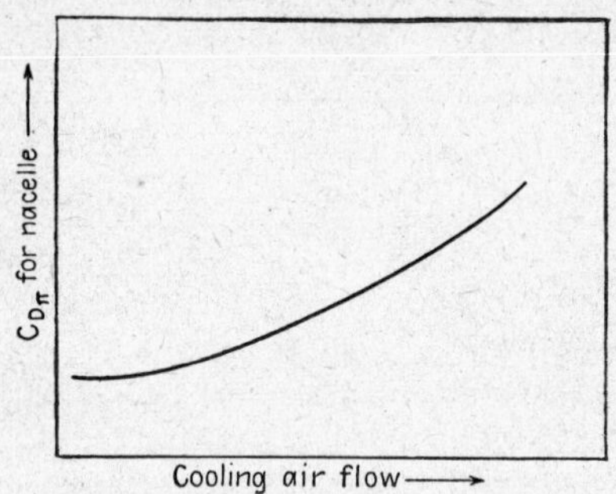

FIG. 3:5.—Effect of cooling air flow on nacelle drag.

3:3. Tail-surface Drag Data.—For tail surfaces it is customary to use thin symmetrical sections such as the NACA 0009, and the drag of tail surfaces alone can be taken from the airfoil-section data, with suitable correction to the low-aspect ratio common in tail surfaces. For the 0009 wing section, the minimum profile-drag coefficient listed in Table XVI on page 387 is 0.0058. The *increments* of drag coefficient due to *addition* of 0009 tail surfaces, as measured in the variable-density tunnel, are shown in Table XXXV on page 436 to be as low as 0.0039 for horizontal tails alone with the stabilizer and wing both set at zero incidence to the fuselage axis. Page 436 shows, however, that this large negative-interference drag (over 33 per cent of the tail-surface drag) is not actually obtained with a practical stabilizer setting such as -4 deg, and for this case, as in the next to the last item on the page, there is a positive interference of over 40 per cent of the horizontal tail drag. Most of the items in the table show that $\Delta C_{D\pi}$ is substantially greater for a combination of horizontal and vertical tails than for horizontal tails alone. This is presumably because of interference at the triple junction of the vertical and horizontal tails with the fuselage. Some negative interference is to be expected, for it is customary to consider that the horizontal tail area consists of a projected area extending all the way through the fuselage at the tail. Tests on tail surfaces consisting of only two members in the form of a V, as shown in Fig. 3:6, instead of the usual three as on page 436, have shown substantially less interference drag as well as other favorable effects and are likely to come into fairly wide use.

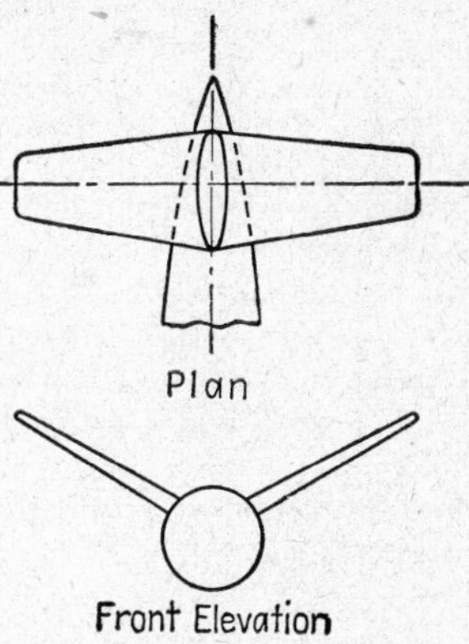

FIG. 3:6.—V-type tail.

Note on page 436 that the effect of adding a fixed horizontal tail surface is to increase the slope of the lift curve and the $C_{L\,max}$, but this does not correspond to the flying conditions, where the elevator must be set to trim the airplane; the net result of the addition of the tail is more likely to be a reduction than an increase in lift-curve slope and $C_{L\,max}$. In nearly every case there was about a 5 per cent reduction in efficiency factor e due to the wing-fuselage function and negligible additional reduction in the efficiency factor due to the tail. The effect of the tail in every case was to move the aerodynamic center well aft, resulting in an increase in stability of the airplane. In the light of the above information, it is customary to assume zero interference drag for the level-flight condition of an airplane.

3:4. Problems

1. For a particular wing-fuselage combination the drag added by the fuselage per square foot of fuselage frontal area at 100 mph at sea level is 10 lb. Find $\Delta C_{D\pi}$ for the fuselage.

2. Using the NACA wing-fuselage-combination data in Table XXXII on page 433, write the equations for the aerodynamic characteristics of the first combination there listed, and calculate the interference-drag coefficient $\Delta C_{D\pi\ \text{interference}}$.

3. Using the NACA wing-fuselage-tail data on page 436, write equations for the aerodynamic characteristics of the first combination of this sort listed, and calculate the tail interference-drag coefficient in per cent of drag of tail alone.

3:5. Drag of Landing Gears and Miscellaneous Exposed Parts.—Full-scale drag data on wheels, landing gears, struts, wires, and other items sometimes exposed to the air stream on low-speed airplanes are given on pages 432 to 441. For most of the items, the critical Mach number has not been determined, for these items are never exposed on airplanes that go very fast. Reynolds-number corrections are also not available for most of these parts, but the tests were run at nearly full-scale Reynolds number so the Reynolds number correction should be small. An exception is the case of struts and wires, for which there may be a large Reynolds number correction as given on page 440. Two examples of the calculation of drag of these items follows:

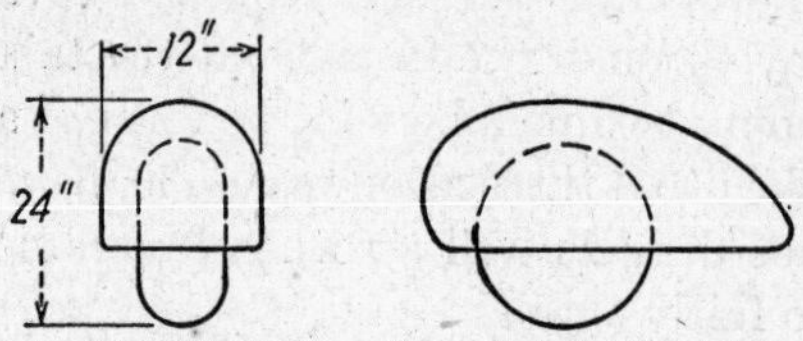

FIG. 3:7.—Cowled wheel.

Example 1.—Cowled-wheel problem. Find the drag at 100 mph in standard sea-level air and the equivalent flat-plate area f_e for the cowled wheel shown in Fig. 3:7.

Solution.—On page 438, item 2, read $C_{D\pi}$ for fairing A as 0.120 based on S_π = circumscribed rectangle. From Fig. 3:7 calculate $S_\pi = 2$ sq ft, $f_e = C_{D\pi} S_\pi = 0.12 \times 2 = 0.24$ sq ft, and $D_{100 \text{ at S.L.}} = 25.6 f_e = 6.1$ lb.

Example 2.—Round-strut problem. Find the drag at 75 mph at 6,000 ft standard altitude of a 1-in. round strut, 3 ft long with end fittings.

Solution.—For 6,000-ft standard altitude, read on chart A in the back of the book $\nu_0/\nu = 0.87$, and calculate $1/\nu = 0.87 \times 6{,}380 = 5{,}550$. At 75 mph, $V = 75 \times 1.467 = 110$ ft per sec. For a 1-in. round cylinder,

$$d = \tfrac{1}{12} \text{ ft} = 0.083 \text{ ft}$$

Calculate $Re = Vd/\nu = 110 \times 0\ 083 \times 5{,}550 = 50{,}800 \approx 5 \times 10^4$. On page 440, in Fig. A26, read $C_{D0}(= C_{D\pi}) = 1.2$. Following the instructions on page 441, item 1, allow 1 ft of length for the two end fittings; hence assume an equivalent length of 3 ft + 1 ft = 4 ft for infinite cylinder data. The area S_π is then

$$4 \text{ ft} \times \tfrac{1}{12} \text{ ft} = 0.33 \text{ sq ft}$$

To calculate $q = \rho V^2/2$, read on the air chart $\sigma = 0.835$, and calculate

$$\rho = 0.835 \times 0.00238 = 0.00199$$

and $q = \rho V^2/2 = 0.00119 \times 110^2/2 = 7.20$ lb per sq ft. Then calculate $D = C_{D\pi} S_\pi q = 1.2 \times 0.33 \times 7.2 = 2.9$ lb. This is the answer called for.

3:6. Problems

1. A streamlined strut of the type shown in Fig. A29(a) is 6 ft long and 1 in. wide and has faired end fittings. Following the instruction on page 441, item 5, (a) calculate the drag of this strut at 150 mph in standard sea-level air, and (b) find the equivalent flat-plate area f_e.

2. An elliptic wire of nominal ¼-in. size (= diameter of threaded end) has a cross section 0.087 in. wide and 0.348 in. long. Following the instructions on page 441, item 3, (a) calculate the drag of a 12-ft length of this wire with two end fittings at 100 mph in standard sea-level air, and (b) find the equivalent flat-plate area f_e.

3. A standard low-pressure airplane tire of Goodrich nominal size 8.50-10 has an outside diameter of 25.5 in. and an over-all width of 8.6 in. Using data on page 438, (a) calculate the drag of this tire on a wheel in flight at 200 mph in standard sea-level air, and (b) find the equivalent flat-plate area f_e.

3:7. Drag Estimate for a Complete Airplane.—For most of the airplanes for which statistical data are given in this text (Table A in the back of the book) the drag is only that due to the major parts such as wing, fuselage, nacelles, and tail, other exposed items having negligible drag. The drag of the parts can be estimated separately and added together to get the total drag, as expressed in equation (3:6). When equation (3:6) is multiplied by S, the items in the equation are in the form of increments of equivalent flat-plate area (Δf_e) and can be numerically added as illustrated in the following example.

Example.—Lockheed Lodestar problem. (*a*) Estimate the flat-plate area equivalent to the parasite drag of a Lockheed Lodestar airplane, assuming the data given below, and (*b*) use the result calculated in (*a*) to write an equation for C_D in terms of C_L^2 for the airplane. Use $v_L = 270$ mph for high-speed Re calculation.

Part	S_π, sq ft	$\Delta C_{D\pi}$	Δf_e, sq ft
Wing, assumed equivalent to NACA 23012 section, span 65.5 ft	551	0.0054	3.0
Fuselage, length = 50 ft	40	0.080	3.2
Nacelles, total for two, including cooling drag	35	0.10	3.5
Tail surfaces, total	200	0.006	1.2
Total	...	......	10.9

Solution.—Wing. To estimate the minimum profile-drag coefficient of the wing, calculate the mean wing chord $c = S/b = 551/65.5 = 8.4$ ft and

$$V = 270 \times 1.467 = 396 \text{ ft per sec}$$

and $Re = 396 \times 8.4 \times 6{,}380 \approx 21{,}000{,}000$. For a 23012 wing section, read, in Table XVII on page 389, $C_{D\,\min} = 0.0061$. Plot this point on page 412, extrapolate parallel to the turbulent-flow line to $Re = 21{,}000{,}000$, and read

$$C_{D0}(=C_{D\pi}) = 0.0054$$

Insert this value as the proper drag coefficient in the above table, calculate

$$f_e = 0.0054 \times 551 = 3.0$$

and insert this value in the table.

Fuselage. For the proper drag coefficient of the fuselage refer to page 432, and note that the range of GALCIT data on large transports is from 0.070 to 0.105; assume a value of 0.080 at the lower end of this range as reasonable. This is higher than any of the drag increments $\Delta C_{D\pi}$ for the ideal NACA fuselage data given in Table XXXII on page 433. With this value of $\Delta C_{D\pi}$, calculate

$$\Delta f_e = 40 \times 0.080 = 3.2 \text{ sq ft}$$

of equivalent flat plate, and insert this value in the table.

Nacelles. For the nacelles, refer to page 435, and note that GALCIT data show a range of values of $\Delta C_{D\pi}$ from 0.080 to 0.120 from large to small airplanes; since this is a medium-sized airplane the nacelle drag of 0.100 including cooling drag is reasonable. The Lockheed nacelles were the subject of intensive development with a view to the reduction of drag, and it is quite possible that a substantially lower value was actually obtained. Using $\Delta C_{D\pi} = 0.10$, calculate

$$\Delta f_e = 0.10 \times 35 = 3.5 \text{ sq ft}$$

of equivalent flat plate, and insert this value in the table.

Tail surfaces. From Table XVI, page 387, assume $\Delta C_{D\pi} = 0.0060$ for tail surfaces equivalent to the NACA 0009, and neglect interference drag as suggested in the discussion of tail-surface drag. Calculate $\Delta f_e = 200 \times 0.006 = 1.2$ sq ft of equivalent flat plate, and insert this value in the table.

Adding the values of Δf_e in the above table gives a total equivalent flat-plate area of $f_e = \Sigma\Delta f_e = 10.9$ sq ft. Using this value, calculate the total parasite-drag coefficient as $C_{Dpe} = f_e/S = 10.9/551 = 0.0196$.

To get the induced drag, calculate the wing aspect ratio as

$$AR = 65.5^2/551 = 7.8$$

Read in Fig. 2:30 for tapered wings $e_w = 0.87$ and calculate $1/e_w = 1.15$. For the contribution of the fuselage to the induced drag, read, in Fig. 3:4,

$$[\Delta(1/e)_{\text{fus}}]/(S_{\pi\,\text{fus}}/S) = 0.075$$

for round fuselages without nose engine, and calculate

$$\Delta(1/e)_{\text{fus}} = 0.75 \times {}^{40}\!/_{550} = 0.055$$

Hence $1/e = 1.15 + 0.055 = 1.205$, and $e = 1/1.205 = 0.83$. Calculate

$$1/\pi e AR = 1/\pi \times 7.8 \times 0.83 = 0.049$$

The desired equation relating the drag and lift coefficients is then

$$C_D = 0.0196 + 0.049C_L^2$$

This is the answer called for.

3:8. Problems

1. For the Ercoupe airplane sketched in Fig. I:3, assume the data given below. (*a*) Estimate the equivalent parasite flat plate, and (*b*) write the equation for C_D *vs.* C_L^2. Use $v = 120$ mph to calculate *Re* for the high-speed wing-drag estimate.

Part	S_π, sq ft	$\Delta C_{D\pi}$	Δf_e, sq ft
Wing, 4412 section, $b = 30$ ft	142.6		
Fuselage length 20 ft 9 in	12	0.12	
Tail surfaces	30	0.006	
Nose wheel (low pressure)	0.60		
Nose-wheel support, fairing streamlined like Fig. A29 (*d*), section 2 in. wide and 6 in. long, equivalent to streamlined strut 3 ft long + end fittings, not faired			
Main wheels, each of two (low-pressure)	0.75		
Main-wheel supports, each of two, each equivalent to 1 ft of 3-in. round tubing with end fittings			
Total			

2. For the Lockheed Constellation airplane, a photograph of which is shown in Fig. I:4*c*, assume the data given below. (*a*) Estimate the equivalent parasite flat plate, and (*b*) write the equation for C_D *vs.* C_L^2. Use $v = 350$ mph to calculate *Re* for the high-speed wing-drag estimate.

Part	S_π, sq ft	$\Delta C_{D\pi}$	Δf_e, sq ft
Wing, mean effective section 23015, span 123 ft	1,650		
Fuselage length 95 ft	100	0.070	
Nacelles, total for four, mean cooling air flow	70	0.080	
Tail surfaces	700	0.006	
Total			

3:9. Power Required for Level Flight at Sea Level.—The principal forces acting on an airplane in level flight are seen in Fig. 3:8 to be the lift L, the weight W, the drag D, and propeller thrust T; there is also usually a tail force F_t necessary to balance, but if L is considered to be lift on the entire airplane, it can include F_t. For level flight at constant velocity

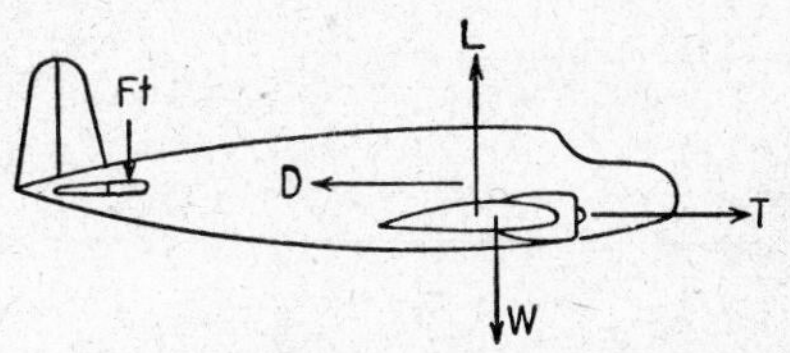

FIG. 3:8.—Forces acting on an airplane in level flight.

$$W = L = \frac{C_L \rho S V^2}{2} = C_L q S \tag{3:11}$$

from which it follows that the lift coefficient necessary for level flight is

$$C_L = \frac{W}{Sq} \tag{3:12}$$

The drag and lift coefficients are usually related by an equation such as was determined in Art. 3:7 of the form

$$C_D = a + bC_L^2$$

or are given by an experimental equation based on wind-tunnel tests, and corrected for Reynolds and Mach numbers, as in Fig. 3:1.

The drag of the airplane may be calculated from

$$D = \frac{D}{L} W = \frac{C_D}{C_L} W \tag{3:13}$$

Since *power* = *force* × *velocity* and 1 hp = 550 ft-lb per sec, the horsepower required for level flight is

$$hp_r = \frac{DV}{550} = \frac{Dv}{375} \tag{3:14}$$

where V is in feet per second and v is in mph.

An example of the calculation of power required for level flight at sea level follows:

Example.—For a Lockheed Lodestar airplane, for which statistical data are given in Table A, assume that the lift and drag coefficients are related by the equation $C_D = 0.0196 + 0.049C_L^2$, as found in Art. 3:7, and calculate the power required for level flight at sea level with a gross weight of 17,500 lb at speeds (mph) of 300, 250, 200, 150, 125, 100, and stalling speed (flaps up), assuming $C_{L\,max} = 1.55$ for a power-on stall with flaps up. Plot hp_{r0} *vs.* v.

Solution.—In Table A, read $S = 551$ sq ft, and calculate

$$W/S = 17{,}500/551 = 31.7 \text{ lb per sq ft}$$

Using $q = 0.00256v^2$ at sea level and equations (3:12) to (3:15), the power required for level flight at sea level is calculated in Table 3:1 (below) and plotted in Fig. 3:9.

TABLE 3:1.—CALCULATION OF POWER REQUIRED FOR LEVEL FLIGHT AT SEA LEVEL OF A LOCKHEED LODESTAR AIRPLANE

v, mph	$q = 0.00256v^2$, lb per sq ft	$C_L = \frac{31.7}{q}$	$C_{Di} = 0.049C_L^2$	$C_D = 0.0196 + C_{Di}$	$D = \frac{WC_D}{C_L}$, lb	$hp_{r0} = \frac{Dv}{375}$
300	230	0.138	0.0009	0.0205	2,600	2,080
250	160	0.198	0.0019	0.0215	1,900	1,268
200	102.4	0.310	0.0047	0.0243	1,375	733
150	57.8	0.548	0.0147	0.0343	1,095	438
125	40.0	0.792	0.0307	0.0503	1,110	370
100	25.6	1.24	0.0752	0.0948	1,340	358
89.1 min	20.4	1.55 max	0.118	0.138	1,560	370

When the horsepower available from the engine and propeller is plotted on the same sheet, the sea-level performance of the airplane can be determined. Methods of calculating the power available are discussed and illustrated in Chap. 4.

3:10. Problems

1. For an Ercoupe airplane for which statistical data are given in Table A, assume that the drag and lift coefficients are related by the equation

$$C_D = 0.030 + 0.066C_L^2$$

and calculate the power required for level flight at sea level with a gross weight of 1,260 lb at speeds (mph) of 120, 100, 80, 70, 60, 50, and minimum speed, assuming $C_{L\,max} = 1.50$ at minimum speed, power on, and plot hp_r *vs.* v as in Fig. 3:9.

2. For a Lockheed Constellation airplane, for which statistical data are given in Table A, assume that the drag and lift coefficients are related by the equation $C_D = 0.0154 + 0.0426C_L^2$, and calculate the power required for level flight at sea level with a gross weight of 86,250 lb at speeds (mph) of 400, 350, 300, 250, 200,

150, 125, 100, and minimum speed (flaps retracted), assuming $C_{L\,max} = 1.60$ at minimum speed (flaps retracted), power on, and plot hp_r *vs.* v, as in Fig. 3:9.

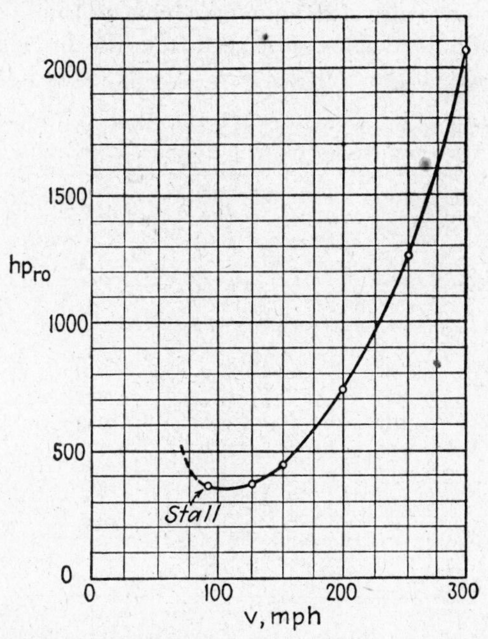

FIG. 3:9.—Power required for level flight at sea level for Lockheed Lodestar airplane as calculated in Table 3:1.

3:11. Level Flight at Altitudes above Sea Level. Minimum-drag Condition and Development of General Power-required Chart.—Equations (3:11) to (3:15) are applicable to either sea-level or altitude conditions if the proper air density is used in equation (3:11). If the same speeds are assumed for the calculation of power required at altitude as at sea level, new values of C_L and C_D and hp_r may be calculated, the air density at altitude in equation (3:11) being used. It is much more convenient, however, to assume instead the same values of C_L as were found for the sea-level calculations; it is then necessary to calculate only the values of v and hp_r for the altitude condition. The equations for calculation of power required at altitude are then

$$D_{alt} = D_{S.L.} \text{ for const. } C_L \tag{3:15}$$

$$v_{alt} = v_{S.L.} \sqrt{\frac{1}{\sigma}} \text{ for const. } C_L \tag{3:16}$$

$$hp_r = hp_{r0} \sqrt{\frac{1}{\sigma}} \text{ for const. } C_L \tag{3:17}$$

The calculation of power required at sea level in Table 3:1 is continued below in Table 3:2 for the speed and power at 10,000 ft standard altitude at the same values of C_L as in Table 3:1, and the results from both figures are plotted in Fig. 3:10, which differs from Fig. 3:9 only in that logarithmic scales of 125 mm base have been used. At 10,000 ft standard altitude the density ratio read from the air chart in the back of the book is $\sigma = 0.738$ and $\sqrt{1/\sigma} = 1.164$. Note in Fig. 3:10 that

TABLE 3 2.—CALCULATION OF POWER REQUIRED FOR LEVEL FLIGHT AT 10,000 FT ALTITUDE FOR LOCKHEED LODESTAR AIRPLANE

S L., from Table 3:1			10,000 ft, $\sigma = 0.738$, $\sqrt{\frac{1}{\sigma}} = 1.164$	
v	C_L	hp_{r0}	v	hp_r
300	0.138	2,080	349	2,420
250	0.198	1,268	291	1,475
200	0.310	733	233	854
150	0.548	438	174.7	510
125	0.792	370	145.5	431
100	1.24	358	116.4	416
89	1.55	370	103.6	431

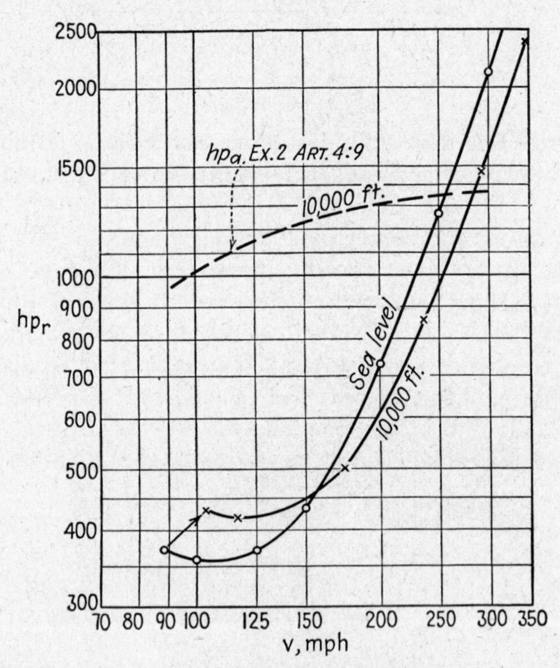

FIG. 3:10.—Replot of Fig. 3:9 with logarithmic scales and with power required at 10,000 ft altitude added from Table 3:2.

each sea-level point plotted is moved *to the right* and *up* the same distance on the logarithmic chart. The equality of distance *over* and *up* is due to the peculiar feature of logarithmic scales: a given ratio is represented by a given distance on the scale.

Figure 3:10 can be put in general form if the speed and power are plotted as ratios to some arbitrary standard speed and power. The arbitrary standard commonly selected is the speed and power at the condition of maximum L/D (minimum D/L). The condition for maximum L/D may be found for an airplane whose aerodynamic characteristics are given by equation (3:13) as follows:

Calculate first

$$\frac{C_D}{C_L} = \frac{a}{C_L} + bC_L \tag{3:18}$$

Setting the derivative of equation (3:18) with respect to C_L equal to zero, and designating this condition (of minimum D/L or maximum L/D) by $(\ )_1$ it is found that

$$bC_{L1}^2 = a \tag{3:19}$$

so that

$$C_{L1} = \sqrt{\frac{a}{b}} \qquad C_{D1} = 2a \tag{3:20}$$

and for a gross weight of W

$$V_1 = \sqrt{\frac{W/S}{\rho C_{L1}/2}} \tag{3:21}$$

At any other speed V

$$V = \sqrt{\frac{W/S}{\rho C_L/2}} \tag{3:22}$$

so

$$\frac{V}{V_1} = \sqrt{\frac{C_{L1}}{C_L}} \tag{3:23}$$

At point $(\ )_1$

$$P_1 = \frac{D_1 V_1}{550} = C_{D1} \frac{\rho}{2} \frac{SV_1^3}{550} \tag{3:24}$$

and at any other point

$$P = \frac{DV}{550} = C_D \frac{\rho}{2} \frac{SV^3}{550} \tag{3:25}$$

so

$$\frac{P}{P_1} = \frac{C_D V^3}{C_{D1} V_1^3} \tag{3:26}$$

but

$$\frac{C_D}{C_{D1}} = \frac{a + bC_L^2}{a + bC_{L1}^2} = \frac{a + bC_L^2}{2a} = \frac{a + bC_L^2}{2bC_{L1}^2} = \frac{1}{2} + \frac{C_L^2}{2C_{L1}^2}$$

$$= \frac{1}{2}\left(1 + \frac{C_L^2}{C_{L1}^2}\right) \tag{3:27}$$

Substituting equations (3:21) and (3:25) in (3:24),

$$\frac{P}{P_1} = \frac{1}{2}\left(1 + \frac{V_1^4}{V^4}\right)\frac{V^3}{V_1^3} = \frac{(V/V_1)^3}{2} + \frac{1}{2(V/V_1)} \qquad (3:28)$$

Equation (3:29) is plotted in Fig. 3:11, an enlarged copy of which, along with other graphs to be explained later, is provided in the pocket in the back of the book and is designated Chart C.

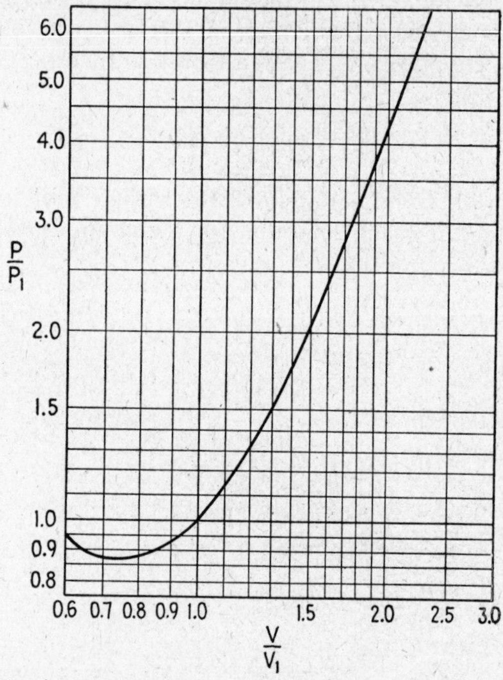

FIG. 3:11.—General logarithmic plot of power required *vs.* speed for level flight for any airplane at any altitude, plotted in terms of power P_1 and speed V_1 at the maximum L/D condition. An enlarged transparent copy of above chart is provided in the back of the book (Chart C).

If, for any particular airplane, the results of calculations of power required for level flight *vs.* speed are plotted to the same logarithmic base as Chart C, the two graphs should be identical except for a displacement of the scales horizontally and vertically. Hence, Figs. 3:11 and Chart C are called *general logarithmic graphs of power required for level flight vs. speed.* They are applicable to any airplane at any altitude. To get a graph of hp_r *vs.* v for any particular airplane, it is thus simply necessary to calculate V_1 from equation (3:22) and P_1 from equation (3:25); the graph is available as Fig. 3:11 or Chart C for any airplane at any altitude in terms of these reference values of power and speed. Chart C can be used in connection with properly plotted engine and propeller data for quick calculation of airplane performance, as explained in Chaps. 4 and 5. It was originated by George S. Schairer in his capacity of director of aerodynamics for the Boeing Aircraft Corporation and is there known as part of the "Boeing quick-performance method."

3:12. Problems

1. For the Ercoupe airplane, calculate the speed and power required for level flight at 12,000 ft standard altitude at the same values of C_L as in Prob. 1, Art. 3:10, and plot on 250-mm-base logarithmic ruled graph paper. Check by superposing the transparent general graph (Chart C) from the back of the book. Read v at $V/V_1 = 1.0$ when the graphs are superposed, and check by equation (3:22).

2. For the Lockheed Constellation airplane, calculate the speed and power required for level flight at 20,000 ft standard altitude at the same values of C_L as in Prob. 2, Art. 3:10, and plot on 250-mm-base logarithmic ruled graph paper. Check by superposing the transparent general graph (Chart C) from the back of the book. Read v at $V/V_1 = 1.0$ when the graphs are superposed, and check by equation (3:22).

CHAPTER 4

ENGINE AND PROPELLER CHARACTERISTICS

4:1. Airplane Engines.—Airplanes are usually propelled by internal-combustion engines that drive propellers. The following brief survey of airplane-engine operation is intended chiefly as a background of nomenclature for an explanation of the principal characteristics that effect airplane performance. Typical engines and propellers are shown on pages 32 to 37.

The principal elements of one cylinder of such an internal-combustion engine are shown in Fig. 4:1 and are assumed to be familiar to most students of technical aerodynamics. An airplane engine consists essentially of a group of cylinders in various arrangements, some of which are shown on page 32. The cylinder sketched in Fig. 4:1 includes (*a*) a piston, which is connected by means of a *connecting rod* to a *crankshaft* that delivers power to the propeller; (*b*) a carburetor, with jets that atomize the fuel in air and a *manifold* that conducts the mixture to the cylinders; (*c*) a system of *valves* for admitting the mixture into the cylinder at the proper *time* in the stroke of the piston, which first close off the cylinder from the manifold to form a *combustion chamber* and later permit the products of combustion to be discharged after burning; and (*d*) a timed *ignition system* for starting the combustion in the cylinder.

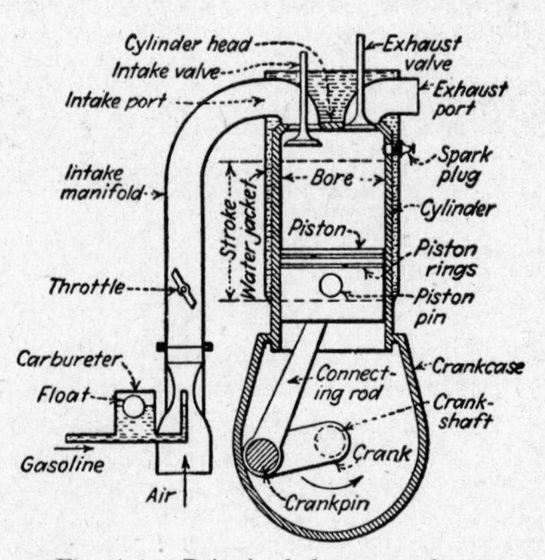

FIG. 4:1.—Principal elements of a gasoline engine. (*From Chatfield and Taylor, "The Airplane and Its Engine."*)

Measurements of the pressure inside one of the cylinders while the engine is running yield an *indicator diagram* similar to that shown in Fig. 4:2. The indicator diagram in Fig. 4:2 shows that a *cycle* of operation consists of *four strokes* of the piston as follows: (1) an intake stroke during which the mixture flows into the cylinder; (2) a compression stroke during which the mixture is compressed approximately adiabatically and at the end of which the mixture is ignited and burns, with a resulting rise in pressure and temperature; (3) a power stroke during which the products of combustion expand and do work on the piston; (4) an exhaust stroke during which the products of combustion flow out of the exhaust valve and through an exhaust pipe to be discharged to the atmosphere. This cycle of operation is known as the *four-stroke cycle* and is the cycle of operation used in most airplane engines.

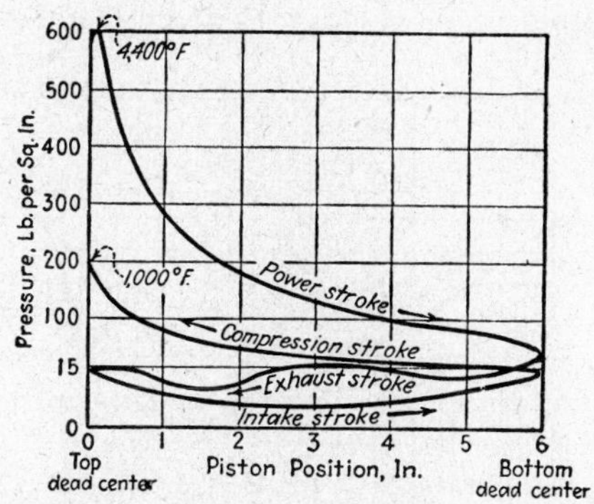

FIG. 4:2.—Indicator diagram for one cylinder of airplane engine.

It is possible, though usually uneconomical, to have the exhaust and intake occur simultaneously at the end of the power stroke, in which case the cycle of operation is known as a *two-stroke cycle*.

The ratio of the volume contained in the cylinder when the piston is at "bottom dead center" to the volume when the piston is at "top dead center" is known as the *compression ratio*. With a sufficiently high compression ratio the isentropic rise in temperature on compression is sufficient to ignite the fuel without an ignition system. An engine that operates in this manner is known as a *Diesel engine;* such engines have occasionally been used on aircraft. A two-stroke-cycle Diesel engine in which the fuel is injected directly into the cylinder near the end of the compression stroke can compare favorably in economy with a typical four-stroke-cycle engine.

The net area of an indicator diagram such as that shown in Fig. 4:2 is a measure of the work per cycle done inside the cylinder and determines what is known as the *indicated horsepower* (Ihp) of the engine. The power delivered by the crankshaft, sometimes measured by a *brake* and therefore called brake horsepower (Bhp), is always less than the indicated horsepower, the relationship being indicated in Fig. 4:3. Where Q is the torque delivered to the crankshaft and N is the rate of rotation of the crankshaft in rpm,

$$\text{Bhp} = \frac{2\pi NQ}{33{,}000} = \frac{Q \times \text{rpm}}{5{,}250} \tag{4:1}$$

A typical variation of brake horsepower with rpm for a small airplane engine is shown in Fig. 4:2.1. With the throttle wide open, very small changes in the brake load will permit large changes in the rpm of the engine, and it is proper to assume that the full-throttle torque is constant for the normal operation of an engine of this sort. Actually, as the rpm increases there is not only an increase in friction horsepower but also an increased loss of energy in the mixture flowing through the manifold and valves. Airplane engines are usually *rated*

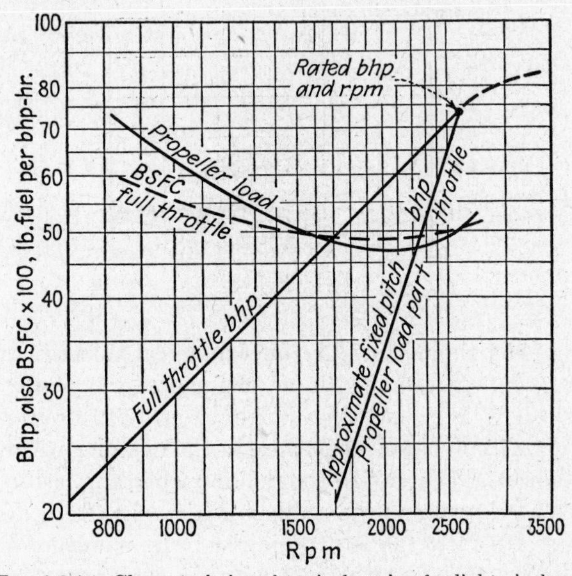

FIG. 4:2.1.—Characteristics of typical engine for light airplane.

however at a brake horsepower and rpm where these losses are small. The rating is somewhat arbitrary, being determined primarily by considerations of durability of the engine parts. Ratings of many airplane engines currently manufactured in the United States are shown on Table C in the back of the hook. Figure 4:2.1 also shows a "propeller-load" curve drawn through the rated brake horsepower and rpm at a slope of 3:1 on the logarithmic graph because brake horsepower varies as rpm cubed for a fixed-pitch propeller. The figure shows also the variation of brake specified fuel consumption (BSFC) with rpm for full throttle and for the typical fixed-pitch propeller load.

4:2. Sea-level Superchargers.—An airplane engine can usually be built lighter for a given delivered power if the air flowing into the cylinders is compressed by means of a rotary blower before it is admitted to the cylinders. The considerations leading to this sort of arrangement are shown in Fig. 4:4, and a cutaway view of a typical supercharger is shown in Fig. 4:5. Engines designed for use on land

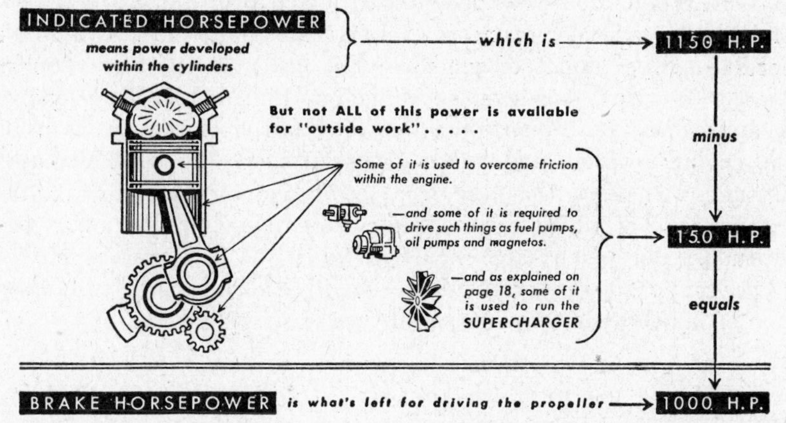

FIG. 4:3.—Sea-level aircraft engine, indicated horsepower *vs.* brake horsepower. (*Figs.* 4:3 *to* 4:5 *from General Motors Corporation booklet Airplane Power, published in* 1944.)

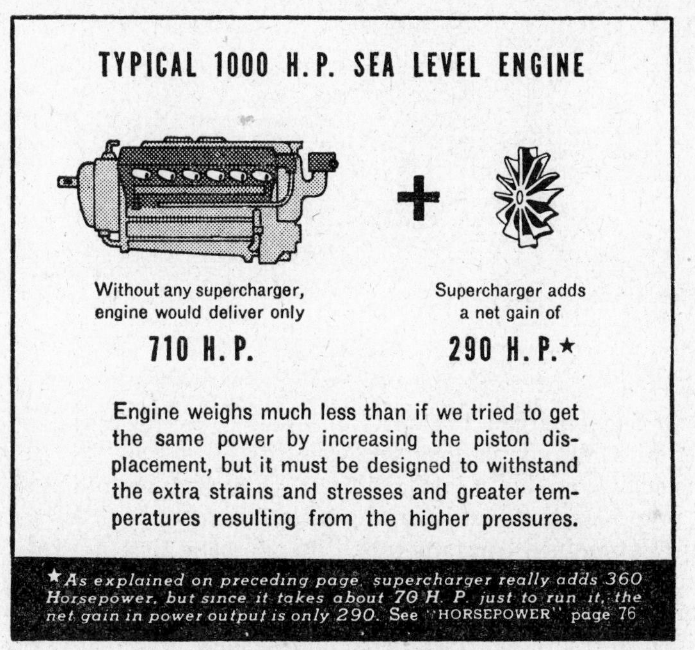

FIG. 4:4.—Typical 1,000-hp sea-level engine.

and water vehicles, in which weight is considerably less important, rarely use sea-level superchargers for "ground boosting." The ground boost was long thought to be uneconomical, but the decision as to its economy rested on typical weight data of engine and supercharger parts; with improvements in structural design of airplane parts its ground boost has been found to give a substantial increase in brake horsepower per pound of engine, although not necessarily brake horsepower per dollar of expense. For an engine without a supercharger or with a sea-level supercharger, the indicated horsepower is approximately proportional to the density of the air in which the engine is flying and hence drops off markedly with increasing altitude. The fact that the friction horsepower is approximately independent of altitude accentuates this reduction in power with altitude. For an airplane engine in which the friction torque Q_f is 13 per cent of the sea-level brake torque Q_0 (which is typical), the variation of full-throttle torque with altitude is given by

$$\frac{Q_{\text{alt}}}{Q_0} = 1.13\sigma - 0.13 \tag{4:2}$$

Equation (4:2) represents the loss in power with altitude at a given rpm assumed in *NACA Tech. Note* 579.

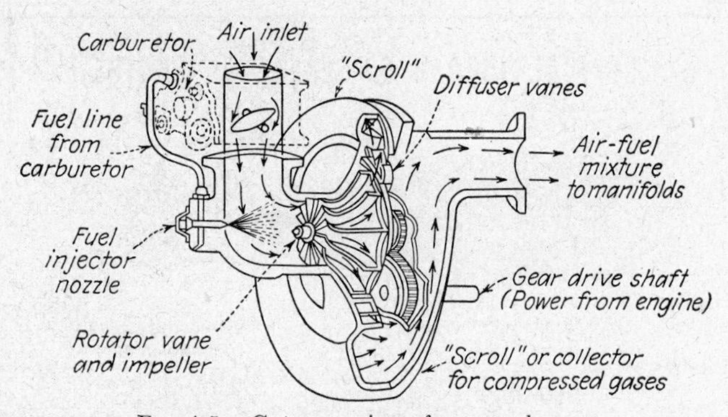

FIG. 4:5.—Cutaway view of a supercharger.

4:3. Supercharged Engines.—In order to avoid excessive loss of power with altitude various arrangements of blowers are connected to the engine, as shown in Fig. 4:6. Such engines are ordinarily used with propellers that can be set by means of a governor to operate at any predetermined constant rpm. The throttle then determines the pressure in the intake manifold. The most useful form of graph of performance for such engines is shown in Fig. 4:7, in which rpm and manifold pressure are considered independent variables. Sea-level performance is given in the left-hand graph and the altitude performance in the right-hand graph. Several sea-level "ratings" are shown on this chart, involving limitations of both manifold pressure and rpm. Such ratings, read from the chart, are as follows:

TABLE 4:1.—SEA-LEVEL RATINGS

Point on S.L. chart	Rating	Rpm	Man. pressure, in. Hg	Bhp	Point on alt. chart
	Take-off	2,100	36.5	760	
K	Max. continuous	1,900	34	675	*L*
B	Cruising	1,800	26	430	*C*

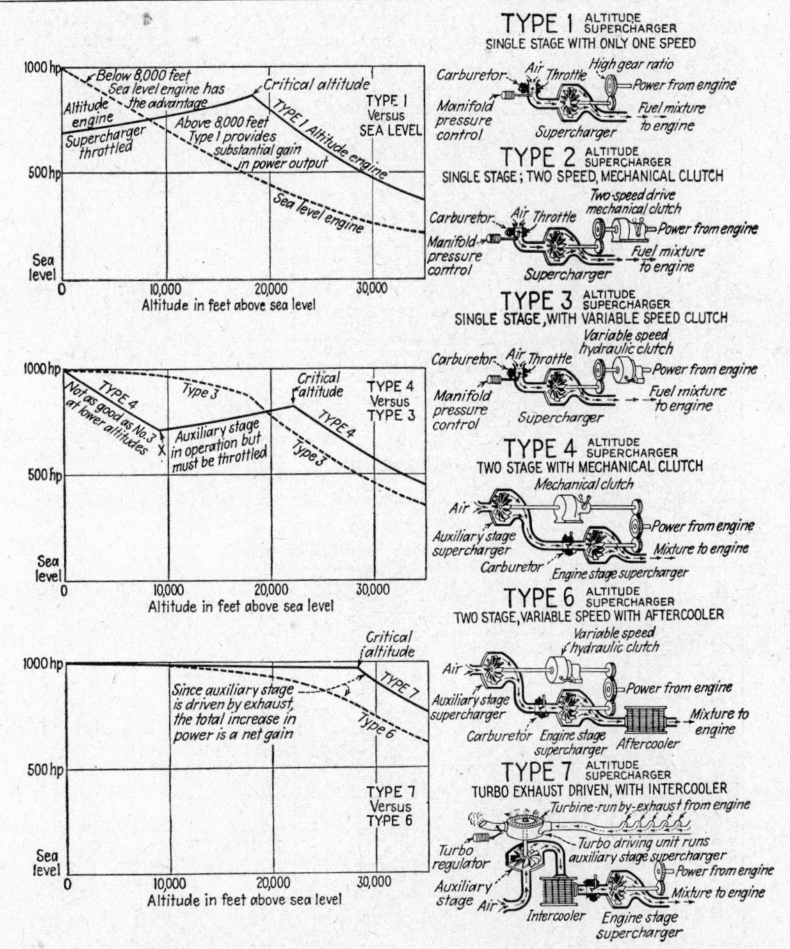

FIG. 4:6.—Types of supercharger arrangement and their effect on engine power at altitude. (*Courtesy General Motors Corporation booklet Airplane Power, published in 1944.*)

The altitude chart is plotted on the following basis: *At constant rpm* and full throttle, the brake horsepower is very nearly directly proportional to the density ratio. Accordingly, lines of constant rpm

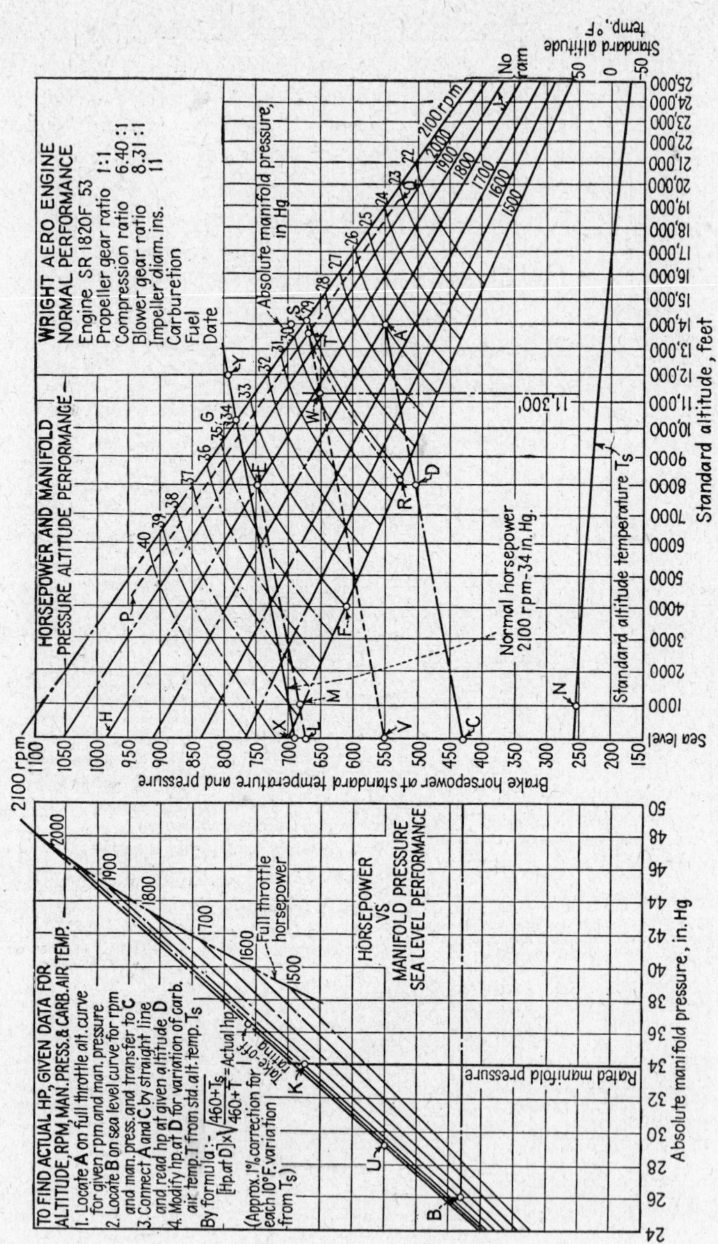

FIG. 4:7.—Typical airplane-engine performance data.

are plotted on the graph as straight, the abscissa being a density-ratio scale (1.00 at left with a base of 10.7 in., so that zero is off the paper at the right) though it is labeled with the corresponding standard altitudes. For each altitude and rpm, full throttle will give a determinable manifold pressure; therefore, lines of constant *full-throttle manifold pressure* may be drawn, and these are the arcs sloping diagonally upward from left to right. The other diagonal lines *XY*, *LE*, *VW*, and *CA* are graphical constructions to determine various part-throttle limitations at other altitudes with a *given rpm and manifold pressure.* (For a given rpm and manifold pressure, brake horsepower increases with altitude because of reduced *exhaust pressure*, and interpolation should be a function of *pressure ratio*, but the density-ratio scale can be used if the use is restricted to *standard altitudes*, for which P/P_0 and ρ/ρ_0 are definitely related, and if corrections are made for *departures from standard temperature.*) A graph of standard temperatures is given to facilitate such corrections that are proportional to $\sqrt{T_{std}/T}$. The procedure for such altitude interpolation is shown in Table 4:2, which is an extension of Table 4:1.

TABLE 4:2.—PART-THROTTLE OPERATING LIMITATIONS AT ALTITUDE

Rating	S.L. ratings (part-throttle)			Alt. ratings (full-throttle)				
	Rpm	Man. pressure	Bhp	Rpm	Man. pressure	Hp	Alt., ft	Point
Max. continuous.....	1,900	34	675	1,900	34	750	8,000	*E*
Cruising...........	1,800	26	43	1,800	26	550	14,000	*A*

Altitude Ratings, Part-throttle, Other Altitudes, Same Rpm and Manifold Pressure as Above

Rating	Alt., ft	Bhp	Point
Max. continuous................................	1,000	685	*M*
Cruising....................................	8,000	505	*D*

Example.—If the above engine is cruising at 2,050 rpm and 29.2 in. Hg manifold pressure at a standard altitude of 11,300 ft, what power is it delivering? The answer is 650 hp.

Solution.—See points *TUVW* on chart.

4:3.1. Other Types of Airplane Power Plants.—As early as 1891 Langley used a steam engine to power his very successful flying models;

the power plant of a steam automobile was used for airplane power in 1925. Consideration has been given to the powering of large airplanes by steam turbines. The "water rate" of a steam engine or steam turbine is usually about ten times the fuel consumption of the gasoline engine of equivalent powers; thus, if steam engines or steam turbines are to be used for airplane power, they must be equipped with condensers to provide for recirculation of the water in order to have reasonable range. Suitable steam-condensing equipment has thus far proved excessively heavy, though it is quite possible that wing-surface condensers can be built at a reasonable weight, similar to the wing-surface radiators used with some liquid-cooled gasoline engines.

Several airplanes built and flown in 1944 and 1945 have been powered by *gas turbines* such as that shown at the bottom of page 218. A gas turbine is essentially simple in construction and had been developed to a point of fairly trouble-free operation at that time. Most gas turbines use the exhaust-jet reaction for propulsion, although consideration has also been given to combining the exhaust-jet reaction with a gear-driven propeller. This combination gives promise of excellent fuel economy, which the jet alone cannot obtain.

Another type of power plant in successful use in 1945 was the intermittent-firing duct engine sketched on page 218, which powered the German V-1 "buzz bomb." The intermittent-firing duct engine has poor fuel economy, and its maximum speed is limited to about 600 mph by compressibility effects on the inlet grill; the fuel economy is less at lower speeds. For speeds over 600 mph the continuous-firing-duct engine (the aerothermodynamic duct, or "athodyd"), or rocket engine, appears to be necessary. Rocket power has been used in the German V-2 bomb with good success. The athodyd, which is nothing more than a barrel open at both ends in which fuel is burned, has been found successful at speeds over 500 mph in the laboratory and may be important for supersonic aircraft at present under development, but it had not been widely used by 1945. Sketches of these various types of power plants and graphs showing the variations of thrust, thermal efficiency, and over-all efficiency are plotted on page 218. Data are also given graphically of the relative frontal area, which is a measure of drag due to the power plant and the relative weight of fuel for a given duration of flight. This chart, which has been reprinted from a study of the Westinghouse Company, suggests that a reasonable upper limit for speed of aircraft powered by propellers and supercharged internal-combustion engines is about 450 mph.

A well-designed airplane propeller has high efficiency as long as the tips do not get into compressibility trouble. This usually occurs at about 500 mph. Some form of jet propulsion appears to be necessary beyond this speed. Flight at supersonic speeds appears to be quite possible and will unquestionably be used for military operations; but it is doubtful whether the traveling public will pay the excessive premium necessary for travel in the region of large compressibility effects, and it is much less likely that they will be willing to pay the additional premium for flight in which shock waves are a major factor in the drag.

The problem of selecting the best type of power plant for a given service is basically a problem of economics and cost accounting, for the solution of which insufficient data are available at present. A study by Carmichael[1] comparing the total weight of power plant and fuel for different types of power plants and different speeds of distances is summarized in Table 4:2.1. Note in the table that the "turbo jet" (gas-turbine-jet propulsion unit on page 418) is far superior to any of the other types of power plant considered for a short trip (300 mph) at high speed (550 mph) in spite of its high fuel consumption and because of the low power-plant weight. When cost figures are available, it may be even more attractive for short trips because of low first cost, low service costs, and low fuel costs (kerosene *vs.* high-octane gasoline), in spite of the reduced payload due to the additional fuel

TABLE 4:2.1.—COMPARISON OF WEIGHTS OF POWER PLANT AND FUEL FOR TWO DIFFERENT RANGES AND SPEEDS

Type of power plant	Power-plant weight per cruising hp	Thermal efficiency, %	Propulsive efficiency, %	Total weight, lb per trip per Thp
For 300-mile trip at 550 mph				
Turbo jet	0.51	16	64	0.9
Turbo propeller	1.1	16	52	3.1
Compound *	3.0	40	52	5.9
Gasoline†	3.4	31	52	6.9
Diesel	3.9	40	52	7.8
For 3,000-mile trip at 300 mph				
Compound*	3.0	40	83	8.6
Diesel	3.9	40	83	9.7
Gasoline†	3.4	31	83	10.5
Turbo propeller	1.1	16	83	14.0
Turbo jet	0.51	16	40	26.5

* Engine and gas turbine.
† Turbo-supercharged.

[1] *Machine Design*, April, 1945.

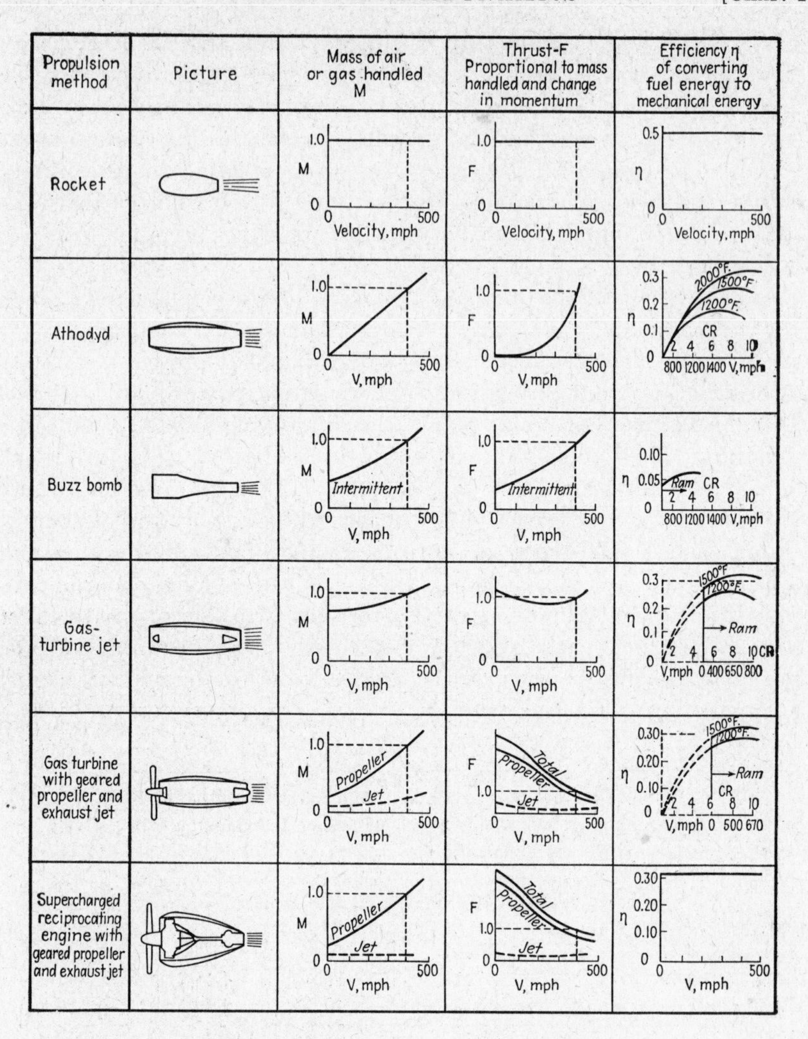

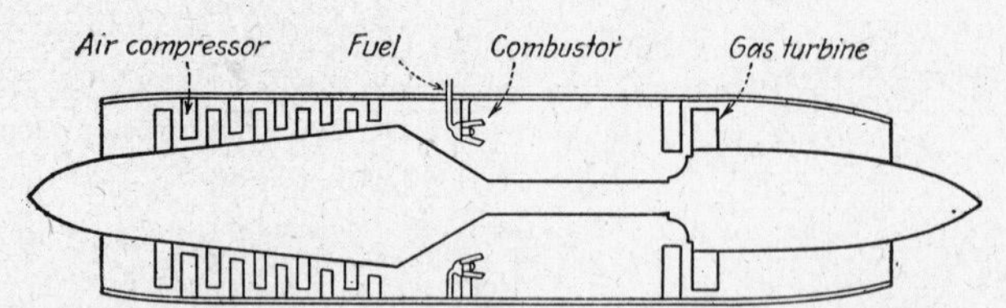

FIG. 4:7.01.—A comparison of the present successful forms of jet-propulsion and reciprocating engines. (*Reprinted from March, 1945, issue of Westinghouse Engineer.*)

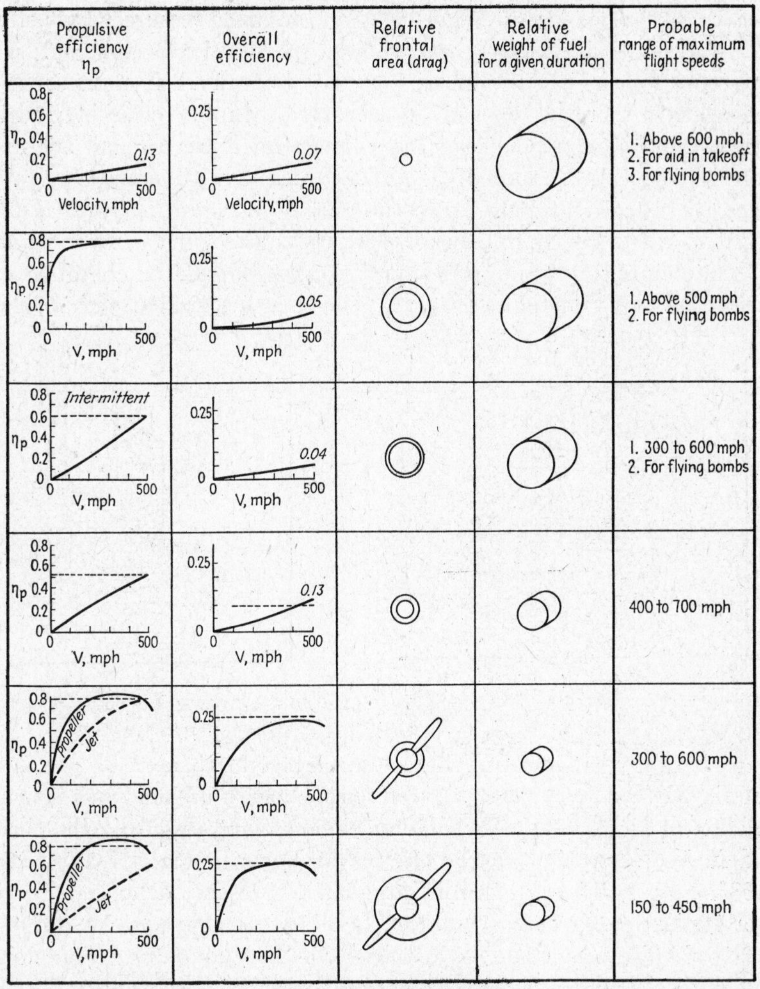

Propulsive efficiency η_p	Overall efficiency	Relative frontal area (drag)	Relative weight of fuel for a given duration	Probable range of maximum flight speeds
0.8, 0.6, η_p 0.4, 0.2, 0; 0, 500; 0.13; Velocity, mph	0.25, 0; 0, 500; 0.07; Velocity, mph			1. Above 600 mph 2. For aid in takeoff 3. For flying bombs
0.8, 0.6, η_p 0.4, 0.2, 0; 0, 500; V, mph	0.25, 0; 0, 500; 0.05; V, mph			1. Above 500 mph 2. For flying bombs
Intermittent; 0.8, 0.6, η_p 0.4, 0.2, 0; 0, 500; V, mph	0.25, 0; 0, 500; 0.04; V, mph			1. 300 to 600 mph 2. For flying bombs
0.8, 0.6, η_p 0.4, 0.2, 0; 0, 500; V, mph	0.25, 0; 0, 500; 0.13; V, mph			400 to 700 mph
0.8, 0.6, η_p 0.4, 0.2, 0; 0, 500; Propeller; Jet; V, mph	0.25, 0; 0, 500; V, mph			300 to 600 mph
0.8, 0.6, η_p 0.4, 0.2, 0; 0, 500; Propeller; Jet; V, mph	0.25, 0; 0, 500; V, mph			150 to 450 mph

FIG. 4:7.01.—*Continued.*

needed. Note also that for long trips (3,000 miles) at low speed (300 mph) the turbo jet goes to the bottom of the list because of fuel weight. It may be inferred that there is a definite field in which the turbo jet is commercially advantageous on a suitably designed transport airplane and that this field may include the typical two-step transcontinental airplane service in the United States but is even more likely to include the typical five-stop transcontinental service.

4:3.2. Turbo-jet Characteristics.—The ideal cycle of operations of the simplified turbine-jet unit sketched at the bottom of page 218 is shown in Figs. 4:7.1 and 4:7.2. It is seen to consist of AB, an approximately isentropic compression; BC, a constant-pressure combustion; and CD, an approximately isentropic expansion in the turbine. The difference in specific volumes between D and A is a measure of the velocity increase for a given area ratio of inlet to outlet, and the thrust developed depends on the velocity increase ΔV and the mass per second of air handled, m, in accordance with equation (1:89). Once the rotor is brought up to the minimum operating rpm (usually about three-fourths of maximum rated rpm), the rpm can be controlled by controlling the rate of fuel supply to the combustion chamber, and this is the only control necessary. The thrust variation with airplane

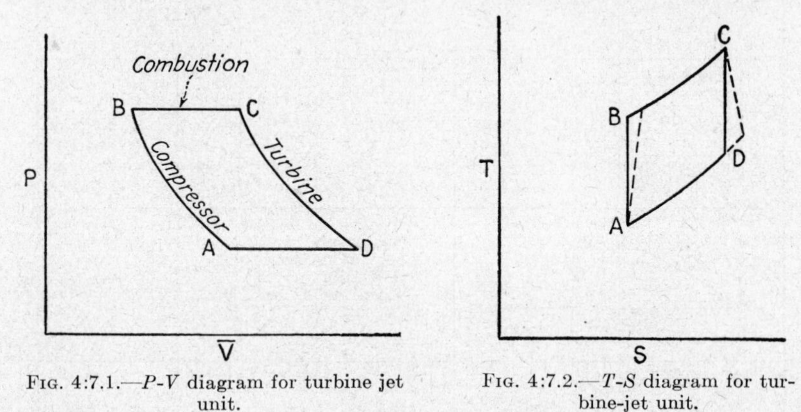

FIG. 4:7.1.—*P-V* diagram for turbine jet unit.

FIG. 4:7.2.—*T-S* diagram for turbine-jet unit.

speed is small, as shown in the column labeled "thrust" on page 218, but the necessary rpm for a given thrust varies greatly with altitude and initial air density. A common means of representing the thrust and fuel-consumption characteristics is shown in Fig. 4:7.3 (AAFTR 5193 by R. E. Hage) which is intended to present the characteristics of a typical small gas-turbine jet at 35,000 ft altitude. A different chart of this sort would be required for each altitude. The thrust available at a given airplane speed can be approximately constant up to a critical altitude at which the maximum safe rpm of the rotor is reached. This type of plot can include a cross plot of fuel consumption in pounds per mile for each jet unit involved. A logarithmic replot of Fig. 4:7.3 in terms of power rather than thrust, to the same logarithmic scales as on Chart C in the back of the book, for a hypothetical turbo jet of four times the thrust, appears as Figure A61.

4:4. Problems

1. For the engine data given in Fig. 4:2.1, read values from the graphs, and calculate (*a*) the full-throttle torque, (*b*) the fuel-consumption rate in pounds per hour at 2,550 rpm, full throttle, and (*c*) the fuel-consumption rate in pounds per hour at 1,550 rpm on propeller load.

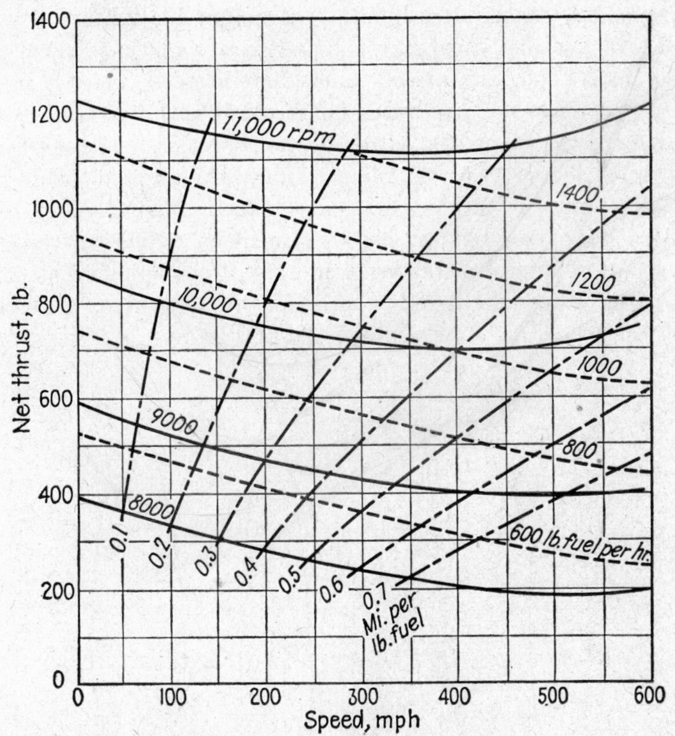

FIG. 4:7.3.—Typical gas-turbine-jet characteristics at 35,000 ft. (*From Army Air Forces Tech. Rept.* 5193 *by R. E. Hage.*)

2. For the engine data in Fig. 4:7, at 14,000 ft standard altitude and 1,800 rpm, read Bhp = 550 with 26 in. Hg manifold pressure (point *A* on the graph). For the same rpm and manifold pressure at sea level read Bhp = 430. Using the method of Art. 4:3, (*a*) find the brake horsepower available at this rpm and manifold pressure at 8,000 ft standard altitude, and (*b*) find the brake horsepower available at this rpm and manifold pressure at 8,000 ft pressure altitude and a temperature of −10°F.

3. The engine shown in Fig. 4:2.1 is rated 75 hp at 2,550 rpm at sea level. Using equation (4:2), find the power developed at 12,000 ft standard altitude at (*a*) 2,550 rpm and (*b*) 2,000 rpm.

4. On page 219, extend the over-all efficiency graphs to 700 mph, select the most efficient type of power plant, and estimate its over-all efficiency.

5. Using the typical turbo-jet characteristics shown in Fig. 4:7.3, calculate the thrust horsepower available at 11,000 rpm and 500 mph for a hypothetical turbo jet giving four times as much thrust as that shown in Fig. 4:7.3, and check with Fig. A61 page 466.

4:5. Propeller Geometry and Construction: Pitch-change Mechanisms.—Airplane propellers, or *airscrews*, as the British more descriptively call them, are usually forged, machined, and ground from strong aluminum-alloy material or built up as hollow blades out of welded-steel sheet. Smaller airplane propellers are sometimes carved from selected hardwood or formed out of reinforced plastic material. Wooden propellers are most often constructed with two blades set at a fixed angle to the plane of rotation of the propeller. Metal blades are usually built separately from the hubs, and the angle of blade setting is *adjustable* on the ground or *controllable* in flight. Most wooden propellers have two blades; larger propellers, which are usually of metal, usually have three blades or more. Propellers with as many as six blades have been flight-tested; propellers with as many as ten blades have been tested in wind tunnels. Photographs of typical three-,

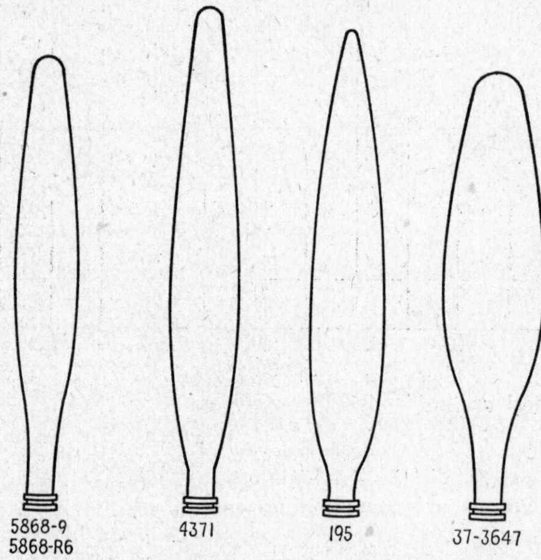

FIG. 4:8.—Typical propeller-blade shapes tested and reported in *NACA Tech. Rept.* 639.

four-, and five-blade propellers are shown on page 35, which also shows details of some typical hubs in which the blades are mounted and of electrical and hydraulic pitch-change mechanisms. Typical propeller-blade shapes tested by the NACA and recorded in *NACA Tech. Rept.* 639 are shown in Fig. 4:8.

A propeller advances as it revolves. The advance per revolution is called the *effective pitch* of the propeller. Any section of the propeller blade travels on a helical path, as shown in Fig. 4:9. A development of the helical path is indicated in Fig. 4:9, which also shows the *geometric pitch* and the *aerodynamic* or the *zero-thrust pitch.* The geometric pitch of an element of a propeller is the distance that the element would advance along its axis of rotation if it was moving along a helical path of slope equal to its blade angle. Propellers are usually constructed with the blade angle varying along the radius so that the geometric pitch is approximately uniform, though wide variations in geometric-pitch distribution have been tested. Since the outer half of the propeller does most of the work, when a single pitch or blade angle must be specified to characterize the entire propeller, the pitch and angle are usually taken at three-fourths of the tip radius. A propeller with a uniform geometric pitch must, of course, have non-uniform blade angles, the elements farthest from the axis having the smallest blade angle. Most propellers do not have exactly uniform

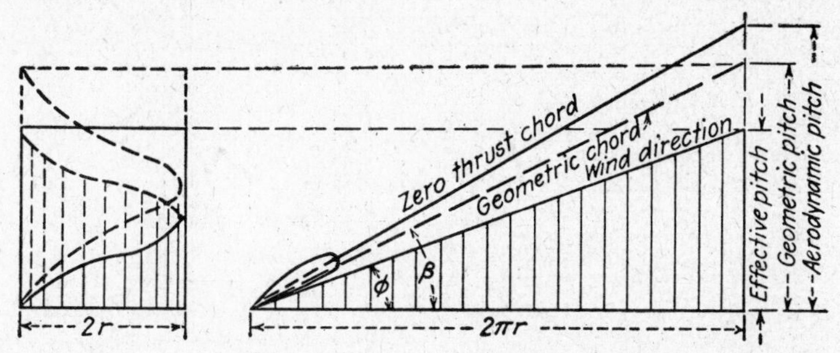

FIG. 4:9.—Illustration of effective, geometric, and aerodynamic pitch.

geometric pitch; the pitch is made smaller near the axis where the air stream is obstructed by the nacelle or fuselage.

For satisfactory operation all the blades of a propeller must have the same angle within approximately 0.5 deg, and the blades must "track" within approximately ⅛ in. (*i.e.*, the tips should rotate in planes not over ⅛ in. apart). Propellers are checked for pitch and track by mounting on a vertical test shaft, which is fixed at right angles to a horizontal bedplate; the blade angles are measured by means of a protractor whose base slides on the bedplate. Track is checked by measuring the height of each blade tip above the bedplate. Propellers must also be carefully balanced both statically and dynamically.

The diameter in the circle in which the propeller-blade tips revolve is usually designated by D. The radius is half the diameter. The ratio of pitch to diameter is called the *pitch ratio*. From the geometry of Fig. 4:9, the tangent of the blade angle at any point is the ratio of the pitch to the circumference at that point. Hence,

$$\left(\frac{p}{D}\right)_{0.75R} = 0.75\pi \tan \beta_{0.75R} = 2.36 \tan \beta_{0.75R} \tag{4:3}$$

Typical propeller-blade airfoil sections are the RAF6 and Clark Y sketched in Fig. 4:10. (Clark Y family ordinates are on page 405.) If the tip of a propeller blade must travel at a speed close to that of sound ($M = 0.8$), high-speed sections like the 16 series sketched in Fig. 2:42 are sometimes used for the outer 25 per cent of the blades. Figure 4:10 also gives a typical presentation of width, thickness, and pitch distribution for two of the propellers sketched in Fig. 4:8. Note in Clark Y (Fig. 4:10) that the geometric pitch is approximately uni-

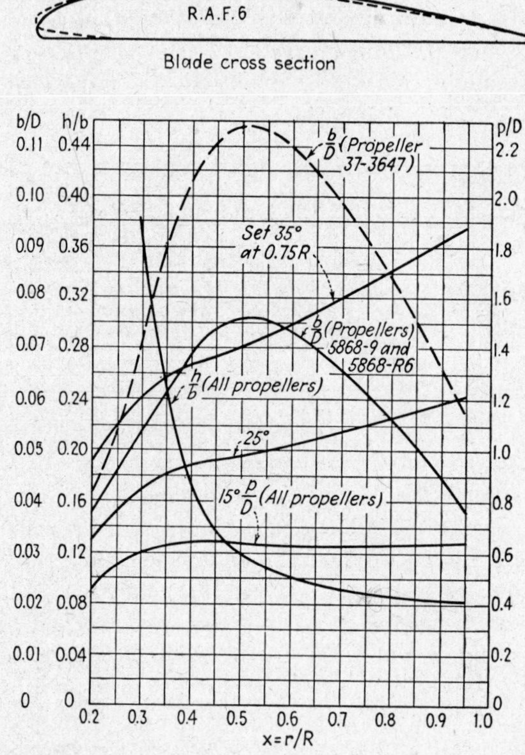

FIG. 4:10.—Blade-form curves for propellers 5868-9, 5868-R6, and 37-3647, r = station radius, b = section chord, h = maximum section thickness, p = geometric pitch. (*From NACA Tech. Rept.* 640.)

form, except for the middle third of the blade when the blade setting at $0.75R$ is 15 deg. With larger values of $0.75R$, the geometric-pitch ratio increases sharply toward the tip. The blade-pitch ratio at $0.75R$ and blade-thickness ratio at $0.75R$ are usually taken as the most typical values of the blade. The characteristic blade widths (b/D) for the two propellers shown in Fig. 4:10 are 0.061 and 0.092, respectively; the characteristic blade thicknesses $(h/b)_{0.75R}$ is 0.090 for both propellers.

While the width and thickness of a propeller blade at $0.75R$ are indicative in a general way of the power that will be absorbed at a given rpm with a given diameter, a better measure of the power absorption is obtained if some account is taken of the shape of the blade, particularly near the tip. Such a blade width and shape factor are known as the *activity factor*, defined by

$$\text{A.F.} = \frac{100{,}000}{16} \int_{0.2}^{1.0} \frac{b}{D} x^3 dx \tag{4:4}$$

where $x = r/R$, as in Fig. 4:10. The activity factor of a propeller blade can be conveniently calculated from data such as are given in Fig. 4:10 by means of Simpson's rule or other rule for approximate integration, as shown in Table 4:3.

TABLE 4:3.—CALCULATION OF ACTIVITY FACTOR OF NACA 5868-9 PROPELLER BY SIMPSON'S RULE

Station No.	0	1	2	3	4	5	6	7	8
$\frac{r}{R} = x$	0.2	0.3	0.4	0.5	0.6	0.7	0.8	0.9	1.0
(b/D), Fig. 4:10	0 038	0.053	0.069	0.076	0.073	0.066	0.056	0.0445	0
b/Dx^3, × 100,000:									
End	30								0
Odd		143		950		2,260		3,250	
Even			441		1,580		2,870		

Sums	Factors	Sums times factors
30	1	30
6,603	4	26,412
4,891	2	9,782
Total...	..	36,224

$x = 0.1$ in above table.

Simpson's rule is

$$\int y\,dx = \frac{\Delta x}{3}\left(\sum y_{\text{end}} + 4 \sum y_{\text{odd}} + 2 \sum y_{\text{even}}\right)$$

Hence,

$$\text{A.F.} = \frac{0.1}{3} \times \frac{36{,}224}{16} = 75.5$$

The numbers 100,000 and 16 are inserted arbitrarily in the definition of activity factor for convenience in calculation and to give an answer that will usually lie between 50 and 150.

Typical hydraulic, electric, and mechanical pitch-change mechanisms are shown on pages 35 to 37.

4:6. Momentum Theory of Propellers.—A propeller produces thrust by causing the stream of air approaching it to be accelerated. The thrust produced can be calculated from the mass per second m of air stream affected and the change in velocity ΔV of the air stream as in equation (1:89), which becomes for this case

$$T = m\Delta V \tag{4:5}$$

Let A_0 be the area of the entering air stream and V_0 its velocity, as shown in Fig. 4:11. Also let A_1 be the area of the

$$\text{propeller disk} = \frac{\pi D^2}{4}$$

where the velocity is Vd. Then, for air of mass density ρ,

$$m = \rho V_0 A_0 = \rho V_d A_d \tag{4:6}$$

and

$$\Delta V = V_s - V_0 \tag{4:7}$$

and, therefore,

$$T = \rho V_d Ad(V_s - V_0) = \rho V_0^2 A_0 \left(\frac{V_s}{V_0} - 1\right) \tag{4:8}$$

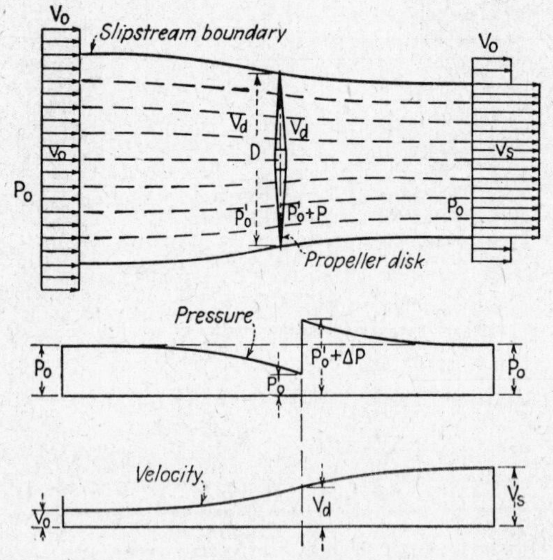

FIG. 4:11.—Assumed velocity and pressure relationship for momentum theory of propellers. (*Arrangement suggested by Nelson, "Airplane Propeller Principles."*)

The thrust may also be calculated from the pressure difference across the propeller $T = A\Delta P$, and ΔP calculated from Bernoulli's theorem as

$$\Delta P = \frac{\rho(V_s^2 - V_0^2)}{2} \tag{4:9}$$

or

$$T = \frac{\rho A_d(V_s^2 - V_0^2)}{2} \tag{4:10}$$

Comparison of equations (4:8) and (4:10) gives

$$V_d = \frac{V_s + V_0}{2} \tag{4:11}$$

and reveals the interesting conclusion that one-half the velocity change has taken place in front of the propeller disk.

The power delivered by the propeller is TV ft-lb per sec; the energy lost in the slip stream per second is

$$\text{Loss} = \frac{1}{2}\, m(V_s - V_0)^2 = \frac{\rho V_0 A_0}{2}\,(V_s - V_0)^2 = \frac{\rho V_0^3 A}{2}\left(\frac{V_s}{V_0} - 1\right)^2 \tag{4:12}$$

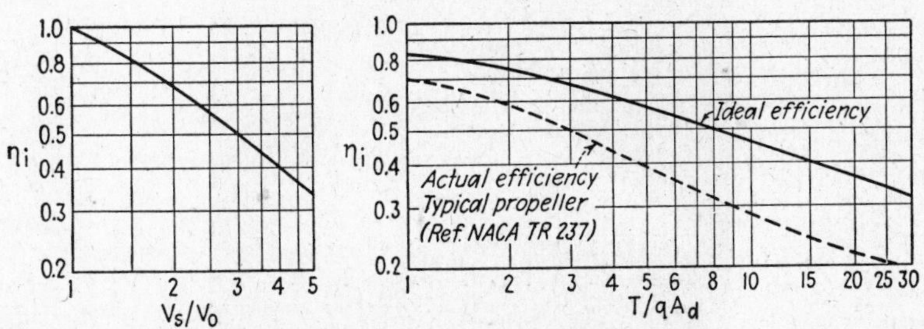

FIG. 4:12.—Ideal efficiency as a function of slip-stream velocity and disk loading.

The efficiency of the propeller calculated by this method, which may be called an ideal efficiency (since the only loss considered is that in translation of the slip stream, slip-stream rotation being neglected), may be designated by the symbol η_i and is generally given by the equation

$$\begin{aligned}\eta_i &= \frac{\text{output}}{\text{input}} = \frac{\text{output}}{\text{output} + \text{loss}} \\ &= \frac{\rho V_0^3 A_0[(V_s/V_0) - 1]}{\rho V_0^3 A_0[(V_s/V_0) - 1] + (\rho V_0^3 A_0/2)[(V_s/V) - 1]^2} \\ &= \frac{2}{1 + (V_s/V_0)} \end{aligned} \tag{4:13}$$

Equation (4:13), which is plotted in Fig. 4:12, shows that for best efficiency V_s/V should be as small as possible. But equation (4:8) shows that small V_s/V_0 gives small thrust. Solving equations (4:8) and (4:13) together gives

$$\eta_i = \frac{4}{4 + (2T/\rho V_0^2 A)} \tag{4:14}$$

or

$$\frac{\eta_i}{2 - \eta_i} = \sqrt{\frac{1}{1 + (2T/\rho V_0^2 A_d)}} \tag{4:15}$$

The quantity $2T/\rho V_0^2 A_d = T/qA_d$ is called the disk-loading coefficient. Equation (4:15) is also plotted in Fig. 4:12.

Equation (4:14) shows that, other factors being constant

1. Ideal efficiency decreases with increase of thrust.
2. Ideal efficiency increases with increase of forward velocity.
3. Ideal efficiency increases with increase of fluid density.
4. Ideal efficiency increases with increase in propeller diameter.

The principal practical conclusions from this analysis are that the propeller diameter should be as large as possible and that propulsion by means of a small-diameter high-velocity jet is necessarily inefficient.

FIG. 4:13.—Wind-tunnel model of German Jaeger P-12 supersonic fighter under test in 1945, intended to get 1,500 mph with ram-jet propulsion. (*Courtesy Aviation News.*)

Jet propulsion, however, is finding wide use in spite of its inefficiency, for airplane propellers also become very inefficient when the helical tip speed of the propeller reaches a high Mach number. When the tip-speed correction (discussed later in the chapter) is excessive owing to high forward velocity, it is possible that a jet will be just as efficient as a propeller; this condition is usually reached at airplane speeds in the region of 450 to 500 mph. Typical jet-propulsion apparatus under current development is shown in Fig. 4:13 and typical jet-propelled fighter aircraft in Fig. 4:14. While either a jet or a propeller is inefficient at these high speeds, it is possible that the jet engine can be built and maintained at a lower cost per flying hour than a conventional airplane engine; thus, the high-speed jet may have commercial as well as military significance, the significance depending on cost data yet to be obtained.

4:7. Blade-element Theory of Propellers.—To determine a relationship between the thrust horsepower delivered by the propeller and the brake horsepower of the engine, it is convenient to consider the propeller blade divided into small elements, as shown in Fig. 4:15, each of which is a revolving airfoil. If the propeller has a forward

FIG. 4:14.—Lockheed P-80 Shooting Star, powered by large General Electric turbo-jet unit, reported to have high speed over 600 mph. Wing-tip auxiliary tanks can be dropped. (*Courtesy Aviation News.*)

velocity of V ft per sec and a speed of rotation of n rps, the resultant air velocity strikes any element at radius r at an angle with the plane of rotation given by the equation

$$\tan \phi = \frac{V}{2\pi rn} \qquad (4:16)$$

FIG. 4:15.—Element of propeller blade.

as shown in Fig. 4:16.

For a blade angle β, the angle of attack α of the resultant velocity on the blade element is seen to be

$$\alpha = \beta - \phi \qquad (4:17)$$

In Fig. 4:16, the resultant of the lift and drag forces on the blade element is shown analyzed into the thrust and torque components. Let γ be the angle between the lift component and the resultant force;

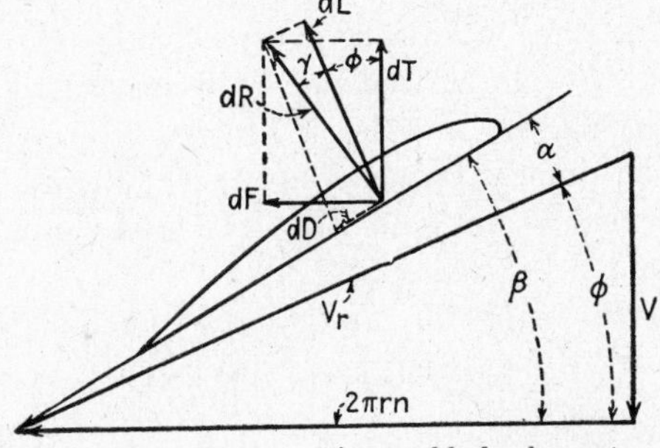

FIG. 4:16.—Forces acting on blade element.

then $\tan \gamma = D/L$. Since $dL = C_L(\rho/2)drV_r^2$

$$dR = \frac{C_L(\rho/2)bdrV_r^2}{\cos \gamma} \tag{4:18}$$

and, from Fig. 4:16, the thrust and torque components of force are

$$dT = dR \cos (\phi + \gamma) \tag{4:19}$$
$$dF = dR \sin (\phi + \gamma) \tag{4:20}$$

The useful work per second done by the thrust force on the blade element is VdT; the work per second done against the force dF is $2\pi rndF$. The efficiency of the blade element is the ratio of output to input, or

$$\eta_e = \frac{VdR \cos (\phi + \gamma)}{2\pi rndR \sin (\phi + \gamma)} \tag{4:21}$$

Since $V/2\pi rn = \tan \phi$, equation (4:21) may be written

$$\eta_e = \frac{\tan \phi}{\tan (\phi + \gamma)} \tag{4:22}$$

The extreme limits of γ for propellers in current use are 2 to 6 deg corresponding to values of L/D for the blade element of 28.6 and 9.5,

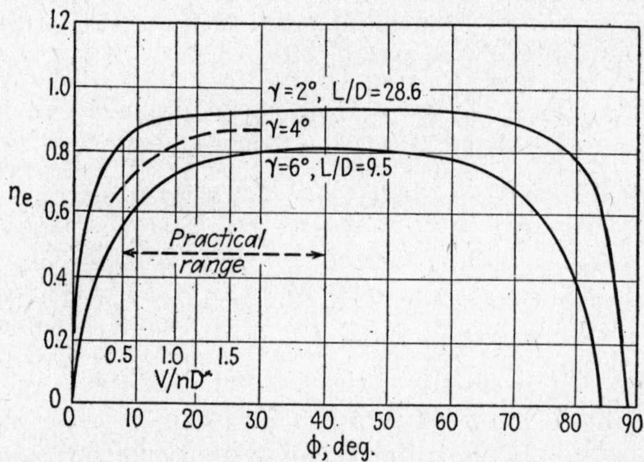

FIG. 4:17.—Blade-element efficiency as a function of effective pitch angle.

respectively, and the variation of η_e with ϕ for these values is shown in Fig. 4:17. The dotted line between these extreme limits in Fig. 4:17 corresponds to $\gamma = 4$ deg ($L/D = 14.3$) and gives efficiencies typical of complete metal propellers of recent design. Note that the shape of the efficiency curves in Fig. 4:17 is the same as that of efficiency curves for mechanical screws.[1]

Equations (4:18) to (4:21) can be used to calculate by integration the thrust, torque, and efficiency of a propeller if reasonable assump-

[1] KIMBALL, D. S., and J. H. BARR, "Machine Design."

tions can be made as to the L/D ratio or the effective aspect ratio of the blade elements. Since the effective aspect ratio is determinable only by experiments on propellers, it is customary to use the foregoing analysis chiefly as a basis for study of experimental data in which pressure and velocity distribution on the blades are involved and to treat the characteristics of the complete propeller in terms of coefficients described in Art. 4:9.

4:8. Problems

1. Using the data in Fig. 4:10 and using equation (4:3), calculate the pitch distribution for the 5868-9 propeller when $\beta_{0.75R}$ is set 20 deg. Assume values of $r/R = 0.2, 0.3, 0.4, 0.5, 0.6, 0.7, 0.8$, and 0.9 for the calculation, and base the calculations on the given values of p/D with $\beta_{0.75R} = 15$ deg.

2. For the same values of r/R as in Prob. 1, calculate the distribution of ϕ and α for $V/nD = 0.8$, using $\beta_{0.75R} = 20$ deg.

3. Using equation (4:4) and the method outlined in Table 4:3, calculate the activity factor for the 37-3647 propeller, for which data are given in Fig. 4:10.

4. Using equation (4:13), calculate the slip-stream velocity ratio V_s/V_0 necessary to get an ideal efficiency η_i of 90 per cent.

5. An airplane traveling at a velocity v_0 of 500 mph is propelled by a jet that has a discharge velocity $V_s - V_0$ of 1,000 ft per sec. Using equation (4:13), calculate the ideal efficiency.

6. In flying at 200 mph in standard sea-level air, a propeller has a disk loading T/A_d of 10 lb per sq ft. Using equation (4:15), find η_i.

7. Using equations (4:18) to (4:20), extend Probs. 1 and 2 to the calculation of thrust and torque distribution on the propeller, and integrate by Simpson's rule to find the total thrust and torque for a propeller of diameter $D = 10$ ft, rpm $= 2{,}000$, and $V = 147$ ft per sec. Assume a Clark Y family of airfoils of $AR = 6$ to calculate airfoil characteristics. Assume $e = 0.9$ in calculating induced drag; plot a_6 and $C_{D\,\min}$ *vs.* t/c to help solve.

4:9. Propeller Coefficients and Problem Types.—The theoretical considerations presented in Arts. 4:6 and 4:7 are of use primarily in connection with dimensional analysis in setting up a suitable form for the presentation and use of experimental results of propeller testing. Such considerations lead to the definition of propeller coefficients of thrust, torque, and power as shown in equations (4:23) to (4:25); these coefficients are indicated by the blade-element theory to be functions of $V/nD = J$.

$$C_T = \frac{T}{\rho n^2 D^4} \tag{4:23}$$

$$C_Q = \frac{Q}{\rho n^2 D^5} \tag{4:24}$$

$$C_P = \frac{P}{\rho n^3 D^5} \tag{4:25}$$

Equations (4:23) to (4:25) represent the most useful form of coefficient where the diameter and rpm ($= 60n$) are known, as in the case of a constant-rpm propeller of known diameter. If n is not known but V is known, as in some performance problems where the propeller rpm is not governed by a governor, it is convenient to eliminate the n from the coefficient equations by multiplying equations (4:23) to (4:25) by a suitable power of J. This procedure gives

$$C'_T = \frac{T}{\rho V^2 D^2} \tag{4:26}$$

$$C'_Q = \frac{Q}{\rho V^2 D^3} \tag{4:27}$$

$$C'_P = \frac{P}{\rho V^3 D^2} \tag{4:28}$$

For problems in which the diameter is unknown, as in cases where it is still to be selected, D can be eliminated from equations (4:23) to (4:25) by multiplying these equations by $(1/J)^4$ or $(1/J)^5$, giving

$$C''_T = \frac{Tn^2}{\rho V^4} \tag{4:29}$$

$$C''_Q = \frac{Qn^3}{\rho V^5} \tag{4:30}$$

$$C''_P = \frac{Pn^2}{\rho V^5} \tag{4:31}$$

Any power or root of equations (4:23) to (4:31) may also be considered a suitable propeller coefficient for plotting and analysis of experimental data. Such coefficients are

$$C_S = \sqrt[5]{\frac{1}{C''_P}} = \frac{V}{\rho^{1/5} P^{1/5} n^{2/5}} \tag{4:32}$$

$$C_{QS} = \sqrt{\frac{1}{C'_Q}} = V \sqrt{\frac{\rho D^3}{Q}} \tag{4:33}$$

Equation (4:32) is known as a *speed-power coefficient* and is used in selecting a propeller diameter when the power and rpm are known. Equation (4:33) is a *torque-speed coefficient* used in calculating propeller performance for a constant-torque engine with a known propeller diameter when the engine rpm is not constant. The propeller efficiency is given by the equation

$$\eta = \frac{TV}{P} = \frac{C_T J}{C_p} \tag{4:34}$$

If T is the tension in the propeller shaft, equation (4:34) gives what is called the *propeller efficiency*. If T is the net thrust delivered by the propeller, the increase in drag, due to slip stream, of the nacelle or fuselage on which it is tested being taken into account, η is called the *propulsive efficiency.* All efficiencies plotted in Appendix 6 are *propulsive efficiencies,* which are the proper efficiencies to use in connection with the drag estimates made in Chap. 3.

For cruising calculations in which the velocity, drag, and drag coefficient are known it is necessary to use thrust and power coefficients based on equations (4:26) and (4:28), which are usually modified to read

$$P_c = \frac{P}{\rho(V^3/2)(\pi D^2/4)} = \frac{8}{\pi} C'_P \tag{4:35}$$

$$\eta P_c = \frac{T}{qA_d} = \frac{8}{\pi} C'_T \tag{4:36}$$

in which $A_d = \pi D^2/4 =$ disk area of one propeller. Since

$$\text{drag} = C_D qS = T \times n_e$$

for cruising, where n_e is the number of engines and T is the thrust on one propeller, the relation between ηP_c and the drag coefficient C_D for the complete airplane may be written

$$\eta P_c = \frac{C_D qS}{qA_d n_e} = C_D \frac{S}{A_d n_e} \tag{4:37}$$

A guide to the selection and use of the proper equation for various types of problems is provided in Table 4:4, which is illustrated by examples following the table.

The propeller graphs usually considered by NACA as basic and plotted for all experimental data are the graphs of C_T and C_P *vs.* $V/nD = J$. Typical graphs of this sort are sketched in Figs. 4:18 and 4:19; such graphs are presented for all propellers for which graphs are supplied in Appendix 6. For special purposes, special derived graphs like those in Fig. 4:20 are plotted from the basic graphs as needed. A physical explanation of Figs. 4:18 and 4:19 in terms of the blade-element theory follows:

The solid line in Fig. 4:18 shows the variation of C_T with V/nD for a fixed blade angle at $0.75R$ of 20 deg. For any given blade angle such as 20 deg there is some value of $V/nD = f(\phi)$ that will give zero mean effective absolute angle of attack on the propeller blade and zero C_T. As V/nD is reduced from the zero-thrust value, the angle of attack on all elements of the propeller blade increases and C_L for each propeller-blade element increases, giving an increase in C_T almost in direct proportion to the reduction in V/nD until an angle of attack is reached where the propeller blade stalls. Further reductions of V/nD below the stalling value yield no increases in C_T. For other blade angles, such as 15 and 25 deg, shown in dotted lines, the V/nD

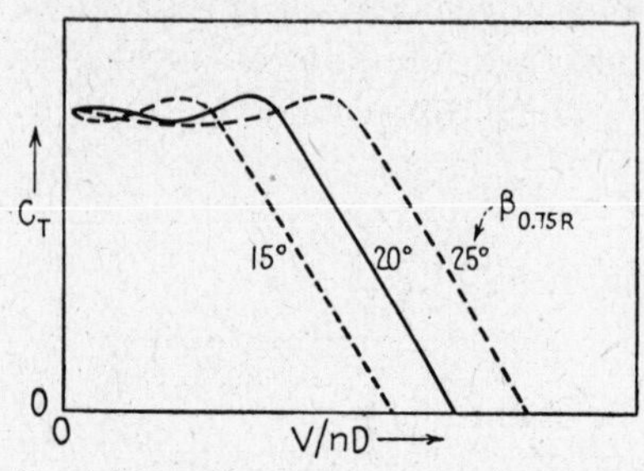

FIG. 4:18.—Typical graph of C_T vs. V/nD for constant β.

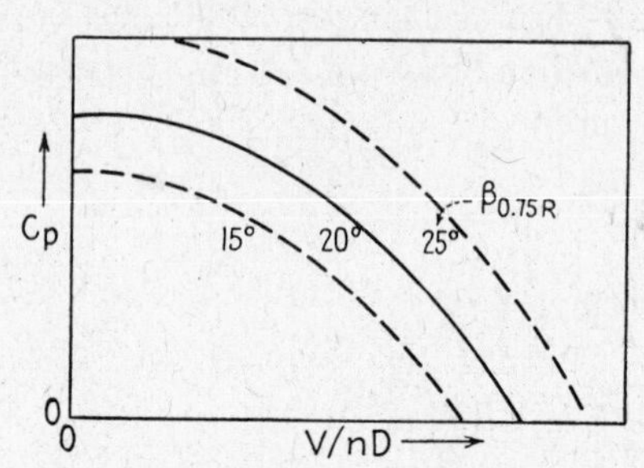

FIG. 4:19.—Typical graph of C_P vs. V/nD for constant β.

for zero thrust is different, and the stalling V/nD is different, but the maximum C_T reached where the blades stall is approximately the same, as shown in Fig. 4:18.

Figure 4:19 follows from Fig. 4:18 and the usual relationship between c_d and c_l for the propeller blade elements. For example, with $\beta_{0.75R} = 20$ deg there will be a small value of C_P when $C_T = 0$, corresponding to the power necessary to turn the propeller when it is delivering no thrust. As the thrust coefficient increases, an induced drag is developed on the propeller-blade elements, which increases the power required, as shown in Fig. 4:19.

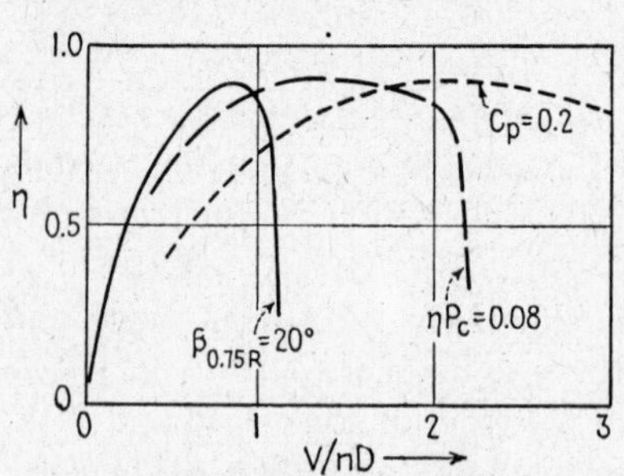

FIG. 4:20.—Typical graphs of η vs. V/nD for constant β, constant C_P, and constant C_T.

For a fixed blade angle such as 20 deg, the graph of propulsive efficiency η vs. V/nD follows from the explanation of C_T and C_P variations in Figs. 4:18 and 4:19. Since $\eta = C_T J / C_P$ [equation (4:34)], it follows that η will be zero where $J = V/nD = 0$ and also $\eta = 0$ where $C_T = 0$. Therefore, η will reach a maximum somewhere between these two values.

For the special purpose of calculating performance of a constant-rpm propeller, lines of C_P = const. can be read from Fig. 4:19 and the corresponding values of η plotted in Fig. 4:20. For cruising calculations, Fig. 4:18 can be replotted with $C_T' = C_T/J^2$ as an ordinate, and

TABLE 4:4.—OUTLINE OF PROCEDURE FOR SOLVING PROPELLER PROBLEMS OF VARIOUS TYPES

Problem type	Given	To find	Procedure: Calc. = calculate Read = read on chart
Selection of diameter	V, n, P, ρ	D, T, η, (also β if fixed-pitch)	1. Calc. C_S, equation (4:32) or (4:38) 2. Read $\frac{V}{nD}$, η, on max η line as on p. 454, Fig. A46 3. Calc. $D = \frac{V/n}{V/nD}$; $T = \frac{\eta P}{V}$
Thrust-power calculation, const. rpm	V, n, P, ρ, D	T, η, Thp	1. Calc. C_P, equation (4:25) or (4:39) 2. Calc. $\frac{V}{nD}$ 3. Read η, as on Fig. A50, p. 456 4. Calc. $Thp = \eta\ Bhp$; $T = \frac{\eta P}{V}$
Thrust-power calculation, const. torque	V, Q, ρ, D, β	T, Thp, η, n	1. Calc. C_{QS}, equation (4:37) 2. Read $\frac{C_T}{C_Q}$ and $\frac{V}{nD}$, as on Fig. A55, p. 461 3. Calc. $T = \frac{C_T}{C_Q}\frac{Q}{D}$, $n = \frac{V/D}{V/nD}$ 4. Calc. $Thp = \frac{TV}{550}$; $= \frac{TV}{P}$
Best cruising fuel consumption	V, T, ρ, D $C = f(P, n)$, lb/(hp)(hr)	η, P, n, best fuel, lb per mile	1. Calc. ηP_c, equation (4:37) 2. Assume several V/nD values 3. Read η, as in Fig. A52, p. 458 4. Calc. $P = \frac{TV}{\eta}$, $n = \frac{V/D}{V/nD}$ 5. Read C, Fig. A59, p. 464 6. Calc. fuel, lb per mile $= \frac{550PC}{v}$ 7. Select best of assumed $\left(\frac{V}{nD}\right)$'S for minimum fuel, lb per mile

Charts referred to are typical only; most applicable chart of this type to be used.

See Chap. 5 for simplified solution for problem types 2, 3, and 4 using superposed transparent charts.

lines with $\eta P_C = 8C'_T/\pi$ = const. for a parameter can be plotted in Fig. 4:20.

Example 1.—Propeller-selection problem, Lockheed Lodestar airplane. Given the airplane power-required calculations in Tables 3:1 and 3:2, the engine data on page 214, and the propeller data on pp. 454 to 456 referred to above. Find the propeller diameter for maximum efficiency at a speed of 240 mph at 10,000 ft standard altitude and 2,100 constant rpm; also find η, Thp, and T.

Solution.—Following the procedure outlined in Table 4:4, calculate first C_S. A more useful form of equation (4:32) defining C_S for practical calculation is

$$C_S = \frac{0.638\ mph\ \sigma^{1/5}}{Bhp^{1/5} rpm^{2/5}} \tag{4:38}$$

for which the fifth-root terms may be conveniently read in Fig. 4:21 if a "log-log" slide rule is not available.

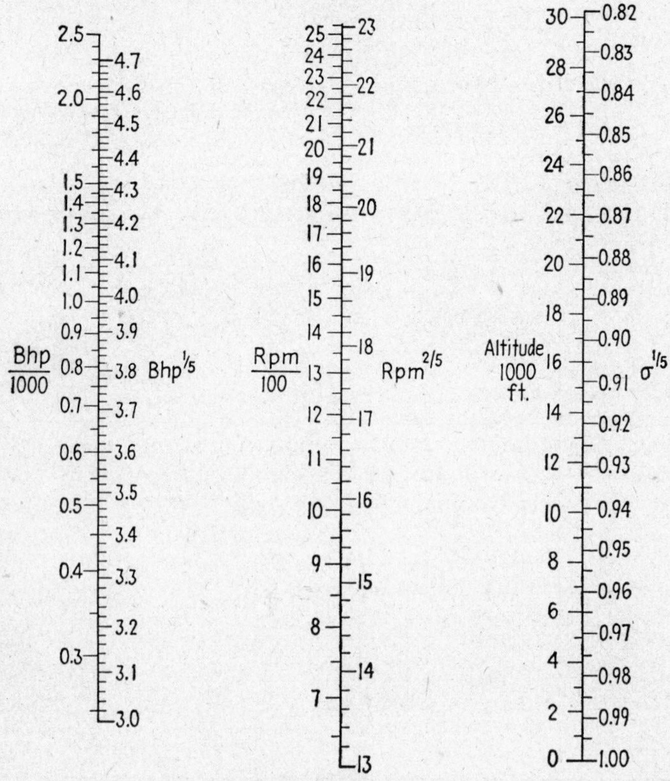

FIG. 4:21.—Graphs to facilitate calculation of C_S in equation (4:38). (*Suggested by Weick, "Airplane Propellers."*)

In the specified engine data read Bhp = 780 per engine, and for this brake horsepower and the specified rpm and altitude read in Fig. 4:21 $\sigma^{1/5} = 0.941$; $Bhp^{2/5} = 3.79$; $rpm^{2/5} = 21.3$; and calculate

$$C_S = \frac{0.638 \times 240 \times 0.941}{3.79 \times 21.3} = 1.79$$

On page 454, Fig. A46, for this value of C_S read on the maximum η line $\beta_{0.75R} = 24.5$ deg and $V/nD = 1.01$. At the same C_S, read $\eta = 0.88$.

$$D = \frac{V/n}{V/nD} = \frac{240 \times (88/2{,}100)}{1.01} = 9.95 \text{ ft}$$

Calculate also

$Thp = 0.88 \times 780 = 687$ per engine and $T = 687 \times 375/240 = 1{,}073$ lb

These are the answers called for.

Example 2.—Power-available calculation, Lockheed Lodestar airplane. Given the airplane, engine, and propeller data in Example 1, and assume that a propeller diameter of 10 ft 6 in. was selected on the basis of additional considerations to those in Example 1. Find the full-throttle power available at 10,000 ft standard altitude, 2.100 constant rpm, and airplane speeds (mph) of 291, 233, 175.5, 145.5, 116.4, and 103.6 (same speeds as in Table 3:2).

Solution.—Following the procedure outlined in Table 4:4, calculate first C_P (which applies to all airplane speeds, because P and n are known and V is not involved in the definition $C_P = P/\rho n^3 D^5$). A more useful form of equation (4:25) defining C_P for practical calculations is

$$C_P = \frac{0.5}{\sigma} \frac{Bhp/1{,}000}{(rpm/1{,}000)^3 (D/10)^5} \qquad (4.:39)$$

Using $Bhp = 780$, $\sigma = 0.738$, $rpm = 2{,}100$, and $D = 10.5$, calculate

$$C_P = \frac{0.5}{0.738} \frac{0.780}{2.1^3 \times 1.05^5} = 0.045$$

Calculate also

$$\frac{V}{nD} = mph \times \frac{88}{2{,}100} \times 10.5 = \frac{\text{mph}}{251}$$

and list this value opposite each value of *mph* as in Table 4:5 below. For each V/nD, with $C_P = 0.045$, read $\beta_{0.75R}$ in Fig. A49, page 455, and η on page 454, and calculate $Thp = 780\eta \times 2$ for two engines, giving the results shown. These values may be plotted in Fig. 3:10 to determine the full-throttle performance at 10,000 ft altitude as explained in Chap. 5.

TABLE 4:5.—CALCULATION OF FULL-THROTTLE THRUST HORSEPOWER AVAILABLE FOR LOCKHEED LODESTAR AIRPLANE AT 10,000 FT ALTITUDE

Mph	V/nD	$\beta_{0.75R}$	η	*Thp*
291	1.16	26°	0.87	1,360
233	0.93	22°	0.86	1,340
175.5	0.70	18°	0.82	1,280
145.5	0.58	16°	0.79	1,230
116.4	0.464	15°	0.72	1,120
103.6	0.412	14.5°	0.68	1,060

Table 4:5 gives the answers called for in this example.

Example 3.—Power-available calculation, Piper Cub airplane with fixed-pitch propeller. Given a Piper Cub airplane

$$(W = 1{,}400 \text{ lb}, S = 180 \text{ sq ft}, C_D = 0.046 + 0.060\, C_L^2)$$

powered by a Lycoming six-cylinder opposed-type engine rated 120 hp at 2,600 rpm and equipped with a fixed-pitch propeller of diameter $D = 6.5$ ft set at

$$\beta_{0.75R} = 18 \text{ deg}$$

of characteristics shown on pages 460 to 463. Find the full-throttle power available at sea level at speeds (mph) of 120, 100, 80, 70, 60, and 50. Calculate also the thrust at mph = 0.

Solution.—Following the procedure outlined in Table 4:4, calculate first $C_{QS} = V\sqrt{\rho D^3/Q}$ (equation 4:37), using $= 0.00238 = 1/420$, $D^3 = 6.5^3 = 275$, $Q = 120 \times (5{,}250/2{,}600) = 242$ lb-ft, and $V = mph \times 1.467$.

$$C_{QS} = mph \frac{1.467}{\sqrt{420 \times 242/275}} = \frac{mph}{13.1}$$

For each speed (*mph*), calculate C_{QS}, and list as in Table 4:6. For each C_{QS}, on page 461, Fig. A55 for $\beta_{0.75R} = 18$ deg, read CT/C_Q and V/nD. Calculate

$$T = (C_T/C_Q)(Q/D) = (C_T/C_Q)(242/6.5) = 37.2(C_T/C_Q)$$

$Thp = (T \times mph)/375$, and

$$rpm = 60n = 88\ mph/[6.5(V/nD)] = 13.5\ mph/(V/nD)$$

giving the results shown in the table.

TABLE 4:6.—CALCULATION OF FULL-THROTTLE THRUST HORSEPOWER AVAILABLE FOR 120-HP PIPER CUB AIRPLANE

Mph	C_{QS}	$\frac{C_T}{C_Q}$	$\frac{V}{nD}$	T	Thp	Rpm
120	9.16	6.3	0.74	234	75.0	2,190
100	7.64	6.9	0.65	257	68.5	2,010
80	6.11	7.45	0.57	277	59.1	1,830
70	5.35	7.9	0.51	294	54.9	1,800
60	4.58	8.15	0.45	303	48.5	1,740
50	3.82	8.5	0.38	316	42.1	1,720
0	0	9.8	0	364	0	Indeterminate

Since the values of rpm in Table 4:6 come out well under the rated 2,600, it is evident that the propeller is not properly selected or set; the proper diameter and setting could have been determined by the method of Example 1, the data on page 460 being used.

Example 4.—Calculation of best cruising fuel economy for Lockheed airplane. Given the same airplane, engine, and propeller data as in Example 2, plus the specific fuel-consumption data in Fig. 4:22. Find the engine rpm and brake horsepower for most economical cruising at 233-mph true air speed at 10,000 ft standard altitude, and find the corresponding number of miles the airplane will go on 6 lb ($\approx$ 1 gal) of fuel.

Solution.—Following the procedure outlined in Table 4:4,

Step 1. Calculate P_c from equation (4:37), taking the value of C_D from Table 3:1 as $C_D = 0.0243$ for 200 mph at sea level or 233 mph at 10,000 ft. Then, with

$A_d = \pi D^2/4 = \pi \times (10.5^2/4) = 86.5$ sq ft, $S = 551$ sq ft, and $n_e = 2$,

$$\eta P_c = 0.0243 \times \frac{551}{86.5} \times 2 = 0.078$$

Draw this line by interpolation on the cruising-propeller chart on page 458, Fig. A52.

Step 2. As a guide to the range of values of V/nD to assume for the specified trial calculation, a range to the right of the peak of propeller efficiency is suggested; for high V/nD values will give lower values of rpm, and Fig. 4:21 shows that low

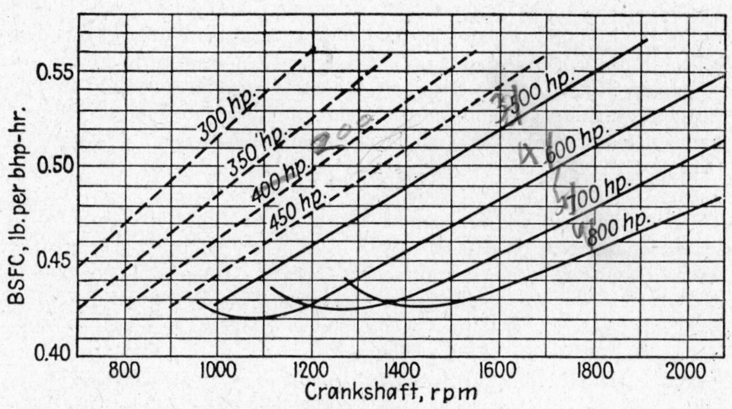

FIG. 4:22.—Assumed fuel-consumption data for engine data on page 214.

rpm favors low fuel consumption. Accordingly, the range of values of V/nD from 1.4 to 2.2 is chosen for tabulation, as in Table 4:7 below, for each value of V/nD assumed, as outlined in Table 4:4.

Step 3. Read η from graph, *e.g.*, at $V/nD = 1.4$ read $\eta = 0.889$.

Step 4. Using $Thp = {}^{854}\!/_{2} = 427$ per engine from Table 3:2, calculate $Bhp = Thp/\eta$ for each V/nD, *e.g.*, at $V/nD = 1.4$, $Bhp = 427/0.889 = 480$. For this condition, $rpm = 60(V/D)/(V/nD) = (88 \times 233/10.5)/1.4 = 1{,}400$.

Step 5. Read C in Fig. 4:21. For the same V/nD as above, read $C = 0.495$ lb per hp-hr.

Step 6. Calculate fuels pounds per mile $= Bhp \times C/v$. For the same V/nD as above, calculate fuels pounds per mile $= 480 \times 0.495/233 = 1.02$ per engine (2.04 lb per mile for two engines).

TABLE 4:7.—CALCULATION OF BEST CRUISING FUEL ECONOMY FOR LOCKHEED LODESTAR AIRPLANE WHEN CRUISING AT 233 MPH TRUE AIR SPEED AT 10,000 FT STANDARD ALTITUDE

$\frac{V}{nD}$	η	Bhp, 1 engine	Rpm	C	Lb per mile, 2 engines
1.4	0.889	480	1,400	0.495	2.04
1.6	0.880	485	1,220	0.467	1.94
1.8	0.870	490	1,080	0.444	1.87
2.0	0.855	500	980	0.425	1.82, optimum cruising
2.2	0.815	523	890	0.425	1.91

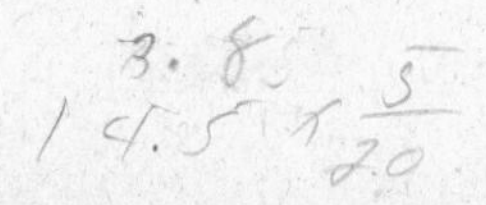

Step 7. Select the lowest pounds per mile in Table 4:7. In this case, the best rpm is 980, corresponding to Bhp = 500 per engine and giving a fuel consumption of 1.82 lb per mile for the airplane (gas mileage = 6/1.82 = 3.30 miles per 6 lb gallon).

4:10. Problems

1. An Ercoupe airplane is to be powered by an engine rated 75 hp at 2,550 rpm. Using the design chart on page 460, Fig. A54, select a propeller diameter and blade angle for maximum efficiency at 120 mph at sea level, and find the propulsive efficiency at this speed.

2. Assume that a two-blade propeller of diameter 6 ft set at $\beta_{0.75R} = 16$ deg is selected for the Ercoupe airplane powered by the engine of characteristics shown in Fig. 4:2.1 (direct drive, no reduction gear) and with the propeller characteristics shown on page 461, Fig. A55. Assume the same airplane speeds as in Prob. 1, Art. 3:10, and calculate the maximum full-throttle thrust horsepower available for level flight at sea level and the engine rpm at each flight speed.

3. Using Fig. A55, calculate the static thrust ($V/nD = 0$) for the airplane-engine-propeller combination in Prob. 2.

4. Assume the Lockheed Constellation airplane to be powered by four engines of characteristics shown on page 464, with a propeller reduction-gear ratio of 0.5. Assume the propeller characteristics shown in Figs. A46 to A50 on pages 454 to 455, and select a propeller diameter for maximum efficiency when delivering the maximum rated power (1,940 hp at 2,550 rpm) at 10,000 ft standard altitude at a true air speed of 375 mph. Find also η_{max}.

5. Assume three-blade propellers of diameter $D = 15$ ft are selected for the Lockheed Constellation airplane powered by the engine of characteristics given on page 464 (propeller-gear ratio 0.5) and with the propeller of characteristics given on pages 454 to 457. Assume the same airplane speeds as in Prob. 2, Art. 3:12, and calculate the maximum full-throttle thrust horsepower from four engines available for level flight at 10,000 ft altitude at 2,550 rpm.

6. For the Lockheed Constellation airplane with engines and propellers as in Prob. 5 and power-required calculations as in Prob. 2, Art. 3:10, use the cruising-propeller chart on page 458, and find the minimum fuel consumed per mile for sea-level cruising at 250 mph. Find also the brake horsepower and rpm for most economical cruising.

4:11. Logarithmic Plotting of Power Available.—If propulsive efficiency is plotted to the same logarithmic base as P/P_1 in Fig. 3:11 or Chart C and 100 per cent propulsive efficiency is taken to correspond to the *brake* horsepower of the engine, the lines of propulsive efficiency are then lines of thrust horsepower and can be traced from a suitably plotted propulsive-efficiency graph onto Chart C. For the plotting to be suitable, the speed scales on Fig. 3:11 or Chart C must correspond to the abscissa on the plot of propulsive efficiency. If a type of power-coefficient analogous to C_{QS} is defined as

$$C_{PS} = \frac{J}{\sqrt[3]{C_P}} = V \sqrt[3]{\frac{\rho D^2}{P}} \qquad (4:40)$$

the resulting coefficient C_{PS} is proportional to V and independent of engine rpm and is related to the V/V_1 scale in Chart C as follows: In equation (3:25), let $C_{D1}S = 2f_e$, where f_e is the flat-plate area equivalent to the minimum drag previously defined; the coefficient C_{PS} at the speed of maximum L/D may be designated

$$C_{PS1} = \sqrt[3]{\frac{n_e D^2}{f_e}} \qquad (4:41)$$

From equations (4:40) and (4:41) it follows that

$$C_{PS} = \frac{V}{V_1}\sqrt[3]{\frac{P}{P_1}}\sqrt[3]{\frac{n_e D^2}{f_e}} \qquad (4:42)$$

Hence, for each value of $f_e/n_e D^3 = (1/C_{PS1})^3$ there can be in Chart C a reference line of slope 3:1 on logarithmic ruled paper with P/P_1 plotted against V/V_1. It is accordingly possible to properly relate the V/V_1 scale on the power-required graph to a propeller-abscissa scale if the propeller abscissa is $J/\sqrt[3]{C_P}$. The graphs in Fig. A50 on page 456 have been replotted in this manner in Fig. A51 on page 457 and may be used to get the results obtained in the example in Art. 4:9 with considerably less calculation as illustrated in the following example.

Example 1.—Power available for Lockheed Lodestar by method of logarithmic plotted propeller chart. Given the airplane, engine, and propeller data as in Examples 1 and 2, Art. 4:9. Find the full-throttle power available as in Example 2 by means of the propeller chart on page 457 and the transparent loose-leaf general power-required chart (Chart C) in the back of the book.

Solution.—1. Calculate $f_e/n_e D^2$. In this case, $n_e = 2$, $D^2 = 10.5^2 = 110$, $f_e = C_{D\,\min}$, $S = 0.0196 \times 551 = 10.8$ sq ft, $f_e/n_e D^2 = 10.8/(2 \times 110) = 0.049$.

2. Calculate V_1 and P_1 from equations (3:22) and (3:25). In this case

$$C_{L_1} = \sqrt{\frac{.0196}{0.049}} = 0.632$$

and, at 10,000 ft, $V = \sqrt{2W/S\rho C_{L_1}} = \sqrt{31.7/(0.738 \times 0.00119 \times 0.632)} = 239$ ft per sec (163 mph), and

$$P_1 = C_{D1}\rho S V_1^3/2 = 0.0196 \times 2 \times 0.738 \times 0.00238 \times 551 \times 239^3/2 = 259{,}000 \text{ ft-lb}$$

per sec (472 hp).

3. Align charts with $f_e/n_e D^2 = 0.049$ on reference line and

$$\frac{P}{P_1} = \frac{(780 \times 2)}{472} = 3.30$$

at 100 per cent efficiency as shown in Fig. 4:23, and trace the line of $C_P = 0.045$ (from page 457) onto Chart C. Then for each value of *mph* in Table 4:5 calculate $V/V_1 = mph/163$, and read P/P_1 from the traced graph. Calculate $Thp = (P/P_1) \times 472$ hp, and list as in Table 4:8 below, which checks Table 4:5 with reasonable accuracy:

TABLE 4:8.—CALCULATION OF FULL-THROTTLE THRUST HORSEPOWER AVAILABLE FOR THE LOCKHEED LODESTAR AIRPLANE AT 10,000 FT ALTITUDE FROM LOGARITHMIC PLOTTED PROPELLER CHART

Mph	$\frac{V}{V_1}$	$\frac{P}{P_1}$	*Thp*
291	1.78	2.91	1,370
233	1.43	2.86	1,350
175.5	1.075	2.73	1,290
145.5	0.891	2.60	1,230
116.4	0.713	2.43	1,140
103.6	0.635	2.30	1,080

The foregoing procedure is possible only if C_P is constant and can be calculated for tracing from Fig. A51, page 457, on Chart C. For airplanes with fixed-pitch propellers the full-throttle engine performance is characterized not by constant C_P but by constant torque. For such an airplane-engine-propeller combination, the full-throttle torque at sea level, $Q_{0\,max}$, may be considered a characteristic constant of the problem, and the propeller-characteristic plotting necessary for this case is a plot of $C_T/C_Q = TD/Q$ *vs.* $C_{QS} = V\sqrt{\rho D^3/Q}$. Such a plot for a typical light airplane propeller is shown facing page 462, plotted to the same logarithmic scales as Chart C. Since lines of constant thrust or drag are 45-deg diagonal lines in Chart C, the C_T/C_Q coordinate facing page 462 is drawn at 45 deg to the C_{QS} coordinate. If Chart C is properly superimposed on Fig. A56, and traced, the lines for constant blade angle in Fig. A56 facing page 462, become lines of thrust horsepower available on Chart C. Proper superposition of the graphs requires that $C_{QS1} = V_1\sqrt{\rho D^3/Q}$ be aligned with $V/V_1 = 1.0$ and that the point $P/P_1 = 1.0$, $V/V_1 = 1.0$ lie on the line $T_1D/Q = D_1D/Q$, where $T_1 = D_1$ = minimum drag of the airplane in level flight if the airplane is approximately level. This procedure is illustrated in Example 2.

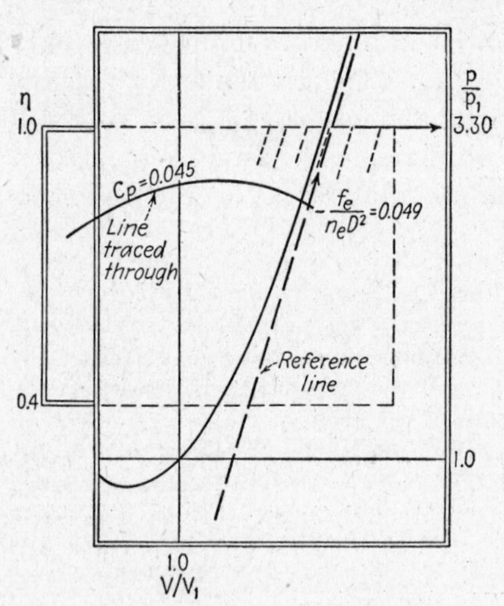

FIG. 4:23.—Superposition of charts for solution of Example 1.

Example 2.—Power available for Piper Cub with fixed-pitch propeller by method of logarithmic plotted propeller chart. Given the same airplane, engine, and propeller data as in Example 3, Art. 4:9. Find the full-throttle thrust horsepower available at sea level for $\beta_{0.75R}$ = 18 deg at the same speeds as in Example 3, Art. 4:9.

Solution.—1. Calculate first C_{L1}, V_1, D_1, and P_1, from equations (3:21) to (3:25) as follows:

$$C_{L1} = \sqrt{\frac{a}{b}} = \sqrt{\frac{0.046}{0.060}} = 0.818$$

$$C_{D1} = 2a = 2 \times 0.046 = 0.092$$

$$V_1 = \sqrt{\frac{2W}{S\rho C_{L1}}} =$$

$$\sqrt{2 \times \frac{1,400}{180} \times 0.00238 \times 0.818} = 89.1 \text{ ft per sec (60.9 mph)}$$

$$D_1 = \frac{C_{D1}W}{C_{L1}} = 0.092 \times \frac{1,400}{0.818} = 157.4$$

$$P_1 = \frac{D_1V_1}{550} = 157.4 \times \frac{89.1}{550} = 25.5 \text{ hp}$$

2. Calculate Q, C_{QS1} from equation (4:33), using $V = V_1$ and $T_1D/Q = D_1D/Q$ as follows:

$$Q = \frac{120 \times 5,250}{2,600} = 242 \text{ lb-ft}$$

$$\sqrt{\frac{\rho D^3}{Q}} = \frac{1}{\sqrt{420 \times 242/6.5^3}} = \frac{1}{19.2}$$

$$C_{QS1} = \frac{V_1}{19.2} = \frac{89.1}{19.2} = 4.65$$

$$\frac{D_1D}{Q} = \frac{T_1D}{Q} = \frac{157.4 \times 6.5}{242} = 4.23$$

3. Align charts as shown in Fig. 4:24 with the point ($P/P_1 = 1$, $V/V_1 = 1$) at the intersection of the calculated values of C_{QS1} and D_1D/Q, and trace the 18-deg blade-angle line from Fig. A56, facing page 462, on Chart C. For the same assumed speeds as in Table 4:6, calculate V/V_1, and read P/P_1 from the traced line. Then calculate $Thp = (P/P_1) \times 25.5$. The resulting values are tabulated in Table 4:9 and are seen to check Table 4:7 with reasonable accuracy. The actual tracing of lines on Chart C from Figs. A50 and A56 for Examples 1 and 2 above are shown in Fig. 4:25.

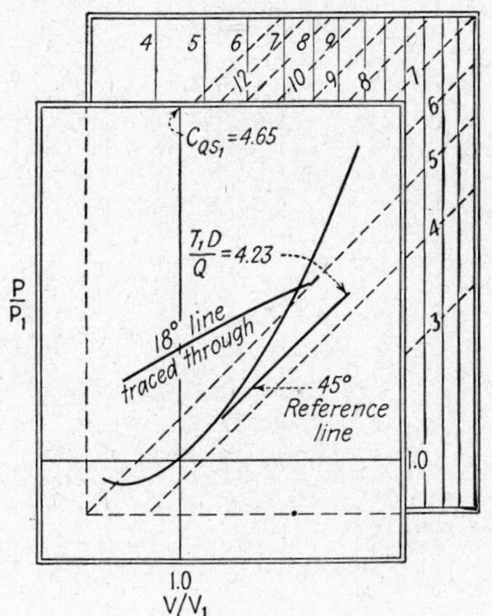

FIG. 4:24.—Superposition of charts for solution of Example 2.

TABLE 4:9.—CALCULATION OF FULL-THROTTLE THRUST HORSEPOWER AVAILABLE AT SEA LEVEL FOR 120-HP PIPER CUB AIRPLANE WITH FIXED-PITCH PROPELLER BY USE OF LOGARITHMIC PLOTTED PROPELLER CHART

Mph	$\frac{V}{V_1}$	$\frac{P}{P_1}$	*Thp*
120	1.97	2.90	74.0
100	1.64	2.63	67.0
80	1.31	2.31	58.9
70	1.15	2.14	54.5
60	0.985	1.92	48.9
50	0.820	1.67	42.5

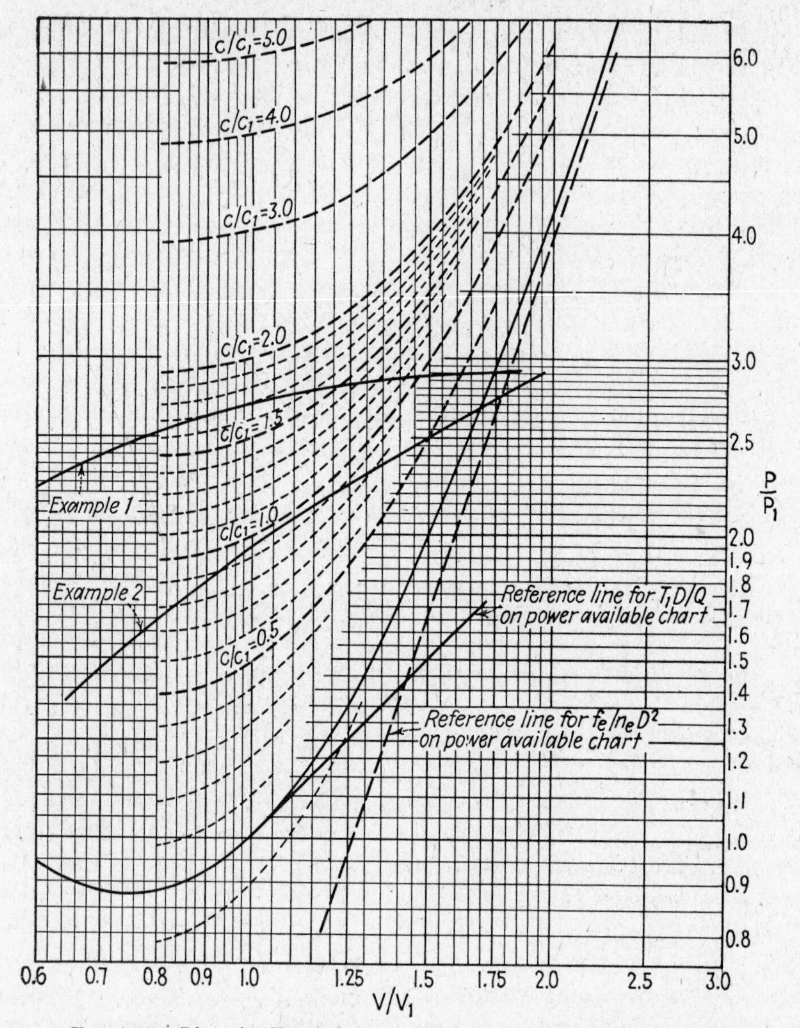

FIG. 4:25.—Lines for Examples 1 and 2, Art. 4:11, traced on Chart C.

4:12. Problems

1. For an Ercoupe airplane powered by an engine rated 75 hp at 2,550 rpm with propeller characteristics as in Fig. A56, plot on Chart C, by tracing from Fig. A56, a graph of P/P_1 *vs.* V/V_1, and check the answers to Prob. 2, Art. 4:10.

2. For the Constellation airplane, check the answers to Prob. 5, Art. 4:10, by tracing the proper propeller-efficiency graph from Fig. A51, page 457 onto Chart C when the two graphs are properly aligned as described in Art. 4:11.

4:13. Correction Factors for Propeller Characteristics.—Wind-tunnel tests on propellers are seldom available for the exact arrangement contemplated in a proposed new design. In making performance estimates it is accordingly necessary to use such test data as are available and make corrections for the difference between the test conditions and the proposed conditions. The principal items for which corrections are made are (1) number of blades, (2) blade width and planform, (3) blade thickness ratio, (4) blade airfoil section, (5) body interference, between propeller and nacelle or fuselage, and (6) tip speed (compressibility correction due to high Mach number at the blade tips). Each of these items has an appreciable, though sometimes minor, effect on the optimum diameter, on the efficiency, and for fixed-pitch propellers on the blade-angle setting necessary to absorb a given power at a given rpm. These effects are discussed below, and quantitative correction factors on efficiency from Thomas, Caldwell, and Rhines[1] are presented in graphical form for each item.

a. Number of Blades.—In 1929, Weick[2] summarized the results of a large number of NACA tests on propellers in the following statement:

> Two-blade propellers are used in all ordinary cases, for the fewer the blades the lighter, cheaper, simpler, and more efficient will be the propeller; and *two* is the smallest number of blades with which proper balance of mass and air forces can be obtained. . . . Vibrations are however set up in two-bladed propellers when the airplane is turning due to the varying gyroscopic moment of the two-bladed arrangement and, when the airplane is sideslipping, due to the uneven air loading. . . . Vibration difficulties considered it is usually desirable to have three or more blades in large-geared propellers.

This statement is still excellent. It may have inspired attempts to develop a one-bladed propeller, using a blade-stump counterweight for mass balance and a rubber-mounted pivot to permit the centrifugal couple to balance the air forces and give simultaneous adjustment of pitch. This development is usually not considered successful, for the drag of the blade-stump balance more than offsets the gain in efficiency. Moreover, as airplane designs have developed to larger forward speeds and slower rotative speeds, the effect of number of blades on efficiency has become small to negligible, so that at present (1947), while three- and four-blade designs predominate because of simplicity and smoothness, five, six, and even ten blades have been selected after careful study on several designs (see Fig. I:13*b*, page 35, for photograph of five-blade installation). A general procedure for correcting the results of tests on propellers of one number of blades, so that they will apply for performance calculations on a propeller of a different number of blades, is not available. Reasonably accurate corrections for most

[1] *J. Roy. Aeronaut. Soc.*, January, 1938, pp. 1–86.
[2] WEICK, F. E., "Aircraft Propeller Design," p. 252.

other factors are available, but it is necessary to start with propeller-test results of the desired number of blades. Full-scale two-blade and three-blade propeller data from NACA reports are given in Appendix 6.

b. Blade Width and Planform.—The effects of blade width and blade-width distribution along the rad us are usually properly and completely accounted for in terms of the *activity factor*, defined and calculated in Art. 4:5. According to data in the paper of Thomas, Caldwell, and Rhines,[1] the effect of activity factor on the line of J *vs.* C_s for "maximum efficiency for a given C_s" (the broken line on the design charts of Figs. A37 to A46, pages 449 to 454) is given for three-blade propellers by the empirical equations

$$J_m = KC_s^{5/4} \tag{4:43}$$

$$K = 0.415 + \frac{\text{A.F.}}{1{,}200} \tag{4:44}$$

in which J_m is the value of V/nD for maximum η for a given C_s. Equations (4:43) and (4:44) permit solving for the diameter of a "best-performance" three-blade propeller in terms of the design airplane speed V_0, the rated engine power and rpm P_0 and n_0, and the activity factor of a propeller blade. The effect of increasing activity factor is to decrease efficiency, as shown in Fig. 4:26; but there is a compensating gain in maximum static thrust, and there may be a reduced compressibility loss at the tips because of the smaller diameter associated with the higher activity factor.

c. Blade Thickness Ratio.—The blade-section thickness ratio at $0.75R$ is usually taken as a typical single measure of the propeller-blade thickness ratio. Metal propeller blades are sometimes made as thin as 6 per cent, although 7.5 or 9 per cent is a more typical value. Wooden blades are rarely less than 12 per cent thick, and 15 per cent is a more common value. The effect of blade thickness on efficiency is shown in Fig. 4:27, the efficiency of a 7.5 per cent thick propeller being used as a reference value. Note that the efficiency loss due to thick blades is low for high values of J_m.

d. Blade Airfoil Section.—The blade-section families most commonly used in propellers are the Clark Y (ordinates on page 405) and the RAF6. Typical propeller data using these sections are given on pages 448 to 455. The RAF6 section has a slightly larger value of α_{l0}; thus, the geometric blade-angle settings are different for the same aerodynamic characteristics. The RAF6 family also has a slightly higher $C_{L\,\max}$, and the RAF6 propellers have a correspondingly higher

[1] *Op. cit.*

$C_{T\,max}$. For a given thickness ratio, the maximum propulsive efficiencies are about the same for all good airfoil sections. Most current propeller designs operate on the verge of tip-speed losses; many current designs, therefore, use high-speed sections (*e.g.*, those listed in Table XIX on page 392) for the outer 20 per cent of the blades. No systematic correction factors for blade airfoil section are available; it is best to use data based on the proper airfoil section, but if such data

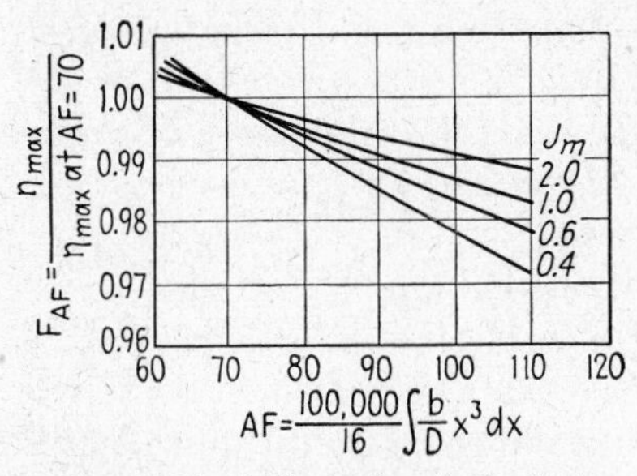

FIG. 4:26.—Effect of activity factor on maximum propulsive efficiency. (*From J. Roy. Aeronaut. Soc.*, *January*, 1938.)

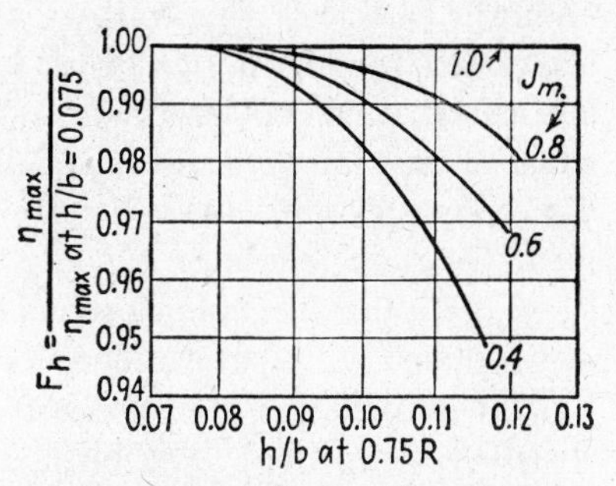

FIG. 4:27.—Effect of blade-thickness ratio on maximum propulsive efficiency. (*From J. Roy. Aeronaut. Soc.*, *January*, 1938.)

are not available the effects of blade section may be safely neglected except for fixed-pitch propellers, where the blade-angle setting will be appreciably lower for an RAF6 section than for a Clark Y section.

e. Body Interference.—A large nacelle or fuselage in front of or behind a propeller has a serious adverse effect on the propulsive efficiency. This is partly because the propulsive efficiency, as defined, includes the effect of the drag added by the slip stream. Most propeller test data (*e.g.*, Figs. A37 to A49, pages 448 to 455) are obtained with propeller mounted in front of a nacelle; many have been obtained with an air-cooled engine nacelle of diameter equal to 42 per cent

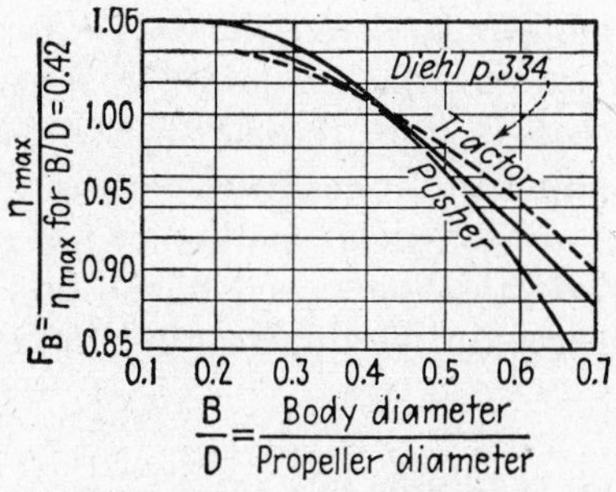

FIG. 4:28.—Effect of body diameter on maximum propulsive efficiency. (*From J. Roy. Aeronaut. Soc.*, *January*, 1938.)

of the propeller diameter. A propulsive-efficiency correction factor for other ratios of nacelle diameter to propeller diameter is shown in Fig. 4:28, which also shows in broken lines for comparison the body-size correction factors reported by Diehl.[1] Note that for a

[1] DIEHL, W. S., "Engineering Aerodynamics," p. 334.

given size of nacelle (measured about one propeller diameter from the plane of rotation of the blade center lines) the pusher propeller appears inferior to the tractor, but this result may be misleading as to the relative merits of pushers and tractors, for pusher installations can conveniently be built with a long extension shaft and the body interference thus made negligible. A proper comparison is between a pusher of $B/D = 0.1$ and a tractor of $B/D = 0.3$ to 0.4, and on this basis the pusher is seen to have several per cent higher efficiency. At least one large new design in 1944 was planned for six pusher propellers absorbing over 3,000 hp each. This arrangement was selected on the basis of maximum cruising efficiency, but the arrangement has the disadvantage that a part-throttle slip stream cannot be used to augment $C_{L\,\max}$ for landing.

f. Tip Speed.—Many propellers operate at speeds beyond the critical (defined as v_{tip} when some local v exceeds the speed of sound) for the level high-speed condition; some even operate at supercritical speeds for cruising. The local Mach number of the blade tips may reach 1.2 without excessive shock-wave losses, as seen in Fig. 2:43 (page 155). For estimating efficiency losses at supercritical speeds it is convenient to approximate the curve of Fig. 2:43 by two straight lines, neglecting losses below $M_1 = 1.2$ and decreasing the efficiency lineally with M_1 as M_1 exceeds 1.2. A good approximation to Fig. 2:43 is obtained if the efficiency is assumed reduced 3 per cent for each 10 per cent increase in M_1. A procedure equivalent to this is used in commercial aerodynamics work at the Boeing Aircraft Company. The local Mach number M_1, however, is not obtainable directly from the helical tip speed since it depends on the mean blade thickness and mean lift coefficient of the affected region of the blade.

A convenient method of taking account of altitude (temperature), blade thickness, and blade angle of attack is to calculate first the helical tip speed from Fig. 4:29 and the equation

$$\text{HTS} = \pi n D \sec \phi_t \qquad (4:45)$$

and then calculate an *effective helical tip speed* (EHTS) from

$$\text{EHTS} = \text{HTS} \times f_c \times f_h \times f_\alpha \qquad (4:46)$$

reading f_c, f_h, and f_α from Figs. 4:30, 4:31, and 4:32, respectively. Figure 4:30 is the usual correction for the effect of temperature on the speed of sound; Fig. 4:31 is consistent with the fundamental flow-pattern equation around elliptic cylinders (Fig. 1:49) for a high-speed tip section and involves an empirical correction factor for Clark Y or RAF6 section; Fig. 4:32 takes account of the increased flow velocity with increased angle of attack and lift at the blade tips, for the high-speed condition α is usually small and the f_α correction can often be neglected.

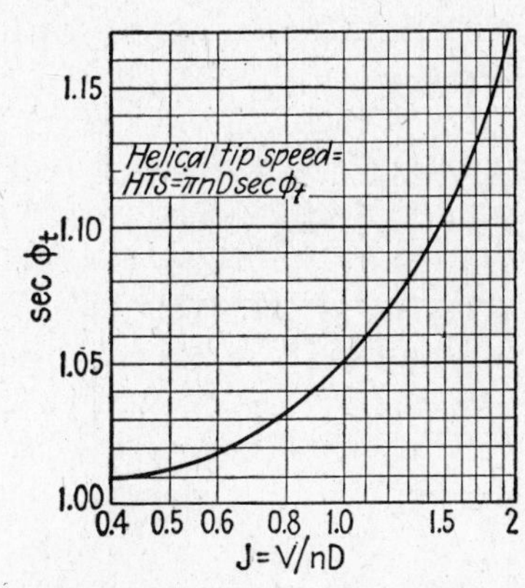

FIG. 4:29.—Graph for calculating helical tip speed (HTS) from rotative tip speed πnD.

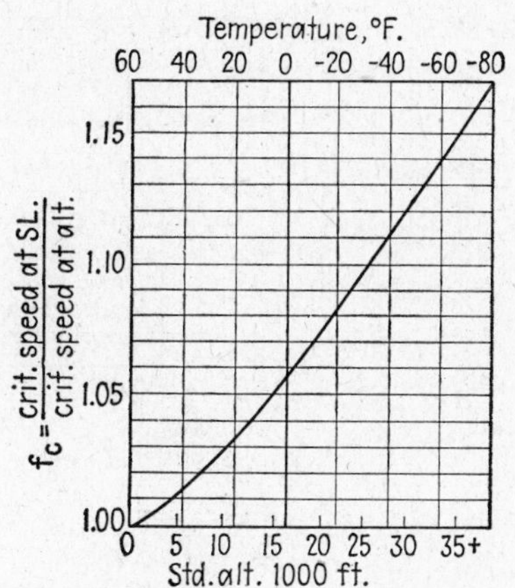

FIG. 4:30.—Temperature factor in effective helical tip speed (EHTS).

The corrected efficiency can be read on Fig. 4:33 as a function of effective helical tip speed. Figure 4:33 is a modification of Fig. 2:43

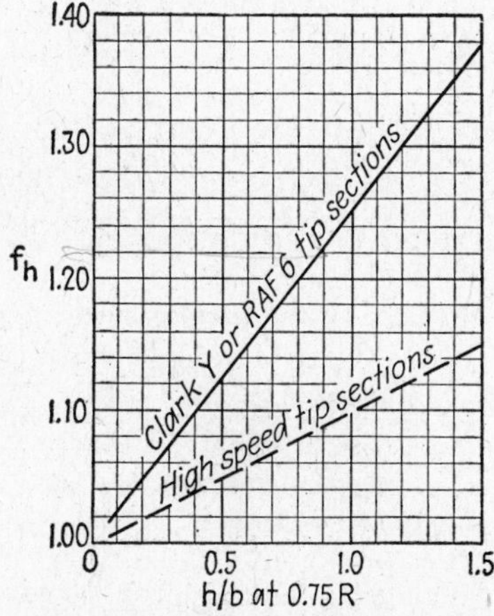

FIG. 4:31.—Thickness factor in effective helical tip speed (EHTS). (*Solid portion of line from J. Roy. Aeronaut. Soc., January,* 1938, *adapted to modified procedure.*)

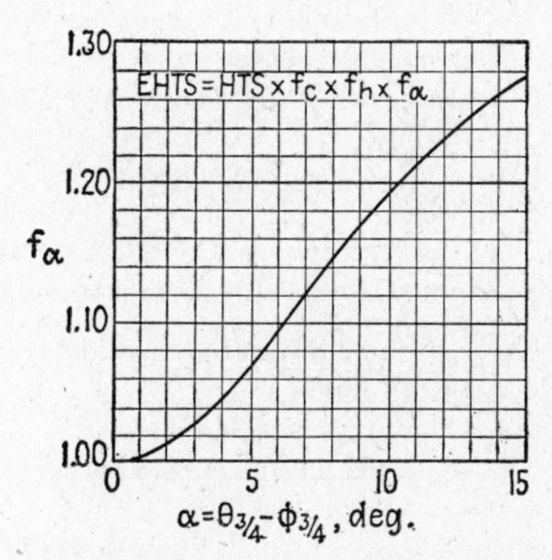

FIG. 4:32.—Angle-of-attack factor in effective helical tip speed (EHTS). (*From J. Roy. Aeronaut. Soc., January,* 1938.)

and assumes a 3 per cent loss of efficiency for a 10 per cent excess of effective helical tip speed over $M_1 = 1.00$ (Boeing minimum) to $M_1 = 1.1$ (probable upper limit). The shaded area represents the present limits of uncertainty of the data. Tip-speed corrections from other sources (in which the effect of α was not considered) are shown in

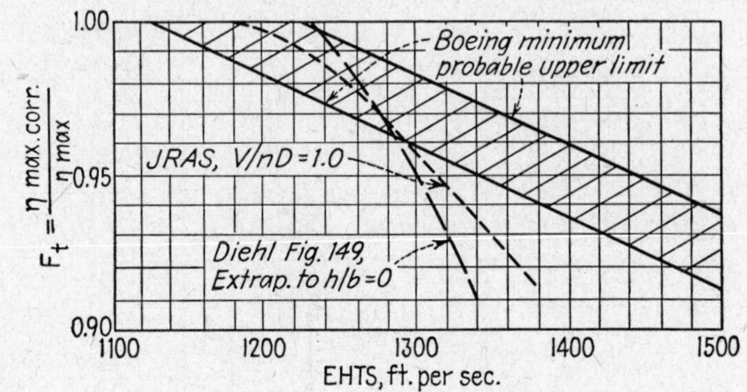

FIG. 4:33.—Efficiency-correction factor for tip speed.

broken lines. The use of this procedure is illustrated by the following example:

Example.—Given a 16-ft-diameter propeller rotating at 1,200 rpm on an airplane traveling 350 mph at 15,000 ft standard altitude. The chart efficiency of the propeller is $\eta_{\max} = 0.88$, and the blade thickness at 0.75R is 7.5 per cent. Neglect f_α. Find the efficiency corrected for tip-speed effect, using the probable upper limit in Fig. 4:33.

Solution

1. Calculate $J = \frac{V}{nD} = \frac{88 \times 350}{1{,}200 \times 16} = 1.60.$
2. Read in Fig. 4:29, sec $\phi_t = 1.12$.
3. Calculate HTS $= \pi n D \sec \phi_t = \pi \times 20 \times 16 \times 1.12 = 1{,}120$ ft per sec.
4. In Fig. 4:30, read $f_c = 1.05$ for 15,000 ft.
5. In Fig. 4:31, read $f_h = 1.19$ for $h/b = 0.075$.
6. Neglecting f_α, calculate EHTS $= 1{,}120 \times 1.05 \times 1.19 = 1{,}400$ ft per sec.
7. Read in Fig. 4:33 on probable-upper-limit line $F_t = 0.96$.
8. Calculate $\eta_{\max\ \text{corr}} = 0.96 \times 0.88 = 0.845$. This is the answer called for.

Summarizing the foregoing corrections,

$$\eta_{\text{corr}} = \eta_{\text{chart}}\, F_{AF} \times F_h \times F_B \times F_t \tag{4:46.1}$$

4:14. Problems

1. The propeller characteristics in Fig. A50 on page 456 are for a propeller of A.F. = 75, blade thickness at $0.75R$ of 9 per cent, and body diameter of 40 per cent of the propeller diameter. At $V/nD = J = 1.5$ and $C_p = 0.10$, the chart efficiency is $\eta_{\max} = 0.89$. Using Figs. 4:26 to 4:28, estimate the maximum efficiency for a similar propeller installation with the following different conditions: A.F. = 90, $h/b = 0.075$, $B/D = 45$ per cent.

2. A 12-ft-diameter propeller rotating at 1,500 rpm drives an airplane 400 mph at 20,000 ft standard altitude. The chart efficiency of the propeller for this condition is $\eta_{\max} = 0.89$; the blade thickness at $0.75R$ is 9 per cent, and a high-critical-speed blade section is used for the outer 20 per cent of the blade. Neglecting f_α, find $\eta_{\max}$ corrected for tip-speed effect, using the probable-upper-limit correction line in Fig. 4:33.

4:15. Detail-design Considerations.—Propeller blades are usually constructed of wood, dural, or steel in the manner shown in Fig. 4:34. The hollow-steel construction is usually lighter for propeller diameters over 8 ft, as shown in Fig. 4:35. Over 80 per cent of the propellers reported by McCoy[1] were within 10 per cent of the lines drawn on Fig. 4:35. Complete propellers weigh 1.6 to 2 times the total weight

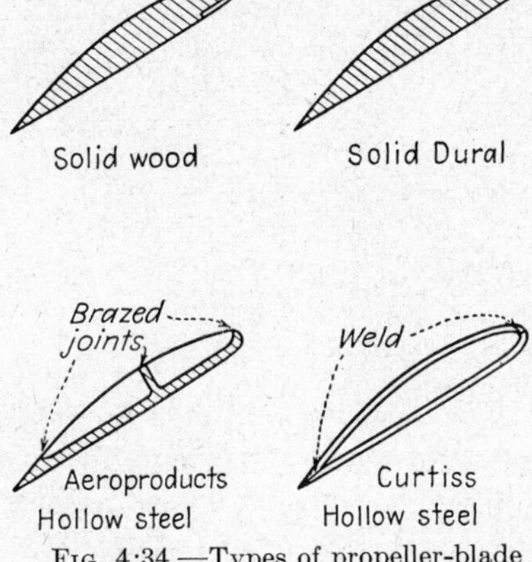

FIG. 4:34.—Types of propeller-blade construction. (*From Nelson, "Aircraft Propeller Principles."*)

FIG. 4:35.—Comparison of weights of dural and hollow-steel blades. (*From McCoy, J. Aeronaut. Sci., July,* 1944.)

of the blades depending on the material and number of blades, as shown in Table 4:6. By using Fig. 4:35 and Table 4:10 the total weight of a complete propeller can be estimated within 10 per cent. For example, note in Fig. 4:35 that a 10-ft-diameter dural propeller blade weighs 47 lb. Three such blades would weigh 141 lb, and a complete three-blade dural propeller of 10 ft diameter would, according to Table 4:10, weigh 1.78 times this amount, or 250 lb.

TABLE 4:10.—AVERAGE RATIOS OF TOTAL PROPELLER WEIGHT TO TOTAL BLADE WEIGHT*

	Weight Ratio
Hollow-steel propellers:	
Six-blade dual rotation	2.0
Four-blade dual rotation	1.75
Three-blade dual rotation	1.85
Dural propellers:	
Four-blade dual rotation	1.61
Three-blade dual rotation	1.78
Two-blade dual rotation	1.92

* From McCoy, *J. Aeronaut. Sci.*, July, 1944.

[1] McCOY, H. M., *J. Aeronaut. Sci.*, July, 1944.

Propeller blades and hubs must be carefully analyzed for the combination of bending and tensile stresses set up by the thrust and centrifugal forces, as shown in Fig. 4:36. If the blade or hub fails, it is thrown out with enormous energy. In such an event, the unbalance of the remaining blades usually tears the engine out of the airplane; such a disaster was the initial cause of the destruction, chiefly by fire, of the first experimental Martin Mars flying boat. The centrifugal and thrust forces can be made partly to offset each other by having a small amount of forward tilt in the blade shown in Fig. 4:36, the usual amount of tilt being approximately ½ deg. The

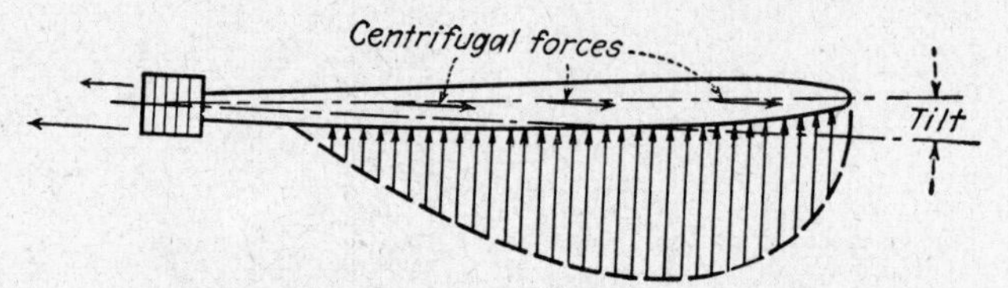

FIG. 4:36.—Forces acting on propeller blade.

deflection of the propeller blades under load, which sometimes amounts to 2 or 3 in. at the tips for large propellers under maximum thrust, gives an effective additional tilt that must be considered in making an accurate stress analysis. A systematic procedure for doing this is outlined by Nelson.[1] Additional gyroscopic bending stresses are

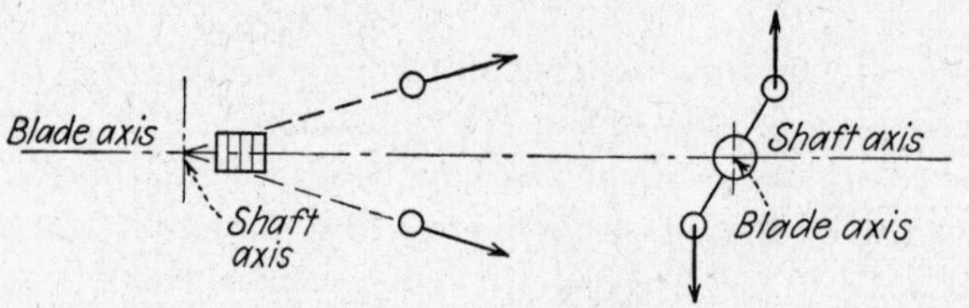

FIG. 4:37.—Sketch showing source of centrifugal couple tending to reduce pitch of controllable blades.

added to the propeller blade when the airplane has a rapid rate of pitch or yaw; the procedure for calculating the gyroscopic bending stresses is also outlined by Nelson.

A rotating propeller blade that is free to turn about the blade axis is acted on by a powerful centrifugal couple tending to set the blade at zero pitch. The cause of the centrifugal couple is illustrated in Fig. 4:37 in which the blade is assumed to be represented by its dynamic equivalent of two weights displaced slightly from the blade axis. Inspection of Fig. 4:37 shows that the centrifugal forces tend to rotate the blade about its own axis in such a way as to reduce the

[1] NELSON, W. C., "Aircraft Propeller Principles," John Wiley & Sons, Inc., New York, 1944.

pitch. In some propellers the centrifugal couple is balanced out by a pair of weights located in a plane perpendicular to the mean plane of the blade, but in most controllable-pitch propellers this centrifugal couple represents simply an additional load to be taken by the pitch-changing mechanism. The pitch-changing mechanism, which may

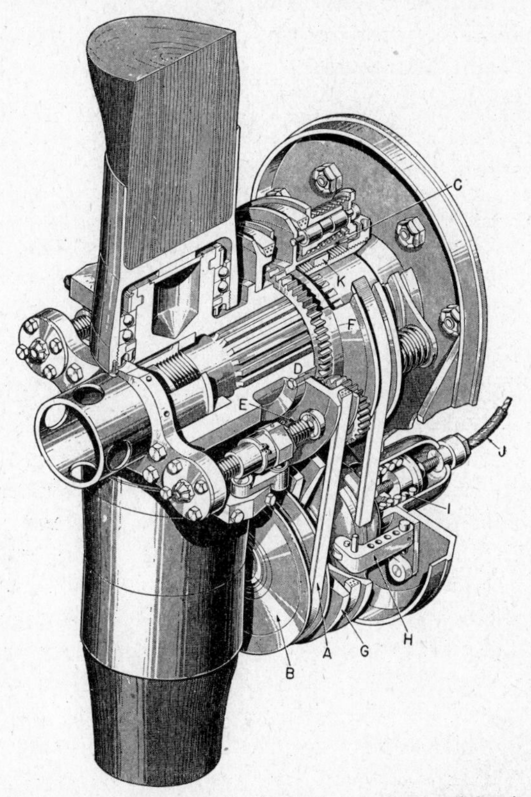

FIG. 4:38.—Variable-ratio V-belt controllable-pitch propeller for light airplane operating on the principle of the Reeves pulley. (*Courtesy Aviation.*)

be either mechanical (as in Fig. 4:38), electrical (as in Fig. I:13*d*, page 37), or hydraulic, not only must overcome the friction of the blade bearings but also must counteract the centrifugal couple when the pitch is being increased and the aerodynamic couple due to the pitching moment on the blade, which usually acts in the same direction as the centrifugal couple. The efficiency of the pitch-changing mechanism is usually made somewhat less than 50 per cent to make it irreversible. For propellers that do not have to be feathered or to be reversed in pitch (for use as aerodynamic brakes) a rate of pitch change of 5 or 6 deg per sec has been found satisfactory, but rates of pitch change as high as 45 deg per sec are reported by McCoy[1] to be necessary for quick feathering or for aerodynamic braking by means of reverse pitch. Quick feathering is necessary to avoid engine damage in case of engine failure in flight; aerodynamic braking by means of reverse pitch is being incorporated in many designs because aerodynamic braking has been found to be considerably more effective than braking by means of wheel brakes. Sample computations of pitch-change power are illustrated by the following example.

Example.[2]—Given a three-blade propeller for which each blade weighs 60 lb and has a center of gravity 25.9 in. from the shaft axis. The centrifugal force (C.F.) per blade is 105,800 lb, and the friction-torque coefficient is 0.014 in. ($= Q_f/\text{C.F.}$, where Q_f = friction torque in in.-lb). The centrifugal torque Q_c per blade is 7,000 in.-lb maximum, and the rate of pitch change is 5 deg per sec. Neglecting the aerodynamic torque and assuming 50 per cent efficiency of the pitch-changing mechanism, find the power required to change the pitch.

Solution.—Calculate $Q_f = 105{,}800 \times 0.014 = 1{,}480$ in.-lb.

$$Q = Q_c + Q_f = 7{,}000 + 1{,}480 = 8{,}480$$

Calculate power required

$$\frac{2\pi \times 5/360 \times 3 \times 8{,}480}{550 \times 12 \times 0.50} = 0.672 \text{ hp}$$

On airplanes with three or more propellers it is practically impossible for the pilot to synchronize the propeller governors of constant-rpm propellers manually; therefore, some means of automatic synchronization must be provided. This is usually accomplished by means of synchronous motors in the propeller-governing circuit for electrically operated propellers. Most propeller governors are not being made "anticipatory" in that they include an accelerometer element that decreases the governor speed as the desired speed is approached and makes for "dead-beat" governing and avoidance of hunting.

Most propellers are also equipped with slinger-rings for spraying the blades with antifreeze liquid to minimize the detrimental effects of ice formation on the blades. Rubber deicers, such as sometimes have been used on the leading edges of wings, having been found unsatisfactory on propeller blades.

4:16. Problems

1. Using Fig. 4:35 and Table 4:10, estimate the total weight of a six-blade dual-rotation hollow-steel propeller 14 ft in diameter.

2. A four-blade hollow-steel propeller blade of 12 ft diameter weighs 65 lb and has a center of gravity 40 per cent of the radius from the shaft axis. It is acted on

[1] *Op. cit.*

[2] From Nelson, *op. cit.*

by a centrifugal force of 150,000 lb and has a maximum centrifugal blade torque of 10,000 in.-lb. Using a blade-friction-torque coefficient of 0.014 in., pitch-changing-mechanism efficiency of 50 per cent, and a rate of pitch change of 45 deg per sec, calculate the maximum power required to change the pitch.

4:17. Static Thrust; Propellers for Slow Vehicles.—The static thrust of an airplane propeller is of particular importance in the calculation of the take-off of an airplane. Air propellers are also occasionally used for the propulsion of slow vehicles such as boats, sleds, and bicycles. Since such propellers operate at a very small value of V/nD compared with airplanes, they may usually be designed primarily from static-thrust considerations.

For a constant-rpm propeller, the static thrust can be obtained by reading at $V/nD = 0$, on the usual graphs of propeller characteristics or those on pages 448 to 455, $\beta_{0.75R}$ and C_T for the specified C_P. For propellers with fixed blade angles, the static thrust can be obtained from a graph such as Fig. A55 by reading $C_T/CQ = TD/Q$ at $C_{QS} = 0$. Graphs of C_T, C_T/C_P $(= C_T/2\pi C)$ are commonly plotted against blade angle to represent the static-thrust characteristics of fixed-pitch propellers over a wide range of blade angles, as in Fig. A58 on page 463, which represents the static-thrust characteristics of a particular two-blade propeller. Similar static-thrust characteristics for three-blade propellers are shown in Fig. 4:39.

If, as in the design of a slow vehicle, it is desired to get the maximum thrust for a given amount of horsepower, a proper propeller-blade angle may be selected from the following considerations:

For a specified tip speed, maximum T/Bhp requires maximum

$$\frac{C_T}{C_P} = \frac{\pi n D}{1{,}730}\,\frac{T}{Bhp} \qquad (4{:}46.2)$$

For a specified rpm, maximum T/Bhp requires maximum

$$\frac{C_T^{5/4}}{C_P} = \frac{T^{5/4}n^3}{\rho^{1/4}n^{5/2}P} = \frac{T}{P}\sqrt{\frac{Tn^2}{\rho}} \qquad (4{:}47)$$

For a specified diameter, maximum T/Bhp requires maximum

$$\frac{C_T^{3/2}}{C_P} = \frac{T^{3/2}}{PD\rho^{1/2}} = \frac{T/Bhp\,\sqrt{T/\pi R^2}}{26.8\,\sqrt{\sigma}} \qquad (4{:}48)$$

Equation (4:48) is sometimes called "figure of merit" in the design of helicopters, where it is also desired to have maximum thrust for a given power. Values of C_T/C_P, $C^{5/4}/C_P$, and $C^{3/2}/C_P$ are plotted against blade angle for a typical three-blade propeller on Fig. 4:39. Note that for this propeller, which has a Clark Y family of sections, the optimum blade angle for maximum T/Bhp is $2\frac{1}{2}$, $7\frac{1}{2}$, or 10 deg depending on whether the *rpm* or *diameter* or tip speed is assumed specified in the design. When the optimum blade angle has been selected, C_P and C_T can be read from Fig. 4:39 (or from a similar graph experi-

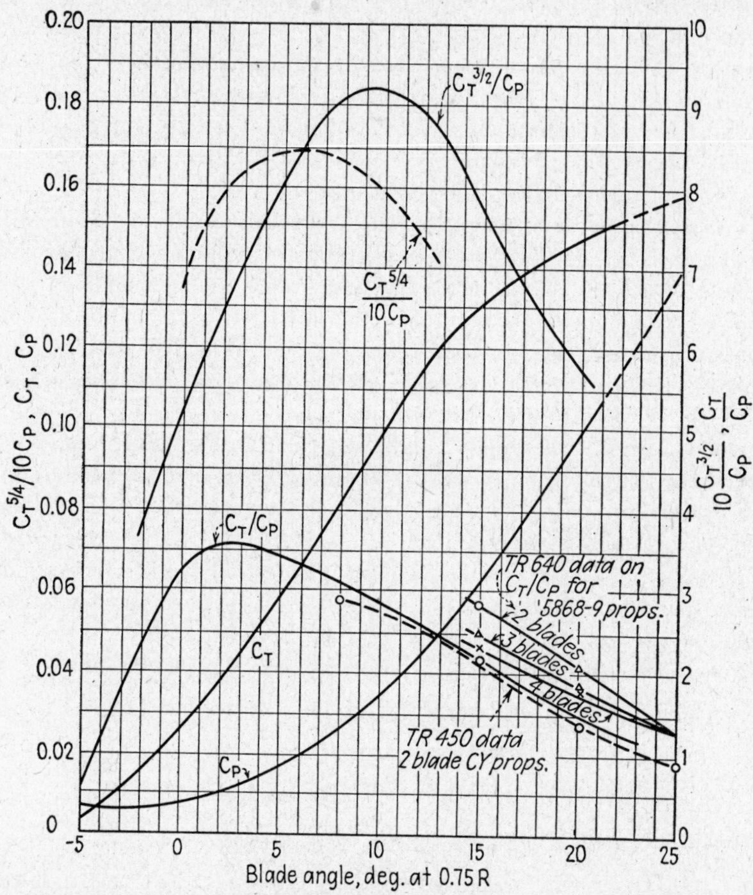

FIG. 4:39.—Static-thrust characteristics of NACA 5868-9 three-blade propeller; helicopter design factors shown also.

mentally determined for a propeller of the desired activity factor, blade thickness, blade section profile, and number of blades). The known values of C_P and C_T can be used to calculate the unknown factors in the design. This procedure is illustrated by the following example:

Example.—Given a bicycle, to be propelled by an air-cooled outboard motorboat engine rated 5 hp at 4,000 rpm. (*a*) For a direct drive at 4,000 rpm, find the maximum thrust and corresponding propeller diameter. (*b*) For a 24-in.-diameter propeller with a belt drive of ratio to be determined, find the maximum thrust and the corresponding rpm. (*c*) For drives at constant tip speeds of 900, 700, 500, 300, and 100 ft per sec, find the maximum thrust and corresponding diameter and rpm.

Solution.—a. For this propeller it may be noted that $C_T^{5/4}/C_P = 1.67$ at $\beta_{0.75R} = 7.5$ deg and $C_P = 0.025$. For the example above, using $Bhp = 5$ and $rpm = 4{,}000$, use $C_P = 0.025$ to calculate the optimum diameter of a three-blade propeller thus:

$$C_P = 0.025 = \frac{(0.5 \times Bhp)/1{,}000}{(rpm/1{,}000)^3(D/10)^5} = \frac{2.5/1{,}000}{64 \times (D/10)^5}$$

$$\frac{D}{10} = \sqrt[5]{\frac{0.0025}{0.025 \times 64}} \qquad D = \frac{10}{\sqrt[5]{640}} = \frac{10}{3.64} = 2.75 \text{ ft} = 33.3 \text{ in.}$$

and, from equation (4:47),

$$T_0^{5/4} = \frac{C_T^{5/4}}{C_P}\frac{P\rho^{1/4}}{\sqrt{n}} = 1.67\,\frac{5 \times 550 \times \sqrt[4]{0.00238}}{\sqrt{66.7}} = \frac{1.27 \times 2{,}750 \times 0.22}{8.16} = 124$$

or $T_0 = 47.5$ lb.

b. Note that $C_T^{3/2}C_{P\,\max} = 0.92$ at $\beta_{0.75R} = 10$ deg. For the example above, using $Bhp = 5$ and $D = 2$ ft, use $C_P = 0.034$ (read at $\beta_{0.75R} = 10$ deg) to calculate the necessary *rpm* thus:

$$C_P = 0.034 = \frac{0.5}{\sigma}\frac{Bhp/1{,}000}{(rpm/1{,}000)^3(D/10)^5} = \frac{(2.5/1{,}000) \times 10^5}{(rpm/1{,}000)^3 \times 32}$$

$$\frac{Rpm}{1{,}000} = \left(\frac{250}{32 \times 0.034}\right)^{1/3} = \sqrt[3]{230} = 6.11 \qquad Rpm = 6{,}110$$

To calculate thrust, read $C_T = 0.098$ in Fig. 4:39, and calculate

$$T_0 = 0.098 \times 0.00238 \times \left(\frac{6{,}110}{60}\right)^2 \times 2^4 = 38.8 \text{ lb}$$

c. For $C_T/C_P = \max = 3.55$, and $\beta_{0.75R} = 2.5$ deg, read $C_T = 0.042$ and $C_P = 0.012$. For the specified *Bhp*, calculate $T = (5 \times 1{,}730 \times 3.55)/\pi nD$ thus:

πnD =	900	700	500	300	100
T =	34.2	44.0	61.5	102	307

Solve for the diameter from the definition of C_P that gives at sea level

$$D^2 = \frac{550\pi^3\,Bhp}{C_P(\pi nD)^3}\frac{2{,}990{,}000{,}000}{(\pi nD)^3}$$

or

$$D = \frac{54{,}500}{(\pi nD)^{3/2}} \qquad \text{and} \qquad rpm = \frac{60(\pi nD)}{\pi D}$$

which gives

πnD =	900	700	500	300	100
$\frac{(\pi nD)^{3/2}}{1{,}000}$ =	27	18.5	12.2	5.2	1.0
D ft =	2.02	2.95	4.47	7.65	54.5
Rpm =	8500	4530	2140	750	35

These answers permit a wide choice of diameter and rpm based on convenience, but it should be noted that they do not give the maximum thrust for a given *diameter* or *rpm;* these items have been found in parts *a* and *b*. These are the answers called for.

4:18. Problems

1. Using the above method and data, find $\beta_{0.75R}$ for a 2-ft-diameter nine-blade bicycle propeller for direct drive at 4,000 rpm, using an 8-hp Target model engine, and find the thrust of the propeller.

2. Using the above method and data, find the blade angle and thrust available from a 2-ft propeller of three blades driven at 2,200 rpm by a 1-hp gasoline engine.

3. For an engine developing 1 hp driving at 2,200 rpm a three-blade propeller at the static-thrust characteristics shown in Fig. 4:39, find the maximum static thrust that can be developed and the corresponding propeller diameter and blade angle.

4. For an engine developing 1 hp driving a three-blade propeller of the static-thrust characteristics shown in Fig. 4:39 and a *propeller diameter* of 36 in., find the maximum static thrust that can be developed and the corresponding rpm and blade angle.

5. A sled used for servicing high-tension lines in the mountains is powered by a small airplane engine rated 75 hp at 2,550 rpm at sea level. The sled, carrying power plant, equipment, and two servicemen, weighs 800 lb. At 10,000 ft pressure altitude and a temperature of 0°F ($\sigma = 0.77$) the engine develops 55 hp at 2,550 rpm. With this *rpm specified,* find the optimum blade angle and propeller diameter, using the three-blade-propeller data in Fig. 4:39. Also, find the static thrust and the steepest grade climbable.

4:19. Wind-tunnel Propellers.—Airplane propellers have been widely used to move the air in wind tunnels, and propeller characteristics can be applied to estimate the wind-tunnel performance if the proper relationships are observed. For higher speed wind tunnels, however, propellers of much greater solidity than any airplane propeller are necessary to get the best performance. Propellers using a large number of wide blades are commonly called axial-flow fans.

The pressure and velocity relationships for closed-throat wind tunnels have been presented in Art. 2:3.

Propeller-fan data of Keller and Marks[1] are shown in Fig. 4:40. Note that very high solidities are included. The 10-blade and 24-blade propeller fans tested by Keller had large spinners covering approximately the middle fourth and three-eighths of the diameter, respectively. Note in Fig. 4:40 that the pressure rise coefficient $\psi = 2\Delta p/\rho u^2$ is plotted against the flow coefficient

$$\phi = \frac{Q}{A_f u}$$

where

[1] KELLER, E. G., "Axial Flow Fans"; translated by L. S. Marks, original published in German, based on tests run in Switzerland.

Δp = increase in total head across fan, vanes, and diffuser
ρ = air density
Q = volume of air flow
u = fan tip speed = πnn, where n = rps and D = fan diameter
A_f = area of fan disk = $\pi D^2/4$

For wind-tunnel propellers, Δp may be conservatively assumed to be equal to the pressure rise across the fan disk. Since the equation of

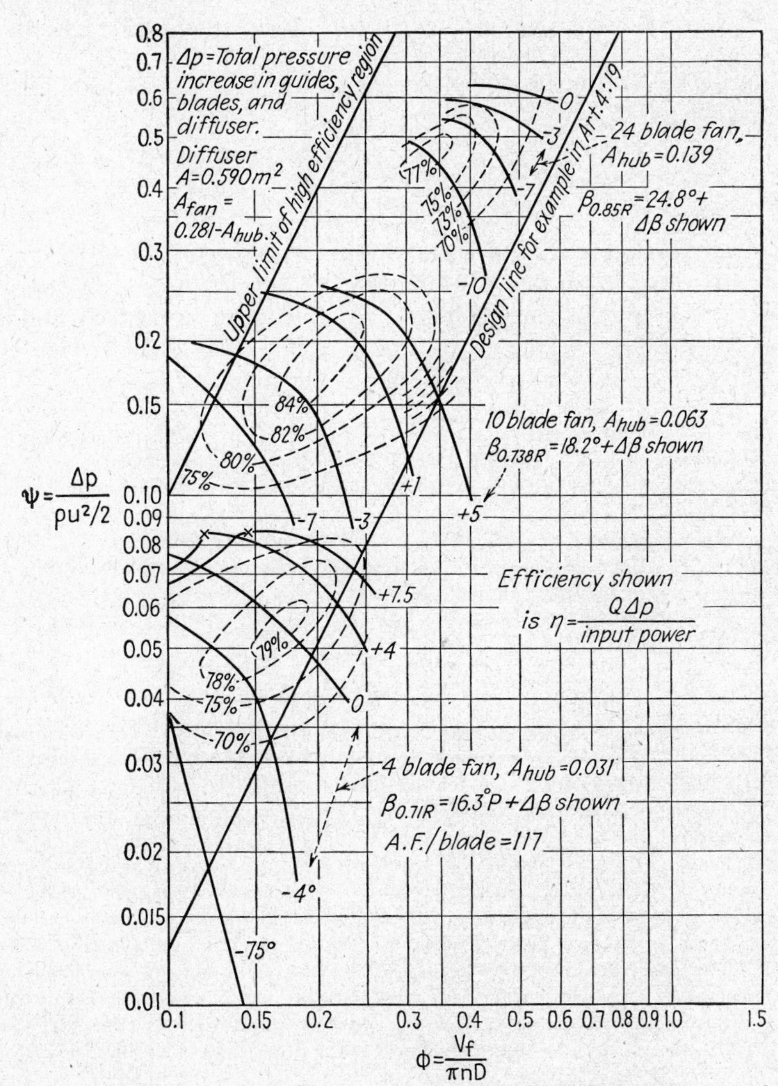

FIG. 4:40.—Characteristics of axial-flow fans from Keller-Marks, Figs. 85, 91, and 97.

continuity applies between the throat of the wind tunnel and the fan disk and since changes in air density between these points are usually negligible,

$$Q = V_f A_f = V_t A_t \tag{4:49}$$

From equations (2:13) and (4:49),

$$\Delta p = \frac{k \rho V_t^2}{2} = \frac{k}{2} V_f^2 \frac{A_f^2}{A_t^2} \tag{4:50}$$

Equation (4:50) can be solved for the pressure ratio ψ as a function of the flow coefficient ϕ as follows:

$$\psi = \frac{\Delta p \times 2}{(\pi n D)^2} = k \frac{V_f^2}{(\pi n D)^2} \frac{A_f^2}{A_t^2} = k \frac{A_f^2}{A_t^2} \phi^2 \tag{4:51}$$

For a wind tunnel with a given estimated-drop coefficient k and a specified ratio of fan-disk area A_f to tunnel-throat area A_t a line of slope 2:1 specified by equation (4:51) can be drawn on the logarithmic plot of fan characteristics shown in Fig. 4:40. This line may be used to select the proper fan as illustrated by the following example.

Example.—A wind tunnel has a throat of 7 by 10 ft (A_t = 70 sq ft) and a propeller diameter of 15 ft (A_f = 176 sq ft). The pressure-drop coefficient $k = \Delta p / q_t$ is 0.20. The propeller is driven by two Chrysler engines, each developing 120 hp at 4,000 rpm. (*a*) Select from Fig. 4:40 a number of blades, and specify the blade angle to get maximum throat velocity. (*b*) Find the throat velocity. (*c*) Find the necessary reduction gear ratio. (*d*) Find the energy ratio of the wind tunnel.

Solution.—For this wind tunnel, calculate

$$k \frac{A_f^2}{A_t^2} = 0.2 \times \frac{(176)^2}{70} = 1.26$$

Draw the line $\psi = 1.26\phi^2$ for this tunnel as shown in Fig. 4:40. This is labeled "design line." For this problem it may be noted that the design line cuts regions of fairly high efficiency for any of the three fans tested. The values of ϕ, ψ, and β for the highest efficiency fan of each number of blades, as read from Fig. 4:40, are given in the table below, which also shows the energy ratio (E.R. $= \eta/k$), the throat velocity V_t in feet per second [equation (2:14)], the mean fan-disk velocity V_f [equation (4:49)], the tip speed ($u = \pi n D = V_f/\phi$), and the fan rpm ($= 60n$). Other things being approximately equal, the fan with the smallest number of blades should be chosen in the interests of economy. If this selection results in excessively high tip speeds (compressibility losses may become excessive at tip speeds over 900 ft per sec), a fan with a larger number of blades should be selected since it will give the required pressure rise at a lower tip speed (higher ϕ). In this case, the answers to the problem are therefore those in the first line of the table below.

Blades	η	ψ	ϕ	β	E.R.	V_t	V_f	u	Rpm	Gear ratio
4	0.78	0.06	0.22	20.3°	3.9	183	73	322	410	0.103
10	0.76	0.16	0.35	23.2°	3.8	182	72.5	207	263	0.066
24	0.65	0.35	0.51	17.8°	3.25	173	69.0	136	173	0.043

The values in the last column are the answers called for.

It will be noted that any given wind tunnel, with fan and throat areas arbitrarily selected, may not have a characteristic line which runs near the high-efficiency region of any of these fans. The high-efficiency region is roughly that between the two inclined lines of 2:1 slope. Hence, if the tunnel is to be driven by a single-stage fan, the value of $k(A_f/A_t)^2$ must be between 1 and 10 (preferably about 2 for a 4-blade fan or about 5 for a 10-blade fan; tests on 40-blade fans show 10 to be a good value). Since $k \approx 0.2$, the area ratios required for efficient single-stage fans are as follows, according to the data of Keller-Marks and related data:

4 blades: $\dfrac{A_f}{A_t} = 3$

10 blades: $\dfrac{A_f}{A_t} = 5$

40 blades: $\dfrac{A_f}{A_t} = 7$

+40% or −30%, for $\dfrac{A_f}{A_t}$ will still be in high-efficiency region

For high-speed wind tunnels, in which it is desired to have $V_t > 900$ ft per sec (615 mph), A_f/A_t is often made from 5 to 7, though values as high as 20 have been used. This keeps the axial velocities through the fan to a low value relative to the speed of sound; thus, the πnD values can be nearly 900 ft per sec without getting into compressibility trouble at the fan blade tips. With $k = 0.2$, $k(A_f/A_t)^2 = 5$ to 10, and with a single-stage fan like Keller-Marks 24-blade fan, $\phi = 0.30$ to 0.25 for high efficiency. If $\pi nD = 900$, then $V_f = 270$ to 225, respectively, and $V_t = 1{,}350$ or 1,570, respectively, compressibility losses in the tunnel being neglected. Thus, speeds well above the speed of sound are obtainable with a single-stage fan. To get still higher speeds, A_f/A_t may be made larger, say 10; then $k(A_f/A_t)^2 = 20$, and no single axial-flow fan of this sort will give good efficiency. High efficiency with so high a value of $k(A_f/A_t)^2$ is obtainable only by using several fans in series. For $k(A_f/A_t)^2 = 20$, four fans in series (four "stages") could each operate on a design line in Fig. 4:40 of

$$k\left(\frac{A_f}{A_t}\right)^2 = 5$$

4:20. Problems

1. A wind tunnel with 3.5- by 5-ft throat and 7.5-ft propeller diameter is to be powered by a single Chrysler engine developing 120 hp at 4,000 rpm. The pressure-drop coefficient is $k = 0.20$. Find the beat gear ratio and number of blades, and estimate the maximum throat velocity.

2. For a particular inexpensive 30- by 48-in. wind tunnel, the pressure-loss coefficient k is 0.66 and two 4-blade fans of diameter 42 in. are used in parallel. If the maximum power available is 80 Bhp at 2,460 propeller rpm, select suitable blade angles from Keller-Marks data for throat velocities of 60, 80, and 100 mph, and find the horsepower required to drive the fans. Use $u = 450$ ft per sec $= \Delta p/242$.

3. A high-speed wind tunnel is to be powered by a 1,000-hp at 2,600 rpm airplane engine. For $k = 0.2$ and $\eta = 0.8$, E.R. $= 4$ and $A_t V_t^3 = 4{,}400{,}000/\rho$. For $\rho = 0.0020$, $A_t V_t^3 = 2.2 \times 10^9$. If A_t is made 2.2 sq ft, V_t can be 1,000 ft per sec if a fan system can be designed to give $\eta = 0.8$. Assume values of $A_f/A_t = 5, 7.07$, and 10 and design fans to give the highest possible efficiency for each sized fan. Tabulate results as shown below, and select optimum tunnel and fan design.

D fan	$\dfrac{A_f}{A_t}$	$k\left(\dfrac{A_f}{A}\right)^2$	Stages	Blades
3.75	5	5	1	4, 10, 24
4.45	7.07	10	2	4, 10, 24
5.30	10	20	4	4, 10, 24

4. Repeat Prob. 3 for $A_t = 0.55$ and $V_t = 1{,}640$.

CHAPTER 5

AIRPLANE PERFORMANCE

5:1. Speed and Climb from Power Required and Available.—The calculations of power required and available at different altitudes for the airplane used in the illustrative examples in Chaps. 3 and 4 are plotted in the same graphs in Fig. 5:1. The intersection of the power-required and -available graphs of any given altitude represents the maximum speed of level flight at that altitude, v_L. For full-throttle

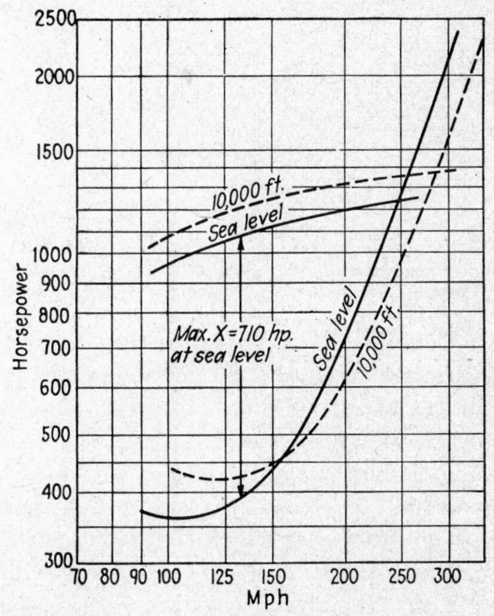

FIG. 5:1.—Power required and available at sea level and 10,000 ft for Lockheed Lodestar airplane.

flight at speeds lower than v_L, there is an excess horsepower X available over that required for level flight, as indicated in Fig. 5:1, and the airplane will climb, the rate of climb in feet per minute being given by the equation

$$C_h = \frac{33{,}000X}{W} \tag{5:1}$$

The rate of climb at any given altitude varies with the airplane speed in the manner shown in Fig. 5:2, which also shows the definitions of maximum rate of climb $C_{h\,max}$ or best climbing speed v_c. The best climbing speed is seen in Fig. 5:2 to correspond to the maximum rate of climb but not to the maximum angle of climb, which usually occurs at a lower speed. Since Fig. 5:2 is a plot of vertical *vs.* horizontal speed, a line drawn from the origin to the graph at any point is a measure of the angle of climb.

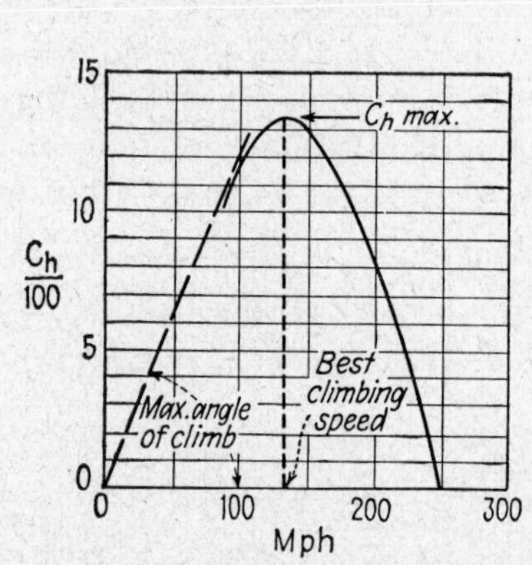

FIG. 5:2.—Rate of climb at sea level as a function of speed for Lockheed Lodestar airplane.

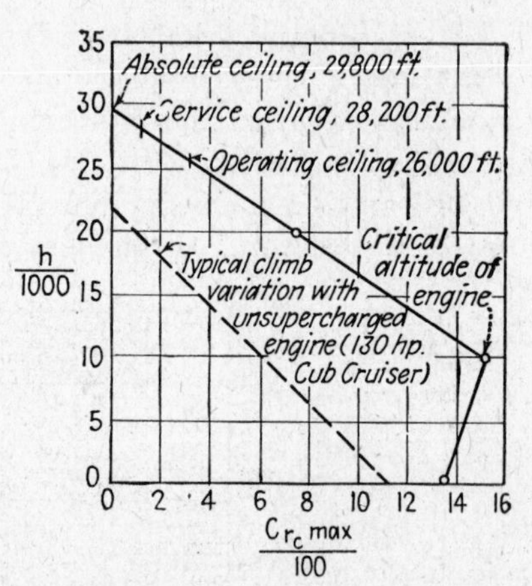

FIG. 5:3.—Graphical determination of ceilings for Lockheed Lodestar airplane.

5:2. Airplane Ceilings.—The full-throttle performance of an airplane is commonly summarized by plotting the maximum rate of climb $C_{h\,max}$ *vs.* altitude, as shown in Fig. 5:3. For airplanes with gear-driven superchargers the graph of $C_{h\,max}$ *vs.* altitude is very nearly a straight line above the critical altitude (for airplanes without superchargers it is a straight line from sea level up). For any airplane there is always some altitude at which the maximum rate of climb is zero, and this is known as the *absolute ceiling* of the airplane. Since the rate of climb is zero, the absolute ceiling is attainable theoretically only in infinite time. A ceiling can be attained only if there is a positive small rate of climb at the ceiling; it is customary to define the *service ceiling* as the altitude at which the rate of climb is 100 ft per min. For commercial flight in unfavorable weather or over mountainous terrain and for military aircraft in formations, this arbitrary 100 ft per min rate of climb does not give a true picture of the maximum feasible operating altitude of the airplane, and it is accordingly becoming customary for certain purposes to speak of an *operating ceiling* corresponding to a somewhat higher rate of climb, usually set at 300 to

500 ft per min. These three ceilings are shown on Fig. 5:3 for one of the airplanes used for illustrative performance calculations in the text.

The speed of maximum rate of climb is shown in its relation to the stalling and level high speeds in Fig. 5:4. Figure 5:4 shows a typical dome-shaped area of speed and altitude within which an airplane can fly. Such a dome area exists because the stalling speed increases with altitude and, above the critical altitude of the engine, the level high

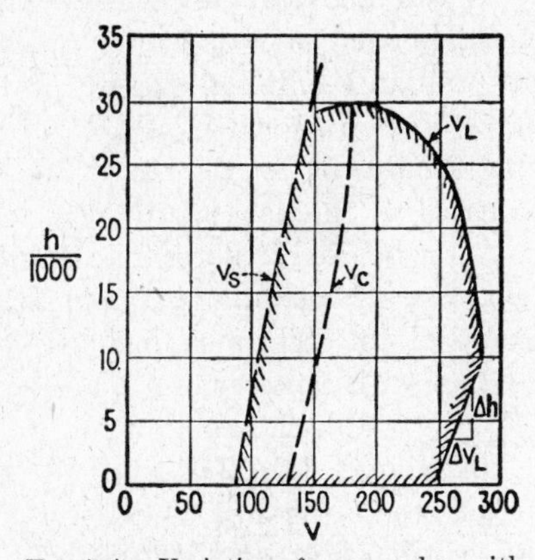

FIG. 5:4.—Variation of v_s, v_c, and v_L with altitude for Lockheed Lodestar.

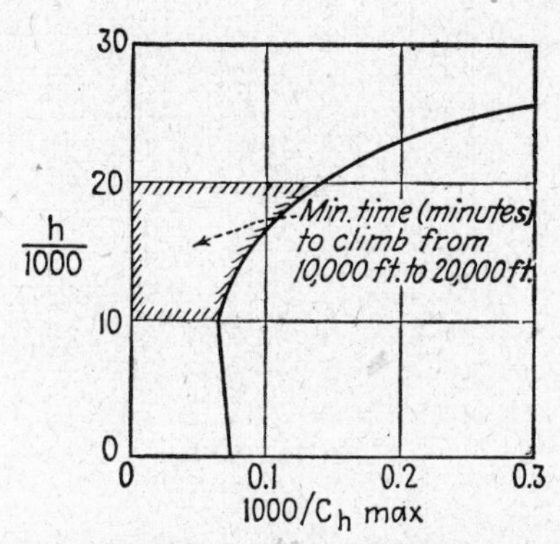

FIG. 5:5.—Plot for determining time to climb between two altitudes.

speed decreases with altitude. Below the critical altitude of the engine there is seen to be an increase in level high speed with altitude, and this increase is usually represented by a straight line of slope such that the level high speed increases almost exactly 1 per cent for each 1,000 ft altitude up to the critical altitude. This feature of the performance of supercharged airplanes is what made possible a new order of high-speed performance unattainable with unsupercharged engines. For example, an airplane that will reach a level high speed of 300 mph at sea level will have a level high speed of nearly 400 mph if its engine has a critical altitude of 33,000 ft.

To determine the time Δt required to climb between two altitudes h_1 and h_2, it is convenient to replot Fig. 5:3 in the form shown in Fig. 5:5. Since $C_{h\,\max} = dh/dt$, it follows that

$$\Delta t = \int_{h_1}^{h_2} \frac{dt}{dh}\,dh = \int_{h_1}^{h_2} \frac{1}{C_{h\,\max}}\,dh \tag{5:2}$$

If $C_{h\,\max}$ plots as a straight line *vs.* altitude as in Fig. 5:3, equation (5:2) can be integrated to give a logarithmic expression for Δt.

5:3. Use of General Logarithmic Charts of Power Required and Available.—If calculations on a particular airplane must be made at a number of gross weights and a number of different altitudes, the calculations may be expedited by tracing power-available lines on the general power-required chart, as in Fig. 4:24. Such lines for the Lockheed Lodestar airplane for the same conditions as in Fig. 5:1 but with an additional altitude of 20,000 ft are shown in Fig. 5:6. The family of curved lines on Chart C in the back of the book may now be used to determine the best climbing speed and maximum rate of climb. The meaning of C_1 is climb with a power of P_1; lines of $C/C_1 = 1.0$, 2.0, and 3.0 are at all points 1.0, 2.0, and 3.0 greater than the heavy line for level flight. This can be checked by noting that at $V/V_1 = 1.0$ the corresponding values of P/P_1 are 2.0, 3.0, and 4.0. Inspection

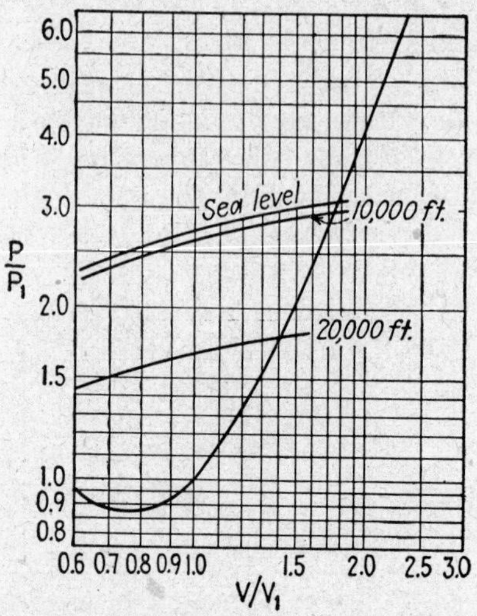

FIG. 5:6.—Power available for Lockheed Lodestar airplane traced onto general power-required chart, two altitudes.

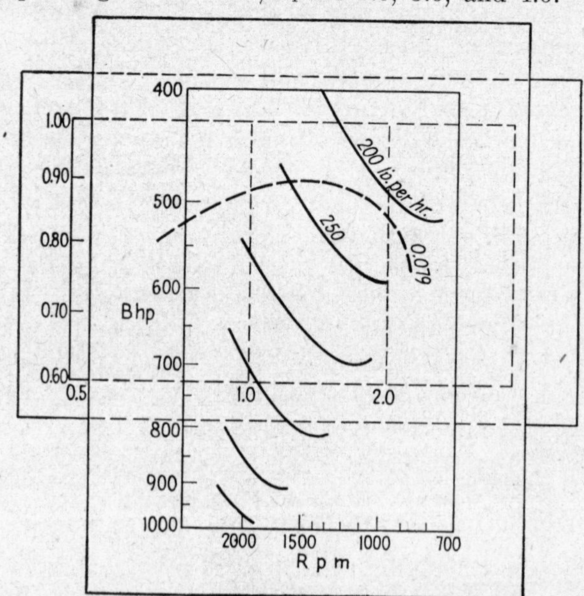

FIG. 5:7.—Superposition of charts for determination of best cruising condition.

of the line in Fig. 4:25 for example 1 shows that the maximum value of C/C_1 approached by the power-available line is 1.30. The best climbing speed in Fig. 4:25, Example 1 (the speed of nearest approach or tangency of the power available with a line of constant C/C_1), is in this case $V/V_1 = 0.97$. Other values necessary for plotting Fig. 5:3 as obtained from Fig. 5:6 are shown in Table 5:1.

TABLE 5:1.—PERFORMANCE CALCULATIONS FOR LOCKHEED LODESTAR AIRPLANE BY USE OF GENERAL LOGARITHMIC GRAPHS OF POWER REQUIRED AND AVAILABLE

$W = 17{,}500$ lb, $\dfrac{f_e}{n_e D} = 0.049$, Rpm $= 2{,}100$, $D = 10.5$ ft

Alt., 1,000 ft	σ	$\sqrt{\frac{1}{\sigma}}$	Bhp	C_P	v_1, mph	P_1	$\frac{Rhp}{P_1}$	C_1	$\frac{v_L}{v_1}$	$\frac{v_c}{v_1}$	$\frac{C}{C_1}$	v_L	v_c	$c_{h\,max}$
S.L.	1.00	1.00	690	0.029	140	405	3.41	765	1.77	0.94	1.76	248	132	1,350
10	0.783	1.164	780	0.045	163	472	3.30	890	1.74	0.94	1.70	284	153	1,510
20	0.533	1.37	530	0.042	192	555	1.91	1040	1.40	0.89	0.70	269	171	733

Performance at other gross weights W than the design gross weight W_0 at other altitudes may be calculated by making the changes indicated by the equations

$$V_1 = V_0 \sqrt{\frac{W}{W_0}} \sqrt{\frac{1}{\sigma}} \tag{5:3}$$

$$P_1 = P_0 \left(\frac{W}{W_0}\right)^{3/2} \sqrt{\frac{1}{\sigma}} \tag{5:4}$$

$$C_1 = C_0 \sqrt{\frac{W}{W_0}} \sqrt{\frac{1}{\sigma}} \tag{5:5}$$

5:4. Problems

1. For the Ercoupe airplane for which calculations of power required for level flight at sea level and 12,000 ft altitude were made in Probs. 1 and 2, Art. 3:10, and for which full-throttle power available for a 75-hp engine at sea level was calculated in Prob. 2, Art. 4:10, (*a*) calculate and plot a graph of rate of climb *vs.* speed at sea level, and find the steepest climbing angle, the maximum rate of climb, and the corresponding air speeds at sea level; (*b*) the maximum rate of climb and level high speed at sea level and at 12,000 ft; (*c*) plot rate of climb *vs.* altitude as a straight line, and find the absolute ceiling, the service ceiling, and the ceiling for 300 ft per min rate of climb. Use the general logarithmic plot of power required for level flight.

2. For the Lockheed Constellation airplane for which calculations of power required for level flight at sea level and 20,000 ft altitude were made in Prob. 2, Art. 3:10, and Prob. 2, Art. 3:12, and for which full-throttle power available at 10,000 ft from four engines of characteristics shown on page 464 was calculated in Prob. 4, Art. 4:10, (*a*) find the maximum rate of climb, best climbing speed, and level high speed at altitudes of sea level, 10,000 ft, and 20,000 ft; (*b*) plot maximum rate of climb *vs.* altitude, assuming a straight line above 10,000 ft, and find the absolute ceiling, the service ceiling, and the ceiling for 300 ft per min rate of climb. Use the general logarithmic plot of power required for level flight.

5:5. Oswald Performance Charts.—Since the power required is a cubic function of speed, as shown in Chart C, the most important items of full-throttle performance, the level-flight speed at sea level v_{L0}, the maximum rate of climb at sea level $C_{h0\,\max}$, and the absolute and service ceilings h_{abs} and h_{serv} can be related to the airplane dimensions, weight, and aerodynamic characteristics if a reasonable estimate can be made of the propeller efficiency and its variations with speed and altitude. A series of charts relating performance to dimensions was developed in 1932 as *NACA Tech. Rept.* 408 by W. B. Oswald, and these charts are given in Figs. A31 to A33 on pages 442 to 444. At the time when these charts were developed, the most important type of engine and propeller combination was the fixed-pitch propeller and unsupercharged engine; these charts are directly applicable to airplane engine-propeller combinations of this type. The basic equations for the charts are developed as follows: From the equations in Chap. 3 it follows that

$$hp_r = C_D \frac{qSV}{550} = \left(C_{Dpe} + \frac{C_L^2}{\pi e A\!\!R}\right)\frac{\rho SV^3}{550} = \frac{\rho f_e V^3}{1{,}100} + \frac{2W^2}{550\pi\rho V e b^2} \quad (5{:}6)$$

for which an approximate solution for the level high speed at sea level v_{L0} can be obtained by equating the horsepower required in equation (5:6) to the maximum thrust horsepower available at sea level $\eta Bhp_{0\,\max}$ This solution is

$$v_{L0} = 52.7\sqrt[3]{\frac{Thp_{0\,\max}}{f_e}} - 0.11\frac{W^2}{eb^2 Thp_{0\,\max}} \quad (5{:}7)$$

Oswald found it convenient in plotting the charts to rewrite equation (5:7) in the form

$$v_{L0} = 52.7\sqrt[3]{\frac{Lp}{L_t}} - 0.11LsL_t \quad (5{:}8)$$

in which

$$L_p = \frac{W}{f_e} = \text{parasite loading} \quad (5{:}9)$$

$$L_t = \frac{W}{Thp_{0\,\max}} = \text{thrust horsepower loading} \quad (5{:}10)$$

$$L_s = \frac{W}{eb^2} = \text{span loading} \quad (5{:}11)$$

Equation (5:8) is plotted as a family of lines on the logarithmic ruled chart in Fig. A31 on page 442. If the three loadings defined by equations (5:9) to (5:11) are calculated, v_{L0} can be read directly from the chart.

For altitude performance Oswald assumed a variation of thrust horsepower with speed given by

$$\frac{Thp_0}{Thp_{0\,\max}} = \left(\frac{V}{V_1}\right)^m = R_v^m \tag{5:12}$$

in which m has the following values based on experimental data on fixed-pitch propellers: $m = 0.55$ for peak-efficiency propellers or for best-performance propellers with a design value of $C_s = C_{sm} > 1.6$. $m = 0.61$ for best performance propellers with $C_{sm} = 1.2$. $m = 0.65$ for best-performance propellers with $C_{sm} = 0.9$. By "peak-efficiency" propeller is meant one that is selected to operate at its peak efficiency. By "best-performance" propeller is meant a propeller selected on the line for maximum efficiency for a given C_s. Oswald further assumed a variation of thrust horsepower with altitude at R_v = const. given by

$$\frac{Thp_h}{Thp_0} = 1.2 - 0.2 \tag{5:13}$$

which is of the same form as equation (4:2) but involves somewhat higher friction horsepower and includes the effect of typical variation of rpm with altitude for a fixed-pitch propeller. The above considerations yielded what Oswald called the general equation for performance,

$$L_tC_h = \frac{33{,}000}{\sigma R_v}(1.2\sigma - 0.2)\sigma R_v^{m+1} - \sigma^2 R_v^4 - \frac{L_sL_t}{3.014V_L}(1 - \sigma^2 R_v^4) \tag{5:14}$$

which is inconvenient to solve directly but can be plotted as families of charts for climb and ceiling as in Figs. A31 and A32 on pages 442 and 443 in terms of the performance parameter

$$\Lambda = L_sL_t^{4/3}Lp^{1/3} = \frac{L_sL_t}{\sqrt[3]{\dfrac{L_p}{L_t}}} \tag{5:15}$$

An example of the application of this procedure to the calculation of the performance of rate 120 hp Cub Cruiser airplane for which power-available calculations were made in Chap. 4 follows:

Example.—120-hp Cub Cruiser performance problem by Oswald charts. W = 1,400 lb, S = 180 sq ft, b = 35.3 ft, f_e = 8.3 sq ft, e = 0.77, $Bhp_{0\,\max}$ = 120. Given a Cub Cruiser airplane with η_m = 0.70 (peak η propeller); assume constant torque (dP/dN = 1.00). *Find* (*a*) the level high speed at sea level v_L, (*b*) the maximum rate of climb at sea level $C_{h0\,max}$, (c) the absolute ceiling h_{abs}, and (d) the service ceiling h_{serv}.

Solution.—Calculate from equations (5:9) to (5:11)

$$L_p = \frac{W}{f_e} = \frac{1{,}400}{8.3} = 169 \text{ lb per sq ft}$$

$$L_s = \frac{W}{eb^2} = \frac{1{,}400}{0.77 \times 35.3^2} = 1.46 \text{ lb per sq ft}$$

$$L_t = \frac{W}{Thp_m} = \frac{1{,}400}{0.70 \times 120} = 16.7 \text{ lb/hp}$$

$$\left.\begin{aligned}\frac{L_p}{L_t} &= 10.1\\ L_sL_t &= 24.4\end{aligned}\right\}\text{Read on p. 442, } v_L = 112 \text{ mph}$$

For the climb and ceiling, calculate $\Lambda = 24.4/\sqrt[3]{10.1} = 24.4/2.16 = 11.3$. For the sea-level maximum rate of climb, read in Fig. A32 on page 443,

$$\frac{L_tC_h}{1{,}000} = 14.2$$

and $C_h = 14{,}200/16.7 = 850$ ft per min. For ceilings, read in Fig. A33 on page 444, $h_{abs} = 20{,}500$ ft ($= h_{serv}$ at $L_t = 0$), $h_{serv} = 17{,}500$ at $L_t = 20$. By interpolation, $h_{serv} = 18{,}000$ at $L_t = 16.7$. These are the answers called for.

The foregoing procedure is quick and simple but cannot be considered as accurate as the procedure called for in Probs. 1 and 2, Art. 5:4, for it cannot take account of specific propeller-efficiency variations with speed and altitude. The charts do, however, show so directly the effects of variations of weight, drag, span, and power on performance that they are widely used for preliminary design of airplanes with unsupercharged engines and fixed-pitch propellers. While the Oswald charts can be adapted to use with supercharged engines and constant-rpm propellers, the more general procedure outlined in Art. 5:7 is recommended for such airplanes.

5:6. Problems

1. For an Ercoupe airplane with $W = 1{,}260$ lb, $S = 142.5$ sq ft, $b = 30$ ft, and $Bhp_m = 75$, assume $f_e = 4.28$ sq ft, $\eta_m = 0.71$, and $e = 0.76$. (a) Calculate L_p, L_s, and L_t from equations (5:9) to (5:11), and use the chart in Fig. A31 on page 442 to find the level high speed at sea level. (b) Calculate Λ from equation (5:15), and use the charts in Fig. A32 and A33 on pages 443 and 444 with $dP/dN = 1.0$ and a peak-efficiency propeller to find the maximum rate of climb at sea level and absolute ceiling.

2. Repeat Prob. 1, (a) for 30 per cent increase in gross weight, (b) for 30 per cent increase in brake horsepower, (c) for 30 per cent decrease in f_e, and (d) for 30 per cent increase in wing span, keeping all other items constant in each case.

3. Repeat Prob. 1 with the following design changes: W increased from 1,260 to 1,600 to allow for one more passenger and heavier engine; brake horsepower increased from 75 to 130 by shifting to six-cylinder engine; f_e reduced from 4.28 to 2.80 by retracting landing gear; b increased from 30 ft to 39 ft to improve altitude performance.

5:7. GALCIT Performance Chart.—Millikan shows[1] that at any altitude of density ratio σ, equation (5:8) may be written

$$v_L = \frac{52.73}{\sqrt{\sigma}} \sqrt[3]{\frac{L_p}{L_{ti}}}\, \Omega_i \tag{5:16}$$

where

$$L_{ti} = L_t \sqrt{\frac{1}{\sigma}} \tag{5:17}$$

$$\Omega_i = f(\Lambda_i) \qquad \text{as on page 446}$$

$$\Lambda_i = \frac{L_s L_{ti}}{\sqrt[3]{\dfrac{L_p}{L_{ti}}}} \tag{5:18}$$

To compute $L_t = W/\eta Bhp$, a value of η must be assumed; when v_L has been found, V_L/nD may be calculated and η looked up on a propeller-efficiency chart. If the calculated η differs appreciably from the assumed η, the calculation must be repeated.

For climb at any altitude h, Millikan plots $L_t C_{mp}$ *vs.* Λ_{ic} and calculates

$$C_h = \frac{L_t C_{mp}}{L_{tc}} \tag{5:19}$$

where

$$L_{tc} = L_t \frac{\eta_0}{\eta_c} \tag{5:20}$$

$$\Lambda_{ic} = \left(\frac{\eta_0}{\eta_c}\right)^{4/3} \Lambda_i R_\Lambda \tag{5:21}$$

where the subscript $(\ )_0$ refers to the high speed, the subscript $(\ )_c$ refers to the climbing condition, and $R = f(\Lambda_i)$. η_c must be read from a propulsive-efficiency chart at the V/nD of the climbing speed, the climbing speed being determined from

$$R_{vc} = \frac{v_c}{v_L} = f(\Lambda_i) \qquad \text{from graph} \tag{5:22}$$

An example of the use of the GALCIT chart follows.

Example.—Lockheed Lodestar performance problem, constant-rpm propellers. Given the same data as in the examples in Chaps. 3 and 4, *viz.*, $W = 17{,}500$, $S = 551$, $Bhp = 780$ at $rpm = 2{,}100$ at 10,000 ft for each of two engines. $D = 10.5$ ft, $C_D = 0.0196 + 0.049C_L^2$, $f_e = 10.8$ sq ft, $b = 65.5$ ft, $e = 0.83$. Propeller characteristics are as on pages 454 to 456. Find the level high speed v_L and the maximum rate of climb C_h at 10,000 ft altitude ($\sigma = 0.738$, $\sqrt{1/\sigma} = 1.64$, $\sqrt{} = 0.859$).

[1] MILLIKAN, C. B., "Aerodynamics of the Airplane." John Wiley & Sons, Inc., New York, 1941.

Solution.—From inspection of Fig. A50, page 456, assume $\eta_0 = 0.89$ (to be verified later), and calculate from equations (5:9) to (5:11)

$$L_p = \frac{W}{f_e} = \frac{17,500}{10.8} = 1,620 \text{ lb per sq ft}$$

$$L_t = \frac{W}{Thp_{\max}} = \frac{17,500}{2} \times 780 \times 0.89 = 12.6 \text{ lb per hp}$$

$$L_s = \frac{W}{eb^2} = \frac{17,500}{0.83} \times 65.5^2 = 5.00 \text{ lb per sq ft}$$

and from equation (5:17)

$$L_{ti} = L_t \sqrt{\frac{1}{\sigma}} = 12.6 \times 1.164 = 14.67 \text{ lb per hp}$$

For the level high speed, proceed in the following steps:

1. Calculate from equation (5:18)

$$\Lambda_i = \frac{5.00 \times 14.67}{\sqrt[3]{1,620/14.67}} = \frac{73.4}{4.80} = 15.3$$

2. Read on Fig. A35, page 446, $\Omega_i = f(\Lambda_i) = 0.965$.
3. Calculate from equation (5:16)

$$v_L = \frac{52.73}{0.859} \sqrt[3]{\frac{1,620}{14.67}} \times 0.965 = 61.5 \times 4.80 \times 0.965 = 285 \text{ mph}$$

4. Check efficiency assumption from Fig. A50, page 456, thus:

Calculate

$$\frac{V_L}{nD} = \frac{285 \times 88}{2,100 \times 10.5} = 1.14$$

Calculate

$$C_p = \frac{0.500}{0.738} \frac{0.780}{2.1^3 \times 1.05^5} = 0.045$$

Read on page 456, $\eta_0 = 0.885$, which is a good check.

Note that the level high speed at 10,000 ft altitude thus calculated is in excellent agreement with the value of 284 mph found by the general logarithmic graph method reported in Table 5:1.

For the maximum rate of climb C_h and corresponding climbing speed v_c, proceed in the following steps:

1. Read on chart on page 446, $R_{vc} = f(\Lambda_i) = 0.60$.
2. Calculate from equation (5:23), $v_c = R_{vc}v_L = 0.6 \times 285 = 171$ mph. (This is intended to be only an approximate value within 10 per cent, a more exact value to be determined by trial; note that the more exact value in Table 5:1 was found to be 153 mph.)
3. Calculate $J_c = (V_c/nD) = R_{vc}(V_L/nD) = 0.60 \times 1.14 = 0.68$, and read η_c on the efficiency chart (Fig. A50, page 456) for the same value of C_p. For this case, read $\eta_c = 0.825$.
4. Calculate L_{tc} from equation (5:21), thus:

$$L_{tc} = 12.6 \frac{0.885}{0.825} = 13.5$$

5. Read $R_\Lambda = f(\Lambda_i)$, and calculate Λ_{ic} from equation (5:22), thus: For $\Lambda_i = 15.3$, read $R_\Lambda = 1.26$, and calculate

$$\Lambda_{ic} = \Lambda_i \left(\frac{\eta_0}{\eta_c}\right)^{4/3} R_\Lambda = 15.3 \times \left(\frac{0.885}{0.825}\right)^{4/3} \times 1.26 = 15.3 \times 1.096 \times 1.26 = 21.1$$

6. Read $L_tC_{mp} = f(\Lambda_{ic})$ on Fig. A35, page 447; for this case read $L_tC_{mp} = 20{,}200$.
7. Calculate C_h from equation (5:20) thus:

$$C_h = \frac{L_tC_{mp}}{L_{tc}} = \frac{20{,}200}{13.5} = 1{,}500 \text{ ft per min}$$

8. Repeat the above calculations for values of R_{vc} 10 per cent higher and lower than found in step 1, to see whether some other value of v_c will not give slightly higher C_h. In this case assuming $R_{vc} = 0.54$ and $v_c = 154$ gives $C_{h\,\max} = 1{,}510$ and checks Table 5:1.

The Schairer-Boeing chart method is usually less laborious than the GALCIT chart method and is somewhat more flexible for the introduction of compressibility for the airplane and propeller.

5:8. Problem.—For the Lockheed Constellation airplane with data as in Prob. 2, Art. 5:4 and preceding problems, use the chart in Fig. A35 on pages 446 and 447 to find (*a*) the level high speed at 10,000 ft altitude, (*b*) the approximate maximum rate of climb at 10,000 ft altitude, and (*c*) the climbing speed corresponding to (*b*).

5:9. Cruising Economy Determination by Logarithmic Chart.—The trial solution for the most economical cruising conditions outlined in Art. 4:9 and illustrated for the Lockheed Lodestar airplane in Table 4:7 (page 239) can be avoided by the use of superposed logarithmic charts of propeller efficiency and fuel economy, as illustrated in the following example:

Example.—Given the Lockheed Lodestar data as in Art. 4:9. Find the best cruising fuel economy at 233 mph true air speed at 10,000 ft standard altitude.

Solution.

1. Replot the cruising propulsive-efficiency data of Fig. A52, page 458, to a large-scale logarithmic base. This has been done in Fig. A53 on page 459.
2. Replot the fuel-consumption data of Fig. 4:22 with a 20-in.-log-base brake-horsepower scale vertically and 10-in.-log-base rpm scale horizontally, and draw lines of constant fuel flow per hour. This has been done on Chart D.
3. Calculate $\eta P_c = 0.078$ as before (Art. 4:9, Example 4, step 1), and assume $Thp = {}^{854}\!/_{2} = 427$ per engine from Table 3:2 as before.
4. Superimpose Chart D on Fig. A53, page 459, with 100 per cent efficiency on the line of $Bhp = 427$, as sketched in Fig. 5:7.
5. Slide the transparent upper chart (Chart D) to the right (keeping $Bhp = 427$ at $\eta = 1.00$) until $V/nD = 1.00$ coincides, with

$$rpm = \frac{88\ mph}{D} = \frac{(88 \times 233)}{10.5} = 1{,}950$$

6. At the point where the lowest fuel flow per hour touches the line of

$$P_c = 0.078$$

read η and *rpm*. For this case, read η = 0.855 and *rpm* = 980. Read also in this case hourly fuel flow = 209 lb per hr for one engine (418 lb per hr for two engines). Calculate pounds per mile = $418/233$ = 1.79, which is a good check with the previous value of 1.81. Read also at this point $V/nD = 2.0$.

The foregoing procedure, suggested originally by George Schairer of Boeing Aircraft Company, saves much calculating time if cruising calculations must be made for a large number of gross weights, speeds, and altitudes, as is usually the case.

5:10. Problem.—For the Lockheed Constellation airplane, repeat Prob. 6, Art. 4:10, (6), using the method of Art. 5:9 and the logarithmic propeller and fuel-consumption charts Fig. A53, page 459, and Chart D in the back of the book.

CHAPTER 6

SPECIAL PERFORMANCE PROBLEMS

Most airplane accidents occur in landing or take-off. Governmental regulations have at times specified an arbitrary upper limit on stalling speed, such as 60 or 70 mph, with a view to minimizing the seriousness of such accidents by requiring less skill on the part of a pilot in making approach turns and glides as well as actual landings and take-offs. This regulation was actually effective, for on an actual airport of a given limited size there is more likelihood of pilot error

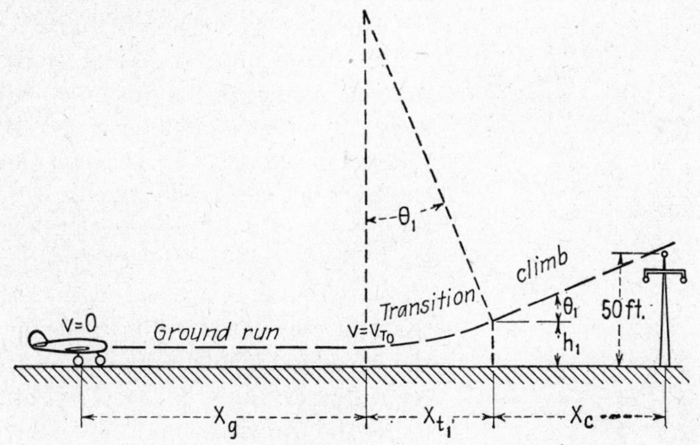

FIG. 6:1.—Components of take-off distance over obstacle.

with a low-speed than with a high-speed airplane. Such arbitrary limitations on stalling speed were found, however, to have a serious detrimental effect on the high-speed performance of airplanes by requiring exceptionally large wing area for a given gross weight. A less arbitrary limitation on the design of aircraft is currently (1946) specified (Civil Air Regulations 04.7533T and 61.7124), requiring that the landing runway used by a transport airplane must be the minimum distance required for landing over a 50-ft obstacle, divided by 0.6. The factor 0.6 is specified to allow room for piloting errors. Such a specification requires that the airplane manufacturer make careful calculations of the landing and take-off performance and performance in related maneuvers; such calculations are the subject of this chapter.

The following take-off and landing calculations are for an airplane equipped with a tricycle landing gear, for this is becoming the dominant type. The calculations are the same for an airplane with a tail wheel except that the time required to raise the tail in taking off and limiting brake pressures to avoid nosing over on landing are neglected.

6:1. Take-off of Landplane over Obstacle.—The horizontal distance necessary to take off and clear a 50-ft obstacle is commonly divided into three phases, as shown in Fig. 6:1: a ground run x_g, during which the airplane accelerates from rest to take-off velocity V_{TO}; a transition distance x_t, which is approximately a circular arc in which the airplane changes direction from the horizontal to a climbing path; and a climbing distance x_c, determined by the climbing performance of the airplane.

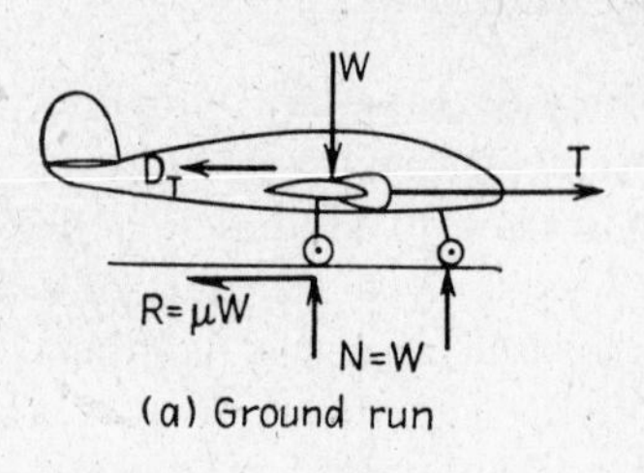

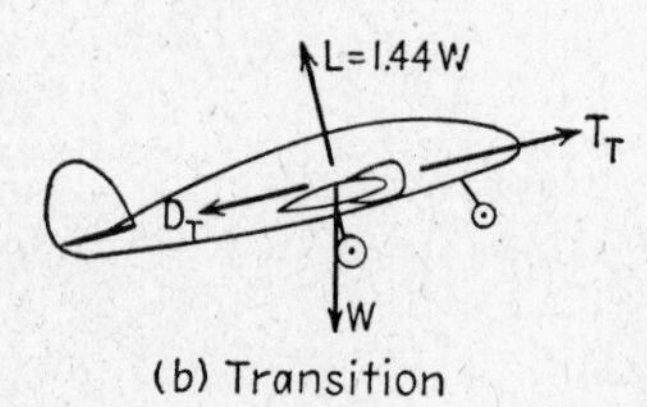

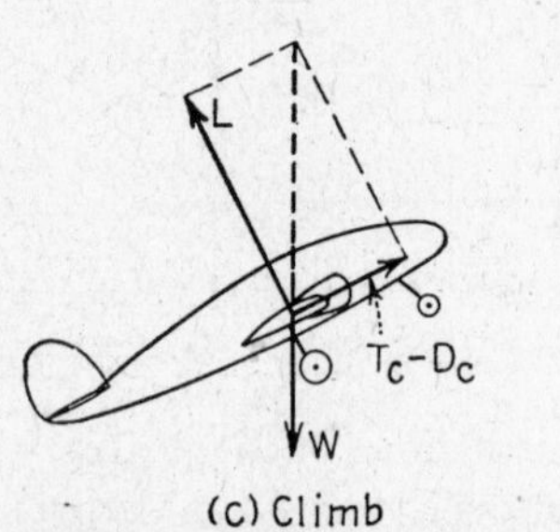

FIG. 6:2.—Forces acting on airplane during three phases of assumed take-off.

The take-off velocity V_{TO} may be any speed in excess of the stalling speed in the take-off configuration (usually with flaps partly down at a predetermined optimum take-off position). In general, the lower the take-off speed, the shorter will be the total horizontal distance to clear an obstacle. The airplane can actually be pulled off the ground at a speed somewhat lower than the calculated stalling speed by using the corrected wind-tunnel value of $C_{L\,max}$, for a higher value of $C_{L\,max}$ is obtainable under the transient condition of increasing angle of attack. This procedure, however, involves the hazard that the airplane will settle down again when conditions become steady. In the interests of safety and to avoid "mushing in" after a too early take-off, it is common practice to set the take-off speed at some arbitrary per cent above the take-off stalling speed V_{STO}. This margin of safety is commonly set at 20 per cent. Hence, it is common to assume

$$V_{TO} = 1.20 V_{STO} \tag{6:1}$$

A smaller value of V_{TO} may be assumed if it is desired to get a shorter take-off distance with correspondingly higher risk.

Forces acting on the airplane during the three phases of the assumed take-off are shown in Fig. 6:2. An analysis of the acceleration and horizontal distance for these three phases is made separately in the following three paragraphs.

a. Ground Run. The airplane accelerates horizontally under the action of the three forces T, D, and $R = \mu W$ so that

$$T - D - \mu W = \frac{W}{g} a \tag{6:2}$$

and the horizontal distance x_g may be calculated by integrating the equation

$$\int_0^{x_g} a dx = \int_0^{V_{TO}} V dV \tag{6:3}$$

TABLE 6:1

Type of surface	Brakes off, average ground-resistance coefficient	Brakes fully applied, average wheel-braking coefficient
Concrete or macadam	0.03 to 0.05	0.4 to 0.6
Hard turf	0.05	0.4
Firm and dry	....	0 33
Soft turf	0.07	
Wet concrete	0.05	0.30
Wet grass	0.10	0.20
Snow- or ice-covered field	0.02	0.07 to 0.10

In equation (6:2) the expression $T - D - \mu W$ may be considered as the net thrust; it varies throughout the take-off from an initial value T_{NI} to a final value of T_{NF}, which can be calculated, plotted, and integrated graphically if the thrust characteristics of the propeller, the drag coefficient of the airplane in the three-point position, and the rolling-resistance coefficient μ are known. Values of T and D may be calculated as in Chap. 5. Values of μ may be taken from Table 6:1, which also shows the resistance coefficients due to braking on landing. If the initial and final net thrust values were substantially the same, the acceleration during take-off could be considered approximately constant and equations (6:2) and (6:3) could be integrated to give

$$x_g = \frac{1}{2g} \frac{V_{TO}^2}{T_{NI}/W} = 0.0156 \frac{V_{TO}^2}{(T_{NI}/W)} \tag{6:4}$$

in which V_{TO} is the take-off velocity in feet per second. In most actual take-off problems, however, the thrust varies with the speed, as shown in Fig. 6:3, and the final net thrust T_{NF} at take-off is considerably less than the initial thrust T_{NI}. For rapid estimation of the ground run, the initial and final net thrust can be calculated and a factor K_s read from Fig. 6:4 that permits calculating

$$x_g = K_s \frac{V_{TO}^2}{T_{NI}/W} \tag{6:5}$$

For more accurate calculations integrate graphically.

b. Transition Distance.—The transition from the level ground run to climb at an angle θ_1 given by the equation

$$\theta_1 = \frac{T_c - D_c}{W} \tag{6:6}$$

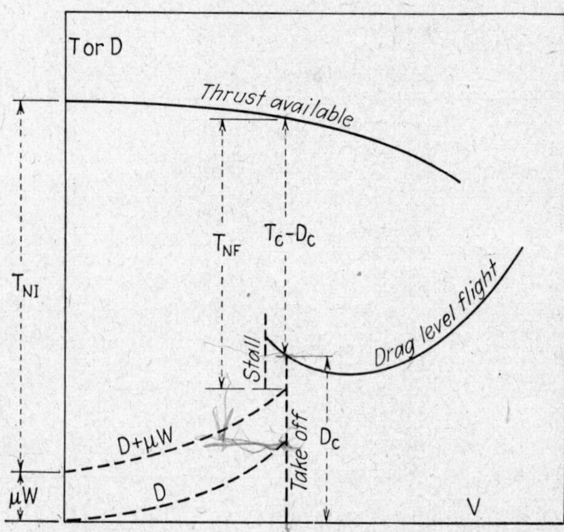

FIG. 6:3.—Variation of forces during take-off.

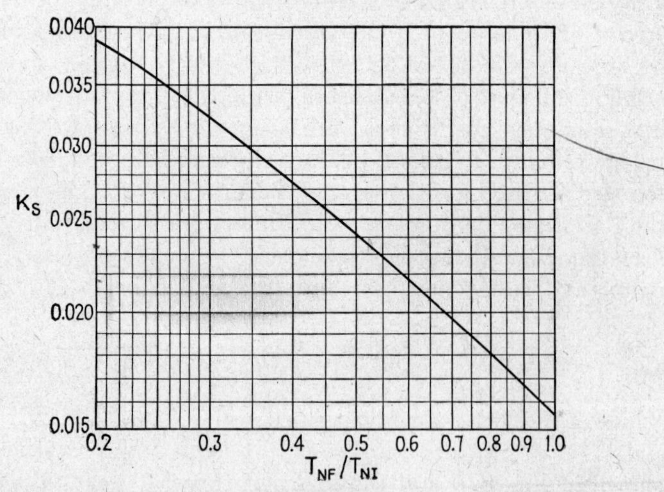

FIG. 6:4.—Diehl's ground-run coefficient K_s for use in equation (6:5).

may be considered to take place at constant normal acceleration due to operating at $C_{L\,\max}$ while traveling at a speed $V_{TO} = 1.2V_{STO}$, giving a lift equal to $1.44W$ and a normal acceleration of $(1.44 - 1)g = 0.44g$. The radius of such a flight path is

$$r = \frac{V_{TO}^2}{0.44g} \qquad (6:7)$$

The horizontal distance is approximately

$$x_{t1} = r\theta_1 = \frac{V_{TO}^2}{0.44g}\frac{T_c - D_c}{W} \qquad (6:8)$$

The corresponding vertical distance, from the geometry of Fig. 6:1, is

$$h_1 = \frac{x_{t1}\theta_1}{2} \qquad (6:9)$$

In some cases, the distance h_1 will turn out to be greater than 50 ft, in which case the transition distance necessary to reach 50 ft altitude may be calculated from the proportionality $x_t/50 = x_{t1}/h_1$.

c. Climbing Distance.—Equilibrium of the forces in Fig. 6:2*c* for steady climb at an angle θ_1 requires that $W \sin \theta_1 = T_c - D_c \approx W\theta_1$ as indicated by equation (6:6). The horizontal distance necessary to climb to $50 - h_1$ ft is accordingly

$$x_c = \frac{50 - h_1}{(T_c - D_c)/W} \qquad (6:10)$$

The total take-off distance x_{TO} is

$$x_{TO} = x_g + x_t + x_c \qquad (6:11)$$

The foregoing simplified approximate take-off calculations are original with the author and are not presented elsewhere in the literature. They are believed to be sufficiently accurate because of the diversity of assumptions involved in other treatments and because of the diversity of practices in actual take-offs. An example illustrating the application of the above method follows:

Example.—An airplane (the Lockheed Lodestar previously used as an example) weighs 17,500 lb and has a wing area of 551 sq ft. The drag and lift coefficients for the take-off configuration may be assumed related by the equation

$$C_D = 0.0196 + 0.049C_L^2 \text{ up to } C_{L\,\max} = 1.55(v_s = 89\text{ mph})$$

The two engines develop 760 Bhp each and are governed to 2,100 rpm for sea-level take-off. The propellers are 10 ft 6 in. in diameter and have the characteristics shown in Fig. A49, page 455. The rolling-resistance coefficient of the wheels during take-off is $\mu = 0.10$. Find the take-off distance to clear a 50-ft obstacle at the end of the runway at sea level with no wind, assuming $v_{TO} = 1.2v_s$.

Solution.—a. To calculate the ground run. 1. Calculate the thrust available at start and at take-off thus: Since the rpm is governed to 2,100, calculate

$$C_P = 0.5\,\frac{\text{Bhp}/1{,}000}{\left(\dfrac{\text{rpm}}{1{,}000}\right)^3\left(\dfrac{D}{10}\right)^5} = \frac{0.5 \times 0.760}{2.1^3 \times 1.05^5} = 0.032$$

At $v_{TO} = 1.2v_s = 1.2 \times 89$ mph $= 107$ mph, $V_{TO} = 157$ ft per sec, and

$$\frac{V_{TO}}{nD} = \frac{157 \times 60}{2{,}100 \times 10.5} = 0.428$$

In Fig. A50, page 456, read $\eta = 0.72$ at $V/nD = 0.428$; in Fig. A49, page 455, read (extrapolating) $C_T = 0.105$ at $V/nD = 0$. From these values calculate at start

$$T_0 = C_T\rho n^2D^4 = \frac{0.105}{420}\left(\frac{2{,}100}{60}\right)^2 \times 10.5^4 = 3{,}730 \text{ lb per engine}$$

At take-off,

$$T_{TO} = \frac{760 \times 550 \times 0.72}{157} = 1{,}920 \text{ lb per engine}$$

2. Calculate the rolling resistance, drag at take-off, and initial and final net thrust as follows:

$$\text{Rolling resistance} = \mu W = 0.10 \times 17{,}500 \text{ lb}$$

Drag at take-off, based on $C_{D\,\min} = q_{TO} = \dfrac{\rho V_{TO}^2}{2} = \dfrac{157^2}{2 \times 420} = 29.3$ lb per sq ft

$$D_{TO} = C_{D\,\min}\, qS = 0.0196 \times 29.3 \times 551 = 316 \text{ lb}$$
$$\text{Initial net thrust} = T_{NI} = 2 \times 3{,}730 - 1{,}750 = 5{,}710 \text{ lb}$$
$$\text{Final net thrust} = T_{NF} = 2 \times 1{,}920 - 316 = 3{,}526 \text{ lb}$$

3. Calculate the ground run by Diehl's method as follows:
Calculate $T_{NF}/T_{NI} = 3{,}526/5{,}710 = 0.617$.
Read, in Fig. 6:4, $K_s = 0.021$.
Calculate from equation (6:5)

$$x_g = 0.021 \times \frac{157^2}{5{,}710/17{,}500} = 1{,}584 \text{ ft}$$

b. To calculate the horizontal and vertical transition distances x_{t1} and h_1: 1. Calculate the drag D_c in climb at take-off speed thus: With $q_{T0} = 29.3$ lb per sq ft as before, $S = 551$, and $W = 17{,}500$.

$$C_{LT0} = \frac{W}{qS} = \frac{17{,}500}{29.3 \times 551} = 1.08$$
$$C_D = 0.0196 + 0.049 \times 1.08^2 = 0.0770$$
$$D_c = \frac{C_D}{C_L}W = \frac{0.077}{1.08} \times 17{,}500 = 1{,}250 \text{ lb}$$

2. Calculate θ_1, x_{t1}, and h_1 from equations (6:6) to (6:9) thus:

$$\theta_1 = \frac{T_c - D_c}{W} = \frac{2 \times 1{,}920 - 1{,}250}{17{,}500} = \frac{2{,}590}{17{,}500} = 0.148 \text{ radian}$$

$$r = \frac{157^2}{0.44 \times 32.2} = 1{,}740 \text{ ft}$$

$$x_{t1} = r\theta_1 = 1{,}740 \times 0.148 = 257 \text{ ft}$$

$$h_1 = \frac{x_{t1}\theta_1}{2} = \frac{257 \times 0.148}{2} = 19 \text{ ft}$$

(If h_1 had turned out to be over 50 ft, the 50-ft obstacle would be cleared before the end of transition and x_c need not be calculated.)

c. To calculate the horizontal distance in climbing the remainder of the distance to 50 ft, use equation (6:10) thus:

$$x_c = \frac{50 - h_1}{\theta_1} = \frac{50 - 19}{0.148} = 210 \text{ ft}$$

The total take-off distance is thus

$$x_{T0} = x_g + x_t + x_c = 1{,}584 + 257 + 210 = 2{,}051$$

This is the answer called for.

The foregoing calculation neglects the effect of *wind*, which is seen in Fig. 6:5 to be a major effect. In Fig. 6:5 the solid line represents the average of a large number of flight-test results reported by Diehl.[1]

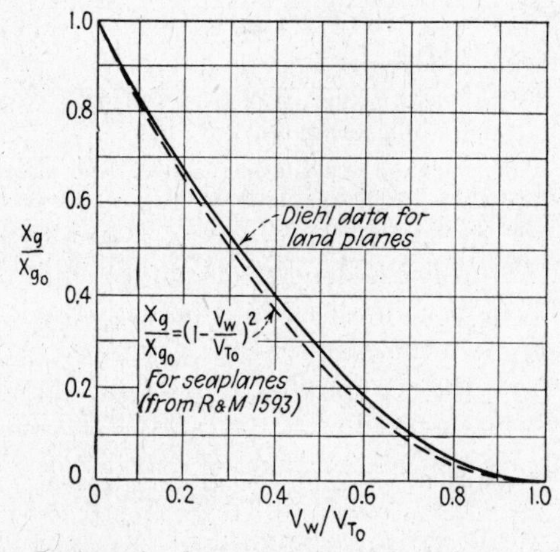

FIG. 6:5.—Effect of wind on x_g. (*From Diehl, "Engineering Aerodynamics," rev. ed.*)

For a first approximation, the total landing distance may be considered to be affected in the same way as the ground run, though for more accurate calculations the effect of wind on transition and climbing distances should be taken into account by adding these results vectorially.

Another major factor affecting take-off distance is altitude; this

[1] DIEHL, W. S., "Engineering Aerodynamics," rev. ed.

effect is large because altitude affects the stalling speed and therefore the take-off speed, which enters into the ground run as a squared term, as seen in equation (6:4).

The effects of both wind and altitude on the take-off and landing distances for a particular airplane (the Lockheed Constellation) at a particular gross weight are plotted in Fig. 6:6. The take-off lines there plotted show a break at 5,000 ft altitude because the calculated take-off distances (from the Constellation Airplane Operating Manual)

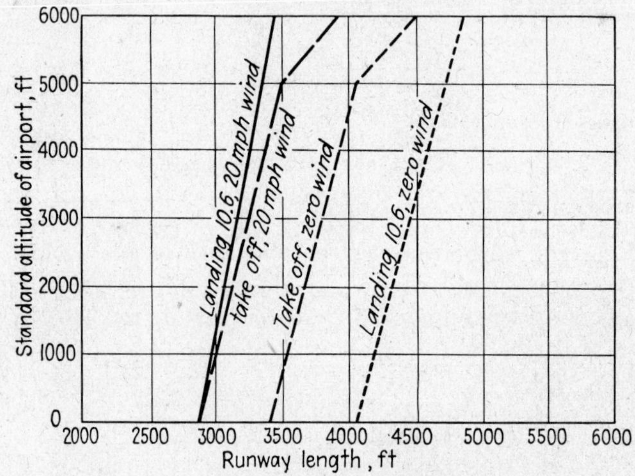

FIG. 6:6.—Effects of wind and altitude on necessary runway length, Lockheed Constellation airplane at W = 82,600 lb gross weight. (*Replotted from Lockheed mode 49 Operating Manual.*)

are the more critical of *two* distances, (1) those required to accelerate to speed v_1 = 106 mph with all engines operating at take-off power, and to stop therefrom in the event of engine failure, or (2) the distance to climb to a 50-ft height at a speed v_2 = 113 mph when the one engine is made inoperative at a speed v_1 = 106 mph. The calculations show that if one of the engines fails on take-off and the corrected indicated air speed is less than 106 mph the climb should be continued on three engines. Below 5,000 ft airport altitude the greater distance is required if the airplane is stopped; above 5,000 the greater distance is required if the climb is continued; this accounts for the break in the curves.

6:2. Landing of a Landplane over an Obstacle.—The process of landing over an obstacle, like that of take-off over an obstacle, may be considered to consist of several phases: the steady glide, a curved-path transition, and a ground run. In the case of landing with a tricycle landing gear, a small additional time must be allowed between the curved-path transition and the braked ground run because of the time necessary to lower the nose wheel carefully. The net effect of the change from conventional to tricycle landing gear is, however, greatly in favor of the tricycle landing gear for short landings, because of the large friction coefficient that can be assumed (and actually applied) without danger of nosing the airplane over. The following treatment is based on a study by Crockett and Bonney[1]

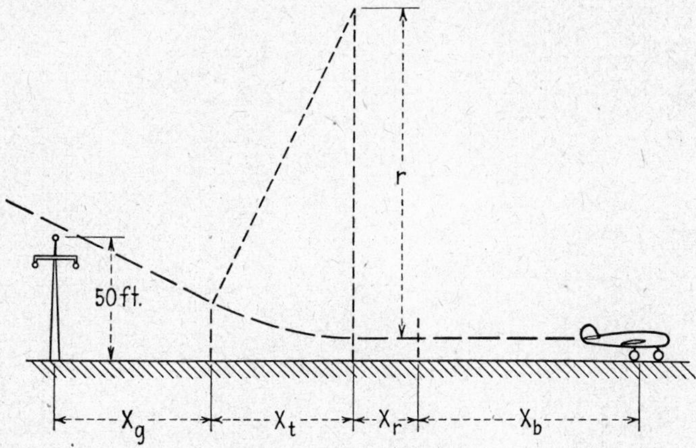

FIG. 6:7.—Components of landing distance over 50-ft obstacle.

which gave special consideration to the use of reversed propeller thrust in retarding the airplane during transition and after landing. This study indicated that the use of reversible-pitch propellers might become common in the attempt to keep landing distance down on heavily loaded airplanes such as are necessary for optimum cruising performance.

In the following analysis the landing distance X_L over an obstacle will be considered to consist of four components that are additive, as shown in the equation

$$X_L = X_g + X_t + X_r + X_b \tag{6:12}$$

in which X_g is the glide distance, X_t the transition distance, X_r the free-rolling distance before brakes and/or reversed propellers are applied, and X_b the braking distance. These distances are shown graphically in Fig. 6:7.

The calculating procedure recommended by Crockett and Bonney is based on the following assumptions: (1) that the glide is at a speed of $1.3V_{SL}$, where V_{SL} is the stalling speed in the landing configura-

[1] CROCKETT, HAROLD B., and E. ARTHUR BONNEY, Reverse Pitch Propellers as Airplane Landing Brakes, *J. Aeronaut. Sci.*, October, 1945, pp. 441–447.

tion; (2) that the transition involves a deceleration from $V_g = 1.3V_{SL}$ to $V_g = V_{SL}$; (3) that a time of 3 sec is required to lower the nose wheel of the tricycle landing gear; (4) that the brakes are applied (and, if reversed-pitch propeller braking is used, the reversed pitch is applied) as soon as the nose wheel is down and until the airplane stops. The equations that express these relationships are

$$X_g = 50 \frac{C_{Lg}}{C_{Dg}} \tag{6:13}$$

$$X_t = \int_{1.3V_{SL}}^{V_{SL}} \frac{1}{a_t} V dV \tag{6:14}$$

where

$$a_t = \frac{D_g + D_S}{2(W/g)} \tag{6:15}$$

giving

$$X_t = \left(\frac{W}{S}\right) \frac{18.00}{(1.69C_{Dg} + C_{DS}\text{ ground})\sigma} \tag{6:16}$$

$$X_r = 3V_{SL} \tag{6:17}$$

$$X_b = \int_{V_{SL}}^{0} \frac{1}{a} V dV \tag{6:18}$$

where

$$a = -\frac{Fg}{W} \tag{6:19}$$

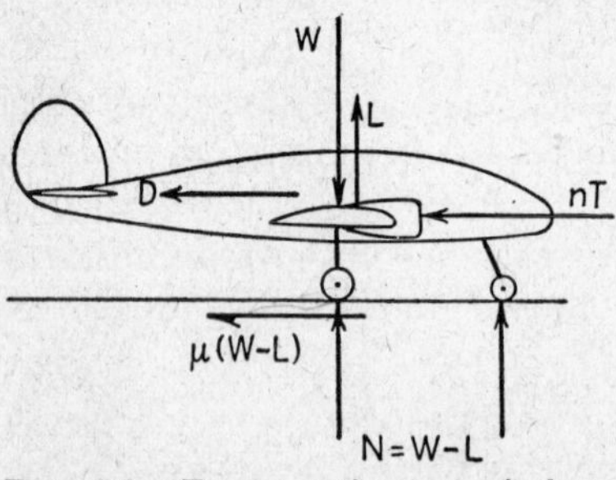

FIG. 6·8.—Forces acting on airplane during braked ground run.

In equation (6:19), F is the net retarding force shown in Fig. 6:8; subscripts g and S refer to glide and stall, respectively. If the variation of reverse-pitch thrust with speed is assumed to be given by an equation of the form

$$T = K_1 + K_2V^2 \tag{6:20}$$

and the coefficients K_1 and K_2 are determined from the propeller characteristics, the net retarding force becomes

$$F = \frac{C_D\sigma\rho_0V^2S}{2} + n(K_1 + K_2V^2) + \mu\left(W - \frac{C_L\sigma\rho_0V^2S}{2}\right) \tag{6:21}$$

where n is the number of engines on which reversed pitch is applied. Using this force in equations (6:19) and (6:18) gives as a result of integration

$$X_b = \frac{0.0334v_S^2}{(\mu C_L - C_D)/C_{LS} - (2.15nK_2v_S^2/W)} \log_e \frac{\mu + (K_1n/W)}{\mu + \dfrac{K_1n}{W} + \dfrac{2.15K_2nv_S^2}{W} - \dfrac{\mu C_L - C_D}{C_{LS}}} \quad (6:22)$$

Equation (6:22) is, of course, greatly simplified if the terms involving propeller thrust are removed, giving

$$X_b = \frac{0.0334v_S^2}{(\mu C_L - C_D)/C_{LS}} \log_e \frac{\mu}{\mu - (\mu C_L - C_D)/C_{LS}} \quad (6:23)$$

Crockett and Bonney suggest that reverse-pitch braking can not only provide for a much shorter ground run on ice-covered runways but can also be used to reduce the transition distance, though the safety of this procedure is still (1946) open to question.

It is possible that rocket jets may prove to be more economical than reverse-pitch propeller braking as this matter is studied further. Rocket jets for assisting take-off proved quite satisfactory in military operations during the Second World War.

6:3. Problems

1. Given the following data on an Ercoupe light airplane, find (*a*) the horizontal distance necessary on *landing*, at sea level with no wind, to clear a 50-ft obstacle and come to a full stop using brakes, and neglecting the drag of idling propellers: and (*b*) the horizontal distance necessary on *take-off*, from sea level with no wind, to clear a 50-ft obstacle after starting from rest. All data are intended to be the same as in previous problems on this airplane.

Airplane data. $W = 1{,}260$ lb, $S = 142.6$ sq ft, $C_D = 0.030 + 0.066C_L^2$. No flaps; $C_{L\,max} = 1.50$. $h/b = 0.085$ on ground. $C_L = 0.30$ on ground.

Engine data. Full throttle sea level $Bhp/rpm = 75/2{,}550$, direct drive.

Propeller data. $D = 6$ ft 0 in., fixed pitch, $\beta_{0.75R} = 16$ deg, characteristics as in Fig. A55, page 461.

Ground data. Rolling-traction coefficient for take-off, $\mu = 0.05$. Sliding-friction coefficient for tires on landing, $\mu = 0.60$.

2 Given the following data on a Lockheed Constellation airplane, find (*a*) the horizontal distance necessary on *landing*, at sea level with no wind, to clear a 50-ft obstacle and come to a full stop, using wheel brakes only, (*b*) the *landing* distance, at sea level with no wind, to clear a 50-ft obstacle and come to a full stop, using full-throttle reverse pitch on two engines, as well as brakes; and (*c*) the horizontal distance necessary on take-off, from sea level with no wind, and clear a 50-ft obstacle after starting from rest.

Airplane data. $W = 86{,}250$ lb, $S = 1{,}650$ sq ft, $C_D = 0.0154 + 0.0426C_L^2$ (retracted flaps). $C_{L\,max} = 1.60$ (flaps retracted). For take-off flap setting, assume $C_D = 0.020 + 0.043C_L^2$ to $C_{L\,max} = 1.8$. For landing flap setting, assume $C_L = 0.030 + 0.043C_L^2$ to $C_{L\,max} = 2.0$. Assume $C_L = 0$ on ground.

Engine data. Sea-level take-off, $Bhp/rpm = 2{,}200/2{,}800$. Propeller gear ratio 0.4375 to 1; characteristics as on page 464.

Propeller data. $D = 15$ ft 2 in., three blades, assume the characteristics in Fig. A49, page 455; constant rpm governed; assume reverse-pitch characteristics as in forward flight.

Ground data. Rolling-traction coefficient for take-off, $\mu = 0.05$. Sliding-friction coefficient for tires on landing, $\mu = 0.60$.

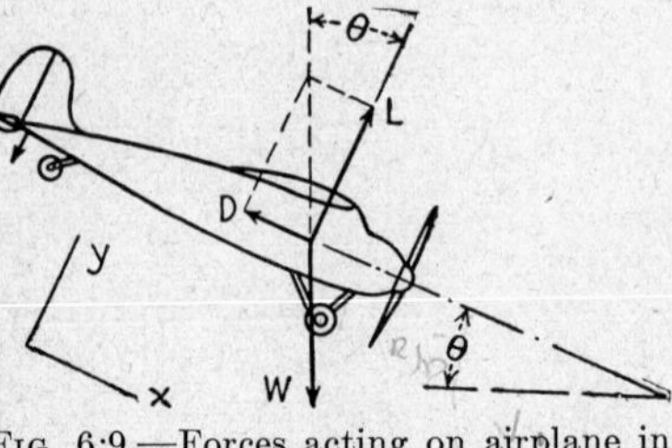

FIG. 6:9.—Forces acting on airplane in glide.

6:4. Gliding and Diving.—The forces acting on an airplane in a steady glide without power are shown in Fig. 6:9. (The tail force is negligible compared with L, D, or W, but its moment about the center of gravity is not negligible and must be considered when calculations of balance in glide are made.) The drag force D must include the drag of the idling propeller. Since acceleration = 0 in steady glide and $\Sigma F_x = 0$ and $\Sigma F_y = 0$, with x and y axes as shown, these equations give

$$L = W \cos \theta \tag{6:24}$$
$$D = W \sin \theta \tag{6:25}$$
$$\frac{L}{D} = \cot \theta \tag{6:26}$$

where θ is the angle of the path of glide with the horizontal. The angle θ is determined by the stabilizer and elevator settings.

The speed of glide at sea level in mph, from equation (6:24) and $L = 0.00256\sigma v^2 SC_L$, is

$$v = \sqrt{\frac{W/S}{0.00256\sigma C_L\{\cos \theta + [\sin \theta/(L/D)]\}}} \tag{6:27}$$

For small angles of glide, $\cos \theta \approx 1.0$, and $\sin \theta/(L/D)$ is negligible compared with 1.0; therefore,

$$v = \sqrt{\frac{W/S}{0.00256\sigma C_L}} \tag{6:28}$$

For a vertical dive, $\cos \theta = 0$, $\sin \theta = 1.0$, and

$$v_m = \sqrt{\frac{W/S}{0.00256\sigma C_{D\,\min}}} \tag{6:29}$$

For any assumed angle of glide θ, L/D can be calculated from equation (6:26) and the corresponding angle of attack C_L, and C_D can be read from a graph of the airplane characteristics; thus, equation (6:27) can be used to calculate the speed of glide. If speed of glide is plotted against angle of glide as in Fig. 6:10, the resulting graph is called a gliding-velocity diagram, a special form of hodograph.

The limiting speed of vertical dive is commonly calculated in connection with the problem of determining design loads for the wings of the airplane. Under these conditions the drag of the idling propeller is a major factor and cannot be neglected. The speed at which the propeller will rotate when idling depends on the friction horsepower of the engine if "dead" and on the idling-jet adjustment of the carburetor if throttled. Terminal dive calculations for determination of design loads for wings are commonly made on the assumption that the propeller rpm is governed or limited to some arbitrary value. Since the propeller-drag coefficient depends on V/nD, the propeller drag cannot be estimated until the terminal dive velocity is known; hence, the solution for terminal dive velocity must be by trial.

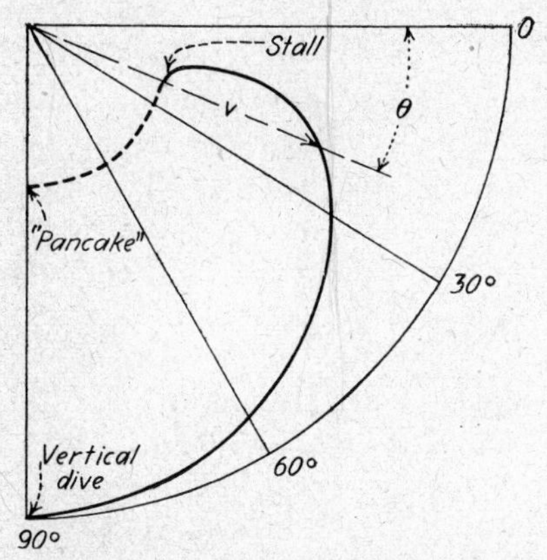

FIG. 6:10.—Polar diagram of gliding speed *vs.* angle of glide.

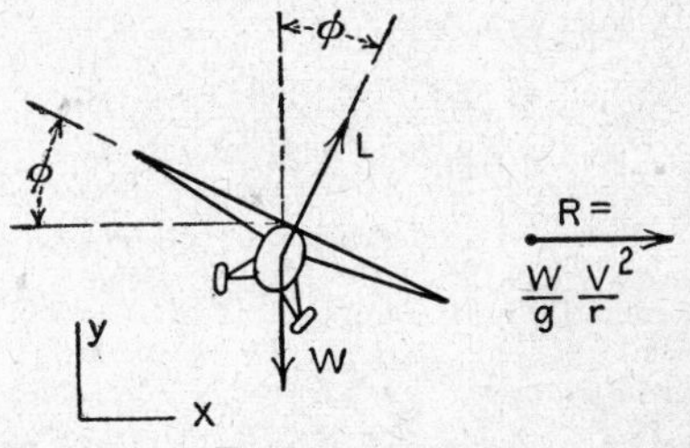

FIG. 6:11.—Forces acting on airplane in horizontal turn without sideslip.

6:5. Level and Gliding Turns.—The forces acting on an airplane in a properly banked horizontal turn are shown in Fig. 6:11. The lift L must be greater in a turn than in horizontal flight, for only the vertical component of the lift is available for supporting the weight. In Fig. 6:11, $\Sigma F_y = 0$ and $\Sigma F_x = \left(\frac{W}{g}\right)\left(\frac{V^2}{r}\right)$; hence,

$$L \cos \phi = W \tag{6:30}$$

$$L \sin \phi = \frac{W}{g}\frac{V^2}{r} \tag{6:31}$$

where r is the radius of turn and ϕ is the angle of bank. Solving equations (6:30) and (6:31) together gives

$$\tan \phi = \frac{V^2}{gr} \tag{6:32}$$

For minimum radius of turn the wings must operate at their maximum lift coefficient, and the airplane must be banked at the maximum angle at which the power available will supply the speed necessary to support the weight. A logarithmic graph of Hp_r and Hp_a against speed, as in Fig. 6:12, can be used for graphical determination of minimum radius of turn in the following manner: At a given angle of attack (*e.g.*, at $C_{L\ max}$) Hp_r varies as V^3; hence, a line through Hp_r at $C_{L\ max}$ with a slope of 3:1 represents the locus of power required at $C_{L\ max}$ at different speeds. The speed at which the power available will propel the airplane at $C_{L\ max}$ is determined by the intersection A in Fig. 6:12. For the particular airplane for which curves are plotted in Fig. 6:12, this speed is seen to be 70 mph, whereas the speed of level flight at $C_{L\ max}$ was 59 mph. From equation (6:30), $L/W = \sec \phi$; and if V_t is the speed of turn at minimum radius and V_s is stalling speed,

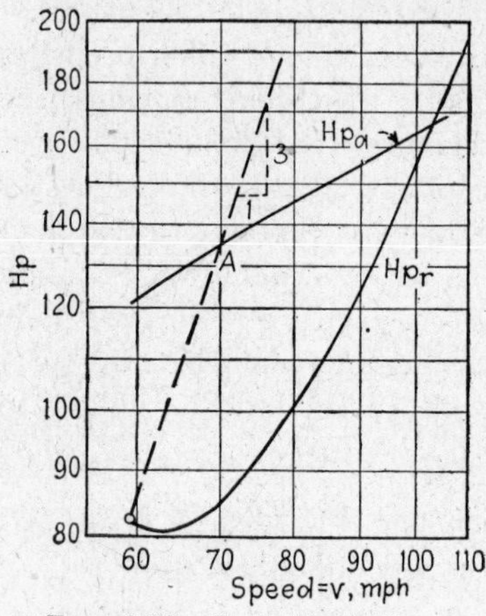

FIG. 6:12.—Logarithmic horsepower-speed graph for graphical determination of minimum radius of turn. (*From Diehl, "Engineering Aerodynamics," rev. ed.*)

$$\sec \phi = \left(\frac{V_t}{V_s}\right)^2 \tag{6:33}$$

For the example in Fig. 6:12

$$\sec \phi = (70/59)^2 = 1.41$$
$$\phi = 44.5° \quad \tan \phi = 0.98$$

and, from equation (6:32),

$$r_{min} = \frac{70 \times (88/60)^2}{32.2 \times 0.98} = 335 \text{ ft}$$

A general equation for r_{min}, derived from equations (6:32) and (6:30), is

$$r_{min} = \frac{W/S}{0.00119\sigma g C_{L\ max} \sin \phi} \tag{6:34}$$

where ϕ is determined from equation (6:33). A pilot should know the minimum radius of turn of his airplane for maximum safety in maneuvering around small fields. Equation (6:34) points out the fact that r_{min} depends chiefly on wing loading, more heavily loaded airplanes requiring a larger radius to turn.

Calculations on *gliding turns* are of practical importance because they permit determining the minimum altitude from which a return to the airport is possible in the event of motor failure soon after take-off. The forces acting on an airplane in a gliding turn are shown in Fig. 6:13. For the axes shown in Fig. 6:13 and for a constant speed of glide in a helical path of radius of curvature $= r$, angle of bank $= \phi$, and angle of glide $= \theta$, $\Sigma F_z = 0$, and $\Sigma F_y = R = (W/g)(V^2/r)$;

From $\Sigma F_x = 0$,

$$D = W \sin \theta \tag{6:35}$$

From $\Sigma F_z = 0$,

$$L = W \frac{\cos \theta}{\cos \phi} \tag{6:36}$$

From $\Sigma F_y = R$,

$$L \sin \phi = \frac{W}{g} \frac{V^2}{r} \tag{6:37}$$

The radius of the cylinder on which the helical path may be considered wound is $r \cos^2 \theta$, and the altitude lost in a complete turn is

$$h = 2\pi r \sin \theta \cos \theta \tag{6:38}$$

The above equations can be solved for minimum loss of altitude in a gliding turn in terms of wing loading, parasite drag, and aspect ratio. For minimum loss of altitude it can be shown that the angle of bank should be about 45 deg, and the wings should operate at maximum lift.

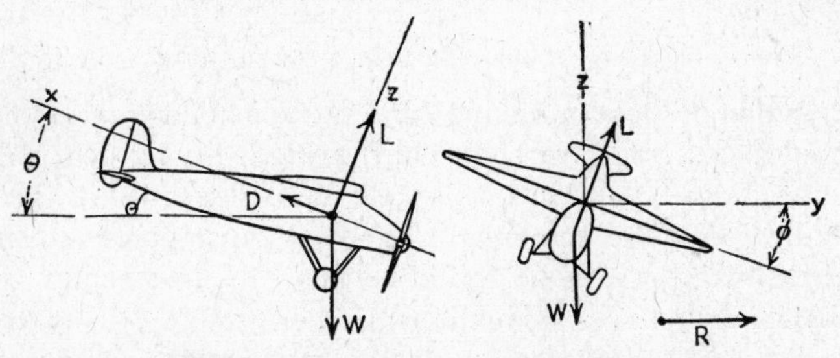

FIG. 6:13.—Forces acting on airplane in gliding turn.

6:6. Problems

1. For the Ercoupe airplane for which data were given in Prob. 1, Art. 6:3, (*a*) find the angle and speed of flattest glide, (*b*) find the terminal velocity of vertical dive, neglecting propeller drag, and (*c*) plot a gliding diagram similar to Fig. 6:10.

2. Using the logarithmic charts of power required and power available for the Ercoupe and Constellation airplanes prepared in Probs. 1 and 2, Art. 5:4, use the method of Art. 6·5 to calculate the minimum radius of level turn at sea level (*a*) for the Ercoupe and (*b*) for the Constellation.

3. For the Ercoupe airplane for which data were given in Prob. 1, Art. 6:3, find the minimum loss of altitude in a 360-deg gliding turn, without power, neglecting the drag of the idling propeller.

CHAPTER 7

SEAPLANES AND FLYING BOATS

Many airplanes are equipped to take off from water and "land" on water. Such airplanes are called *flying boats* if the boat hull replaces the airplane fuselage or *seaplanes* if floats take the place of wheels on a conventional landplane. If flying boats or seaplanes are also equipped with wheels for landing, they are called *amphibians*. In many localities, marine aircraft are safer and more useful than landplanes because of the more widespread facilities for emergency landings and the closer proximity of landing facilities to centers of population.

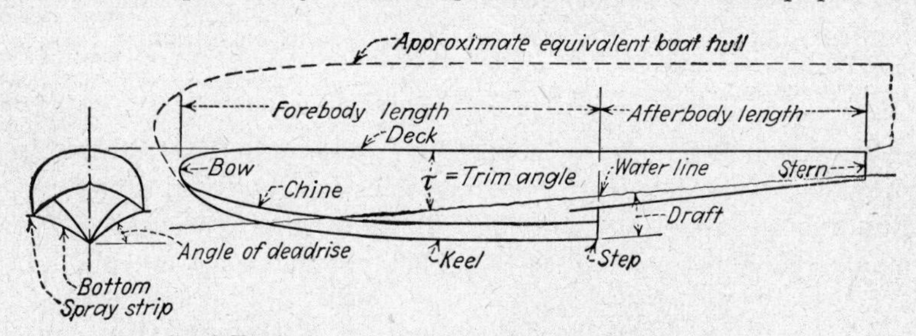

FIG. 7:1.—Typical seaplane float and terms used to describe it.

7:1. Action of Float in Taking Off.—A typical float and some of the terms used to describe it are shown in Fig. 7:1. Flying-boat hulls have similar lines; a boat hull approximately equivalent in side view to the hull is indicated by broken lines. The boat thus appears to have two steps; the forward step is spoken of as the main step or just the step.

A float or hull serves three major purposes:

1. It must displace water so as to have buoyancy to support the weight of the ship when it is standing still. The weight of the displaced water (= displacement = Δ) is usually considered to be 64 times the displaced volume in cubic feet for sea water. Conservative practice usually requires that the Δ of the float completely submerged should be two to four times the weight of the ship. These float displacements correspond to excess buoyancies of 100 to 300 per cent, respectively. The submerged volume is usually 40 to 60 per cent of the product of the three over-all dimensions ("block" coefficient = 0.4 to 0.6).

2. It must offer small resistance to motion at low speed so that a

given amount of power will make it move fast enough to obtain a dynamic reaction from the water that will force it to rise out of the water and ride "on the step" in a "planing" attitude.

3. It must offer small resistance while planing so as to permit the ship to increase its speed beyond the stalling speed and leave the water.

The above process of taking off is of course not the only method. A conventional low-speed watercraft (*e.g.*, a canoe) could be used as a seaplane float and would take off without planing if enough power were supplied, but the necessary power is usually prohibitive.

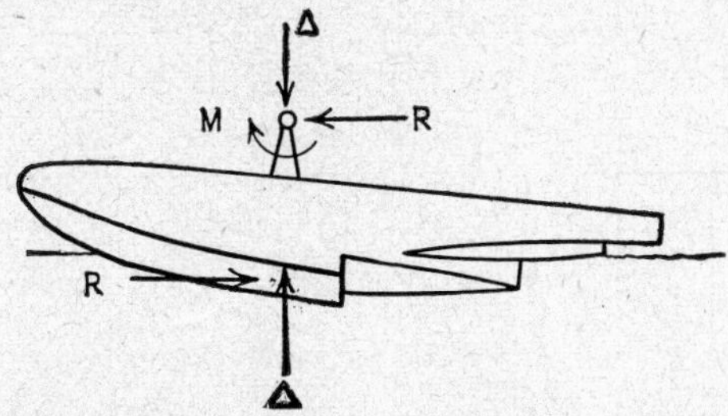

FIG. 7:2.—Forces acting on model hull in tank test.

7:2. Model Tests on Boat Hulls.—Tests to determine the take-off characteristics of hulls and floats are commonly made by towing scale models in a tank. Such tanks are in use at the Washington Navy Yard and at the NACA laboratory at Langley Field. The forces acting on a model hull in a tank test at constant speed and trim angle are shown in Fig. 7:2. For a given load and speed there is in general only one angle of trim that will give zero moment M. Tests run at zero moment are spoken of as "free to trim."

Tests on hulls differ from tests on airfoils in that the load on the water can be varied independently of angle of attack and the forces do not vary as the square of the speed. A different group of dimensionless coefficients is therefore necessary to represent the results of hull tests independently of the size of the model. The coefficients[1] in common use are

$$C_\Delta = \frac{\Delta}{wb^3} = \text{load coefficient} \tag{7:1}$$

$$C_R = \frac{R}{wb^3} = \text{resistance coefficient} \tag{7:2}$$

$$C_M = \frac{M}{wb^4} = \text{trimming-moment coefficient} \tag{7:3}$$

$$C_V = \frac{V}{\sqrt{gb}} = \text{speed coefficient} \tag{7:4}$$

[1] From *NACA Tech. Note* 464.

In these definitions, Δ, R, and M are the forces shown in Fig. 7:2, b is the beam of the hull (the maximum width at the water line), and w is the density of the water (63.6 per cu ft in the NACA tank). With V in feet per second, $g = 32.2$ ft per sec².

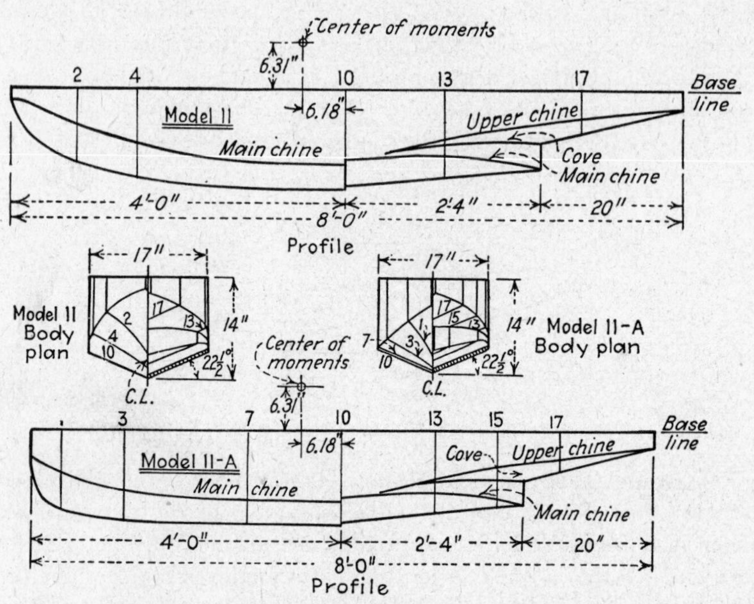

FIG. 7:3.—Lines of NACA hull models Nos. 11 and 11-A. (*From NACA TN* 464, 470.)

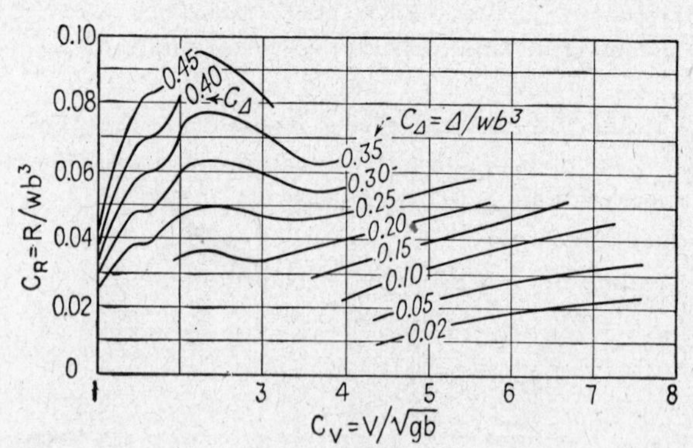

FIG. 7:4.—Resistance coefficient at best trim angle for NACA Model-11 hull. (*From NACA TN* 464.)

Lines of two of the best hulls tested in the NACA tank are shown in Fig. 7:3. Graphs of C_R *vs.* C_V for constant C_Δ are commonly obtained for various angles of trim: graphs for the "best" angles of trim (angles of minimum R/Δ) for these two hulls are shown in Figs. 7:9 and 7:5. Two other ways of plotting the data are shown in Figs. 7:6 and 7:7.

Of these, Fig. 7:6 (Δ/R *vs.* C_V for constant C_Δ) has been most widely used for take-off calculations. Figure 7:7 (Δ/R *vs.* C_Δ for constant C_V at angles of maximum Δ/R) provides a simple summary of the hull characteristics useful in comparing different hulls.

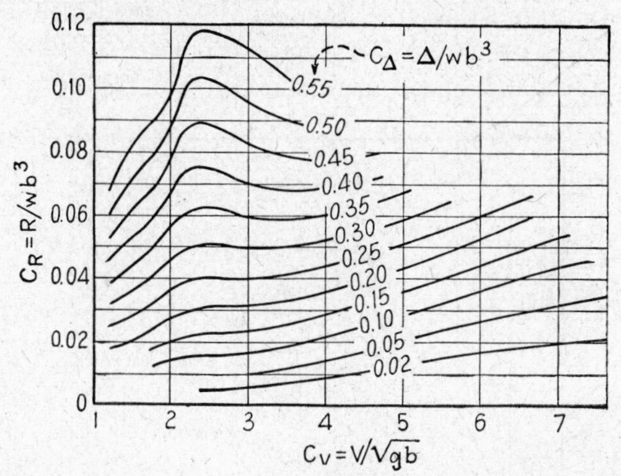

Fig. 7:5.—Resistance coefficient at best trim angle for NACA Model 11-A hull. (*From NACA TN* 470.)

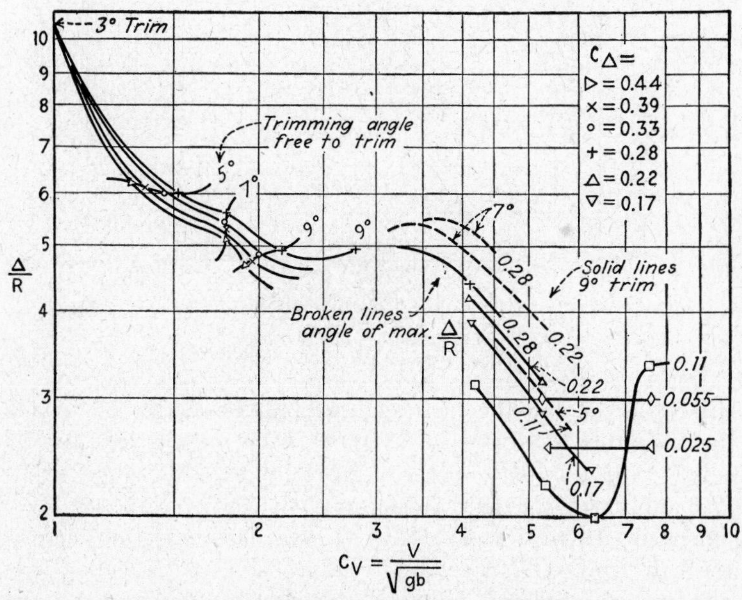

Fig. 7:6.—Water resistance characteristics of NACA Model-11 hull. (*From NACA TN* 464.)

Note in Fig. 7:4 that the resistance increases with speed up to $C_V \approx 2.3$ at all values of constant load. During this speed increase the hull is rising out of the water, getting "on the step." Beyond this speed, the rise out of the water more than offsets the increase in resistance due to friction and eddies, and the resistance passes its "hump"; $C_V \approx 2.3$ is spoken of as the *hump-speed coefficient* for this hull. Beyond $C_V = 3$ or 4, the resistance again rises because of skin friction and induced water resistance (analogous to induced drag of wings), the skin friction becoming the dominant factor at high speeds. In Fig. 7:6, tests at low speed were run free to trim ($C_M = 0$) because

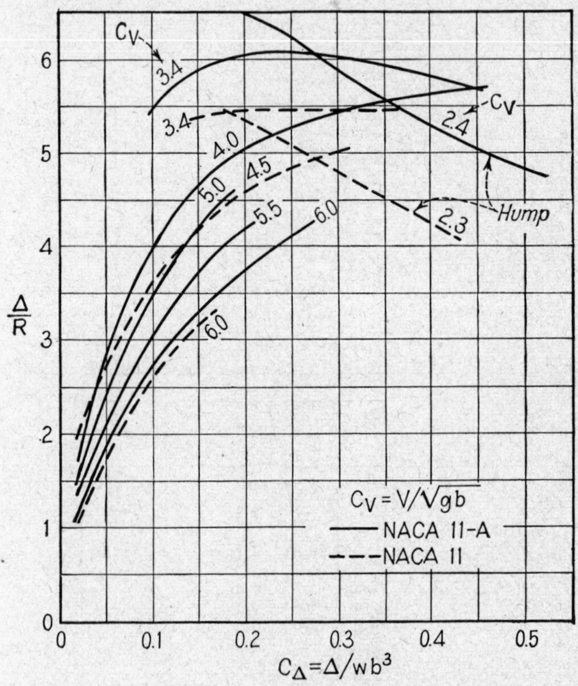

FIG. 7:7.—Δ/R *vs.* C_Δ for trim at angles of maximum Δ/R for NACA hulls Nos. 11 and 11-A. (*From NACA TN* 470.)

on the full-scale ship the trim angle cannot be controlled by means of the elevators at low speeds. Different free-to-trim curves are obtained with different center-of-gravity locations: the curves in Fig. 7:6 apply only for the center-of-gravity location shown in Fig. 7:3; at higher speeds, tests were run at various constant-trim angles. It is useful to think of R/Δ as an effective coefficient of sliding friction on the water; minimum friction requires maximum Δ/R. Good take-off of a flying boat requires large Δ/R at hump speed and at high speed. Note in Fig. 7:7 that NACA hulls 11 and 11-A are compared at hump speed ($C_V \approx 2.3$) and at higher values of constant C_V. Note that hull 11-A is considerably superior (higher Δ/R), particularly at hump speed; the principal difference between the two hulls is that hull 11-A has less curvature on the keel forward of the step.

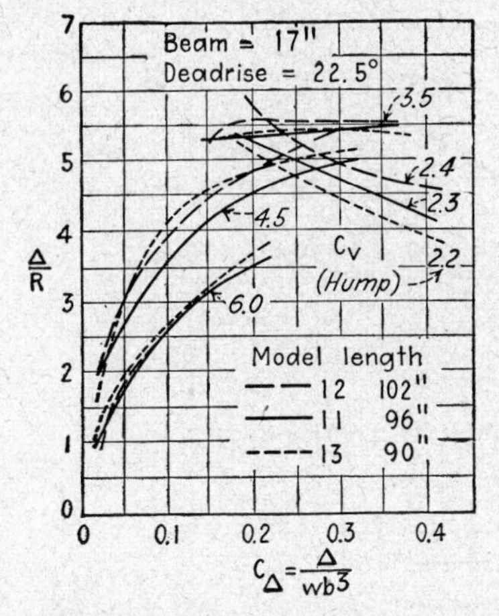

FIG. 7:8.—Effect of change in length on hull characteristics. (*From NACA TN* 491.)

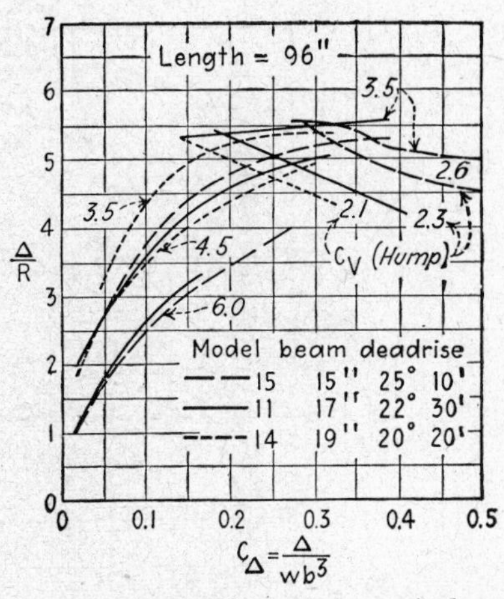

FIG. 7:9.—Effect of change in beam on hull characteristics. (*From NACA TN* 491.)

The effects of variations in hull length and in dead-rise angle on the characteristics of hulls similar to NACA 11 are shown in Figs. 7:8 and 7:9. Note in Fig. 7:8 that a slightly longer hull gives a more favorable (higher) Δ/R at the hump, and note in Fig. 7:9 that a slightly greater dead-rise angle gives a more favorable hump Δ/R, the change making negligible difference in the Δ/R at high speed ($C_V = 6.0$) in either case. Also note by comparison with Fig. 7:7 that the improvements in hump Δ/R due to change in length or dead-rise angle are small compared with the change in forebody keel shape involved in the change from hull 11 to 11-A. For marked improvement in high-speed Δ/R, it appears to be necessary to use a hull with a pointed step (Fig. 7:10), as shown by the characteristics in Fig. 7:11, though for this hull the improvement was made at a sacrifice in hump Δ/R. The sacrifice in hump Δ/R does not appear to be a necessary feature of pointed-step hulls, as is shown by tests on NACA model 35 hull (Fig. 7:12). Note that, at $C_\Delta = 0.5$, model 35 hull gives a Δ/R about 30 per cent better than hull 11-A at all speeds and is slightly inferior to model 22 only at high

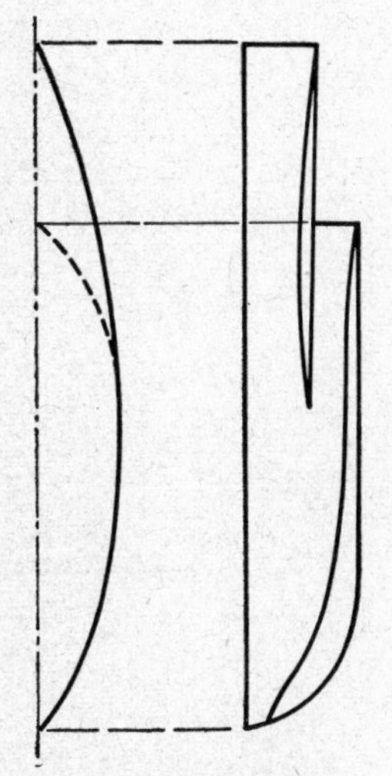

FIG. 7:10.—Lines of NACA Model-22 hull. (*From NACA TN* 488.)

speed ($C_V = 6.0$). Further research is in progress; the latest *NACA Technical Notes* and *Technical Reports* should be consulted.

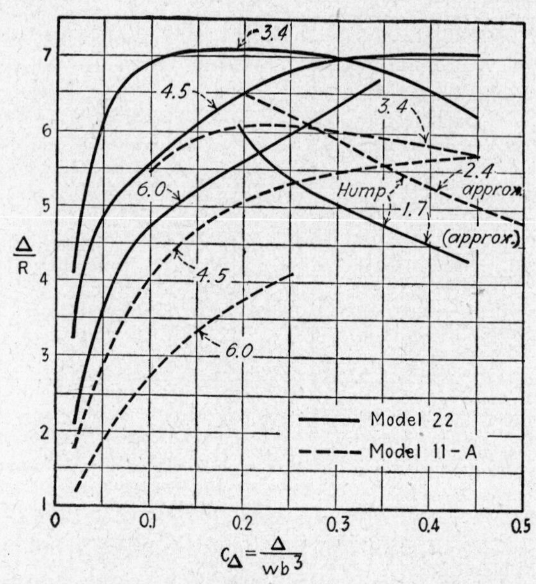

FIG. 7:11.—Characteristics of hull with a pointed step (model 22) compared with NACA 11-A.

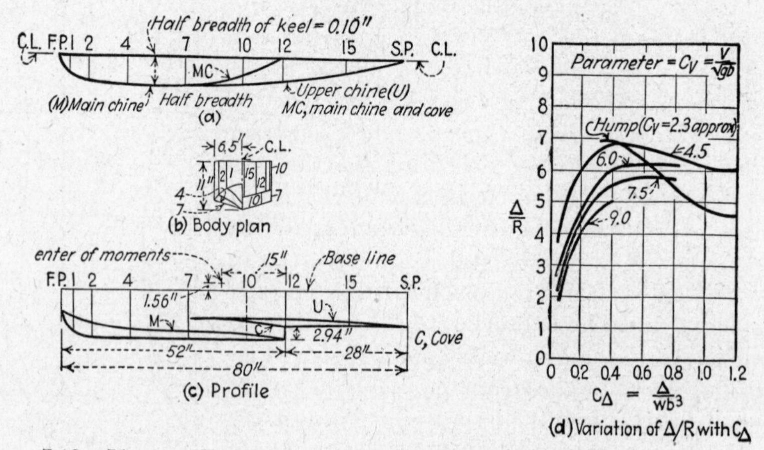

FIG. 7:12.—Lines and characteristics of best pointed-step hull hitherto tested (September, 1934) by the NACA. (*Hull model ao. 35, from NACA TN* 504.)

The above results are based on ⅙-scale models tested in the NACA tank at Langley Field. It is believed that full-scale tests would yield the same conclusions; but because of the differences in Reynolds number and roughness between the models and the full-scale hulls, the numerical values of Δ/R may be 10 to 20 per cent off. Take-off tests have indicated, though not conclusively, that the full-scale hulls have a more favorable Δ/R (at a given C_V and C_Δ) than the models, and studies of skin friction indicate that this should be true for smooth hulls. Sottorf's tests on similar floats of different sizes[1] showed an

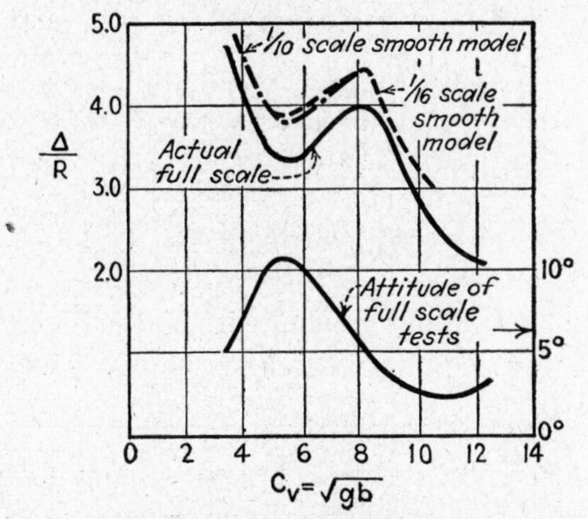

Fig. 7:13.—British data on effect of scale and roughness on characteristics of twin floats of III F seaplane. (*From RM* 1591.)

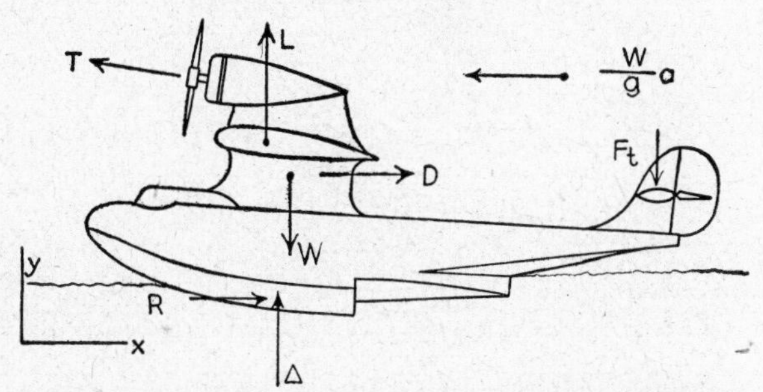

Fig. 7:14.—Forces acting on flying boat during take-off.

increase in hump C_R ($= C_{Rh}$) with increase in scale ratio λ approximately linear to $\Delta C_{Rh}/C_{Rh} = 20$ per cent at $\lambda = 12$; British tests, however (Fig. 7:13), show that the effect of roughness due to rivetheads (and perhaps other factors) more than offsets the effect of scale and that the full-scale results are about 10 per cent less favorable than the tests on smooth models. Because the scale and roughness effects partly compensate, it is believed desirable to use NACA tank test results for take-off calculations without corrections for these factors until more data become available.

7:3. Calculation of Take-off Time.—The forces acting on a typical flying boat during take-off are shown in Fig. 7:14. Since $\Sigma F_y = 0$,

[1] *NACA Tech. Mem.* 704.

if the small vertical component of thrust and the tail force F_t are neglected as compared with the other vertical forces,

$$L + \Delta - W = 0 \tag{7:5}$$

Since $\Sigma F_x = (w/g)a$,

$$T - D - R = \frac{W}{g} a \tag{7:6}$$

The take-off time in a calm, t_0, may be found by integrating $dt = dV/a$ from $V = 0$ to the getaway speed $V = V_G$, the acceleration found in equation (7:6) being used,

$$a = \frac{g}{W} [T - (D + R)] = \frac{g}{W} T_e \tag{7:7}$$

Since R varies in an irregular manner with V, the integration is usually done graphically (or approximately by Simpson's rule). The varia-

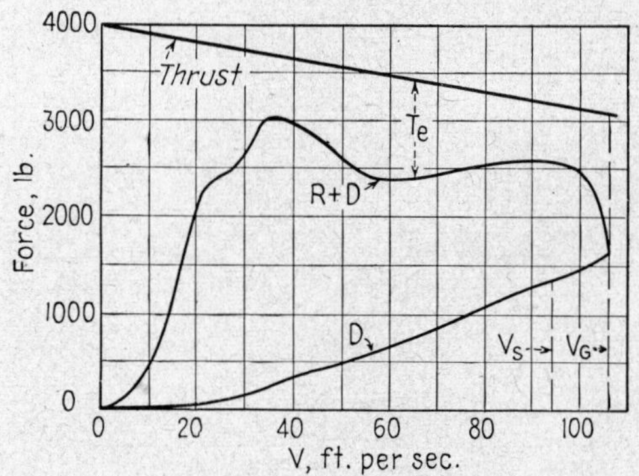

FIG. 7:15.—Variation of forces with speed during take-off for typical flying boat. (*From NACA TN* 464.)

tion of the horizontal forces on a typical flying boat during take-off is shown in Fig. 7:15, and the corresponding plot of $1/a$ *vs.* V for determination of take-off time is shown in Fig. 7:16. These figures are for a getaway speed about 10 per cent greater than stalling speed and imply that the wing is operating at a value of C_L about 20 per cent less than $C_{L\,\max}$. *Minimum* take-off time requires that the ship be "stalled" off the water and $V_G = V_s$. A compromise figure suggested by Stout[1] as an arbitrary standard is $V_g = 1.05V_s$, corresponding to $C_L = 0.9C_{L\,\max}$.

The forces in equation (7:7) may be calculated as follows:

The thrust T should be calculated as explained in Chap. 4, the

[1] STOUT, E. G., Take-off Analysis for Flying Boats and Seaplanes, *Aviation*, August, 1944, p. 150, September, 1944, p. 132.

appropriate procedure for fixed-pitch propeller, constant-rpm propeller, or turbo jet being used in accordance with the specified power plant.

The drag D may be calculated from

$$D = 0.00256\sigma v^2 S C_D \tag{7:8}$$

in which

$$C_D = C_{De\,\min} + \frac{C_L^2}{\pi AR_g e} \tag{7:9}$$

$$C_L = a\alpha_{ag} \tag{7:10}$$

The subscript $(\ )_g$ in equations (7:9) and (7:10) refers to the correc-

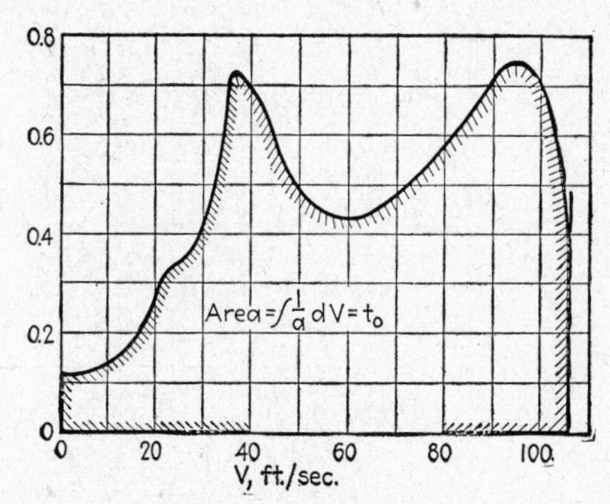

FIG. 7:16.—Plot of $1/a$ *vs.* V for graphical determination of take-off time. (*From NACA TN* 464.)

tions for ground effect, as in Chap. 2, Figs. 2:77 and 2:78, α_{ag} being a function of α_a, which is given by

$$\alpha_a = i_a + \tau \tag{7:11}$$

i_a is the incidence of the zero-lift line of the wing, and τ is the angle of trim.

The water resistance R may be calculated from equation (7:2), with a value of C_R obtained from a graph similar to Fig. 7:4, which requires knowledge of C_V (assumed) and C_Δ from equation (7:1), in which Δ is obtained from equation (7:5) and L is given by the usual equation

$$L = 0.00256\sigma v^2 S C_L \tag{7:12}$$

The principal difficulty in the foregoing procedure is the necessity of making reasonable assumptions for the values of τ and the corresponding wing angle of attack α_a in equation (7:11). At speeds below the hump speed, the angles of trim and attack are usually not controllable by the pilot because of insufficient elevator control. Accordingly, at these speeds, the angles of free trim of the hull for the known center-of-gravity location must be used. Above the minimum speed for longitudinal control, the pilot can set the trim at the best trim angle. The best trim angle for a complete flying boat is the angle of minimum $(D + R)$, and is usually somewhat higher than the best trim angle for the hull (which is the angle of minimum R) because D/L at $C_{L\,max}$ is less than R/Δ at any trim angle, and the greater the portion of the load that can be taken by the wings the quicker will be the take-off. It is difficult, however, to make calculations on this assump-

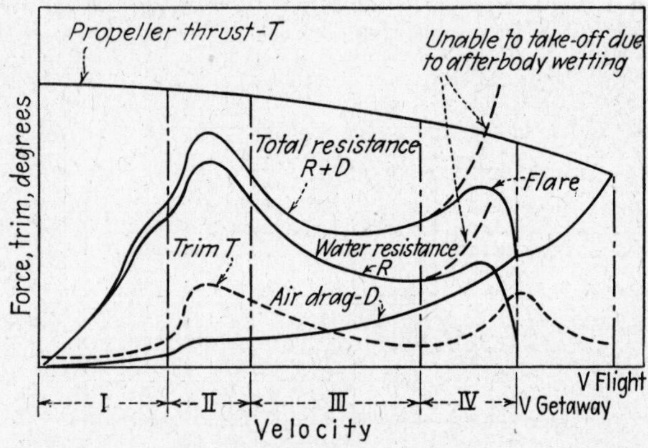

FIG. 7:17.—Phases of take-off.

tion in practice, for the hull data are not usually available at the very high trim angles usually necessary. The angle of wing setting i_a is usually a compromise between the high value desired for quickest take-off and the low value desired for minimum cruising drag. The calculation procedure developed by Stout and widely used in the aircraft industry is to assume that the hull trims at the *best angle for the hull.* This assumption will often result in an apparent inability to take off that does not actually exist, for at high speed, in the region of about 90 per cent of getaway speed, the boat can easily be rocked backward to give maximum lift on the wings and permit take-off. This possibility can be taken account of graphically with sufficient accuracy by drawing an arbitrary *flare* on the curve of total resistance, as shown in Fig. 7:17.

The standard form for take-off computations recommended by Stout is shown in Fig. 7:18. Instructions for filling in Fig. 7:18 follow:

Column 1. Assume arbitrary values of C_V beginning with 1.0 and increasing by increments of 0.2 up to 3.0 and by increments of 0.5 to getaway, which may be at C_V equal to 6 or 7.

Columns 2 and 3. Calculate the corresponding values of v and v^2

from equation (7:4), which is repeated at the bottom of the standard form.

Column 4. At $C_V = 1.0$, with free trim angle (from Fig. 7:19) assume $C_\Delta = C_{\Delta 0} = W/wb^3$, as given at the head of the standard form. For each succeeding value of C_V, assume the C_Δ in the preceding line. Beginning in the region of the hump the value of the trim angle used should be the lower of the two values read from Figs. 7:19 and 7:21.

Engine .... Gross weight, lb. ....

BHP/RPM .... Wing area, sq. ft. ....

Gear ratio .... $C_{\Delta_o} = \frac{G.\ W.}{w\ b^3} =$ ——— Beam, ft. ....

Prop. dia. .... Flaps, deg. ....

Prop. A. F. .... C_L @ V_g (0.9 C_L max.) ....

1	2	3	4	5	6	7	8	9	10	11	12	13	14	15	16	17
C_V	V mph	V^2 mph	T deg.	C_L*	L lb.	Δ lb.	$C\Delta$	CR	R lb.	C_D*	D lb.	$R+D$ lb.	T lb.	T_e lb.	$1/a$	V_{fps}/a

* Use full ground effect

$C_V = V_{fps}/\sqrt{g\,b}$ $V_{mph} = C_V X$ .... $L = .00256\ C_L S V^2 = C_L V^2 X$ ....

$C_\Delta = \Delta/wb^3$ $C\Delta = \Delta/$ .... $D = .00256\ C_D S V^2 = C_D V^2 X$ ....

$C_R = R/wb^3$ $R = C_R X$ .... $1/a = \text{G. W.}/g\ T_e =$ ...... $/T_e$

FIG. 7:18.—Standard form for take-off computations proposed by Stout.

This is because experience shows that the free and best trim angles usually plot as shown in Fig. 7:23 and that control usually becomes possible at the point of intersection of free trim and best trim lines.

Column 5. Calculate C_L from equations (7:10) and (7:11), taking account of the ground effect as previously explained.

Column 6. Calculate L from equation (7:12), which is repeated at the bottom of the standard form.

Column 7. Calculate Δ from equation (7:5).

Column 8. Calculate C_Δ from equation (7:1), which is repeated at the bottom of the standard form.

Column 9. Read C_R from Fig. 7:20 or Fig. 7:22, using the appropriate values C_V and C_Δ in the same line of the table.

Column 10. Calculate R from equation (7:2), which is repeated at the bottom of the standard form.

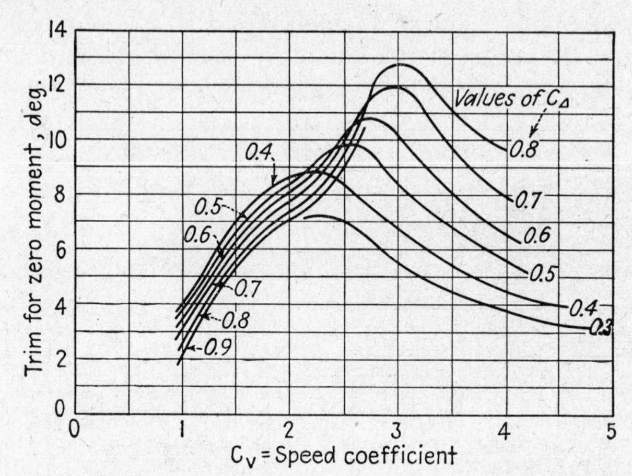

FIG. 7:19.—Variation of trim with C_V and C_Δ, free to trim, model 11 hull.

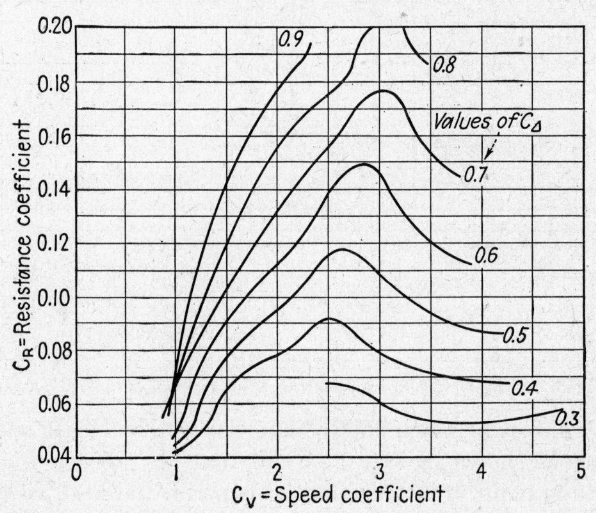

FIG. 7:20.—Variation of C_R with C_V and C_Δ, free to trim, model 11 hull.

Column 11. Calculate C_D from equation (7:9), or read from the graph of aerodynamic characteristics, taking account of ground effect.

Column 12. Calculate D from equation (7:8), which is repeated at the bottom of the standard form.

Column 13. Calculate $R + D$ by adding items in columns 10 and 12.

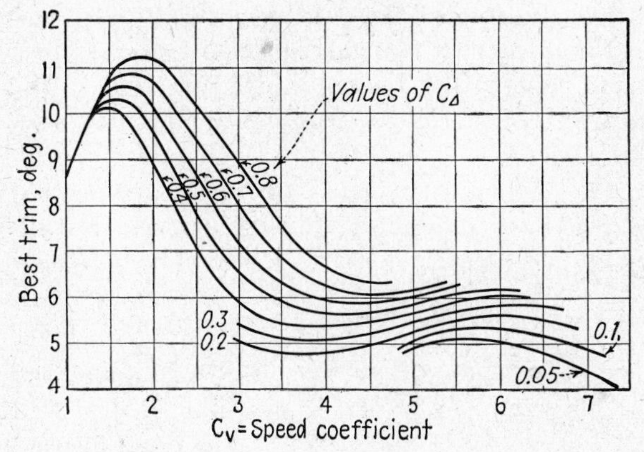

FIG. 7:21.—Variation of trim with C_V and C_Δ, best trim, model 11 hull.

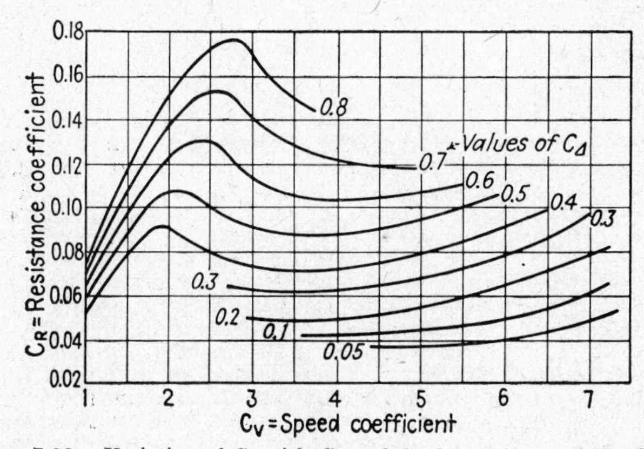

FIG. 7:22.—Variation of C_R with C_V and C_Δ, best trim, model 11 hull.

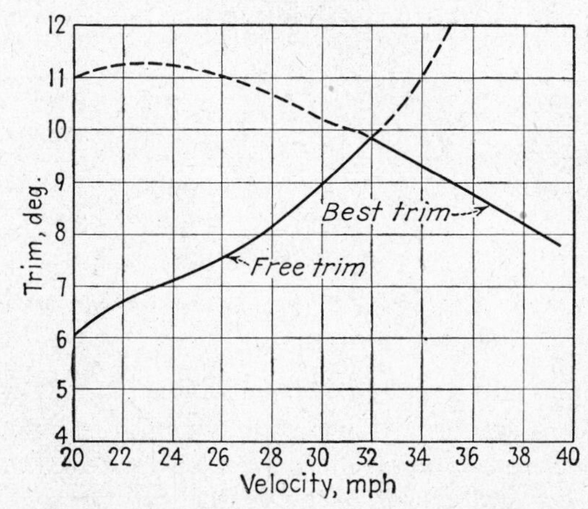

FIG. 7:23.—Trim angle plotted against speed for a particular flying boat.

Column 14. Calculate T as outlined in Chap. 4.

Column 15. Calculate T_e from equation (7:7).

Column 16. Calculate $1/a$ from equation (7:7). The values in this column are to be plotted as in Fig. 7:16 and integrated to get the take-off time.

Column 17. A quantity V/a is also tabulated so that it can be plotted against V to determine take-off distance by integration if desired.

	XX
Engine Bhp,	1,200
rpm	2,700
Gear ratio	2:1
Prop. dia.	13.0
Prop. A.F.	90

$$C_{\Delta 0} = \frac{\text{Gross wt}}{wb^3} = 0.865$$

Gross weight, lb	64,000
Wing area, sq ft	1,600
Beam, ft	10.5
Flaps, deg	20
C_L at V_g (0.9 C_L max)	1.62

(1) C_V	(2) V mph	(3) V^2 mph	(4) τ deg	(5) C_L*	(6) L lb	(7) Δ lb	(8) C_Δ	(9) C_R	(10) R lb	(11) C_D*	(12) D lb	(13) $R+D$ lb	(14) T lb	(15) T_e lb	(16) $\frac{1}{a}$	(17) $\frac{V_{fps}}{a}$
1.0	12.6	159	2.3	0.89	580	63,420	0.856	0.064	4,740	0.062	40	4,780	18,000	13,220	0.150	2.78
1.2	15.1	228	3.5	1.00	935	63,065	0.851	0.095	7,040	0.066	62	7,102	17,850	10,748	0.185	4.09
1.4	17.6	310	4.9	1.14	1,450	62,550	0.844	0.118	8,740	0.071	90	8,830	17,700	8,870	0.224	5.78
1.6	20.1	404	6.0	1.24	2,055	61,945	0.835	0.135	10,000	0.075	0.124	10,124	17,550	7,426	0.268	7.90
1.8	22.6	511	6.8	1.32	2,760	61,240	0.827	0.149	11,040	0.080	0.168	11,208	17,400	6,192	0.322	10.65
2.0	25.1	630	7.3	1.36	3,510	60,490	0.815	0.159	11,780	0.083	0.214	11,994	17,250	5,256	0.378	13.90
2.2	27.6	762	8.0	1.43	4,465	59,535	0.804	0.166	12,300	0.088	0.275	12,575	17,100	4,525	0.440	17.80
2.4	30.1	906	9.1	1.53	5,680	58,320	0.787	0.170	12,600	0.096	0.357	12,957	16,950	3,993	0.499	22.00
2.6	32.6	1,063	9.7	1.58	6,880	57,120	0.771	0.168	12,450	0.100	0.436	12,886	16,800	3,914	0.509	24.30
2.8	35.1	1,233	9.0	1.52	7,680	56,320	0.759	0.164	12,160	0.095	481	12,641	16,650	4,009	0.496	25.60
3.0	37.6	1,414	8.4	1.47	8,520	55,480	0.749	0.155	11,500	0.090	521	12,021	16,500	4,479	0.444	24.50
3.5	43.9	1,930	7.0	1.33	10,520	53,480	0.721	0.134	9,930	0.081	641	10,571	16,050	5,479	0.363	23.40
4.0	50.2	2,520	6.2	1.25	12,900	51,100	0.690	0.120	8,900	0.076	785	9,685	15,650	5,965	0.333	24.50
4.5	56.5	3,190	5.9	1.23	16,100	47,900	0.647	0.111	8,230	0.075	980	9,210	15,200	5,990	0.332	27.50
5.0	62.8	3,940	5.9	1.23	19,870	44,130	0.595	0.106	7,850	0.075	1,210	9,060	14,600	5,540	0.359	33.00
5.5	69.0	4,760	6.1	1.24	24,200	39,800	0.538	0.102	7,560	0.076	1,486	9,046	14,150	5,104	0.390	39.50
6.0	75.3	5,670	6.1	1.24	28,800	35,200	0.476	0.099	7,340	0.076	1,770	9,110	13,700	4,590	0.433	47.80
7.8	98.2	9,650	10.1	1.62	64,000	0	0	0	0	0.105	4,150	4,150	11,650	7,500	0.266	38.30

* Use full ground effect.

$$C_V = \frac{V_{fps}}{\sqrt{gh}} \qquad V_{mph} = C_V \times 12.55 \qquad L = 0.00256 C_L S V^2 = C_L V^2 \times 4.10$$

$$C_\Delta = \frac{\Delta}{wb^3} \qquad C_\Delta = \frac{\Delta}{74{,}090} \qquad D = 0.00256 C_D S V^2 = C_D V^2 \times 4.10$$

$$C_R = \frac{R}{wb^3} \qquad R = C_R \times 74{,}090 \qquad 1/a = \frac{\text{Gross wt}}{g T_e} = \frac{1{,}990}{Te}$$

FIG. 7:24.—Sample take-off computations in standard form.

The formulas given at the bottom of Fig. 7:18 are for sea-level take-off, which is the usual case. For take-off from mountain lakes, which is sometimes of importance, the equations used must be those given in the text, which include the density-ratio factor.

The following numerical example[1] illustrates the use of this standard form in making take-off calculations.

Example.—Given the following data on a flying boat, calculate the take-off time and distance at sea level and with no wind.

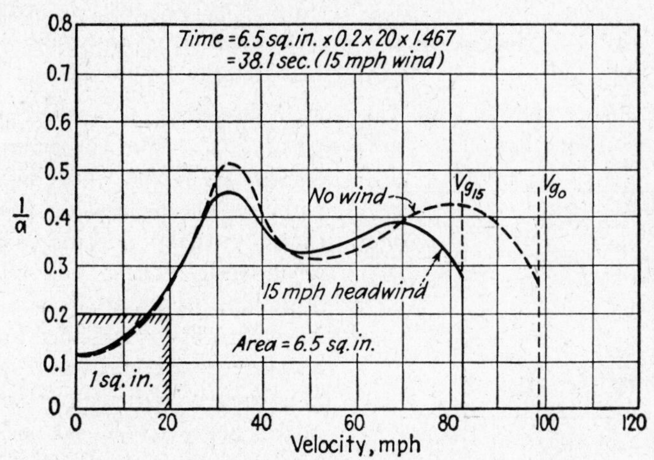

FIG. 7:25.—Graph of $1/a$ *vs.* v for graphical integration of take-off time. Effect of 15-mph head wind also shown.

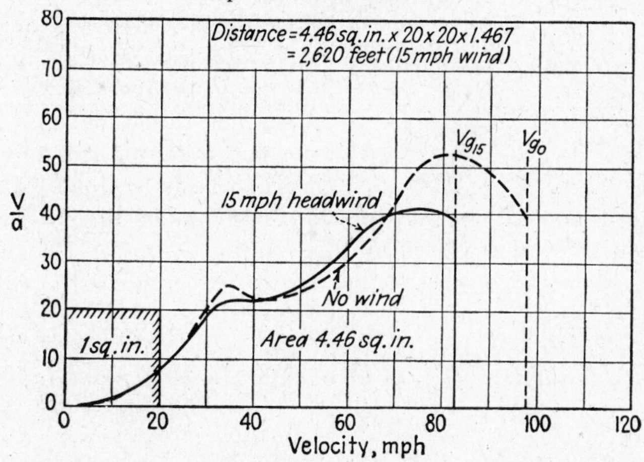

FIG. 7:26.—Graph of v/a *vs.* f for graphical integration of take-off distance. Effect of 15-mph head wind also shown.

Airplane data. Gross weight 64,000 lb., wing area 1,600 sq ft, wing span 120 ft, aspect ratio 9, flaps at take-off 20 deg, $C_{L\,max} = 1.8$, height of wing above water level (mean) 11 ft.

Hull data. Beam 10.5 ft, characteristics as shown in Figs. 7:19 to 7:22.

Engine data. Four engines, take-off brake horsepower per engine 1,200, take-off rpm 2,700, propeller gear ratio 2:1.

[1] From Stout, *op. cit.*

Propeller data. Diameter 13 ft, three blades, propeller activity factor 90.

Solution.—Follow the procedure outlined above, and enter the results in the standard form, as shown in Fig. 7:24. The propeller computations are based on a power coefficient of $C_p = 0.0625$, $J = 88V/(1{,}350 \times 13) = 0.005 \times v$, and $T = 130{,}300C_T$. The propeller characteristics used in this example are practically the same as those on Fig. A49, page 455 (with minor correction for difference in Activity Factor). Plots of columns 16 and 17 against column 2 are shown in Figs. 7:25 and 7:26.

7:4. Effect of Wind on Take-off.—The effect of a head wind of velocity V_W on take-off is shown in Fig. 7:27. The thrust and drag curves are moved to the left by an amount V_W, decreasing the mean thrust available and increasing the mean drag during take-off. The hump still comes at the same water speed, however; and since the lift at hump speed is greatly increased, the Δ is greatly reduced. The hump Δ/R is slightly reduced because of the lower C_Δ at the hump (see Fig. 7:7). The mean net thrust is considerably increased, as shown in Fig. 7:27; the take-off time is reduced not only because of the greater mean net thrust but also because the ship takes off at a lower water speed. Tests by Jones[1] show that the ratio of take-off time into a wind, t, to take-off time in a calm, t_0, is given with good accuracy by the equation

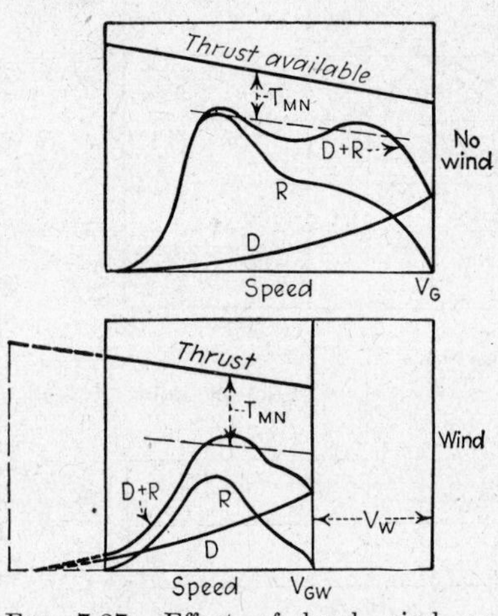

FIG. 7:27.—Effect of head wind on forces during take-off.

$$\frac{t}{t_0} = 1 - \frac{V_W}{V_G} \tag{7:13}$$

and the corresponding ratio of take-off distances, as plotted in Fig. 6:5, is

$$\frac{S}{S_0} = 1 - \left(\frac{V_W}{V_G}\right)^2 \tag{7:14}$$

Stout[2] has pointed out that equation (7:13) is inconsistent with Diehl's graphical method[3] for high wind velocities and long take-off times and that, for a particular flying boat, the take-off calculated by

[1] Reported in *Aeronaut. Research Comm. Rept. Mem.* (*Gt. Brit.*) 1593.

[2] *Op. cit.*

[3] DIEHL, W. S., "Engineering Aerodynamics," rev. ed., p. 503.

integration gives a value intermediate between those of Diehl and Jones. It is accordingly recommended that equations (7:13) and (7:14) be limited to take-off times of less than 60 sec and wind velocities of less than 20 per cent of the getaway speed. For longer times and higher velocities the correction for wing should be by integration, as in the original solution in Art. 7:3.

7:5. Take-off Considerations in Flying-boat Design.—Diehl[1] has shown, as a result of analysis of flight-test data on take-off with various gross weights at constant power, that take-off time is related to gross weight by the equation

$$\frac{W_{max}}{Bhp} = \frac{W}{Bhp} + \frac{140}{t} \tag{7:15}$$

A further study of recent designs of flying boats shows that a take-off time of the order of 70 sec is obtainable with power loading

$$\frac{W}{Bhp} = 16$$

though the design of the hull, wing, and propellers and choice of getaway speed are major factors. Putting 70 sec and $W/Bhp = 16$ in equation (7:15) yields the interesting though approximate conclusion that a flying boat will not take off from calm water with a power loading much greater than 18 lb per Bhp.

On further investigation of this hypothesis, Pierson and Burghardt[2] have proposed that the effect of weight, power, wind velocity, and getaway speed on take-off time be represented by the equation

$$\frac{1}{t} = \frac{1}{t_0} - K_W W + K_p Bhp + K_{VW} V_W - K_{VG} V_G \tag{7:16}$$

in which the factors K are believed to have the following values:

TABLE 7:1

Factor	Range	Average
$10^7 K_w$	5 to 20	16
$10^6 K_p$	5 to 25	13
$10^5 K_{vw}$	20 to 60	35
$10^5 K_{vg}$	30 to 60	47

These factors have dimensional units of pounds, horsepower, mph,

[1] *Ibid.*, p. 504.

[2] PIERSON, JOHN D., and JOSEPH R. BURGHARDT, A Specific Chart for Flying Boat Take-off Performance, *J. Aeronaut. Sci.*, April, 1945, pp. 169–172.

and seconds. As a means of comparing the take-off of a proposed flying boat with different gross weights, brake horsepower, getaway speeds, and head winds, Pierson and Burghardt propose a graphical representation of the form shown in Fig. 7:28. Pierson and Burghardt further show that take-off distance and take-off time are related with excellent accuracy by the empirical equation

$$S = 1.2 \frac{V_G t}{2} = 0.6 V_G t \tag{7:17}$$

in which V_G is in feet per second and t is in seconds, giving a take-off distance in feet.

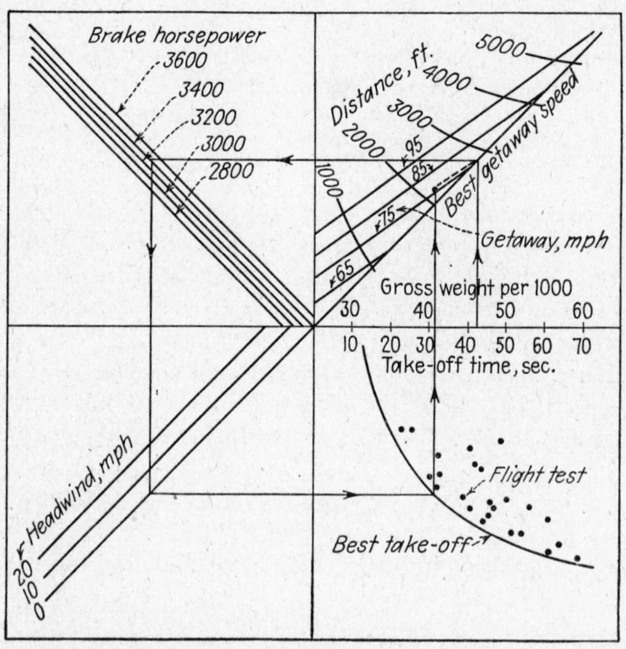

FIG. 7:28.—Chart for comparing effects on take-off of principal variables for a specific flying boat. (*From Pierson and Burghardt, J. Aeronaut. Sci., April, 1945.*)

The flight-test results shown in Fig. 7:28 are believed typical of the discrepancies commonly found between flight-test take-off time and calculated take-off time. The flight tests usually show up more poorly than the calculated results because of imperfections in pilot technique.

7:6. Problems

1. Given the following data on a flying boat, use Stout's standard form (Fig. 7:18) to calculate the take-off time.

Airplane data. Weight 15,000 lb, wing area 1,000 sq ft, wing span 85 ft, wing 10 ft above normal-load water line; lift and drag characteristics of the complete boat in the air related by the equations $C_D = 0.05 + 0.06C_L^2$, where $C_L = 0.080\alpha_a$; $C_{L\,\max} = 1.50$ at $\alpha_a = 19$ deg.

Hull data. NACA model 11, see Fig. 7:4. Beam 8 ft 0 in., $i_a = 8$ deg up from deck.

Engine data. Two engines, each developing 500 hp at 2,000 rpm.

Propeller data. Three blades, $D = 8.7$ ft, direct-drive constant rpm. Characteristics as in Fig. A49, page 455.

2. Given the following data on a flying boat, (*a*) find the equations for C_D *vs.* C_L and C_L *vs.* α_a for the airplane on the water; (*b*) assuming take-off at $C_L = 1.50$, find the take-off time.

Airplane data. Weight 40,000 lb, wing area 1,400 sq ft, wing span 105 ft, wing 8 ft above the normal-load water line. The minimum parasite and profile drag is equivalent to 45 sq ft of flat plate of $C_D = 1.00$, of which 15 sq ft is estimated to be due to hull. The wing is set with the zero-lift chord inclined 10 deg up from the deck line of the hull. Assume $e = 0.80$.

Hull data. NACA model 11-A; 10-ft beam.

Engine data. Four engines each rated 550 Bhp at 2,200 rpm.

Propeller data: Two-position variable-pitch three-blade propellers that can be set back 6 deg for take-off. Characteristics as on Fig. A49, page 455.

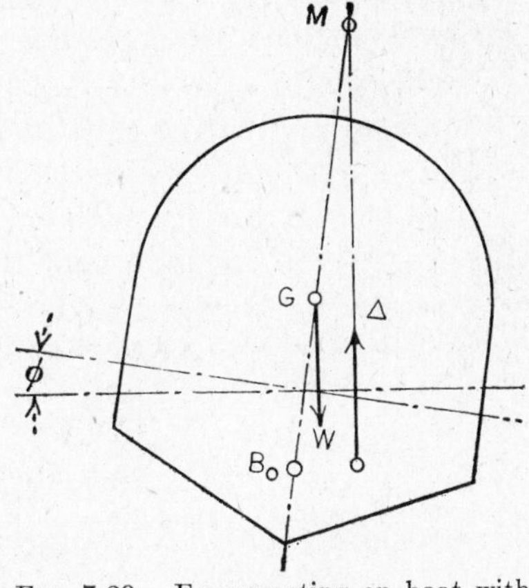

FIG. 7:29.—Forces acting on boat with small angle of heel ϕ.

7:7. Transverse Stability on the Water.—When a boat is tilted ("heeled") to the right through a small heel angle ϕ, as shown in Fig. 7:29, the buoyant force Δ shifts to the right so as to cut the center line at a point M known as the *metacenter*. The weight W acts through the center of gravity G. For small angles of heel the *metacentric height GM* is approximately constant. The moment of the couple ($\Delta = W$) is

$$M = -\Delta \times GM \sin \phi \approx -\Delta \times GM \times \phi \qquad (7:18)$$

the negative sign denoting that the moment is opposite in direction to the angular displacement for a positive metacentric height. The lateral stability on the water is measured by

$$\frac{dM}{d\phi} = -\Delta \times GM \qquad (7:19)$$

and the slope of the curve of heeling moment *vs.* angle of heel is negative (and *GM* is positive) for positive stability.

Metacentric height is determined experimentally by tilting tests on models and

$$\frac{\text{Full-scale } GM}{\text{Model } GM} = \lambda \qquad (7:20)$$

where λ is the linear-scale ratio of the model.

Metacentric height can be determined with good accuracy from the drawings of the hull from the formula

$$B_0M = \frac{I}{V} \qquad (7:21)$$

(derived in most textbooks on naval architecture) where B_0 is the original center of buoyancy, I is the moment of inertia of the water-plane area about its center line, and V is the volume of displacement ($V = W/64$ for sea water).

Fore-and-aft tilting experiments permit determination in a similar manner of *longitudinal metacentric height.* For flying boats, longitudinal GM is rarely calculated, for there is rarely any doubt about the existence of adequate longitudinal stability on the water.

Twin-float seaplanes, such as that shown in Fig. I:5*c*, are stated[1] to have satisfactory static stability on the water if

$$\text{Transverse } GM = 4\sqrt[3]{V} \qquad (7:22)$$

$$\text{Longitudinal } GM = 6\sqrt[3]{V} \qquad (7:23)$$

and this proposal is in fair agreement with that of Diehl,[2]

$$\begin{aligned} \text{Transverse } GM &= \text{about } 5.6\sqrt[3]{V} \\ \text{Longitudinal } GM &\geq \text{transverse } GM \end{aligned} \qquad (7:24)$$

Diehl further proposes the following equations for calculation of transverse and longitudinal metacentric heights in terms of the over-all boat length L, the float spacing on center lines, the beam of each float B, and the displacement volume V:

$$\text{Transverse } GM = (0.28 \text{ to } 0.32)\frac{BL_s^2}{V} \qquad (7:25)$$

$$\text{Longitudinal } GM = (0.06 \text{ to } 0.075)\frac{BL^3}{V} \qquad (7:26)$$

Diehl combines equations (7:24) to (7:26) to give a desirable float length and spacing of

$$L^3 = \frac{86V^{4/3}}{B} \qquad (7:27)$$

$$s = \frac{4.5V^{2/3}}{\sqrt{LB}} \qquad (7:28)$$

[1] *Aeronaut. Research Comm. Rept. Mem. (Gt. Brit.)* 1653.

[2] *Op. cit.*, pp. 494, 495.

Single-float seaplanes and *flying boats* require auxiliary flotation for transverse stability on the water. Three types of such auxiliary flotation are shown in Fig. 7:30. Stabilizing floats are commonly

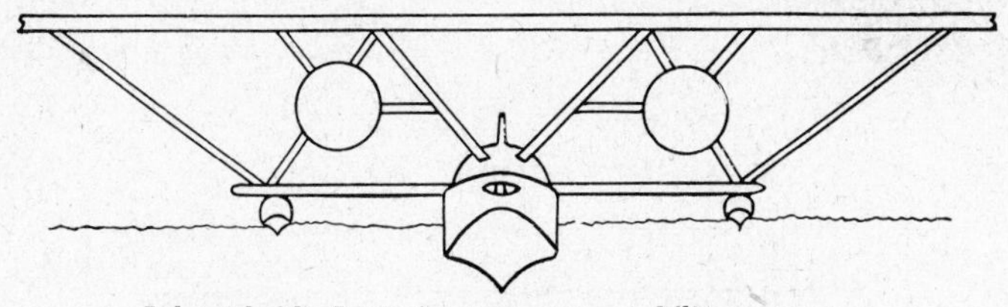

a. Inboard side floats for transverse stability on water.

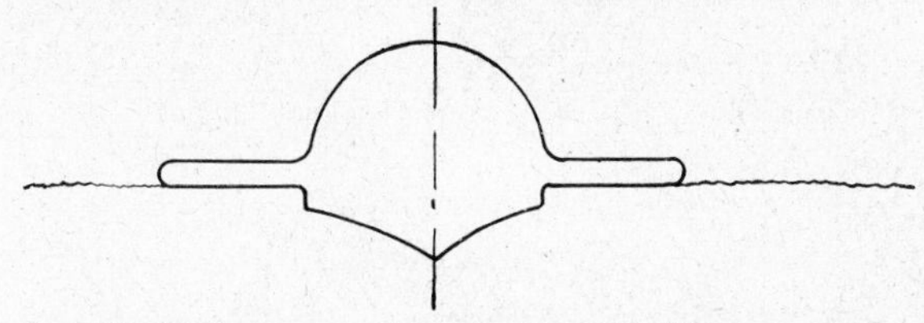

b. Wing-stub sponsons for transverse stability on water.

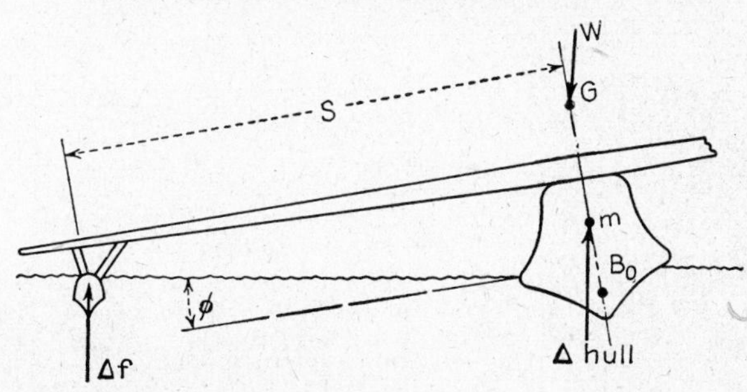

c. Forces acting on boat with hull float submerged.

FIG. 7:30.—Types of auxiliary flotation.

designed in accordance with U.S. Bureau of Aeronautics specification SR-59C, which states

$$\frac{\Delta_f}{W} = \frac{Gm'}{s} \sin \phi + \frac{0.1b/s}{W/S} + 0.06 \frac{\sqrt[3]{W}}{s} \tag{7:29}$$

in which Δ_f is the side-float displacement in pounds, W is the normal gross weight of the seaplane or flying boat in pounds, s is the distance between the center of buoyancy of the side float and the center line of the boat in feet, Gm' is the metacentric height above the center of gravity for the boat hull, ϕ is the angle of heel required to submerge the auxiliary float, b is the wing span, and W/S is the wing loading. In equation (7:29) the first term of the right-hand member is the float displacement necessary to offset the instability of the hull, the second term represents the effect of the wind on the wing, and the third term a reasonable excess restoring moment based on experience. In determining Gm' in equation (7:29), the destabilizing effect of partly full fuel tanks must be considered.

The forces shown in Fig. 7:30*c* may also be considered to consist of a righting couple equal to Δ_f times s and an upsetting couple equal

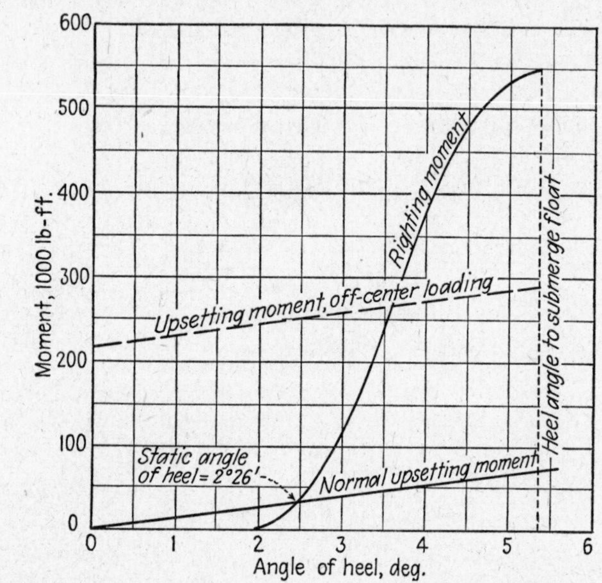

FIG. 7:31.—Upsetting and righting couples plotted against angle of heel. (*From W. J. Griffey, Favoring the Classical in Hydrodynamics, Aviation*, 1944.)

to $WGm' \sin \phi$. A righting factor C may be defined as the ratio of the righting couple to the upsetting couple and is accordingly given by the equation

$$\frac{\Delta_f}{W} = C \frac{Gm'}{s} \sin \phi \qquad (7:30)$$

This relationship between righting and upsetting couple is shown graphically in Fig. 7:31, which also shows the upsetting moment due to some arbitrary off-center loading, such as two men out on one of the wings filling an outboard wing fuel tank, when the opposite wing tanks are empty. A righting factor C between 1.2 and 2 for the worst condition of off-center loading is usually considered to represent a satisfactory margin of stability and provides a check on equation (7:29). The following numerical example by Griffey[1] illustrates the application of equations (7:29) and (7:30).

[1] GRIFFEY, W. J., Favoring the Classical in Hydrodynamics, *Aviation*, October, 1944, pp. 159–163.

Example.—A flying boat of gross weight 145,000 lb and wing area 3,686 sq ft is stabilized by auxiliary floats located 69.6 ft from the hull center line. The wing span is 200 ft, and the effective height of the center of gravity above the hull metacenter, the destabilizing effect of fuel in tanks being taken into account, is 5.1 ft. A heel angle of $\phi = 5°18'$ ($\sin \phi = 0.0927$) is necessary to submerge the wing-tip float. (*a*) Calculate the necessary wing-tip float displacement from equation (7:29). (*b*) For $\Delta_f = 7{,}870$ lb, find the righting factor from equation (7.30). (*c*) For $\Delta_f = 7{,}870$ lb, find the righting factor C with an upsetting moment due to off-center loading of 218,200 lb-ft due to two men and fuel on one wing only.

Solution.—*a.* Substituting in equation (7:29),

$$\frac{\Delta_f}{145{,}000} = \frac{5.1 \times 0.0927}{69.6} + \frac{0.1 \times 200/69.6}{145{,}000/3{,}686} + \frac{0.06\sqrt[3]{45{,}000}}{69.6}$$

which gives

$$\Delta_f = 8{,}610$$

b. Substitute next in equation (7:30) as follows:

$$C = \frac{7{,}870 \times 69.6}{145{,}000 \times 5.1 \times 0.0927} = 8.0$$

c. Adding the moment due to off-center loading to the denominator of equation (7:30) gives

$$C = \frac{7{,}870 \times 69.6}{(145{,}000 \times 5.1 \times 0.0927) + 218{,}200} = 1.9$$

These are the answers called for.

7:8. Analysis of Flying-boat and Seaplane Landings.—Since there is usually plenty of room for landing a flying boat or seaplane, the landing time and distance are usually not computed. The major problems connected with the landing of flying boats are those of minimizing impact loads and minimizing the damage due to skipping, or "porpoising," on landing. This subject has been extensively studied by Stout.[1]

Flying boats are often preferred to landplanes for long over-water hops because of the possibility of landing on water safely in an emergency, although, under many conditions of wind and waves found in the open sea, safe landing of a flying boat requires an unusual combination of skill and good fortune. The size, period, and speed of ocean waves are shown in Fig. 7:32. After a prolonged period of blowing wind, the wave velocity becomes nearly equal to the wind velocity. In one case cited by Cornish,[2] after 1 day of 46-mph wind, the wave velocity reached 30 mph. At the end of 4 days of steady wind, the wave velocity was 43 mph. In times of shifting winds, the

[1] STOUT, E. G., Landing Analyses for Flying Boats and Seaplanes, *Aviation*, October, November, December, 1945

[2] CORNISH, VAUGHAN, "Waves of Sea and Other Waves."

waves and wind may not be moving in the same direction. The ideal condition for seaplane landings is when the wind is blowing at right angles to fairly large waves so that landings can be made in wave troughs. Some pilots favor landing parallel to the wave crests under all conditions, but there is a great risk of hooking a wing or a wing-tip float in a wave. For landings in a sheltered harbor, landing into the wind is of course the only type of landing considered. For a very large harbor (as at Hampton Roads, Va.) the waves existing in high

SIZE AND SHAPE OF WAVES IN OPEN SEA

Wind (and wave) velocity,		Period, sec	Length, ft	Maximum height, ft	Maximum slope $\sin \theta_{max}$,	θ_{max}
Beaufort No.	mph					
5	19	5.5	135	13 3	0.310	18° 5′
6	25	7.2	262	17.5	0.210	12° 7′
7	31	8.9	404	21.7	0.169	9° 45′
8	37	10.6	575	25.9	0.142	8° 5′
9	44	12.6	818	30.8	0.119	6° 50′
10	53	15.2	1180	37.1	0.099	5° 40′

FIG. 7:32.—Wind-wave relationships for open sea.

winds may be more difficult to land on than the open sea, as the size of waves is limited by the size of the harbor.

Stout[1] reports good success in making landing-impact calculations agree with impact-shock measurements by calculating the maximum draft on landing from the "landing integral"

$$S = \int_{V_S}^{0} \frac{W}{g} \frac{V dV}{L_p + \Delta} \tag{7:31}$$

in which V_S is the sinking speed at impact, L_p is the planing lift of the hull, and Δ is the buoyant lift of the hull.

L_p may be calculated from

$$L_p = \frac{C_{Lp} \rho b^2 V^2}{2} \tag{7:32}$$

in which b is the beam in feet and ρ is the water density (usually 1.99 slugs per cu ft for sea water). The planing-lift coefficient C_{Lp} for a particular hull with a particular dead-rise angle is shown in Fig. 7:33. A recommended standard procedure for making these calculations is given by Stout.[2]

[1] STOUT, E. G., *op. cit.*
[2] *Ibid.*

A major factor determining the skipping on landing has been found by Stout[1] to be the depth of the step, as shown in Fig. 7:34. Stout concluded on the basis of a comprehensive series of tests on models dynamically similar to the full-scale flying boats that

1. The depth of step should be not less than 8 per cent of the beam for satisfactory skipping characteristics.

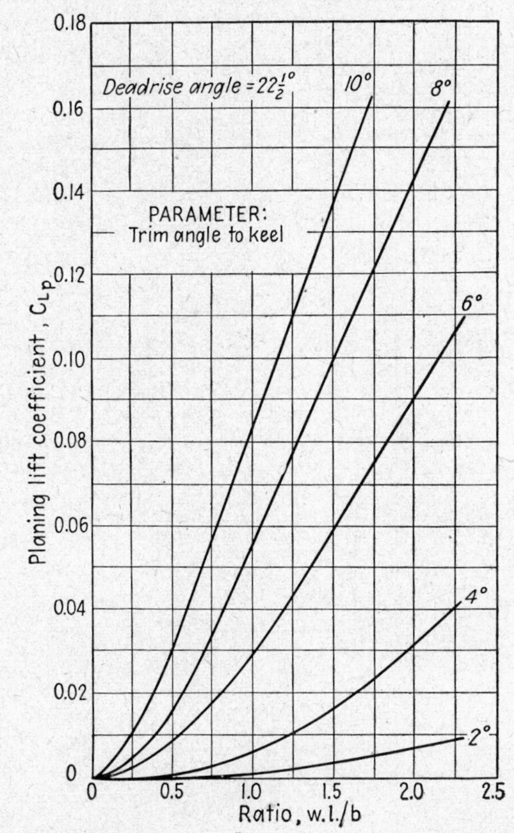

FIG. 7:33.—C_{L_p} *vs.* (wetted length/beam) for 22.5° dead-rise angle on a particular hull. (*From Stout.*)

2. A pointed step, with apex pointed aft, is in general superior to the more usual transverse step.

3. Supplementary ventilation of the step is an effective means of eliminating skipping and should be located behind the step in the afterbody and as close as possible to the center line. Short, straight ventilating shafts are satisfactory, and no appreciable improvement is obtained by ramming the air to increase ventilation.

[1] *Ibid.*

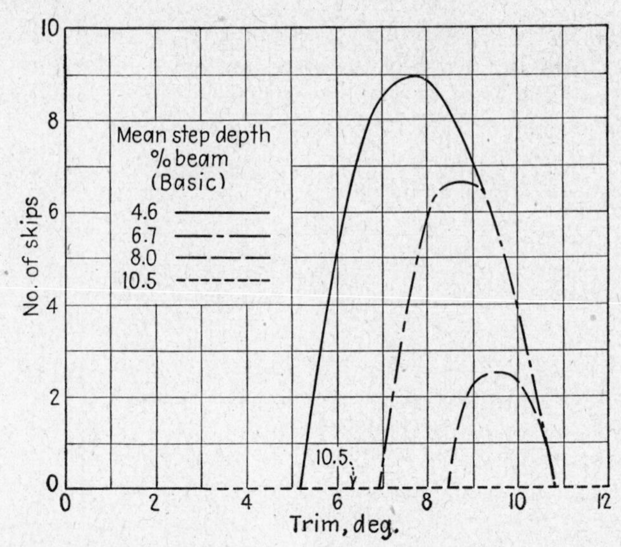

FIG. 7:34.—Effect of step depth on skipping characteristics. (*From Stout.*)

7:9. Problems

1. A flying boat weighs 30,000 lb and has a wing area of 1,400 sq ft. The wing span is 105 ft, and transverse stability is obtained by wing-tip floats located 44 ft from the center line of the boat. An angle of heel of 5.67 deg is required to sub-

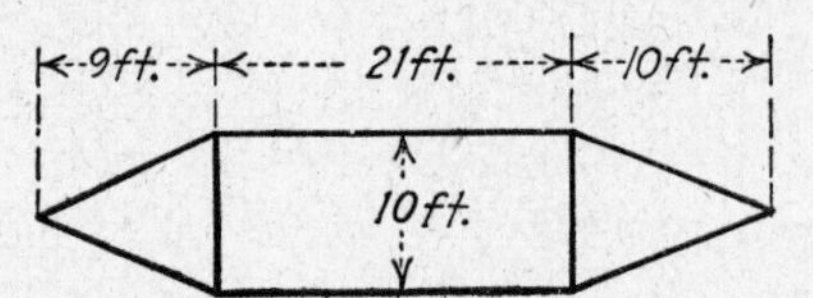

FIG. 7:35.—Water-line area of hull for Prob. 1, Art. 7:9.

merge the float. The normal-load-water-line area of the hull is approximately as shown in Fig. 7:35. Neglecting the destabilizing effect of partly filled gas tanks, find (*a*) the necessary float displacement from equation (7:29) and (*b*) the righting factor C from equation (7:30) for this float displacement. $B_0 G = 8.5$ ft.

2. A twin-float seaplane weighs 1,800 lb and has a wing area of 200 sq ft and wing span of 38 ft. For floats of 28-in. beam, use equations (7:27) and (7:28), and calculate the necessary over-all length and lateral spacing of the floats. Also, calculate the transverse and longitudinal metacentric heights from equations (7:25) and (7:26), and compare the results with equations (7:22) to (7:24).

CHAPTER 8

FLIGHT TESTING FOR PERFORMANCE

8:1. Limitations of Model Testing.—One of the major objectives of work in technical aerodynamics is to make flight-test results more accurately predictable from model-test results. Performance estimates based on model-test results have hitherto proved rather unsatisfactory because of the large and uncertain corrections necessary to make the results correspond to free flight of a full-sized airplane, but model tests on stability have sometimes given very good results.

Airplane design by building, testing, changing, and retesting models is essentially a confession of ignorance. It is an attempt to make design by trial and error *less expensive* than by changing the full-sized airplane. It is actually less expensive for an individual manufacturer only because of the millions that have been spent by government agencies in trying to determine the significance of model tests. In many matters pertaining to airplane design it is well to confess ignorance; there is, for example, no reliable method of estimating the interference drag between two bodies of irregular shape. In other matters, such as wing characteristics, new model tests in a new wind tunnel are of little value because more reliable estimates can be made by the methods outlined in Chap. 2.

Model tests involving fluid forces never completely represent the full-scale condition because of practical limits on the control of the variables involved (for example, the acceleration g due to gravity is not readily controllable, and the density and viscosity of the fluid are controllable only within narrow limits, depending on the range of pressures and temperatures that the apparatus will permit). Model tests, however, have considerable advantage over flight tests in that the testing conditions are more carefully controllable because the laboratory is on steady ground and is largely independent of weather conditions, whereas accurate flight tests cannot be made unless steady, smooth air is available for flying, with only small vertical currents and with a reasonable temperature pattern. Such air most often occurs under conditions of zero visibility.

8:2. Scope and Instrumentation for Flight Tests.—Accurate flight testing requires not only good weather but also, as stated by Allen,[1]

[1] ALLEN, EDMUND T., Flight Testing for Performance and Stability, *J. Aeronaut. Sci.*, January, 1943.

(1) complete and accurate calibrated instrumentation so that all variables can be measured, (2) a technique of flying accurately so that what is measured will be representative of the true optimum performance of the airplane, and (3) a mathematically correct method of applying the flight-test data.

The principal step toward development of flight-test accuracy comparable with wind-tunnel accuracy was the development of technique for photographic recording of all data. This is usually done by collecting the instruments on a panel or in a box where they can be photographed by a motion-picture camera; such a device is known as a "photorecorder."

In flight testing for performance, instruments must be provided for measuring the pressure and temperature of the air, the vertical and horizontal components of velocity of the airplane, and the power and rpm of the engine and propeller. Such instruments must be accurately calibrated to eliminate instrument error. The weight and center of gravity of the airplane must also be accurately recorded; since the weight varies in flight as fuel is consumed, a continuous check on the weight of fuel in the airplane is required for accurate weight calculations. Torque-meter and tachometer readings are ordinarily sufficient for calculation of engine power. However, it is usually not possible to dispense with instruments for measuring manifold pressure, carburetor-air temperature, and exhaust back pressure. Torque-meter readings have frequently been found to be erratic; and unless careful cross checks of chart power against torque-meter power are made, misleading results may be obtained.

The measurement of outside-air temperature, while apparently a simple procedure, is difficult if it is to be done accurately. The type and location of the temperature element and the method of recording temperature must be carefully considered. The temperature element will have a correction because of the temperature rise caused by the compression of air in front of the element and by boundary-layer friction of the air. The adiabatic air-temperature rise, calculated as in Chap. 1, is of the order of 22 5°F at 350 mph true air speed; the actual air-temperature rise is usually found to be about 80 per cent of the full adiabatic rise. A satisfactory method of checking this rise for a particular installation is to run a series of speed runs at both low and high altitude to check the temperature rise over a wide range of speeds.

An accurate wind-tunnel calibration of an air-speed meter is not sufficient, for this instrument has a calibration depending on the angle of attack and is further likely to be in error because of small leaks in the connecting tubing. Air-speed meters must be calibrated by runs over a speed course in which the time is measured for a given distance of flight. Wind effects must be allowed for by running in both directions. The air-speed-calibration plotting recommended by Allen is shown in Fig. 8:1. The data are plotted in the form of the ratio of true indicated air speed V_i to actual indicated air speed V_I as registered through the Pitot installation. This ratio is plotted against the parameter $V_I/(W/W_{std})^{1/2}$. The four calibration runs shown in Fig.

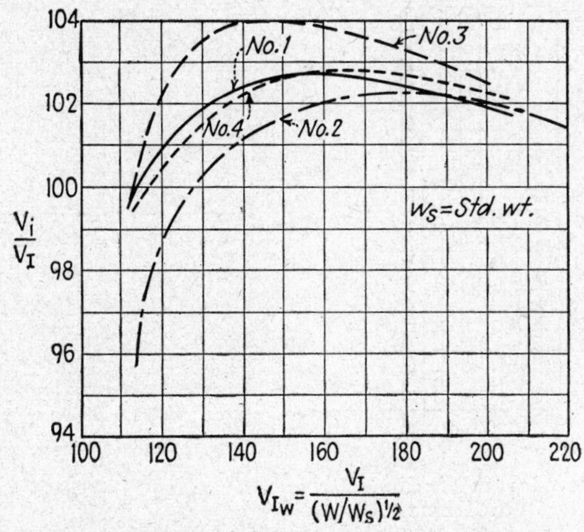

Fig. 8:1.—Air-speed calibration variations obtained with the same airplane. (*From Allen, J. Aeronaut. Sci., January,* 1943.)

8:1 were obtained with minor differences in the airplane, particularly in the surface ahead of the Pitot mast. Runs 1 and 4, representing the two middle lines, were considered the final calibration.

8:3. Flight-tests for Speed and Climb.—The purpose of conducting flight tests on performance is normally (1) to establish compliance with performance guarantees and (2) to determine performance information necessary to permit effective use of the airplane. The accuracy obtainable according to Reed[1] is ± 1 per cent with proper weight control, instrumentation, technique, and evaluation. A flight test for level high speed at low altitude can normally be run as part of the air-speed-instrument calibration. At higher altitudes it is difficult to get flight under exactly level conditions; the rate-of-climb indicator is an extremely unreliable indication of actual rate of change of altitude. The full-throttle level-flight condition is in many cases determined by plotting full-throttle rate of climb against horizontal speed and determining the intercept for zero rate of climb.

[1] Reed, Albert C., Airplane Performance Testing at Altitude, *J. Aeronaut. Sci.*, February, 1941.

The layout of a flight plan for testing climb performance is based on the principle that optimum climb rate may be determined by a series of short, steady climbs at predetermined air speeds. A chart of altitude *vs.* climb for such a test will have the appearance of a saw tooth, as illustrated in Fig. 8:2. The most accurate measurement of rate of climb is obtainable from a barograph or from photorecording of a sensitive altimeter, with records of altitude at regular time intervals. Full-throttle climb is usually determined at several alti-

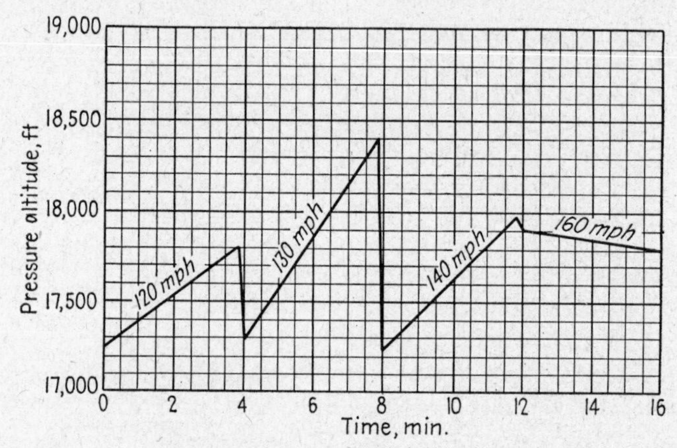

FIG. 8:2.—Observed rate of climb for various constant air speeds. (*From Reed, J. Aeronaut. Sci., February,* 1941.)

tudes and at a sufficient number of air speeds to ensure that the best climbing speed has been bracketed and that an accurately formed curve of velocity *vs.* climb rate is obtained in the region of best climbing speed.

8:4. Analysis of Flight-test Data for Speed and Climb.—The following procedure for analysis of flight-test data for speed and climb, originally developed by Reed[1] and by Allen[2] of the Boeing Aircraft Company, has become widely used throughout the aircraft industry and may be considered to have largely superseded the "equivalent-pressure and density-altitude" method,[3] but an alternate method described as the "temperature-altitude method" was finding some use in 1946.[4]

[1] *Ibid.*, Airplane Performance Testing at Altitude, *J. Aeronaut. Sci.*, February, 1941.

[2] *Op. cit.*

[3] WOOD, K. D., "Technical Aerodynamics," 1st ed., 1935.

[4] BEERER, J. G., The Reduction of Flight Test Performance Data to Standard Air Conditions by the Temperature-altitude Method; *Journal of the Aeronautical Sciences* paper at annual meeting, January, 1946, published in *J. Aeronaut. Sci.*, October, 1946.

The primary effects of weight and altitude on performance of a given airplane, which can be calculated by the methods of Chap. 5, are handled by using the following parameters for flight-test calculations:

$$V_{iw} = \frac{V\sqrt{\sigma}}{\sqrt{W/W_s}} \tag{8:1}$$

$$P_{iw} = \frac{P\sqrt{\sigma}}{(W/W_s)^{3/2}} \tag{8:2}$$

$$N_{iw} = \frac{N\sqrt{\sigma}}{\sqrt{W/W_s}} \tag{8:3}$$

$$C_{iw} = \frac{C_h\sqrt{\sigma}}{\sqrt{W/W_s}} \tag{8:4}$$

in which V = true air velocity
P = brake power of engine
N = rpm of engine
C_h = rate of climb of airplane
σ = air-density ratio at altitude of test
W = gross weight of airplane as tested
W_s = standard reference or design gross weight

A logical derivation of these parameters follows: For *approximately level flight* (including small angles of climb or glide), from equation (2:1),

$$L = W = \frac{C_L \sigma \rho_0 S V^2}{2} \tag{8:5}$$

If a term W_s representing an arbitrary standard gross weight is multiplied into both sides of equation (8:5),

$$V_{iw} = \frac{V\sqrt{\sigma}}{\sqrt{W/W_s}} = \sqrt{\frac{2W_s}{\rho_0 S}}\sqrt{\frac{1}{C_L}} \tag{8:6}$$

Equation (8:6) defines V_{iw}, which, for a given airplane W_s and S constants, depends only on C_L and therefore determines C_L. Flight at a *given lift coefficient* is thus determined by a given V_{iw}, and

$$C_L = \frac{2W_s/\rho_0 S}{V_{iw}^2} \tag{8:7}$$

The power required for level flight, from equation (3:15), is

$$P_r = DV = \frac{C_D}{C_L} W \sqrt{\frac{2W/S}{\sigma \rho_0 C_L}} \tag{8:8}$$

Again introducing a term W_s into both sides of the equations,

$$P_{riw} = \frac{P_r \sqrt{\sigma}}{(W/W_s)^{3/2}} = C_D V_{iw}^3 \frac{\rho_0 S}{2} \tag{8:9}$$

or

$$C_D = \frac{(2/\rho_0 S)P_{riw}}{V_{iw}^3} \tag{8:10}$$

Equation (8:6) points out that, for a given airplane flying at a given *angle of attack* (given C_L and C_D), P_{riw} is constant.

If P is the *brake* power of the engine (foot-pounds per second) and η is the propulsive efficiency, $P_r = \eta P$ for level flight and $P_{riw} = \eta P_{iw}$.

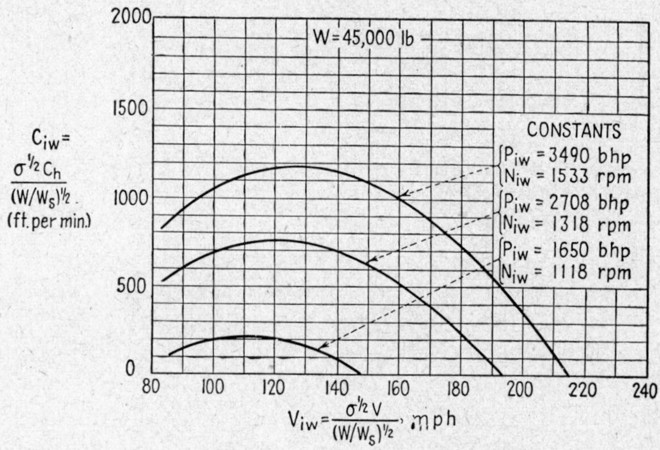

FIG. 8:3.—Climb performance for any weight and altitude at constant P_{iw} and N_{iw}. (*From Reed, J. Aeronaut. Sci., February,* 1941.)

For flight that is not level but involves a rate of climb C_h (in feet per second here), from equation (5:1)

$$\eta P - P_r = WC_h \tag{8:11}$$

If the factor $\sqrt{\sigma}/(W/W_s)^{3/2}$ is introduced into this equation,

$$\eta P_{iw} - P_{riw} = W_s C_h \left(\frac{\sqrt{\sigma}}{\sqrt{W/W_s}} \right) \tag{8:12}$$

and the items in parentheses in equation (8:12) may be called C_{iw}.

If airplane flight-test data are to be compared on a basis of constant angle of attack on the wings (V_{iw} constant) they should also involve constant angle of attack on the propeller-blade sections (V/nD constant); but since V is not constant (V_{iw} *is* constant), the rotative speed of the propeller (n per second or N per minute) must be varied with gross weight and altitude in the same way as the forward speed.

Hence, a corrected rpm $N_{iw} = N\sqrt{\sigma}/\sqrt{W/W_s}$ must be used whenever $V_{iw} = V\sqrt{\sigma}/\sqrt{W/W_s}$ is used.

A typical plot of flight-test data corrected for altitude and weight is shown in Fig. 8:3. The intercepts of these graphs on the horizontal axis are the level-flight speeds V_{iw} for the specified powers P_{iw}. The values of P_{riw} for these values of V_{iw} are known if the propulsive efficiencies η may be assumed. The practice recommended by Allen[1] is to assume the chart efficiencies (as on page 455), calculate C_L and C_D from equations (8:4) and (8:10), respectively, and plot C_L^2 *vs.* C_D as in Fig. 8:4*a* (squared scale is used for C_L plotting). If, as is usually the

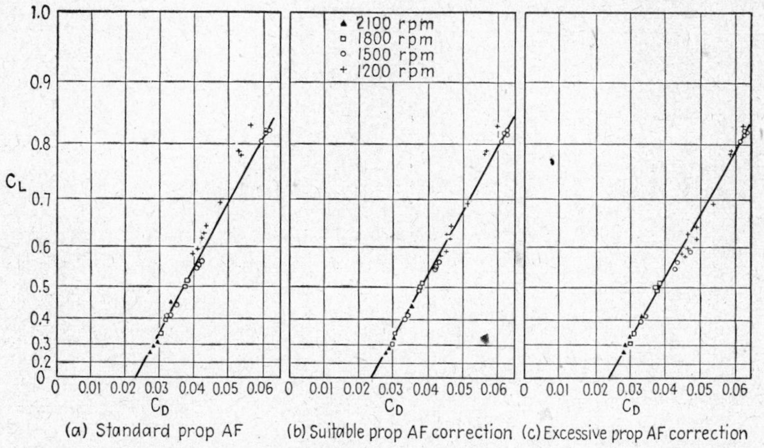

FIG. 8:4.—Airplane polars used to determine suitable activity-factor correction for propeller-power coefficients. (*From Allen, J. Aeronaut. Sci., January,* 1943.)

case, the points appear to deviate systematically from a straight line, various activity-factor corrections on the propeller data may be applied until a straight line will fit the data well. If no activity-factor correction gives a good fit, the propeller-tip Mach number may be investigated by trial in the same manner. Boeing tests reported by Allen[1] show that a propeller-tip Mach number over 0.8 usually results in an apparent increase in airplane drag and therefore requires a correction on flight-test data.

8:5. Problems

1. Given the following data for a hypothetical flight test of an Ercoupe airplane in level flight at part throttle and assuming the propulsive-efficiency data on page 460, calculate and plot C_D *vs.* C_L^2 for the airplane, and find $C_{De\,\min}$ and $A\!\!\!R_e$ for the airplane. W_s = 1,260 pounds, propeller D = 6 ft 0 in., $\beta_{0.75R}$ = 16 deg.

[1] *Op. cit.*

Run No.	1	2	3	4	5	6
Gross weight, lb	1,260	1,250	1,245	1,230	1,215	1,200
True v_i, mph	68	80	92	101	110	117
True torque, lb-ft	103	102	115	126	143	154
True rpm	1,570	1,870	2,115	2,345	2,570	2,720
True air temp., deg F	50	55	45	48	51	53
True pressure altitude, ft	5,000	5,200	5,100	5,500	5,600	5,200

2. Given the following data for hypothetical series full-throttle climb tests at 2,400 rpm of a Lockheed Constellation airplane (W_s = 86,250 lb, propeller D = 15 ft), calculate and plot a graph of C_{iw} *vs.* V_{iw}. Use propeller data in Figs. A47, A48, and A49, pages 454 and 455 and engine data in Fig. A60, page 465.

Run No.	1	2	3	4	5	6
Gross weight, lb	86,250	86,100	85,900	85,000	84,700	83,000
True v_i, mph	120	160	180	200	250	300
True Bhp, each of 4 engines	1,920	1,980	2,020	1,900	1,950	1,970
True air temp., deg F	40	52	55	47	43	38
True pressure alt, ft	3,000	2,800	3,500	3,000	3,700	3,900
Observed rate of climb, true ft per min	1,340	1,560	1,680	1,720	1,300	540

CHAPTER 9

CHARACTERISTICS OF HINGED SURFACES

The control surfaces of an airplane are usually movable flaps, which, in their neutral position, constitute the rear portion of an airfoil. Such flaps may be designated as *ailerons*, *elevators*, or *rudders*, depending on whether they control the movements about the *longitudinal*, *lateral*, or *vertical* axis of the airplane. In order to make calculations on the stability and control of an airplane it is necessary to know the aerodynamic characteristics (lift, drag, and pitching moment) of such hinged surfaces. The control forces necessary to move such hinged surfaces depend on the moment of the aerodynamic forces about the hinge axis; thus, studies of control also involve the aerodynamic hinge moment of the movable surface, designated by H_f. The control forces are often modified by means of a *tab* that constitutes a portion of the trailing edge of the flap. This chapter presents a study of the effect of flap and tab angles and sizes on the lift, drag, and pitching moment for the complete control surface and on the hinge moment of the flap.

9:1. Coefficients and Variables for Doubly Hinged Surfaces.—The forces, moments, angles, and dimensions of a control surface with a movable flap and tab are sketched in Fig. 9:1. The lift and normal force are seen to be approximately the same for small angles of attack. Force coefficients both for finite control surfaces and for sections of such surfaces are defined, as for wings, by the equations (notation as in Chap. 2 and Fig. 9:1)

$$C_N = \frac{N}{qS} \qquad \text{or} \qquad c_n = \frac{n}{qc} \tag{9:1}$$

$$C_D = \frac{D}{qS} \qquad \text{or} \qquad c_d = \frac{d}{qc} \tag{9:2}$$

$$C_M = \frac{M}{qcS} \qquad \text{or} \qquad c_m = \frac{m}{qc^2} \tag{9:3}$$

$$C_{Hf} = \frac{H_f}{qc_fS_f} \qquad \text{or} \qquad c_{hf} = \frac{h_f}{qc_f^2} \tag{9:4}$$

The relationships between these coefficients are the same as for wings when δ_f and δ_t are equal to zero; these relationships are given in Chap.

2. Published data on wing and wing-section characteristics can be applied to tail surfaces if suitable corrections are made for Reynolds number, Mach number, and aspect ratio as outlined in Chap. 2. A special study of hinge-moment coefficients is presented later in this chapter.

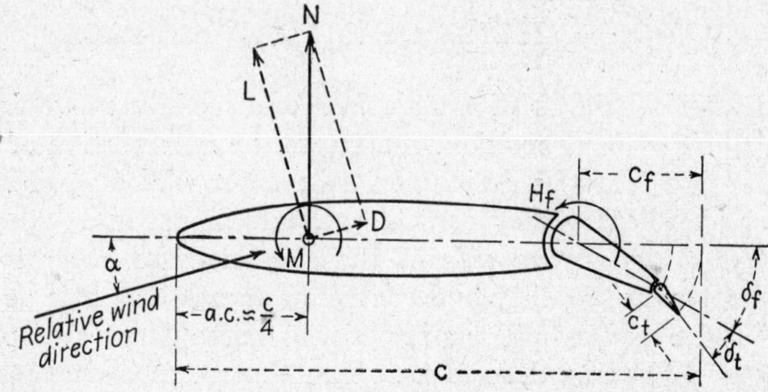

FIG. 9:1.—Forces, moments, angles, and dimensions of a control surface with movable flap and tab.

9:2. Problems

1. A tail surface of aspect ratio 3.4 has a span of 155 in. and an area of 7,015 sq in. and is tested in a wind tunnel at a speed $V = 88$ ft per sec and an angle of attack of 10 deg with $\delta_f = 0$ and $\delta_t = 0$. The airfoil section is of the NACA four-digit series and may be designated NACA 0007.5. Using the methods of Chap. 2 and the airfoil-section data in Table XVI on page 387, estimate C_L, C_D, and C_M and L, D, M.

2. A tail surface has a rectangular planform and aspect ratio of 3.1. The span is 17.7 in., and the area is 100 sq in. The airfoil section is NACA 0008. The tail surface is tested in a wind tunnel at a speed $V = 110$ ft per sec and an angle of attack of 8 deg. Estimate the lift, drag, pitching moment about the aerodynamic center, and the corresponding coefficients.

9:3. Effect of Flap Deflection on Lift, Drag, and Pitching Moment. Coefficients of normal force, lift, and pitching moment may be expressed as a function of the flap deflection δ_f by the equations

$$c_n = a_0(\alpha + k\delta_f) \qquad \text{or} \qquad C_N = a(\alpha + k\delta_f) \tag{9:5}$$

$$c_d = c_{d0}\left[1 + f\frac{c_f}{c}\left(\frac{\delta_f}{10}\right)^x\right] \tag{9:6}$$

$$c_m = -m_f\delta_f \tag{9:7}$$

in which the coefficients k and m_f have the meaning

$$k = \left(\frac{\partial c_n}{\partial \delta_f}\right) \alpha = \text{const}$$

$$m_f = \left(\frac{\partial c_m}{\partial \delta_f}\right) c_n = \text{const}$$

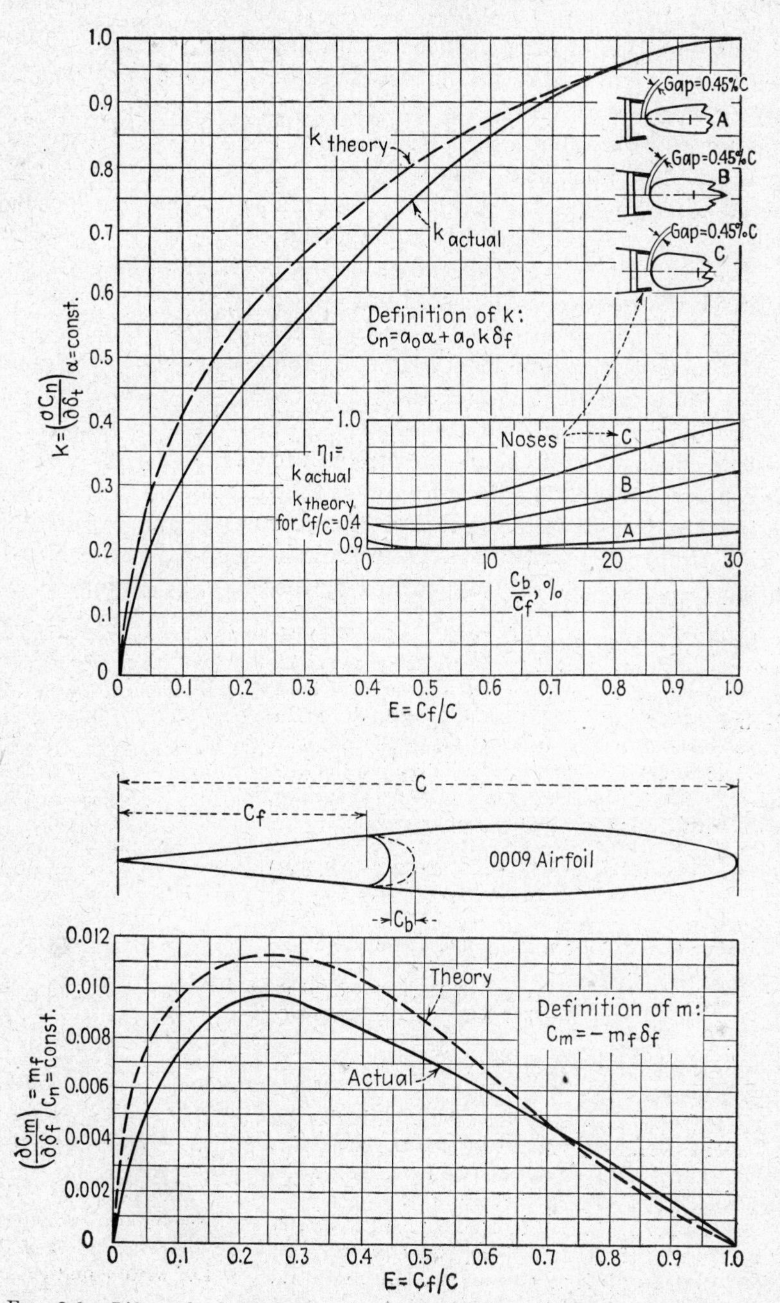

FIG. 9:2.—Lift and pitching-moment characteristics of hinged surfaces. (*From NACA Tech. Rept.* 721.) Effect of aerodynamic balance on lift. (*From L. E. Root, J. Aeronaut. Sci., April*, 1945.)

The variation of drag coefficient with flap angle is usually considered unimportant and is inaccurately known. For one particular tail surface reported in *NACA Tech. Rept.* 688, the coefficients f and x in equation (9:6) are found to be $f = 1.6$ and $x = 2$ for flap deflections up to 15 deg; but these values cannot be considered general, and special wind-tunnel tests should be run on a tail, if the effect of flap deflection on c_d is considered to be important.

The coefficients k and m_f were derived by Glauert[1] on the basis of lifting-line theory, which does not appear to apply very well for the flap sizes ordinarily used for control surfaces. Experimental wind-tunnel determinations of k and m_f are plotted against the chord ratio c_f/c in Fig. 9:2, in which the values obtained by the lifting-line theory are also shown by dotted lines.

The effect of aerodynamic balance on the flap on the value of k is also shown in Fig. 9:2, where it appears that, for some shapes of nose on the flap, the theoretical value of k is more nearly approached than with a simple hinge without aerodynamic balance. The meaning of the coefficients k and m_f is illustrated by the following example:

Example.—A horizontal-tail surface of aspect ratio 3 has a rectangular planform and constant-chord elevator (flap) of 20 per cent of the chord of the tail surface. (*a*) Write equations for C_N and C_M in terms of the flap deflection δ_f, and (*b*) find C_N and C_M for a flap deflection of $\delta_f = 10$ deg and $\alpha = +5$ deg.

Solution.—For $E = c_f/c = 0.20$, read in Fig. 9:2 on the "actual" curves $k = 0.45$ and $m_f = 0.0094$. To determine the lift-curve slope, read in Fig. A10, page 415, for an aspect ratio of 3, $a = 0.055$ per deg.

a. Substituting in equations (9:5) and (9:7),

$$C_N = 0.055(\alpha + 0.45\delta_f)$$
$$C_M = 0.0094\delta_f$$

b. For $\delta_f = 10$ deg and $\alpha = 5$ deg, calculate

$$C_N = 0.055(5 + 4.5) = 0.522$$
$$C_M = 0.0094 \times 10° = 0.094$$

These are the answers called for.

9:4. Problems

1. For the Ercoupe airplane the total horizontal-tail area is 19.6 ft, of which 9.4 sq ft is elevators. Assuming that the effect of twin vertical tails at the end of the horizontal tail is to give an effective aspect ratio of 4.5, write equations for C_N and C_M in terms of the flap deflection δ_f.

2. The horizontal tail of the Lockheed Constellation airplane has a total area of 347.3 sq ft, of which 106.8 sq ft is elevators. Assuming that the effect of the triple vertical tails is to give an effective aspect ratio of 4.0, write equations for C_N and C_M in terms of the flap deflection δ_f.

[1] *Aeronaut. Research Comm. Rept. Mem. (Gt. Brit.)* 1095.

9:5. Effect of Flap and Tab Deflections on Flap Hinge Moments and Control Forces.—Theoretical considerations previously mentioned show that the hinge-moment coefficient of a flap is related to the normal force coefficient on the surface c_n and the flap deflection δ_f by the equation

$$c_{hf} = +h_0 c_n + h\delta_f \tag{9:8}$$

Theoretical and experimental values of h_0 and h are given in Fig. 9:3 for hinged surfaces without aerodynamic balance and without gap

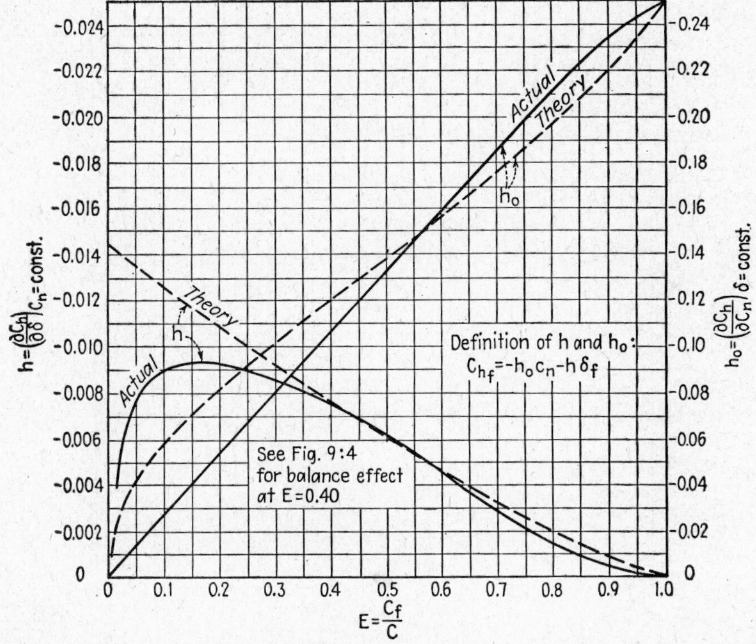

FIG. 9:3.—Hinge-moment characteristics for hinged surfaces without aerodynamic balance or gap. (*From NACA Tech. Rept.* 721.)

between the movable and fixed portions. The effect of aerodynamic balance on the coefficients h_0 and h for a flap size of approximately 40 per cent of the control surface is seen in Fig. 9:4 to depend on the shape of the nose of the flap, the fuller nose shape giving the greater reduction in hinge moments for a given per cent of balance. A flap nose is considered to have zero balance when it is constructed as a circular arc tangent to the airfoil surfaces with the center of the arc at the hinge line. Figure 9:3 also shows the effect of very small changes in the gap between the movable and fixed surfaces: a change from zero to one-half of 1 per cent makes a difference in h of the order of 30 per cent for some nose shapes. Aerodynamic balance of this sort is often used on large airplanes to reduce the control forces, but care must be taken to avoid overbalancing, for this may cause a reversal of control forces for large angles of flap deflection.

The effect of trim-tab deflections on flap hinge moments is shown in Fig. 9:4. Here the lifting-line theory and experimental data are seen to disagree so widely that the theory is unimportant. For flaps

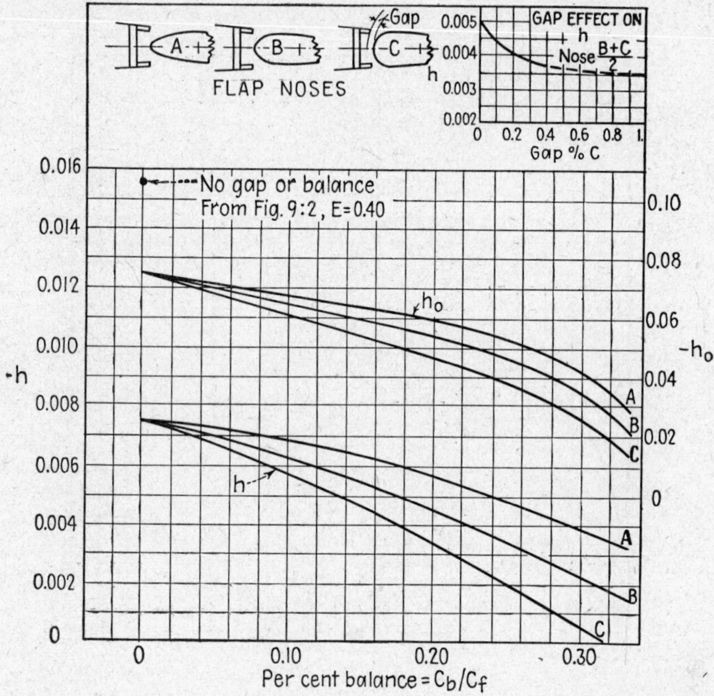

FIG. 9:4.—Effect of aerodynamic balance and gap on hinge-moment parameters in Fig. 9:2 for $E = 0.40 \pm 0.04$. Lower six curves are for gap $\approx$ 0.5 per cent. (*From L. E. Root, J. Aeronaut. Sci., April,* 1945.)

with trim tabs the flap hinge moment of equation (9:8) may be modified to read

$$c_{hf} = +h_0 c_n + h\delta_f + h_1\delta_t \tag{9:9}$$

in which h_1 may be read from Fig. 9:4 as a function of flap size and tab size. The control-stick forces may be calculated from the flap hinge moment H_f in equation (9:4) and the geometrical linkage between the flap and the control stick.

Stability calculations for airplanes are sometimes made on the assumption of fixed elevators and then corrected for the effect of releasing the controls, so that the elevator is free and there is practically zero hinge moment. For zero hinge moment the flap (elevator) will trail at an angle $\delta_{f\,\text{free}}$ determined by putting equation (9:8) or (9:9) equal to zero. The ratio of the normal force coefficient with free elevator to the normal force coefficient with fixed elevator is defined as the "free-elevator factor" and is designated by F_e. The free-elevator factor corresponding to the experimental data in Figs. 9:2 and 9:3 is shown in Fig. 9:6, and the effect of aerodynamic balance on

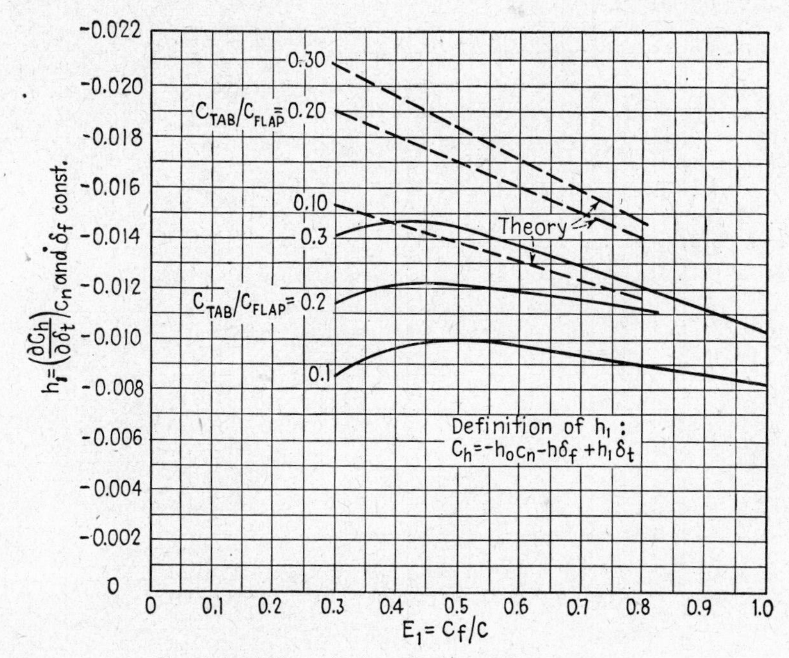

FIG. 9:5.—Effect of trim tab on flap hinge moments.

free-elevator factor based on data on Fig. 9:4 is shown in Fig. 9:7. Tabs are sometimes mechanically linked to the flap so as to provide a geometric relationship between δ_t and δ_f that may serve to reduce the control forces, in which case they are known as *balancing tabs*.

Calculations based on the foregoing explanation are illustrated by the following example.

Example.—Given a horizontal-tail surface that has a total surface of 210 sq ft of which 82 sq ft is elevator. The airfoil section is NACA 0012. The elevator has an aerodynamic balance of 22 per cent of the elevator surface and has a shape halfway between the *B* and *C* nose shapes in Fig. 9:2. There is a gap between elevator and stabilizer equal to 0.5 per cent of the tail-surface chord. The aspect ratio of the tail surface is 4.0. The elevator is equipped with a full-span trim tab of 10 per cent of the elevator chord.

Find (*a*) an equation for C_N in terms of α and δ_f; (*b*) an equation for C_H in terms of C_N, δ_f, and δ_t and also in terms of α, δ_f, and δ_t; (*c*) the free-elevator factor F_e; (*d*) C_N and C_H for $\alpha = 5$ deg, $\delta_f = 10$ deg, and $\delta_t = -6$ deg; (*e*) the elevator hinge moment for the conditions in part (*d*) when standard sea-level air flows by the tail at 100 mph; (*f*) the control-stick forces in part (*e*) if the geometry of the control system is as follows: distance from pilot's hand to control-stick pivot = 24 in., distance from control-stick pivot to elevator cable connection = 6 in., elevator-horn length from elevator hinge = 4 in.

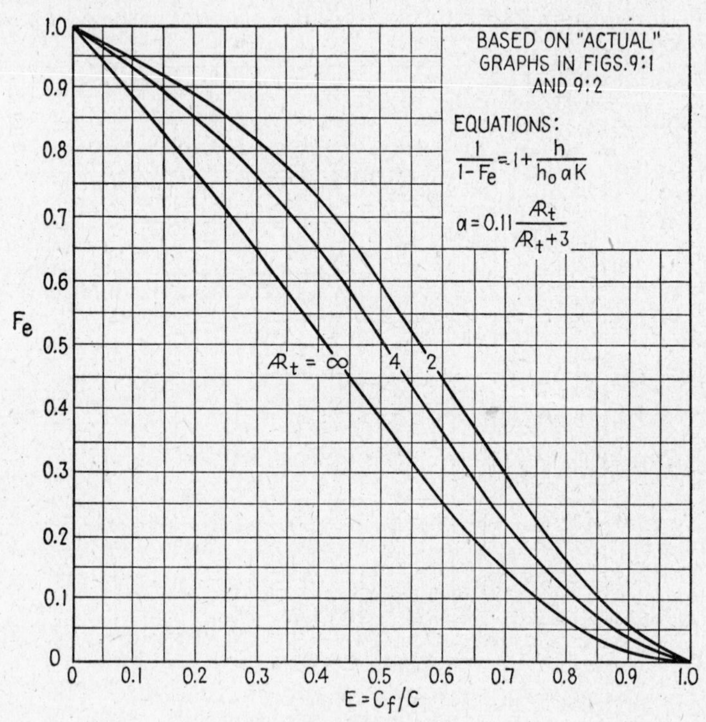

FIG. 9:6.—Free elevator factor for tail surfaces without aerodynamic balance or gap.

Solution.—a. For tail-surface aspect ratio of 4.0, read on page 415, lower line $[a = 0.1095 A\!\!R/(A\!\!R + 3)]$, $a = 0.063$. For a flap (elevator) size of

$$E = c_f/c = {}^{82}\!/_{210} = 0.39,$$

read, in Fig. 9:2, $k_{\text{theory}} = 0.74$; for a nose halfway between B and C, read

$$\eta_1 = k_{\text{actual}}/k_{\text{theory}} = 0.96$$

for $c_b/c_f = 0.22$; hence $k = 0.96 + 0.74 = 0.71$. Substitute these values of a and k in equation (9:5) to get

$$C_N = 0.063(\alpha + 0.71\delta_f) \tag{9:10}$$

b. For a flap size of $E = 0.39$ as before, read in Fig. 9:4 [which is a suitable modification of equation (9:3) for $E = 0.39$], with a balance ratio of $c_b/c_f = 0.22$, and on a line midway between nose shapes B and C, $-h_0 = 0.048$ and $-h = 0.0035$ (these tests are noted in the caption to Fig. 9:4 to be applicable for an elevator gap of 0.5 per cent of the tail-surface chord; hence no other gap correction is necessary). For a tab size of $c_{\text{tab}}/c_{\text{flap}} = 0.10$ and a flap size of $E = C_f/c = 0.39$, read, in Fig. 9:5, $h_1 = -0.0088$. Substitute these values of h_0, h, and h_1 in equation (9:9), and

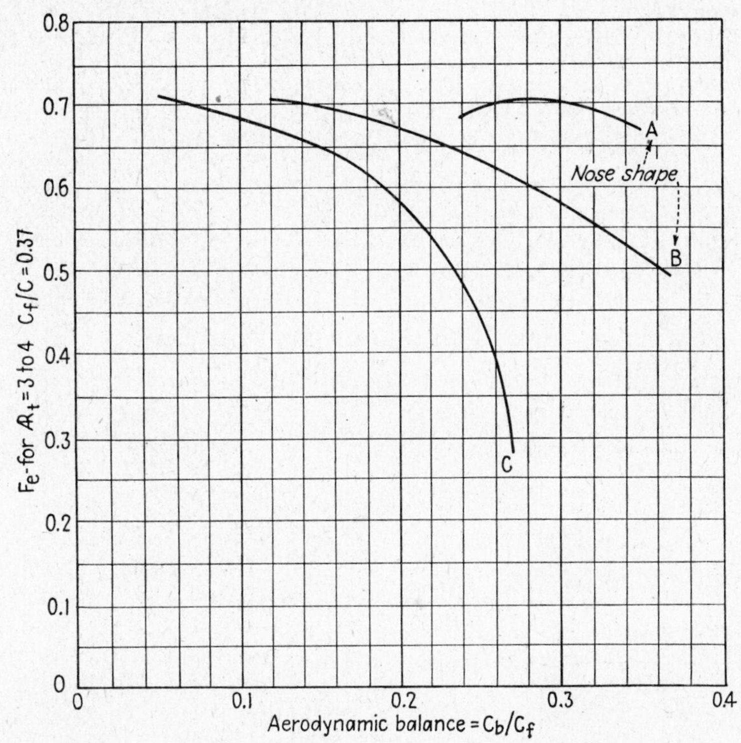

FIG. 9:7.—Effect of elevator balance on free elevator factor for $E \approx 0.40$. (*From L. E. Root, J. Aeronaut. Sci., April, 1945.*)

neglecting the distinction between C_{Hf} and c_{hf} for this purpose (though not for pressure-distribution calculations, discussed later)

$$C_{Hf} = -0.048C_N - 0.0035\delta_f - 0.0088\delta \tag{9:11}$$

Combining equations (9:10) and (9:11) gives

$$C_{Hf} = -0.0030\alpha - 0.0057\delta_f - 0.0088\delta_t \tag{9:12}$$

c. For the free-elevator factor with $E = c_f/c = 0.39$, $Æ_t = 4$, and no gap or balance, Fig. 9:6 would give $F_e = 0.66$. The effect of balance is given only for $E = 0.37$ (in Fig. 9:7), where, on a line drawn midway between noses B and C, for $c_b/c_f = 0.22$, read $F_e = 0.61$. For $E = 0.37$ and no gap or balance, with $Æ_t = 3.5$, which is about the test condition in Fig. 9:7, read $F_e = 0.71$, giving a correction factor for balance of $0.61/0.71 = 0.86$. Applying this same correction factor to the value of $F_e = 0.66$ that was read for the tail surface in this example gives

$F_e = 0.66 \times (0.61/0.71) = 0.57$. This result is uncertain because the effects of Æ and E in Fig. 9:7 are incompletely known; for values of Æ and E greatly different from the test values in Fig. 9:7, the effect of balance on F_e must be considered unknown until further test results have been published. As a check calculation, solve equation (9:12) with $C_{Hf} = 0$ and get $\delta_{f\,\text{free}} = -0.525\alpha$, and substitute in equation (9:10) to get $F_e = C_{N\,\text{free}}/C_{N\,\text{fixed}} = 0.625$ (best answer).

d. For $\alpha = 5$ deg, $\delta_f = 10$ deg, and $\delta_t = -6$ deg, substitute in equations (9:10) and (9:12) to get

$$C_N = 0.063(5 + 0.71 \times 10) = 0.76$$
$$C_H = -0.0030 \times 5 - 0.0057 \times 10 + 0.0088 \times 6 = -0.019$$

The negative sign indicates that the elevator must be held down and corresponds to a forward pressure on the control stick.

e. For 100 mph in standard sea-level air, calculate $q = 0.00256v^2 = 25.6$ lb per sq ft. For $S = 210$ sq ft and Æ $= b^2/S = 4.0$, calculate $b = \sqrt{4 \times 210} = 29$ ft. Calculate $\bar{c}_f = S_f/b = {}^{82}\!/_{29} = 2.82$ ft. Use equation (9:4), and calculate

$$H_f = C_{Hf}q\bar{c}_fS_f = -0.019 \times 25.6 \times 2.82 \times 82 = -112 \text{ lb-ft} = -1{,}360 \text{ lb-in.}$$

f. Calculate control-stick force as follows:

$$\text{Control-stick tension} = \frac{1{,}360 \text{ lb-in.}}{4 \text{ in.}} = 340 \text{ lb}$$
$$\text{Control-stick moment} = 340 \text{ lb} \times 6 \text{ in.} = 2{,}040 \text{ lb-in.}$$
$$\text{Control-stick force} = \frac{2{,}040 \text{ lb-in.}}{24 \text{ in.}} = 85 \text{ lb}$$

These are the answers called for.

9:6. Problems

1. A horizontal tail surface similar to that on the Ercoupe airplane (Prob. 1, Art. 9:4) has an area of 19.6 sq ft, of which 9.4 sq ft is elevators. The effective aspect ratio is 4.5, the actual aspect ratio is 4.0, and there is no aerodynamic balance on the elevator, and no gap between elevator and stabilizer.

Find (*a*) an equation for C_H in terms of C_N and δ_f; (*b*) an equation for C_H in terms of α and δ_f; (*c*) the free-elevator factor F_e; (*d*) C_H for $\alpha = 4$ deg and $\delta_f = 8$ deg; (*e*) the elevator hinge moment for the conditions in part (*d*) when air of 6,000 ft standard altitude flows by the tail at 80 mph; (*f*) the control-stick force in part (*e*) if the geometry of the control system is as follows: distance from pilot's hands to control-stick pivot = 20 in., distance from control-stick pivot to elevator cable connection = 4 in., elevator-horn length from elevator hinge = 3 in.

2. A horizontal-tail surface similar to that on the Constellation airplane (Prob. 2, Art. 9:4) has an area of 347.3, of which 106.8 sq ft is elevator. The effective aspect ratio is 4.0, and the actual aspect ratio is 3.6. There is an aerodynamic balance on the elevator, with nose shape A, and a gap of $0.005c$ between the elevator and stabilizer. The elevator balance is 25 per cent of the mean elevator chord. There is a full-span trim tab of 10 per cent of the elevator chord.

Find (*a*) an equation for C_H in terms of C_N, δ_f, and δ_t; (*b*) an equation for C_N in terms of α, δ_f, and δ_t; (*c*) the free-elevator factor F_e; (*d*) C_H for $\alpha = -2$ deg, $\delta_f = -15$ deg, and $\delta_t = 5$ deg; (*e*) H_f for part (*d*) at 2,000 ft standard altitude and an air speed of 80 mph; (*f*) the control-stick force in part (*e*) if the geometry of the control system is as follows: distance from pilot's hands to control-column pivot = 36 in., distance from control-column pivot to elevator cable = 6 in., elevator-horn length from elevator hinge = 6 in.

3. A vertical-tail surface similar to that on a Douglas DC-3 airplane has an area of 93.4 sq ft, of which 46.3 sq ft is rudder. The aspect ratio is 2.0. There is an aerodynamic balance on the rudder with nose shape midway between nose shapes B and C in Fig. 9:2, and the aerodynamic-balance area is 24 per cent of the rudder area. The rudder is equipped with a balancing tab so linked to the rudder that for each 10-deg movement of the rudder the tab moves 5 deg in the opposite direction. The gap between the rudder and fin is $0.005c$.

Find (*a*) an equation for C_N in terms of α and δ_f; (*b*) an equation for C_H in terms of C_N and δ_f; (*c*) an equation for C_H in terms of α and δ_f; (*d*) the trail angle of the rudder when it is free ($C_{Hf} = 0$) in terms of α; (*e*) the "free-rudder factor" $F_r = C_{N\,\text{fixed}}/C_{N\,\text{free}}$, calculated from the results of parts (*d*) and (*a*); (*f*) C_H for $\alpha = 2$ deg and $\delta_f = 10$ deg; (*g*) M_H for part (*f*) when standard sea-level air flows by the rudder at 100 mph; (*h*) the rudder-pedal force for part (*g*) if the geometry of the control system is as follows: distance from pilot's foot to rudder-pedal pivot = 12 in., distance from rudder pedal to rudder-cable connection = 3 in.; rudder-horn length from rudder hinge = 4 in.

9:7. Pressure Distribution on Control Surfaces.—Typical chordwise pressure distribution on a tail surface, a fin and rudder in this case, is shown in Fig. 9:8. At zero angle of attack and rudder deflection, graph *b* shows the usual equal pressure distribution on upper and lower surfaces with maximum negative pressure at points of maximum local velocity. Note that the pressure on the movable surfaces is practically zero, chiefly because of the gap between the fixed and movable surfaces.

Graph *c* shows the effect of angle of attack on the vertical-tail surfaces to be similar to that on wings, with a high peak of negative pressure (in this case approximately -2.0 times the dynamic pressure) very close to the leading edge.

Graphs *e* and *h* show that the effect of deflection of the rudder is to give a substantial difference in pressure between the upper and lower surfaces on both fin and rudder. Note in graphs *g*, *h*, and *i* that the effect of adding aerodynamic balance is to produce large local surface pressures on the balance area for large angles of rudder deflection.

The local surface pressures near the hinge are even greater if there is no gap. These local pressures can be used as shown in Fig. 9:9 to provide a balancing effect without gap for a limited range of flap angles if the stationary surface is thick enough. This type of balance is known as a *pressure balance* and is considered advantageous for airplanes flying at high subsonic speeds. Elimination of the gap greatly increases the effectiveness of a given area of control surface, and the pressure balance can be used to reduce the hinge moments to an even greater extent than with the more common overhanging aerodynamic balance.

The chordwise pressure distribution of classified airfoils, including most of the NACA four- and five-digit airfoils, can be calculated by an

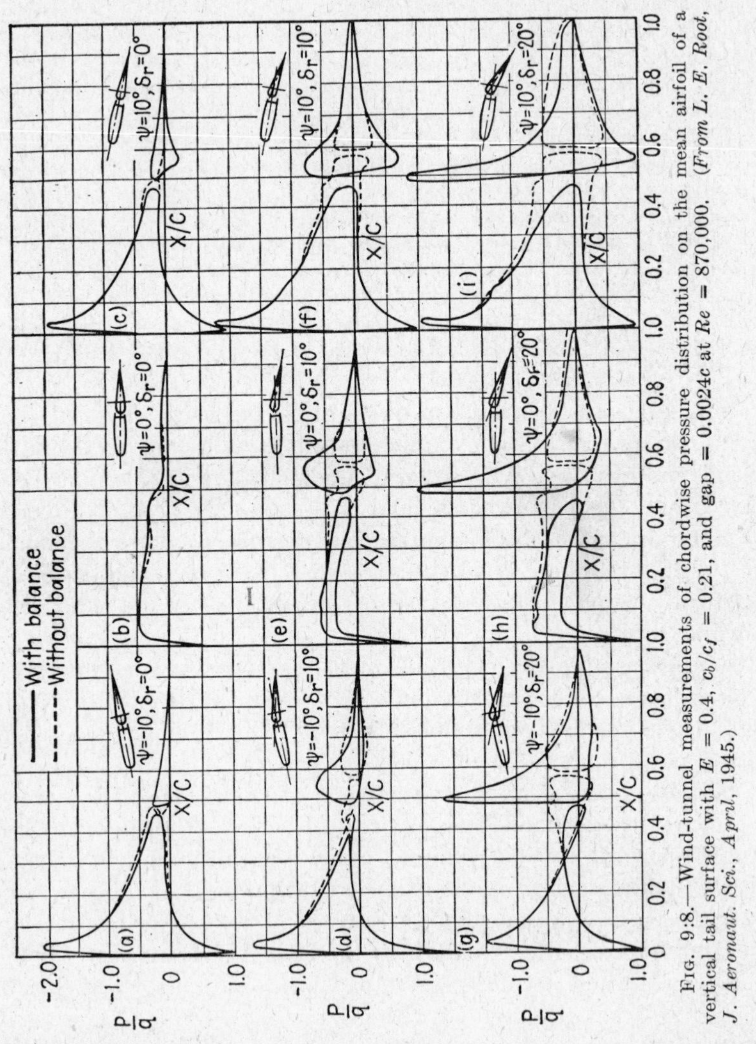

FIG. 9:8.—Wind-tunnel measurements of chordwise pressure distribution on the mean airfoil of a vertical tail surface with $E = 0.4$, $c_b/c_f = 0.21$, and gap $= 0.0024c$ at $Re = 870{,}000$. (*From L. E. Root, J. Aeronaut. Sci., April*, 1945.)

extension of the methods of Art. 2:21 to include the effect of flap deflection in a manner outlined in the Army–Navy–Commerce Committee on Aircraft Design publication ANC-1 (2) entitled Chordwise Air-load Distribution; but this procedure, involving several pages of graphs is considered too elaborate for reproduction here and is in any event applicable only to tail surfaces without gap, which are rather unusual. For actual tail surfaces, test results such as those shown in Fig. 9:8 must be obtained for each new design. A first approximation for preliminary design of tail surfaces, from the U.S. Department of Commerce Civil Air Regulations 04, is shown in Fig. 9:10. The minimum average-limit pressure per square foot is specified in the

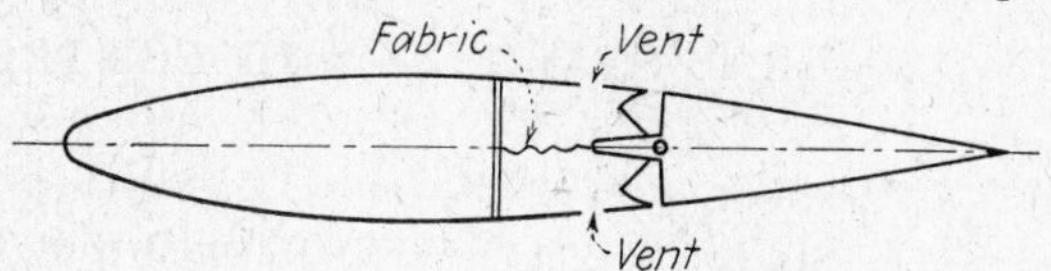

Fig. 9:9.—Pressure balance for hinged flap.

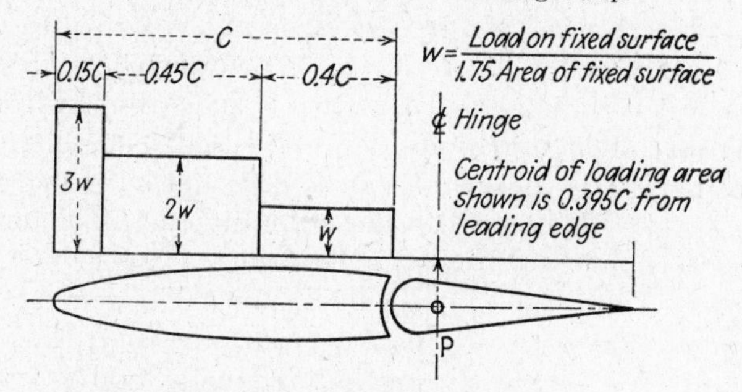

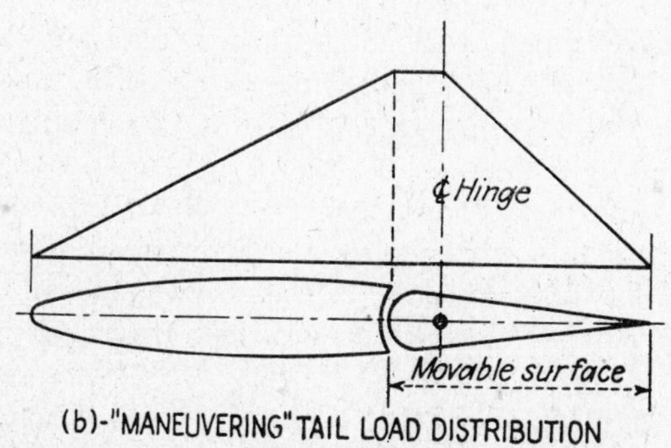

Fig. 9:10.—Approximate chordwise distribution of air loads on tail surfaces for preliminary design. (*From U.S. Civil Air Regulations* OU, *Airplane Airworthiness.*)

regulations; the normal force coefficient is usually assumed to be uniform along the span on the tail surface.

9:8. Problem.—For the horizontal tail of the Ercoupe, for which data are given in Prob. 1, Art. 9:6, and a minimum average horizontal-tail load of 15 lb per sq ft, find the maximum local unit pressure on the horizontal tail for the maneuvering pressure distribution shown in Fig. 9:10*b*.

CHAPTER 10

LONGITUDINAL STABILITY AND CONTROL

An airplane is usually considered to have satisfactory *control* if the pilot, by movement of controls, can make the airplane take off, fly in any desired direction, and land safely. It is said to have satisfactory *stability* if, when the pilot releases the controls, the airplane maintains a condition of steady flight. An airplane is said to be *statically stable* if it is so designed that when it is distributed from a condition of steady flight, forces are developed that tend to return it to that condition. It is said to be *dynamically stable* if the oscillations in returning to the stable condition are successively smaller and smaller. An airplane need not be statically or dynamically stable in order to be flyable, provided that the control is satisfactory. In general, the more stable an airplane is, the less sensitive it is to the controls; some military airplanes are purposely made marginally stable or slightly unstable in order to increase their maneuverability. A commercial airplane for private pilots should probably be made statically and dynamically stable, but a commercial air liner to be flown by professional pilots and equipped with an automatic pilot may quite permissibly be unstable in the free-control condition if this condition rarely exists. Satisfactory design procedure for an airplane requires that the control and stability be investigated while the airplane design is still in a preliminary stage and that the preliminary calculation of stability and control be thoroughly verified by wind-tunnel tests before the design has progressed so far that the changes in the control surfaces are expensive. This chapter deals with such preliminary calculations.

10:1. Static Stability of a Wing Alone.—A conventional airplane wing, such as most of the NACA four- and five-digit wings does not make a satisfactory "flying-wing" airplane because, while it can be controlled in flight by means of flaps on the trailing edge, it is statically unstable. Such wings all have negative pitching moments, such as shown in Fig. 10:1, so that for balance in flight the center of gravity must be located aft of the aerodynamic center. With this center-of-gravity location an increase in angle of attack and lift (as for example from L_2 to L_3 in Fig. 10:1) results in a change of moment about the center of gravity, which causes the angle of attack to increase still further. For wings with a reflexed trailing edge, however, such as in Fig. 10:2 or the NACA M6 listed in Table XVIII, page 390, or most of the NACA five-digit series with the number 1 for a middle digit, the pitching moment about the aerodynamic center is positive, and the center of gravity must be located ahead of the aerodynamic center for balance. With such a center-of-gravity location, an increased angle of attack and lift causes a change in moments about the center of gravity so as to reduce the angle of attack; this is, therefore, a statically stable arrangement, though it may be dynamically unstable.

The farther the center of gravity can be located ahead of the aerodynamic center, the greater will be the static stability. For most of

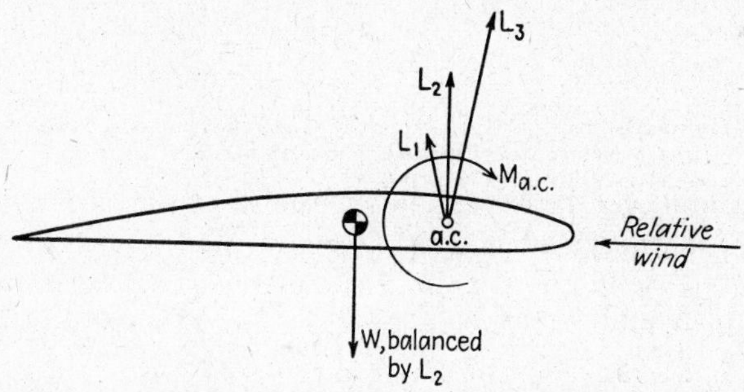

FIG. 10:1.—Wing with negative $C_{M\,a.c.}$; center of gravity (c.g.) aft of aerodynamic center (a.c.) for balance; unstable in flight.

the airfoils listed in Appendix 4, $C_{M\,a.c.}$ is only slightly negative, and such airfoils flown without tail surfaces are only slightly stable. The only large values of $C_{M\,a.c.}$ listed in Appendix 4 are for inverted airfoils, from which it may be concluded that most wings will fly satisfactorily upside down without a tail. This arrangement, however, gives a poor stalling lift coefficient, and it is usually considered unsatisfactory, though many workable designs have been built and flown without tails (as, for example, the Northrop XB-35, shown in Fig. I:5*f*).

10:2. Static Stability of a Tandem Monoplane.—In Art. 10:1 it was noted that a wing with trailing edge inclined downward relative to the zero-lift chord, which requires a center-of-gravity location aft of the aerodynamic center for balance, is unstable and a wing with trailing edge inclined upward, requiring center of gravity ahead of aerodynamic center for balance, is stable. A symmetrical wing (with $C_{M\,a.c.} = 0$) has no pitching moment and requires for balance that the center of gravity be located exactly *at* the aerodynamic center. Such a wing is neutrally stable and therefore will not fly by itself. Consider next a combination of two symmetrical wings in tandem, as shown in Fig. 10:3. If the wings are set at equal angles to the body and the effect of flow over the forward wing on the angle of attack on the rear wing (down-wash) is neglected, the center of gravity would have to be located midway between the two aero-

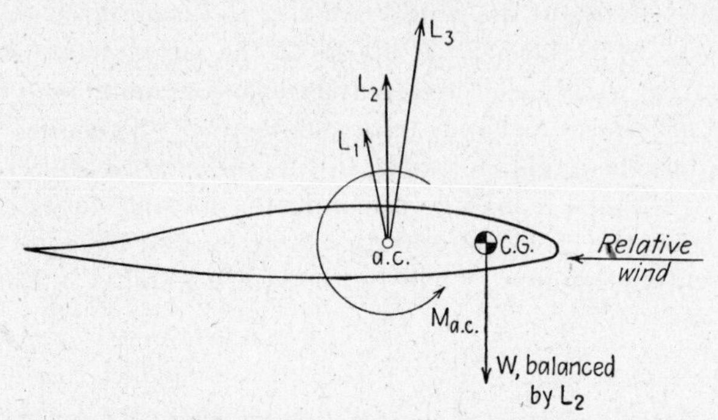

FIG. 10:2.—Wing with positive $C_{M\,a.c.}$; center of gravity (c.g.) ahead of aerodynamic center (a.c.) for balance; stable in flight.

dynamic centers for balance. When the direction of flight changes, the lift on both wings changes equally, and there is no change on moments around the center of gravity, so that such an airplane would be neutrally stable and therefore would not fly satisfactorily by itself.

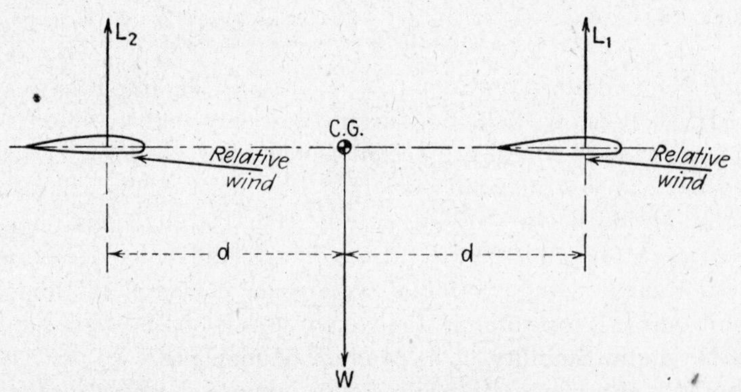

FIG. 10:3.—Tandem monoplane of two symmetrical wings of equal incidence center of gravity (c.g.) midway between aerodynamic centers (a.c.'s) for balance neutrally stable.

If, however, the rear wing is set at a lower angle of incidence than the front wing, as shown in Fig. 10:4, it has a smaller angle of attack and a smaller lift, and the center of gravity must be located nearer the forward wing for balanced flight. For this arrangement, when the angle of attack increases an equal amount on both wings, the percentage increases on the rear wing are greater, and the pitching moments about the center of gravity change so as to produce a net diving moment that will reduce the angle of attack. This arrangement is therefore stable and in principle is the arrangement used in almost all present-day aircraft, though in practice the rear wing is usually made

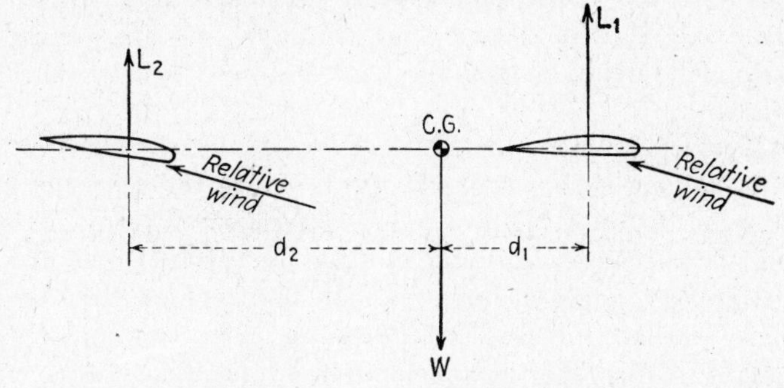

FIG. 10:4.—Tandem monoplane of two symmetrical wings with rear wing at lower incidence; center of gravity (c.g.) nearer to front aerodynamic center (a.c.); stable.

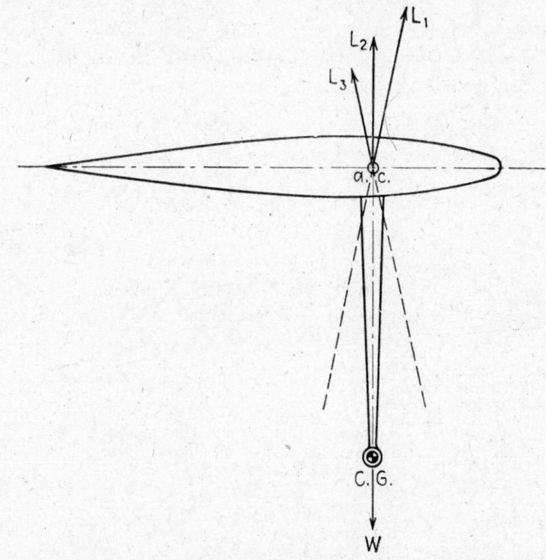

FIG. 10:5.—Center-of-gravity location for stable flight with a wing of constant center of pressure (c.p.) ($C_{M\ a.c.} = 0$).

substantially smaller than on the front wing, so that an even farther forward center-of-gravity location is required for balance. It is stable as long as the rear wing, or "stabilizer," is set at an angle sufficiently negative relative to the main wing and the center of gravity is correspondingly located for satisfactory balance. Many experimenters in glider flight were killed through failure to discover this elementary principle. The principle is equally valid whether the larger surface is the forward surface or the rear surface, though only a few airplanes have been built with the smaller surface forward (such as the Naugle N6 shown in Fig. I:5*e*). Static-stability relationships are developed here only for the conventional case with the wing ahead of the stabilizing and control surface, but the same procedure can be used to develop the relationships for the "tail-first," or Canard, type of airplane.

Another arrangement for satisfactory stability in flight of a neutrally stable wing is shown in Fig. 10:5. With the center of gravity located some distance below the aerodynamic center an increase in angle of attack causes a diving moment of the lift force about the center of gravity, and a decrease in angle of attack causes a nosing up moment of the lift force about the center of gravity and results in stable flight. This wing arrangement was first developed by Spratt about the time of the Wright brothers' first flight but does not usually lend itself to efficient aerodynamic design and is accordingly seldom used.

10:3. Static-stability Relationships with Wing and Stabilizer.—The pitching moments about the center of gravity on an airplane to the

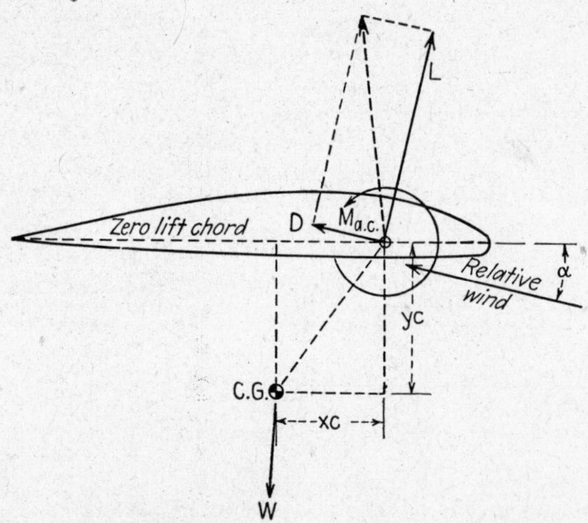

FIG. 10:6.—Sketch for calculating moments of wing forces about center of gravity (c.g.) of arbitrary location.

lift drag and moment on the wing alone may be calculated from the geometric relationships shown in Fig. 10:6, in which the center of gravity is the distance xc behind the aerodynamic center (measured parallel to the zero-lift chord) and yc below the aerodynamic center (measured perpendicular to the zero lift chord). The equation for moment of the aerodynamic forces in Fig. 10:6 about the center of gravity is

$$M_{c.g.} = (L \cos \alpha + D \sin \alpha)xc + (D \cos \alpha - L \sin \alpha)yc + M_{a.c.} \quad (10:1)$$

For small absolute angles of attack (here denoted by α) it is permissible to assume $\cos \alpha = 1$, $\sin \alpha = \alpha = C_L/m$, and $C_D \sin \alpha = 0$. Upon making these approximations and dividing equation (10:1) on cqS, where c is the geometric mean chord of the wing, it follows that

$$C_{Mw} = xC_L + y\left(C_D - \frac{C_L^2}{m}\right) + C_{Ma.c.} \quad (10:2)$$

Since for most airplanes $C_D = C_{De\,\min} + C_L^2/\pi A\!\!R_e$, equation (10:2) may be written

$$C_{Mw} = xC_L + yC_{De\,\min} + yC_L^2\left(\frac{1}{\pi A\!\!R_e} - \frac{1}{m}\right) + C_{Ma.c.} \quad (10:3)$$

Equation (10:3) may be considered to be the pitching-moment coefficient for the wing alone about the center of gravity. The effect of adding fuselage and nacelle to the wing appears to be usually completely accounted for by assuming that such addition results in a foreward movement of the aerodynamic center. Typical values of fuselage and nacelle effects, as given by Millikan,[1] are

Fuselage, $\Delta(a.c.) = 0.02$ to 0.04 average 0.03
2 nacelles, $\Delta(a.c.) = 0.025$ to 0.045 average 0.035

Theoretical methods are available for estimating part but not all of the fuselage effect,[2,3] since the wing-fuselage interference is hardly susceptible to mathematical analysis.

If $(a.c.)'$ is the effective aerodynamic-center location taking account of fuselage and nacelle effects,

$$(a.c.)' = a.c. - \Delta(a.c.)_{\text{fuselage}} - \Delta(a.c.)_{\text{nacelles}}$$

If x' is the distance in mean chords from $(a.c.)'$ to the center of gravity then equation (10:3) may be modified in include fuselage and nacelle effects by writing it

$$C_{Mwfn} = x'C_L + yC_{De\,\min} + yC_L^2\left(\frac{1}{\pi A\!\!R_e} - \frac{1}{m}\right) + C_{Ma.c.} \quad (10:4)$$

[1] MILLIKAN, CLARK B., "Aerodynamics of the Airplane," 1941 ed., p. 149.

[2] LIEPMANN, H. P., An Improved Longitudinal Stability Calculation, *J. Aeronaut. Sci.*, March, 1942.

[3] HOCKMAN, MARION THOMAS, "Elementary Considerations of Longitudinal Stability," *J. Aeronaut. Sci.*, July, 1945.

The force on the tail surface and the geometrical relationships between the angles involved are shown in Fig. 10:7, where it is seen that

$$M_t = -F_t l_t \tag{10:5}$$

Noting that $F_t = C_{Lt} \times q_t \times S_t$, where $q_t = \rho V_t^2/2$ and $C_{Lt} = a_t \alpha_t$, and dividing by cqS give

$$C_{Mt} = \frac{a_t \alpha_t q_t S_t}{cqS} l_t \tag{10:6}$$

Since α_t differs from α by the down-wash ϵ and the stabilizer incidence

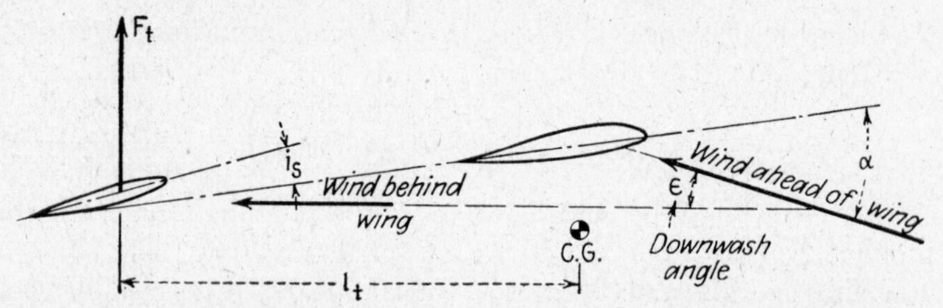

FIG. 10:7.—Sketch illustrating down-wash and angle-of-attack relationships.

i_s, that is, $\alpha_t = \alpha - \epsilon + i_s$, we may write, for stabilizer incidence $i_s = 0$,

$$\frac{\alpha_t}{\alpha} = 1 - \frac{\epsilon}{\alpha} \tag{10:7}$$

Equations (10:6) and (10:7) may be combined to give

$$C_{Mt} = -C_L \frac{a_t}{a} \frac{l_t}{c} \frac{q_t}{q} \frac{S_t}{s} \left(1 - \frac{\epsilon}{\alpha}\right) \quad \text{for } i_s = 0 \tag{10:8}$$

The resultant moment on the airplane is

$$C_M = C_{Mwfn} + C_{Mt} \tag{10:9}$$

Static stability requires that *an increase* in α or C_L must be accompanied by a *reduction* in C_M, or

$$\frac{dC_M}{dC_L} = \text{stability index} = \text{negative for positive static stability}$$

Equations (10:4) and (10:8) may be used to calculate and plot graphs of C_{Mwfn} and C_{Mt} against angle of attack or lift coefficient. The foregoing procedure is illustrated by the following example.

Example.—The data given below are for an airplane similar to the Lockheed Lodestar. Using the foregoing method, (*a*) estimate the aerodynamic-center location for the wing, fuselage, and two nacelles; (*b*) write an equation for C_{Mwfn} in terms of C_L and numerical coefficients; (*c*) write an equation for C_{Mt} in terms of C_L and numerical coefficients for $i_s = 0$ and free elevators; (*d*) plot the equations of parts (*b*) and (*c*) with C_L as abscissa, and plot C_M *vs.* C_L; (*e*) add a new C_M scale for $i_s = -4$ deg and free elevators, and find C_L and v for trim with this stabilizer setting and free elevators for a gross weight of 17,500 lb in standard sea-level air; (*f*) add a scale of elevator angles to the C_M scale for the trim condition found in part (*e*). (*g*) find the static-stability index dC_M/dC_L both analytically and graphically for the trim condition found in part (*e*). Find also the maximum aft center-of-gravity location for static stability at small values of C_L.

Wing data. Surface area = 551 sq ft, span = 65.5 ft, Æ = 7.75, geometric mean chord = 8.41 ft, taper ratio = 2:1; wing 23015-09; 0-0 listed in Table XX on page 393.

Fuselage and nacelle data. Assume $\Delta(a.c.) = 0.03$ for fuselage, $\Delta(a.c.) = 0.04$ for 2 nacelles.

Tail data. Length, center of gravity to $(a.c.)_{\text{tail}}$, $l_t = 28$ ft; surface area = 134 sq ft; span = 21.6 ft; $Æ_t = 3.5$; elevator surface area = 40.4 sq ft. No gap or balance.

Center-of-gravity location. $0.27c$ aft of leading edge of geometric mean chord, $0.05c$ above zero lift chord ($y = -0.05$).

Down-wash and wing wake. Assume $\epsilon = 0.4\alpha$ and $q_t = 0.9q$.

Solution.—a. For the 23015-09 wing, read in Table XX on page 393, a.c. = 2 per cent ahead of $c/4$, = 0.23. For $\Delta(a.c.) = 0.3$ for fuselage plus 0.04 for nacelles, calculate $(a.c.)' = 0.23 - 0.03 - 0.04 = 0.16$.

b. For the 23015-09 wing, read, in Table XX on page 393, $C_{Ma.c.} = -0.007$; $C_{De\,\min} = 0.0067$, $e = 0.91$, $a = 0.074$ for Æ = 6. Correct e and a to Æ = 7.75 graphically by Fig. 2:30 and Fig. A10, page 415, and get $e = 0.88$ and $a = 0.079$. Substitute these values in equation (10:4), and get, with

$$x' = c.g. - (a.c.)' = 0.27 - 0.16 = 0.11,$$

$$C_{Mwfn} = 0.11C_L - 0.05 \times 0.0067 - 0.05C_L^2\left(\frac{1}{\pi} \times 7.75 \times 0.88 - \frac{1}{57.3} \times 0.078\right) - 0.007 = 0.11C_L + 0.009C_L^2 - 0.0073$$

c. To substitute in equation (10:8), read, on page 415, for $Æ_t = 3.5$, $a_t = 0.059$. Note also that the given data specify that $l_t = 28$ ft, $c = 8.41$, $q_t/q = 0.9$,

$$S_t = 134 \text{ sq ft},$$

$S = 551$ sq ft, $1 - (\epsilon/\alpha) = 0.60$, and, from part (*b*), $a = 0.079$. Hence

$$C_{Mt} = -C_L \frac{0.059}{0.079}\frac{28}{8.41}\,0.9\,\frac{134}{551}\,0.60 = -0.327C_L \quad \text{with fixed elevators}$$

For C_{Mt} with *free* elevators, calculate $E = 40.4/134 = 0.302$, and read in, Fig. 9:6, $F_e = 0.78$; hence, with free elevators,

$$C_{Mt} = -0.78 \times 0.327C_L = 0.255C_L$$

d. The above equations for C_{Mwfn} and C_{Mt} as well as $C_M = C_{Mwfn} + C_{Mt}$ are plotted in Fig. 10:8. The negative slope of the graph of C_M *vs.* C_L indicates positive static stability.

e. To get the effect of change of stabilizer setting (with free elevators), note from equation (10:6) that

$$\frac{\partial C_M}{\partial i_s} = \frac{\partial C_{Mt}}{\partial \alpha_t} F_e = -F_e a_t \frac{l_t}{c} \frac{q_t}{q} \frac{S_t}{S}$$

and with numerical values substituted this gives

$$\frac{\partial C_M}{\partial i_s} = 0.78 \times 0.059 \frac{28}{8.41} 0.9 \frac{134}{551} = 0.0336 \text{ per deg}$$

This scale is laid out on the right side of Fig. 10:8. Note that with $i_s = -4$ deg

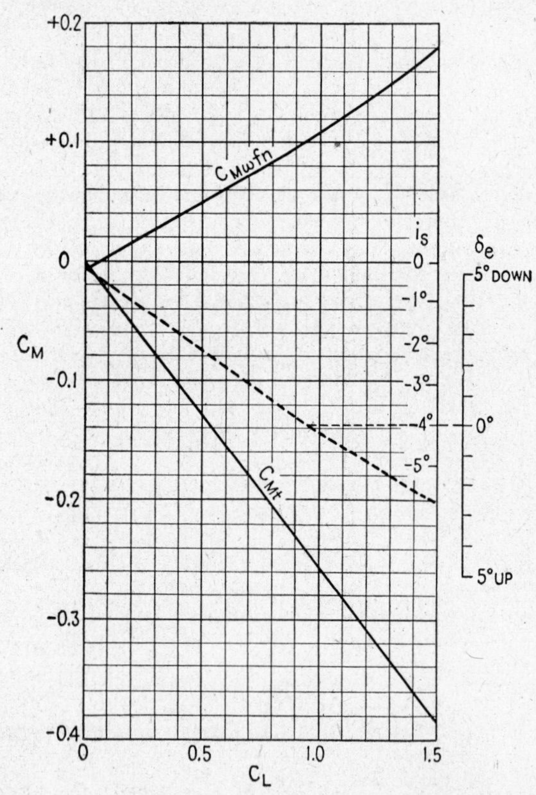

FIG. 10:8.—Plot of pitching moment *vs.* C_L for illustrative example.

the airplane trims at $C_L = 0.95$; the corresponding trim speed for $W = 17{,}500$ and standard sea-level air is

$$v = \sqrt{\frac{17{,}500/551}{0.00256 \times 0.95}} = 116 \text{ mph}$$

f. For elevator effectiveness, read, in Fig. 9:2, $k = 0.58$, and, from equation (10:6),

$$\frac{\partial C_M}{\partial \delta_e} = \frac{\partial C_{Mt}}{\partial \delta_t} k = ka_t \frac{l_t}{c} \frac{q_t}{q} \frac{S_t}{S} = 0.025 \text{ per deg}$$

This scale is also laid out on the right side of Fig. 10:8.

g. Differentiating C_M with respect to C_L gives, for free elevators,

$$\frac{dC_M}{dC_L} = +0.11 + 0.018C_L - 0.255$$

For $C_L = 0.95$,

$$\frac{dC_M}{dC_L} = -0.128$$

For small values of C_L

$$\frac{dC_M}{dC_L} = -0.145$$

Hence, the center of gravity could be 14.5 per cent of the geometric mean chord farther aft before the airplane became unstable at low C_L. This location would be at 28 per cent $\times$ 14.5 per cent = 42.5 per cent of the geometric mean chord.

These are the answers called for.

10:4. Problems

1. The data given below are for an airplane similar to the Ercoupe. Using the method illustrated in Art. 9:3, (*a*) estimate the aerodynamic-center location for the wing and fuselage; (*b*) write an equation for C_{Mwfn} in terms of C_L and numerical coefficients; (*c*) write an equation for C_{Mt} in terms of C_L and numerical coefficients for $i_s = 0$ and free elevators; (*d*) plot the equations of parts (*b*) and (*c*) with C_L as abscissa, and plot C_M *vs.* C_L; (*e*) add a scale of stabilizer angles to the plot, and find i_s for trim at 90 mph in standard sea-level air for a gross weight of 1,260 lb; (*f*) add a scale of elevator angles to the C_M scale for the trim condition found in part (*e*); (*g*) find the maximum rearward center-of-gravity location for positive static stability at small values of C_L.

Wing data. $S = 142.6$ sq ft, $b = 30$ ft, rectangular, 4412 section.

Fuselage data. Assume $\Delta(a.c.) = 0.03$ for fuselage.

Tail data. $l_t = 14$ ft, $S_t = 19.6$ sq ft, $S_{elev} = 9.4$ sq ft, $AR_t = 4.0$. No gap or balance.

Center-of-gravity location. 0.30*c* aft of leading edge; 0.02*c* above zero lift chord.

Downwash and wing wake. Assume $\epsilon = 0.35\alpha$ and $q_t = q$.

2. Find the same items as in Prob. 1, but use the following data, which apply to an airplane like the Lockheed Constellation:

Wing data. $S = 1{,}650$ sq ft, $b = 123$ ft, tapered 3:1, 23018-09 sections.

Fuselage data. Assume $\Delta(a.c.) = 0.04$ for fuselage, $\Delta(a.c.) = 0.06$ for four nacelles.

Tail data. $l_t = 45$ ft, $S_t = 347.3$ sq ft, $S_{elev} = 106.8$ sq ft, $AR_t = 3.6$. Elevator balance = 25 per cent elevator chord; gap = 0.005*c*, as in Prob. 2, Art. 9:6.

Center-of-gravity location. 0.22*c* aft of leading edge of geometric mean chord; vertical location assumed to be exactly *on* the zero lift chord.

Down-wash and wing wake. Assume $\epsilon = 0.30\alpha$ and $q_t = q$.

10:5. Estimation of Down-wash.—In the analysis of Art. 10:3, the down-wash ratio ϵ/α was given or assumed to be known. In practice, it is never accurately known and is difficult to estimate accurately.

A survey of some of the attempts at down-wash estimation is presented in this article.

According to the momentum theory of airfoils, it was shown in Art. 2:7, equation (2:25), that

$$\alpha_{\text{rad}} = \frac{2C_L}{\pi A\!\!R} \tag{10:10}$$

which, with $C_L = m\alpha_{\text{rad}}$ and $m = 2\pi A\!\!R/(A\!\!R + 2.5)$ (from Art. 2:11) gives

$$\frac{\epsilon}{\alpha} = \frac{4}{A\!\!R + 2.5} \tag{10:11}$$

A physical picture of the relation between actual and theoretical vertical velocity distribution in the vicinity of a wing, as presented by Millikan,[1] is shown in Fig. 10:9, where it is noted that equation (10:10)

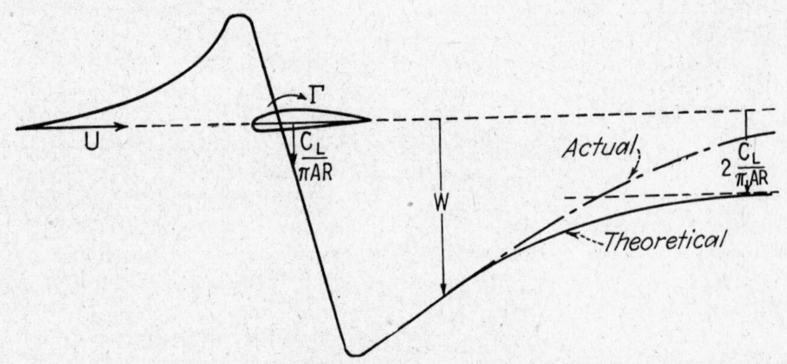

FIG. 10:9.—Vertical velocity (w) distribution in the vicinity of a wing. (*From Millikan, "Aerodynamics of the Airplane."*)

gives the theoretical limiting down-wash at an infinite distance behind the wing. The actual down-wash distribution behind elliptic wings, as reported by Silverstein and Katzoff,[2] is shown in Fig. 10:10, and the actual down-wash at typical tail locations for wings of various aspect ratios and taper ratios is shown in Fig. 10:11. In Figs. 10:10 and 10:11, h/b is a factor representing the vertical location of the horizontal tail relative to the zero-lift chord of the wing, expressed as a fraction of the wing span. Figures 10:10 and 10:11 or the corresponding figures in *NACA Tech. Rept.* 648 for wings with flaps deflected are widely used for estimating down-wash in connection with the assumption that $q_t/q = 1.0$. This assumption is equivalent to neglecting the

[1] *Loc. cit.*

[2] SILVERSTEIN, A., and S. KATZOFF, Design Charts for Predicting Downwash Angles and Wake Characteristics behind Plain and Flapped Wings, *NACA Tech. Rept.* 648 (1939).

loss of velocity due to wing drag and wing-fuselage interference. This loss can be neglected for most angles of attack on a given airplane; but there is always a small region of reduced velocity due to the wing drag, known as the "wake" of the wing, and it usually affects the horizontal tail at some angles of attack on the wing. Charts showing the wake center angle, wake velocity distribution, and the maximum width and dynamic-pressure loss in the wake are given in Fig. 10:13.

The effect of propeller operation on stability and down-wash is difficult to predict accurately. The horizontal tail is usually partly in the propeller slip stream, and, from this consideration only, the operation of the propellers should increase the stability and control.

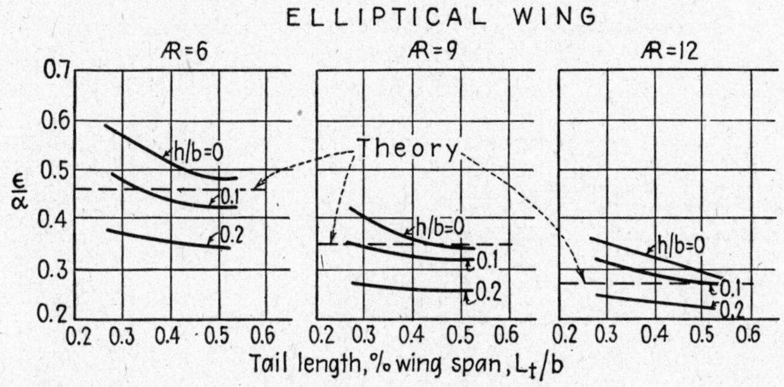

FIG. 10:10.—Theoretical and actual down-wash in the region of typical tail surfaces. (*From NACA Tech. Rept.* 648.)

The propeller thrust is usually greater at lower speeds and for usual center-of-gravity locations has a greater diving moment at high values of C_L, and this factor would also tend to increase the stability. Wind-tunnel tests on models with running propellers, however,[1] usually show that the effect of propeller operation is to *reduce* the stability. Accordingly, wherever possible, wind-tunnel models are equipped with operating propellers to determine the power-on as well as the power-off characteristics.

10:6. Problems

1. Given the data in Prob. 1, Art. 10:4, on an airplane similar to the Ercoupe, and given also a vertical location of the horizontal tail relative to the zero-lift chord of the wing of $h/b = 0.05$. (*a*) Using Fig. 10:11, find the down-wash ratio

[1] MILLER, S. S., and W. H. ALBACH, Wind Tunnel Tests on a Low Wing Monoplane with Propellers Running; Longitudinal and Directional Stability; Elevator Hinge Moments, *J. Aeronaut. Sci.*, February, 1938, p. 141. MILLIKAN, C. B., J. S. RUSSELL, and H. M. MCCOY, Wind Tunnel Tests on a High Wing Monoplane, *J. Aeronaut. Sci.*, January, 1936, p. 79.

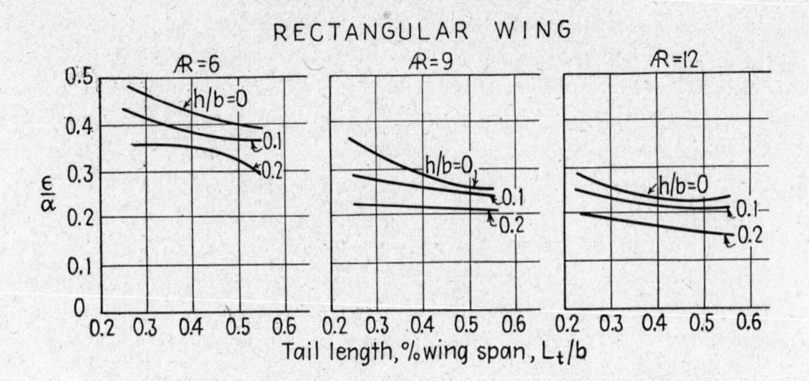

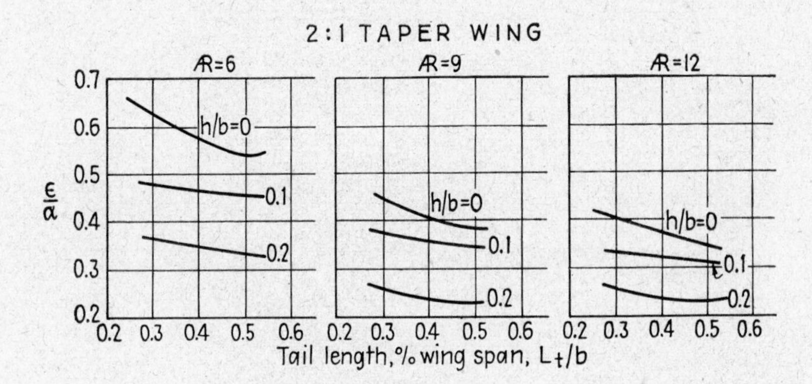

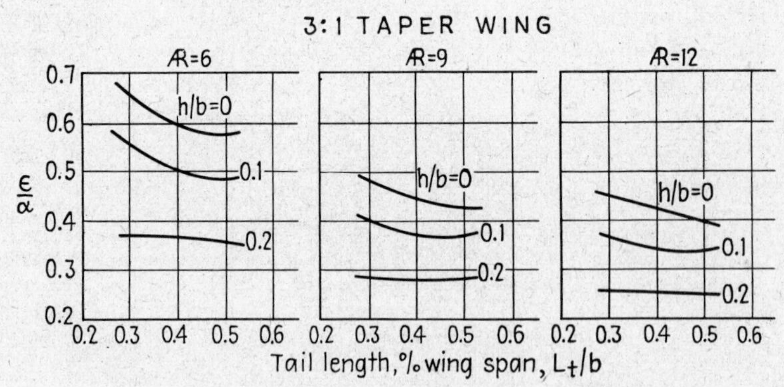

FIG. 10:11.—Down-wash behind wings of various taper ratios and aspect ratios. (*From NACA Tech. Rept.* 648.)

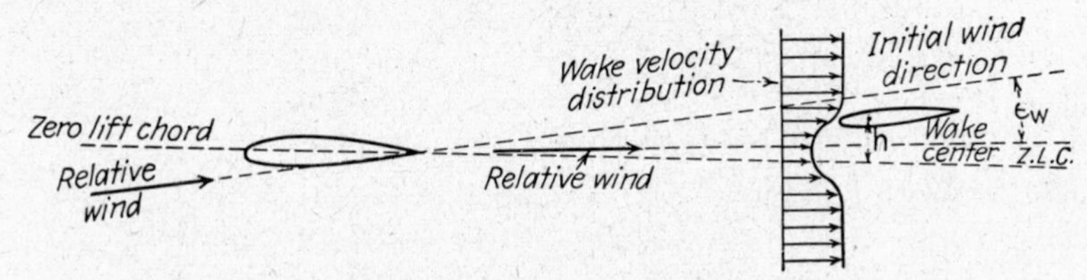

FIG. 10:12.—Wake location and wake velocity distribution.

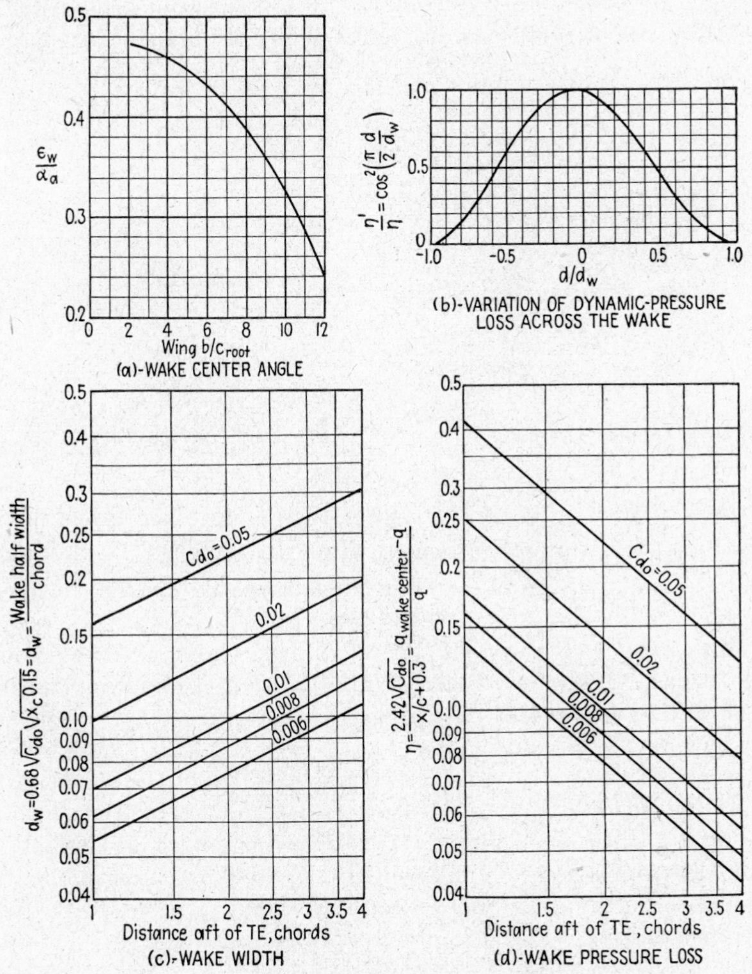

FIG. 10:13.—Data on size and location of a wake behind a wing without fuselage. (*From NACA Tech. Rept.* 648.)

for ϵ/α at the tail. (*b*) Using data in Fig. 10:13, plot to scale a wake velocity distribution as in Fig. 10:12.

2. Repeat Prob. 1 for the Constellation airplane, using data as in Prob. 2, Art. 10:4, and assuming a vertical-tail location $h/b = 0.10$.

10:7. Control Forces.—For a small, low-speed airplane, conventionally designed control surfaces will never require forces in excess of those which can be exerted by a strong pilot (specified by U.S. Department of Commerce Civil Air Regulations 04 as 200 lb on elevator control, 200 lb on rudder control, or 80 lb on aileron control). In fact, consideration of ease of handling the airplane will usually lead the manufacturer to keep the control forces under 5 or 10 lb for any normal

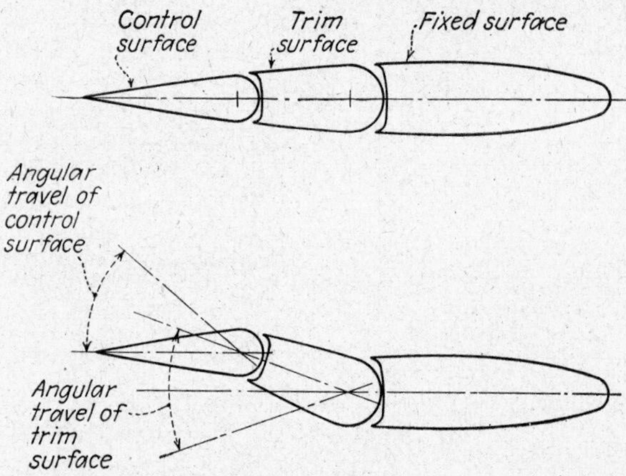

FIG. 10:14.—Tab-control arrangement used satisfactorily on large Boeing airplanes.

maneuvers. As airplanes are made larger, the control forces are kept small by careful design of aerodynamic-balance, tab-balance, or pressure-balance systems, discussed in Chap. 9; but there is always a limit to which a balancing system can go without obtaining overbalance under some conditions. When this limit is reached, owing to the excessive size or speed of the airplane, or both, two other means are used for keeping the control forces low. One is illustrated in Fig. 10:14 and consists essentially of using the trim tabs to fly the airplane by connecting them directly to the control stick and leaving the elevator free to float at the angle determined by the trim-tab setting. Another is illustrated in Fig. 10:15 and consists essentially of using hydraulic pressure to magnify the pilot's efforts by means of a servovalve and other mechanisms. Electric-power boosts have also been satisfactorily used.

In any case, the probable control forces should be carefully studied by preparation of a diagram similar to Fig. 10:8 and calculation of the control force for each elevator angle at the corresponding speed of trimmed level flight. In fact, control forces could be added to the elevator scale of Fig. 10:8 if the dynamic pressure corresponding to the trim C_L for each elevator angle were used with the appropriate hinge-moment coefficient, but the scale of control forces would be nonuniform. In flight tests for stability and control, discussed in Chap. 11, control-stick force is commonly plotted against v or C_L, uniform scale being used for the control-stick-force plot.

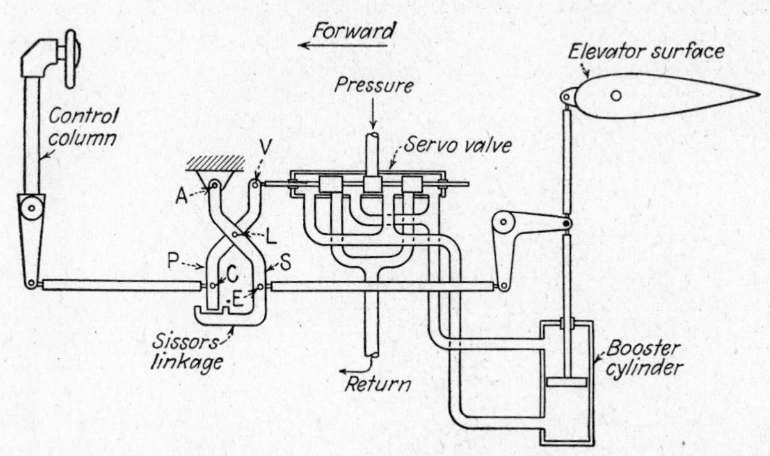

FIG. 10:15.—Schematic diagram of Vickers power-boost control used on large Martin airplanes. (*From Riley, Basic Principles of Power Boost Flight Controls, S.A.E. Journal, February,* 1945, *p.* 110.)

10:8. Dynamic Longitudinal Stability.—Typical oscillations of a dynamically stable airplane in returning to its statically stable equilibrium condition are shown in Fig. 10:16. Analysis of dynamic stability usually involves calculation of the time T and the period P shown in Fig. 10:16. The mathematical analysis is not difficult but is too lengthy for presentation here; it has been well presented elsewhere.[1] The estimation of the time and period of oscillation involve additional uncertainties to those of the static-stability estimate. The following graphical procedure from *NACA Tech. Rept.* 521 is presented chiefly to emphasize the factors involved and the order of magnitude of their effects. The report specifies that the period of oscillation in seconds shall be calculated from

$$P = \frac{2.83\sqrt{C_L W/S}}{\psi'} \tag{10:12}$$

[1] DIEHL, W. S., "Engineering Aerodynamics," rev. ed., Chap. 8.

and the time to damp to half amplitude shall be calculated from

$$T = \frac{-0.313 \sqrt{C_L W/S}}{\zeta'} \qquad (10:13)$$

in which ψ' and ζ' are intended to be read from Figs. 10:17 and 10:18 (or more applicable charts if available). Each chart is a plot of what is called the *rotational-damping factor* $-m_q$ against the *static-stability factor* $(-\mu m_\alpha)$ for specific values of C_L, C_D, $dC_L/d\alpha$, and $dC_D/d\alpha$. The values of the aerodynamic coefficients and slopes with respect to

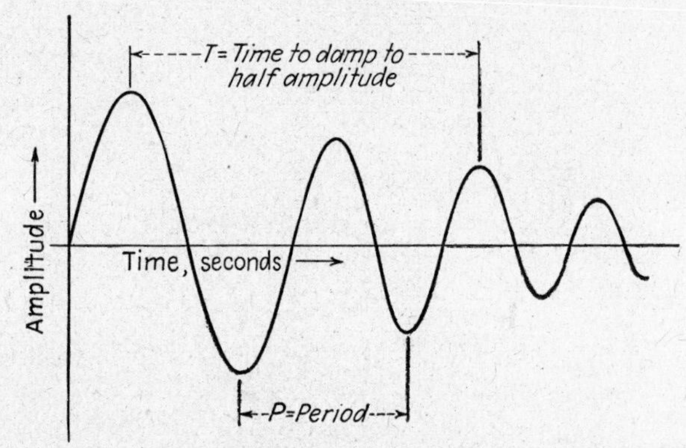

FIG. 10:16.—Longitudinal oscillations of an airplane and quantities determined in dynamic-stability analysis.

α, may be found for the desired condition of flight by the methods outlined in Chap. 2. The rotational-damping factor $-m_q$ is given by

$$-m_q = a_t \frac{l_t^2}{2k_y^2} \frac{S_t}{S} \qquad (10:14)$$

where k_y is the radius of gyration of the airplane around the span axis (other notation as before) and is usually estimated from

$$k_y^2 = C_B(l_1^2 + h^2) \qquad (10:15)$$

where

$$C_B \approx 0.036 \quad \text{(usual range 0.032 to 0.039)} \qquad (10:16)$$

and l_1 and h are the *over-all* length and height of the airplane.

The static stability $-\mu m_\alpha$ is calculated from

$$-\mu m_\alpha = -\frac{6.5cW/S}{\sigma k_y^2} \frac{dC_M}{d\alpha} \qquad (10:17)$$

in which c is the geometric mean chord, σ is the air-density ratio, and other notation is as before; $dC_M/d\alpha$ can be calculated from the static-stability index dC_M/dC_L determined in Art. 10:3 and the lift-curve

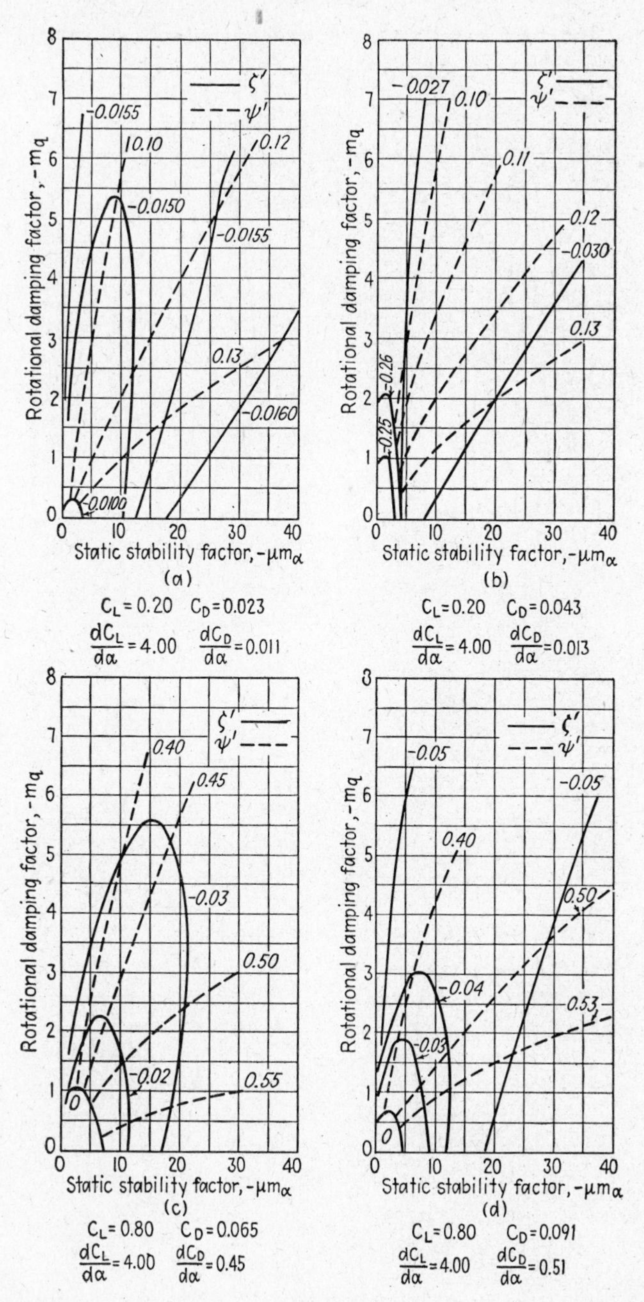

FIG. 10:17.—Charts for dynamic-stability factors. (*From NACA Tech. Rept.* 521.)

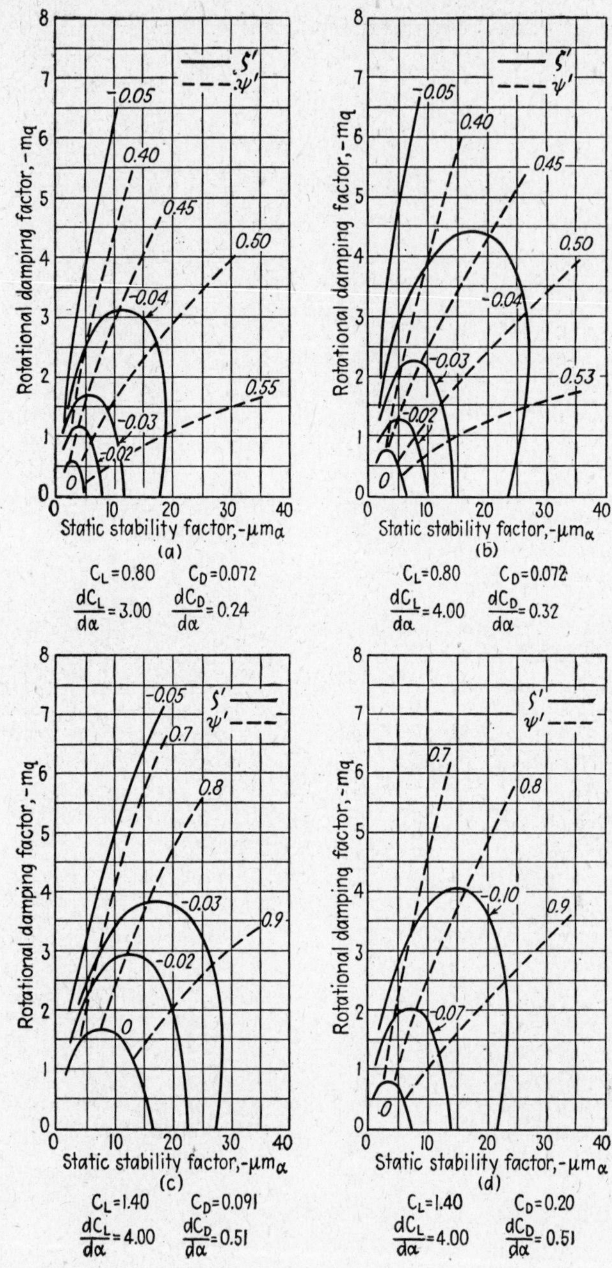

Fig. 10:18.—Charts for dynamic-stability factors. (*From NACA Tech. Rept.* 521.)

slope $dC_L/d\alpha$. The foregoing procedure is illustrated by the following example:

Example.—Given

$$C_L = 0.80 \qquad C_D = 0.080 \qquad \frac{dC_L}{d\alpha} = 3.95 \text{ per radian} \qquad \frac{dC_D}{d\alpha} = 0.39 \text{ per radian}$$

$$-m_q = 2.6 \qquad -\mu m_\alpha = 16.5 \quad \text{(Taken from full-scale flight data)}$$

Find ζ' and ψ'.

Solution.—From Fig. 10:17*d*, $\zeta' = -0.44$, and $\psi' = 0.48$.

From Fig. 10:18*b*, $\zeta' = -0.035$, and $\psi' = 0.48$.

From interpolation between the figures on the basis of C_D, $\zeta' = -0.039$, and $\psi' = 0.48$.

From interpolation between the figures on the basis of dC_D/d, $\zeta' = -0.038$, and $\psi' = 0.48$.

From full-scale unpublished flight test of this airplane, $\zeta' = -0.041$, and $\psi' = 0.72$.

The agreement between calculated and flight-test values is not very good, but the oscillations due to free controls and possible oscillation of the gasoline in partly filled tanks complicate the flight-test measurements.

10:9. Problems

1. Using the Ercoupe data given in Probs. 1, Art. 10:4, and 1, Art. 10:6, and making other reasonable assumptions where necessary, calculate the period of oscillation and time required for oscillations to damp to half amplitude for level flight in standard sea-level air at $C_L = 0.80$.

2. For the Constellation airplane, use data given in Probs. 2, Art. 10:4, and 2, Art. 10:6, and making other reasonable assumptions where necessary, calculate the period of oscillation and time required to damp to half amplitude for level flight in standard sea-level air at $C_L = 0.80$.

CHAPTER 11

LATERAL AND DIRECTIONAL STABILITY AND CONTROL

An airplane is said to be *directionally stable* if, when properly trimmed with a rudder tab, it maintains a steady heading when the pilot takes his feet off the rudder pedals. It is said to be *laterally stable* if, when banked or disturbed from the laterally level position by a gust, it so moves as to regain a level position without operation of the controls by the pilot. The lateral movement necessary to right the airplane laterally usually affects the directional heading of the airplane so that lateral stability cannot be considered independently of directional stability. If an airplane is banked to the right and has excessive vertical-fin area, the sideslip may result in a spiral dive if not controlled. Such an airplane is said to be *spirally unstable.* If, on the other hand, the airplane wing has excessive dihedral, a sideslip to the right will cause a yawing to the left, which may be followed by a left sideslip and right yaw. The resulting movement, sometimes described as a "Dutch roll," may involve increasingly violent oscillations in roll and direction; such an airplane is said to have *unstable oscillations.* An airplane must be carefully proportioned to avoid these two types of combined lateral and directional instability. This sort of instability is essentially a dynamic instability; but static directional stability, or the "weather-vane" effect, is a major factor in the dynamic stability, and since it is readily measured in a wind tunnel it is given first and separate consideration.

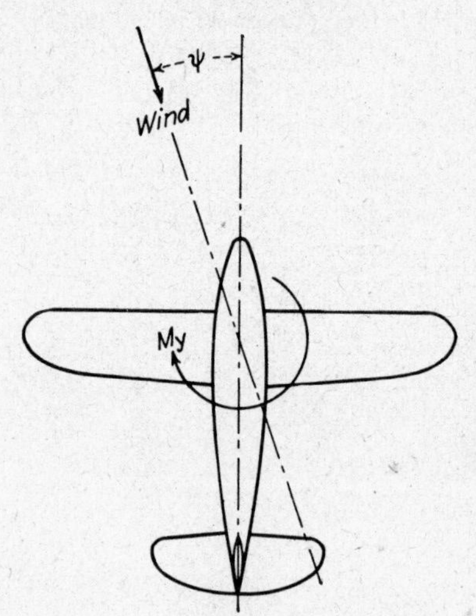

FIG. 11:1.—Yawing moment on airplane.

11:1. Directional Stability and Control.—When an airplane is yawed to the right (or is sideslipping to the left), as shown in Fig. 11:1, the air forces on the wing, fuselage, and tail produce a moment M_y on the airplane. This air moment is arbitrarily shown in Fig. 11:1 in the same direction as the angle of yaw.

If the air moment M_y decreases as the angle of yaw ψ increases, the airplane is said to have positive *static directional stability*. Typical wind-tunnel-test results for static directional stability are shown in Fig. 11:2, in which C_y is defined by

$$C_y = \frac{M_y}{bqS} \tag{11:1}$$

The positive slope of C_y *vs.* ψ without a vertical tail indicates considerable positive stability. Tests are usually also made with the rudder deflected in various amounts, and sometimes also with the rudder free, giving the results shown by the broken lines in Fig. 11:2, though the

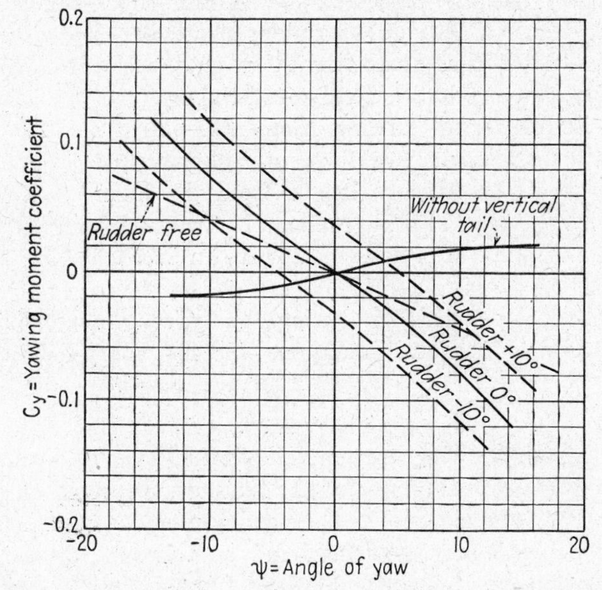

FIG. 11:2.—Typical wind-tunnel-test plot of directional stability and control.

free-rudder condition is more often calculated from the fixed-rudder-test data by the methods of Chap. 9 because of the large-scale effect on free-rudder tests on small models. Figure 9:6, designated as giving a free-elevator factor, can also be used to read the "free-rudder factor" if the proper aspect ratio for the vertical tail is used.

The intersections of the lines of fixed-rudder angle with the axis of zero-yawing-moment coefficient show the angle of yaw that can be held by a given rudder angle; thus Fig. 11:2 shows that 10 deg of rudder will hold approximately 5 deg of yaw. The points of intersection of the fixed-rudder-angle lines with the axis of $\psi = 0$ are the yawing-moment coefficients that can be held by a given rudder angle; these intersections are used in determining the rudder design for multi-engine aircraft, as the principal requirement for the design of the rudder for such an airplane is that it shall be able to hold the airplane at a fixed heading when one of the engines is inoperative.

For single-engine airplanes it is difficult to set up a criterion for the design of rudders or for specifying what constitutes a desirable location of the curves on Fig. 11:2. With a steerable nose wheel, rudders are not necessary for steering on the ground, and a water rudder steers better than an air rudder for flying boats. Apparently the only definite requirements for rudder design for such an airplane is that the rudder shall be large enough to get the airplane out of a spin (discussed later in this chapter). Accordingly, several single-engine airplanes have been designed without any rudder whatever. For airplanes that cannot be stalled because of limitation on the elevator control, the elimination of the rudder has enhanced the safety of the airplane.

11:2. Estimation of Yawing Moments.—Most airplane fuselages are slightly unstable in yaw for center-of-gravity locations of 20 to 40 per cent of the fuselage length from the nose. The wing and nacelles, if any, may also have a small yawing moment at angles of yaw. The vertical tail is designed to give an overbalancing stabilizing moment.

For fuselages tested without wings, the yawing-moment coefficient must be based on fuselage dimensions; the customary definition is

$$C'_{yf} = \frac{M_{yf}}{qL_fS_f} \tag{11:2}$$

where M_{yf} is the yawing moment on the fuselage, L_f is the fuselage length, and S_f is the side area of the fuselage, projected on the plane of symmetry of the airplane. The yawing-moment coefficient C_y of a complete airplane may be considered as the sum of the yawing-moment coefficients due to the fuselage wing and tail as indicated by the equation

$$C_y = C'_{vf}\frac{S_f}{S}\frac{L_f}{b} + C_{yw} + C_{y\,\text{tail}} \tag{11:3}$$

in which C_{yw} and $C_{y\,\text{tail}}$ are coefficients for the wing and tail, which include interference effects. They are obtainable in a wind tunnel by testing first the fuselage alone, then the fuselage-wing combination, and last the fuselage-wing-tail combination.

Since the slope of the graph of C_y *vs.* ψ is the determining factor in static directional stability, it is convenient to designate it by a special symbol $C_{y\psi} = dC_y/d\psi$ for simplicity.

The major factor determining $C_{y\psi f}$ is the location of the center of gravity on the fuselage. Data from Diehl and *NACA Tech. Rept.* 589

are summarized in Fig. 11:3, and the effect of the addition of a wing for a particular case is shown in Fig. 11:4. Some other data for fuselages alone are somewhat higher than the range of data plotted by Diehl,[1] but for a clean oval fuselage with a pointed tail Diehl's upper line will usually be within 20 per cent of test result for a rectangular

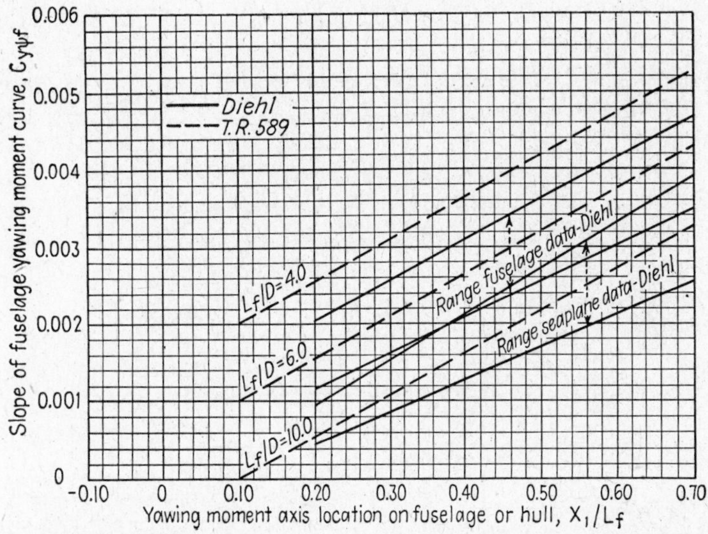

FIG. 11:3.—Summary of data on instability in yaw for fuselages and hulls without wings or tails. L_f/D is length to diameter ratio of fuselage. Fuselage data studied by Diehl were for $L_f/D = 5.5$ to 6.5.

fuselage; with a knife-edge type of tail Diehl's lower limit is recommended. The effect of adding the wing is seen in Fig. 11:4 to reduce the instability about 40 per cent, depending presumably on the value of the ratio Sb/S_fL_f which was 3.95 for the tests reported in Fig. 11:4. For example, consider an elliptic fuselage of length $L_f = 15$ ft and $S_f = 50$ sq ft with center of gravity 5 ft from the nose so that

$$\frac{X_1}{L_f} = 0.33$$

From Fig. 11:3, on Diehl's upper line read $C'_{y\psi f} = 0.0027$ per deg. If the wing area is $S = 90$ sq ft and the wing span $b = 25$ ft, calculate $Sb/S_fL_f = (90 \times 25)/(50 \times 15) = 3.0$, and estimate a reduction of the value 0.0027 by $(3/3.95) \times 40$ per cent $= 30$ per cent, so that

$$C'_{y\psi\,(\text{fus+wing})} = 0.7 \times 0.0027 = 0.0019$$

$$C_{y\,(\text{fus+wing})} = \frac{0.0019}{3.0} = 0.0006$$

[1] DIEHL, W. S., "Engineering Aerodynamics," rev. ed., p. 204.

This unstable yawing-moment-coefficient slope must be balanced by the yawing moment due to the vertical tail. The vertical-tail

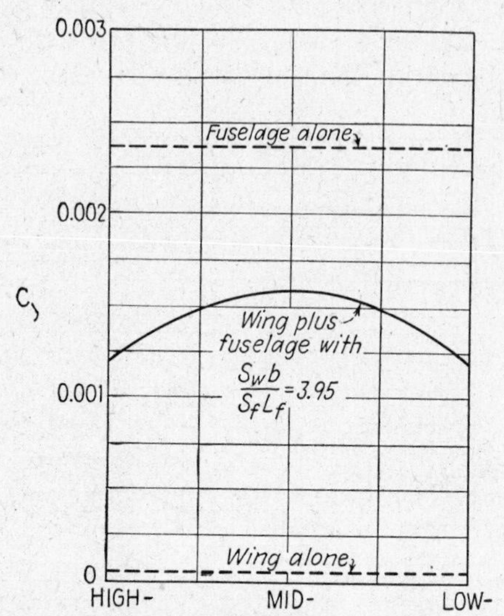

FIG. 11:4.—Effect of wing on fuselage instability. (*From NACA Tech. Note* 730, *Fig.* 21.)

effect may be written

$$C_{y\psi v} = -\frac{S_v}{S}\frac{L_v}{b}a_v\left(1 - \frac{\epsilon_v}{\psi}\right)F_r \qquad (11:4)$$

where S_v = vertical-tail area
S = wing area
L_v = tail length, c.g. to a.c. of vertical tail
b = wing span
a_v = lift-curve slope of vertical tail $\approx 0.1095 A\!\!R_v/(A\!\!R_v + 3)$
$A\!\!R_v$ = aspect ratio of vertical tail
ϵ_v/ψ = "side-wash factor," analogous to down-wash factor in longitudinal-stability problem, assumed zero except for unusual arrangements involving vertical area ahead of the vertical tail
F_r = free-rudder factor (= 1.0 if rudder is fixed), from same graph as free-elevator factor, Fig. 9:8

For example, assume the airplane described above has twin vertical tails, each of 4 sq ft area and aspect ratio 1.5 so that $S_v = 8$ and $a_v = (1.5/4.5) \times 0.1095 = 0.036$. Assume further that $L_v = 10$ ft, $\epsilon_v/\psi = 0$, and $F_r = 1.0$ (fixed rudders); then

$$C_{y\psi v} = -\tfrac{8}{90} \times \tfrac{10}{25} \times 0.036 = -0.0013$$

For this complete airplane, the yawing-moment-curve slope is then

$$C_{y\psi} = C_{y\psi fw} + C_{y\psi v} = +0.0006 - 0.0013 = -0.0007$$

with fixed elevators

With a free-rudder factor of 0.6, $C_{y\psi} = +0.0006 - 0.0008 = -0.0002$, which is still slightly stable.

Millikan[1] states that GALCIT tests show values of $-C_{y\psi}$ in the range from 0.0007 to 0.0015 (presumably with fixed rudder) to be desirable. Diehl[2] suggests that a desirable value is $0.00005(W/S)$, which gives the same result as Millikan's recommendation for wing loadings W/S of 14 to 30 lb per sq ft.

11:3. Problems

1. Using the methods described above, estimate the slope of the graph of yawing-moment coefficient *vs.* angle of yaw for the Ercoupe airplane, using data in problems in Chap. 10, and making other reasonable assumptions where necessary.

2. Repeat Prob. 1 for the Lockheed Constellation.

11:4. Estimation of Dihedral Necessary to Avoid Spiral Instability. The interrelationship between the yawing and rolling motions of an airplane may conveniently be analyzed, as in *NACA Tech. Rept.* 589, by writing and solving the Newtonian equations for lateral acceleration and angular acceleration about the roll and yaw axes. In this way it may be shown that, for an airplane that is directionally stable, the principal requirement for lateral and directional stability is sufficient dihedral to prevent the airplane from going into a spiral dive when the controls are released. An estimate of the necessary dihedral requires numerical evaluation of the following slopes or derivatives, in

Static stability:

$$\frac{dC_r}{d\psi} = C_{r\psi} \quad \text{(rolling moment due to sideslip)}$$

$$\frac{dC_y}{d\psi} = C_{y\psi} \quad \text{(yawing moment due to sideslip)}$$

Damping moments:

$$\frac{dC_r}{d}\left(\frac{pb}{2V}\right) = C_{rr} \quad \text{(rolling moment due to angular velocity of roll)}$$

$$\frac{dC_y}{d}\left(\frac{rb}{2V}\right) = C_{yy} \quad \text{(yawing moment due to angular velocity of yaw)}$$

Cross moments:

$$\frac{dC_r}{d}\left(\frac{rb}{2V}\right) = C_{ry} \quad \text{(rolling moment due to angular velocity of yaw)}$$

$$\frac{dC_r}{d}\left(\frac{pb}{2V}\right) = C_{yr} \quad \text{(yawing moment due to angular velocity of roll)}$$

which p and r are the angular velocities of roll and yaw, respectively.

The necessary and sufficient conditions to avoid spiral divergence may be shown to be

$$C_{r\psi}C_{yy} \geq C_{y\psi}C_{ry} \tag{11:5}$$

[1] MILLIKAN, CLARK B., "Aerodynamics of the Airplane," 1941, p. 158.

[2] *Op. cit.*

Instructions for estimating $C_{y\psi}$ have already been given in Art. 11:2. Instructions[1] for estimating the other quantities in the above equation follow:

Rolling moment due to sideslip, $C_{r\psi}$, depends chiefly on dihedral. With sufficient accuracy, data in *NACA Tech. Rept.* 589 are representable by

$$C_{r\psi} = C_{r\psi 0} + 0.0002\Gamma^\circ \tag{11:6}$$

for rectangular wings of aspect ratio 6 with no taper and no sweepback, where Γ° is the effective dihedral angle in degrees and $C_{r\psi 0}$ is a factor depending chiefly on the wing tip shape as shown in Fig. 11:5. The "effective dihedral" is the geometric dihedral plus or minus a correction for the position of the wing on the fuselage. For a mid-wing monoplane, the correction is zero. For high-wing monoplanes, add about 3 deg; for low-wing monoplanes, subtract about 3 deg; for a conventional high fin, add 1 deg at low angle of attack. Typical data are shown in Fig. 11:6. These values are not general, however, and more research is needed to determine them accurately.

Rolling moment due to yawing, C_{ry}, results from the two wing tips having different velocities. Experimental values are difficult to determine, and few have been published; but Glauert states that

$$\left.\begin{aligned} C_{ry} &= \frac{C_L}{4} \text{ for rectangular wings} \\ C_{ry} &= \frac{C_L}{3} \text{ for elliptic wings} \end{aligned}\right\} \tag{11:7}$$

agree well with such experimental data as are available.

Yawing moment due to yawing, C_{yy}, is a damping moment to which all parts of the airplane contribute. The fuselage and interference effects are usually small and neglected. The effects of the wing and vertical tail may be added algebraically thus,

$$C_{yy} = C_{yyw} + C_{yyv} \tag{11:8}$$

where

$$\left.\begin{aligned} C_{yyw} &= -(0.33C_{De\,\min} + 0.043C_{Di}) \text{ for rectangular wings} \\ C_{yyw} &= -(0.25C_{De\,\min} + 0.33C_{Di}) \text{ for elliptic wings} \end{aligned}\right\} \tag{11:9}$$

and

$$C_{yyv} = -115\left(\frac{L_v}{b}\right)\frac{S_v}{S}\left(1 - \frac{\epsilon_v}{\psi}\right)a_v \tag{11:10}$$

the notation being the same as in the static-directional-stability equation.

[1] Chiefly from *NACA Tech. Rept.* 589.

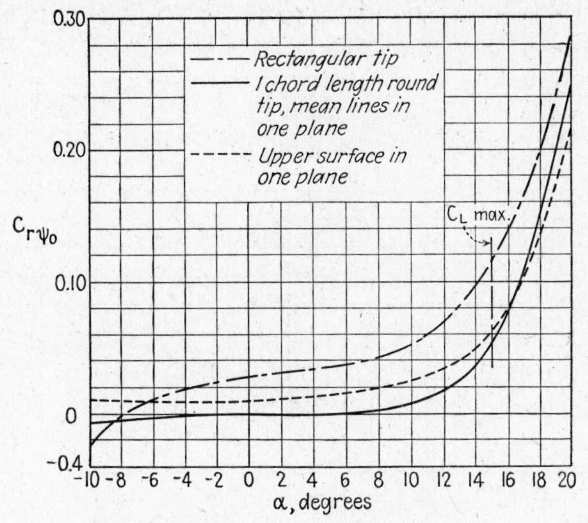

FIG. 11:5.—Effect of wing-tip shape on C_r.

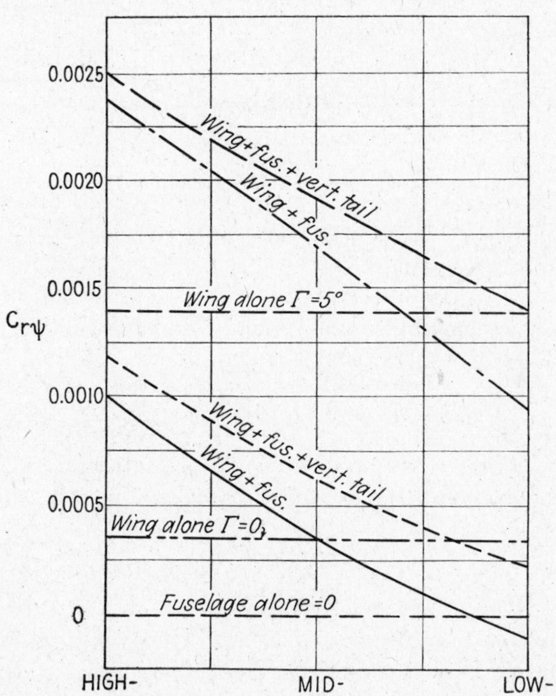

FIG. 11:6.—Effect of wing location and vertical tail on C_r. (*From NACA Tech. Note 730.*)

A family of 23 graphs like Fig. 11:7 for estimating lateral- and directional-instability conditions is given in *NACA Tech. Rept.* 589, but in the interests of simplicity the problem may be limited to determining the conditions for spiral instability. To develop a single chart for this purpose, several simplifying approximations may be

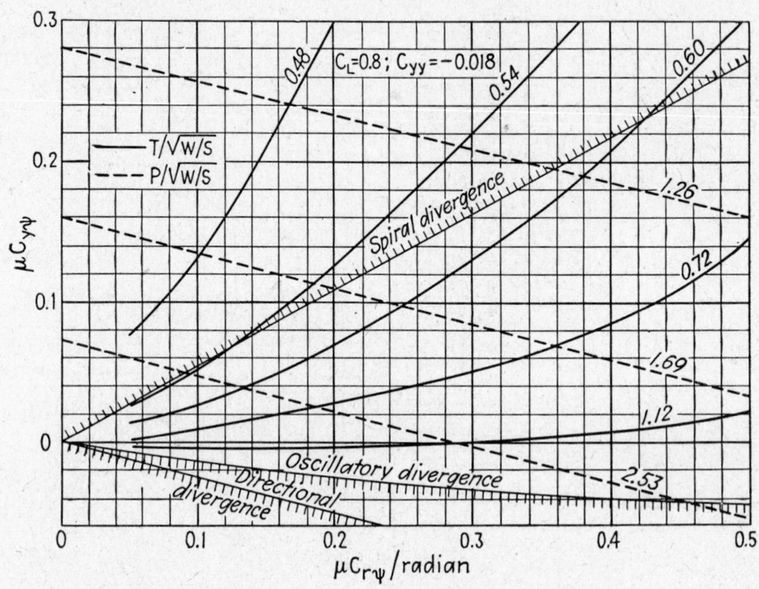

FIG. 11:7.—Graph for determining period of oscillation P and damping time T to one-half amplitude for an airplane with $C_{yy} = -0.108$ flying at $C_L = 0.8$. Regions of stability lie between lines labeled "spiral divergence" and "oscillatory divergence." Airplane density factor = $(13.1W/Sb)/\sigma$. (*From NACA Tech. Rept.* 589.)

made. In view of the uncertainties involved in several of the above estimates, it is reasonable to approximate equation (11:7) by

$$C_{ry} = 0.3C_L$$

It is also helpful in making estimates to consider that the effective dihedral in degrees Γ_e° is defined by the equation $\Gamma_e^\circ = C_{r\psi}/0.0002$. Then the limiting condition for spiral divergence may be written, from equation (11:5),

$$\Gamma_e^\circ = \frac{1{,}500C_LC_{y\psi}}{C_{yy}} \qquad (11:11)$$

and this equation may be plotted as a network chart as in Fig. 11:9, where the numerator is called the static-directional-stability factor and the denominator the yaw-damping factor. The numerical values on the chart facilitate the checking of calculations. The quantity

$1{,}500C_{y\psi}$ usually lies between 1 and 2 for satisfactory directional stability, and C_L ranges from 0.2 to 1.4 for level flight of normal airplanes. The lowest speed (and highest C_L) will determine the necessary dihedral. The following example illustrates the use of Fig. 11:8:

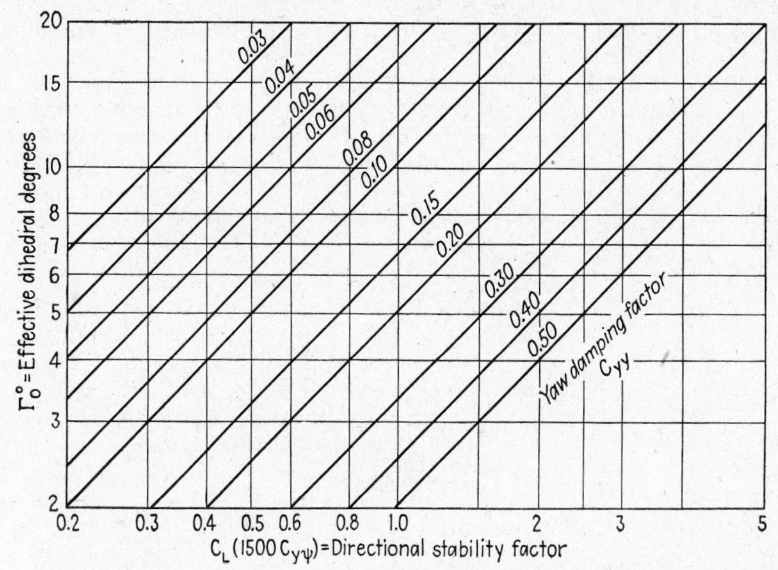

FIG. 11:8.—Chart for estimating dihedral to avoid spiral instability.

Example.—Given data as in the example in Art. 11:2. Find (*a*) the highest value of C_L at which spiral stability will be maintained for 5 deg effective dihedral and fixed rudders, and (*b*) the minimum speed at which the airplane is spirally stable for $W/S = 10$ lb per sq ft in standard sea-level air.

Solution.—$C_{y\psi}$ has already been determined for this airplane as -0.0007; therefore, $1{,}500C_{y\psi} = -1.05$. Since C_L enters into the wing-damping coefficient, it must be either assumed or neglected in a trial solution. Since the wing-damping coefficient C_{yyw} is usually small compared with that due to the vertical tail, calculate first C_{yyv} from equation (11:10) thus:

$$C_{yyv} = -115(\tfrac{10}{25})^2\,\tfrac{8}{90}0.036 = -0.059$$

For this value of C_{yy} and 5 deg effective dihedral, read, in Fig. 11:8,

$$C_L(1{,}500C_{y\psi}) = 0.3$$

For $1{,}500C_{y\psi} = -1.05$ as computed before, $C_L = 0.285$ for spiral stability. For this value of C_L, the hitherto neglected damping moment due to the wing may be calculated. Assume $C_{De\,\min} = 0.01$, and a rectangular wing of aspect ratio 7 for which $C_{Di} = C_L^2/7\pi = 0.285^2/22 = 0.055$. Then, from equation (11:9),

$$C_{yyw} = -(0.33 \times 0.01 + 0.043 \times 0.055) = -0.0033 - 0.0021 = -0.0054$$

and with $C_{yyv} = -0.059$ as before

$$C_{yy} = -0.059 - 0.0054 = -0.064$$

Using this corrected value of C_{yy}, read, in Fig. 11:8, $C_L(1{,}500C_y) = 0.32$ and $C_L = 0.305$.

For a wing loading of $W/S = 10$ lb per sq ft, calculate

$$v = \sqrt{(W/S)/0.00256C_L} = 113 \text{ mph}$$

The airplane will be spirally unstable at speeds below 113 mph. These are the answers called for.

If the solution is for dihedral rather than C_L, the trial solution is avoided. In general, it should be noted that large directional stability requires large dihedral for spiral stability. The effect of slip stream is often to increase greatly the directional stability and hence the necessary dihedral. Gas-powered models are often built with large dihedral to avoid spiral instability at the high values of C_L at which they may operate under some conditions of uncontrolled flight.

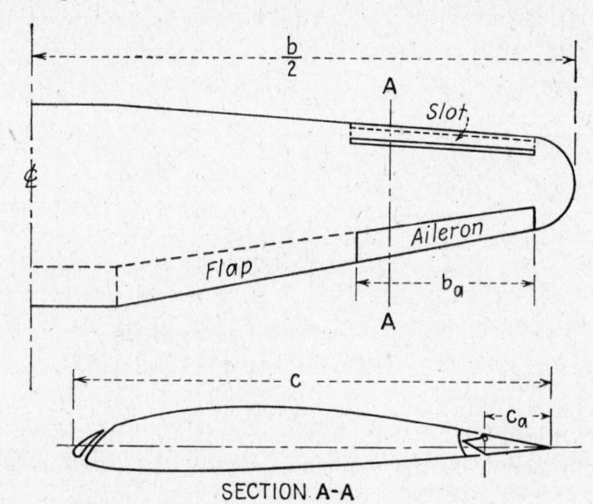

FIG. 11:9.—Plan and section of wing showing typical aileron location. (Balanced-aileron sketch from *NACA Tech. Rept.* 603.) Slot in wing is often omitted.

11:5. Problems

1. For the Ercoupe airplane with data as in Chap. 10 estimate the dihedral necessary to avoid spiral instability at $C_L = 1.0$.

2. For the Lockheed Constellation, with data in Chap. 10, estimate the dihedral necessary to avoid spiral instability at $C_L = 0.5$.

3. Add a scale of effective dihedral angle in degrees, Γ_e° to the abscissa of Fig. 11:7 for $\sigma = 1.00$, $W = 1{,}260$ lb, $S = 1{,}426$ sq ft, and $b = 30$ ft, assuming that $\Gamma_e^\circ = (C_{r\psi} \text{ per deg})/0.0002$ from equation (11:6).

11:6. Lateral Control and Aileron Design.—Airplanes are controlled laterally by means of ailerons. Most ailerons consist of movable flaps constituting the trailing edge of the outer portion of the wing, as sketched in Fig. 11:9, which also shows a typical internal, or pressure, balance to keep the control forces low. Such ailerons operate by changing the effective camber of the outer portion of the wing. Conventional ailerons have the disadvantage that they cannot be used effectively with full-span wing flaps. This disadvantage is overcome by a design such as the Northrop retractable aileron, as sketched in Fig. 11:10. This type of aileron is sometimes designated as a "spoiler" because it serves to spoil the lift (and increase the drag) when it is raised. The linkage between the control stick and a conventional aileron is usually such that the aileron moves up more than it moves down. This arrangement is desirable because downward movement of an aileron increases the drag on the wing on which the lift is increased, and this effect must be compensated by rudder action. Aileron movement is equally effective whether it is up or down when the speed is high and the angle of attack low. The chief problem in aileron design is to maintain good lateral control at low speed and high lift coefficient. When a wing is just about to stall, putting the aileron down may stall it; therefore, ailerons that operate up only are often

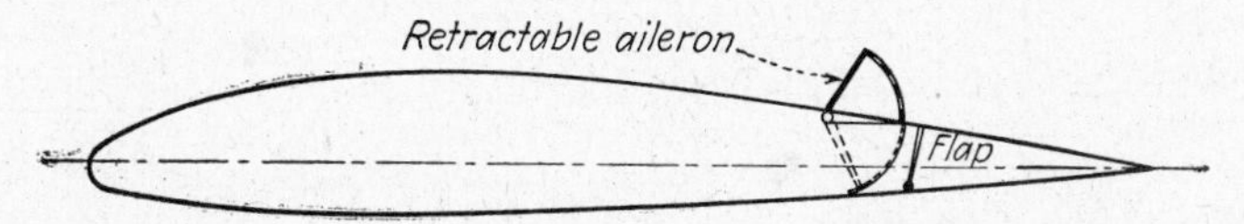

FIG. 11:10.—Section of wing with full-span flap and Northrop retractable aileron.

more satisfactory for this critical condition. The Northrop retractable aileron can also be considered an "up-only" aileron.

When an airplane is flying at an angle of attack below the stall and has an angular rolling velocity of p, it is acted on by a resisting rolling moment $M_r = C_r bqS$ (where C_r is defined as the rolling-moment coefficient) which is greater the greater the angular of velocity of roll. The ratio of C_r to $pb/2V$ (which is the tangent of the helix angle of roll at the wing tip) has been designated in Art. 11:4 as C_{rr}. The fact that wings resist being rolled below the stall is mathematically described by saying that C_{rr} is negative below the stall. The wings resist being rolled because the descending wing operates at a higher angle of attack than the ascending wing and hence gets more lift (beyond the stall, however, C_{rr} is positive, and the wings roll themselves, or autorotate, causing a spin as discussed in Art. 11:7).

For conventional ailerons the rolling-moment coefficient C_r is approximately constant below the stall and is not greatly affected by the proportions of the ailerons for the range of sizes from 10 to 40 per cent of the chord and 30 to 60 per cent of span, as shown in Fig. 11:11. A comparison of various types of ailerons as regards yawing moment is shown in Fig. 11:12, which includes a line for "floating ailerons," so rigged that the hinge moment is zero whenever the control stick is in the neutral position. Note that a favorable yawing moment (*i.e.*, a yawing moment favorable to a normally banked turn) is obtainable only with up-only ailerons.

No ailerons thus far tested will give lateral control much beyond the stall, and most ailerons become inoperative several degrees below the yawed stall. Because of this inherent limitation of ailerons, attempts to design an airplane that is controllable under all conditions

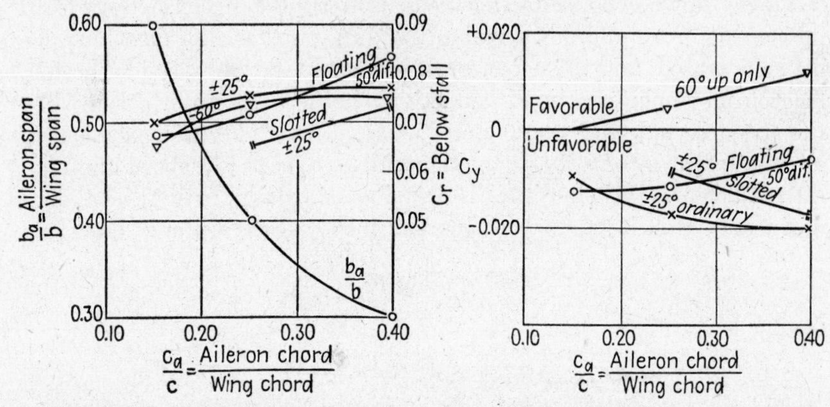

FIG. 11:11.—Proportions of test ailerons and mean rolling moment coefficients below stall.

FIG. 11:12.—Yawing moments due to maximum aileron deflection at $\alpha_2 \approx 15°$.

have usually involved a limit on travel of elevator and/or throttle controls so that a stall is not possible. If it is possible to stall an airplane, it will be laterally uncontrollable under some conditions and will usually get into a spin as described below.

11:7. Spins and Spin Recovery.—Below the stall, wings resist being rolled because the wing moving downward has a larger angle of

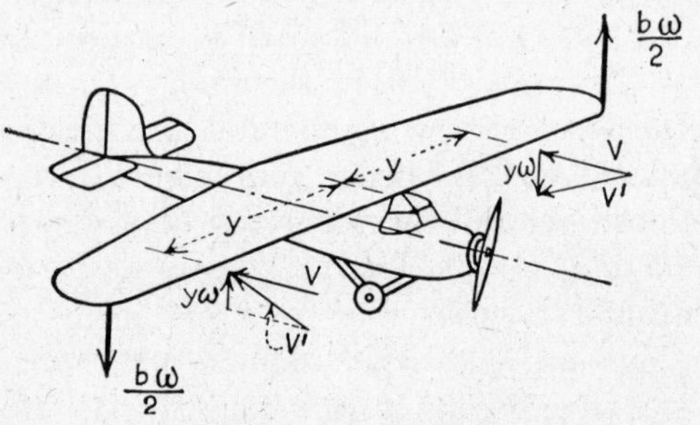

FIG. 11:13.—Resultant wind velocities due to roll.

attack, as shown in Fig. 11:13, and hence gets more lift. Beyond the stall, however, a larger angle of attack gives *less lift*, as shown in Fig. 11:14; thus, the wings roll themselves when they are held at a fixed angle of attack beyond the stall. This is called *autorotation* or *spinning.* It is, in a way, part of the penalty for a high value for $C_{L\max}$; for, in general, the higher C_L goes, the faster it falls beyond the stall. If a model wing or airplane is mounted in a wind tunnel so as to be free to rotate about the axis of the tunnel (wind axis) and is held at an angle of attack beyond the stall, it will rotate itself at an angular velocity that may be designated as p (radians per sec). The tangential component of the wing-tip velocity is $pb/2$, and the ratio $pb/2V$ is a measure of the helix angle of stable autorotation. A typical characteristic curve for $pb/2V$ against angle of attack is shown in Fig. 11:15. The curves for positive and negative autorotation are not quite the

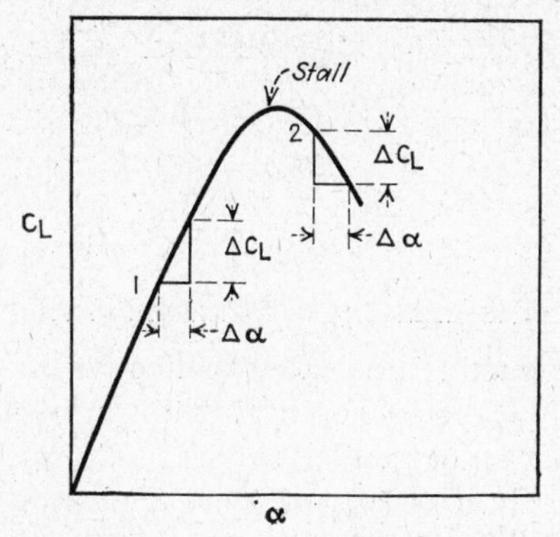

FIG. 11:14.—Effect of change in angle of attack on lift below stall and beyond stall.

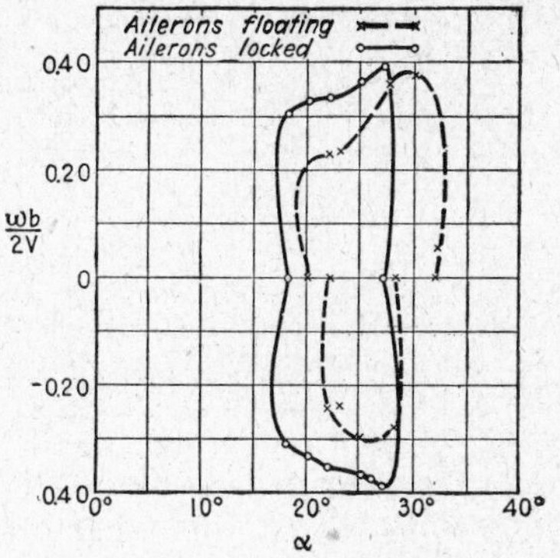

FIG. 11:15.—Rate of stable autorotation for Clark Y wing with locked ailerons.

same because of rotation of the air stream in the wind tunnel. If such a model airplane in a wind tunnel is also given a fixed angle of yaw, the helix angle of stable rotation is considerably increased and the model autorotates faster for a given air speed in the tunnel.

When an airplane in free flight is stalled, it is usually laterally and directionally unstable, as indicated in the analysis of Art. 11:4. The ailerons, moreover, are ineffective at the stall, and regardless of how the pilot moves the controls the airplane starts to roll and because of the autorotative couple discussed above continues to roll itself. If it rolls from an initial horizontal attitude, moreover, the vertical tail causes a yawing displacement and angular velocity, and the combined yaw and roll induce further yaw and roll. This is the usual form of a spin. In a spin, the horizontal tail as well as the wing is often stalled; since the ailerons are ineffective, the rudder is the only control surface that will permit recovery from the spin (though on some airplanes the horizontal tail does not stall in a normal spin and recovery can be effected by pushing forward on the control stick, giving opposite rudder, and pulling out of the resulting dive).

Quantitative analysis of the forces and motions during a spin is beyond the scope of this text; but it should be pointed out that, since the rudder is sometimes the only means of recovery from the spin, particular care should be taken in preliminary design to avoid so

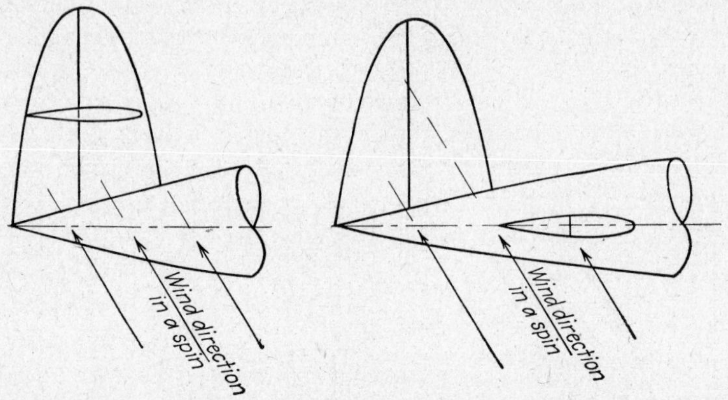

FIG. 11:16.—Horizontal tail locations to avoid blanketing all the rudder in a spin.

locating the horizontal tail that it makes the rudder ineffective as a means of spin recovery. The conventional relationship between horizontal and vertical tails, with the rudder and elevator axes approximately in the same plane, has often been a cause of spins from which recovery was not possible. Two arrangements for avoiding this are

FIG. 11:17.—V-type tail on experimental guided missile. (*Aviation February,* 1946).

shown in Fig. 11:16. Twin vertical tails on the end of the horizontal tail, as in the Ercoupe, are also effective for spin recovery (but the Ercoupe is a spinproof airplane because the elevator control is insufficient to stall it). Another type of tail that cannot be blanketed out in a spin is the V-type tail shown in Fig. 11:17. In this type of tail, the movable surfaces can be operated either together, to serve as elevators, or differentially, to serve as rudders. There is a net saving, not only in the tail surface necessary for satisfactory stability and control, but also in the interference drag between the fuselage and tail. The tail size shown in Fig. 11:17 is believed to be considerably larger than the minimum necessary for satisfactory flying qualities of the airplane.

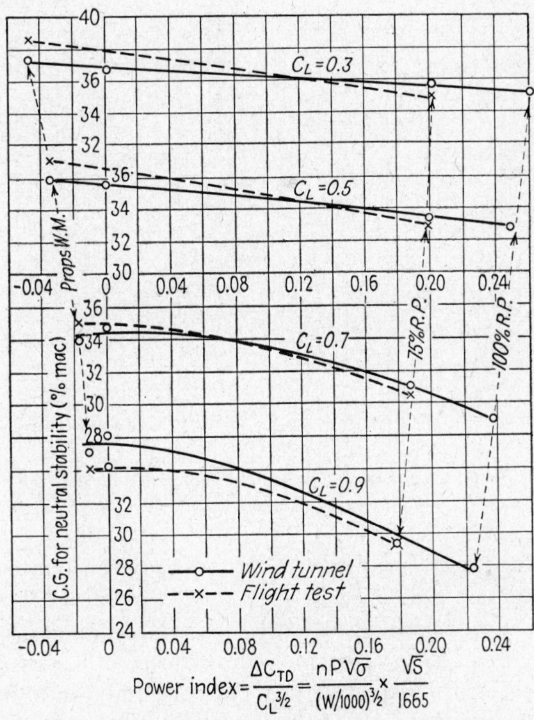

FIG. 11:18.—Comparable wind-tunnel and flight tests of power-on longitudinal stability. (*From Allen, Flight Testing for Performance and Stability, J. Aeronaut. Sci., January,* 1943.)

11:8. Flight Testing for Stability and Control.—Recent improvements in flight-test techniques and instrumentation, especially the photographic recording of all flight-test data on motion-picture-camera film, have made possible a flight-test accuracy comparable with that in wind-tunnel tests so that it has become possible to get a good check between wind-tunnel- and flight-test results, as illustrated in Fig. 11:18. Good arrangement is reported by Allen[1] between wind-tunnel and flight tests for static longitudinal stability and control and for direc-

[1] ALLEN, EDMUND T., Flight Testing for Performance and Stability, *J. Aeronaut. Sci.*, January, 1943, pp. 1–24.

tional control. Accurate studies have also been made in flight of dynamic longitudinal stability and dynamic lateral and directional stability, but these results are as yet inaccurately predictable from wind-tunnel tests, which are in most respects static tests. Allen[1] reports poor agreement between wind-tunnel tests and flight tests with free elevator but excellent agreement with fixed elevators. He explains the descrepancy as due to scale effects on small model tail

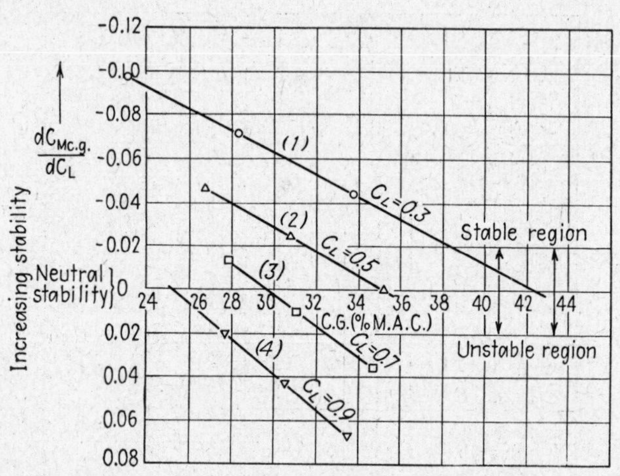

FIG. 11:19.—Extrapolation for determination of the center of gravity (c.g.) for neutral stability. (*From Allen, Flight Testing for Performance and Stability, J. Aeronaut. Sci., January,* 1943.)

surfaces and to tunnel-wall effects not properly accounted for by the usual corrections.

In the Boeing procedure for flight testing for longitudinal stability reported by Allen, measurements are made of all control forces and positions, air speed, angle of attack, rate of climb, and all engine conditions. Autosyn meters are used for the indicators of control-surface position, and indicator dials are located both in the cockpit and the photorecorder. The center of gravity of the airplane is adjusted by means of water ballast tanks in the fuselage. The testing method consists essentially in measuring the change in trim speed associated with change in center of-gravity position. All the other variables (power, altitude, and elevator-trim-tab setting) are held constant. Data are usually cross plotted as shown in Fig. 11:19, where the intersections of lines constant C_L with the axis of

$$dC_{Mcg}/dC_L = 0$$

are the center-of-gravity location for neutral stability (abbreviated

[1] *Ibid.*

c.g.n.s.). These results are compared for different amounts of engine power on the basis of a power index (abbreviation p.i.) defined by

$$\text{p.i.} = \left(\frac{1{,}000}{W_{\text{std}}}\right)^{3/2} \frac{\sqrt{S}}{1{,}665} \eta P_{iw} \tag{11:12}$$

in which P_{iw} is the same as in Chap. 8.

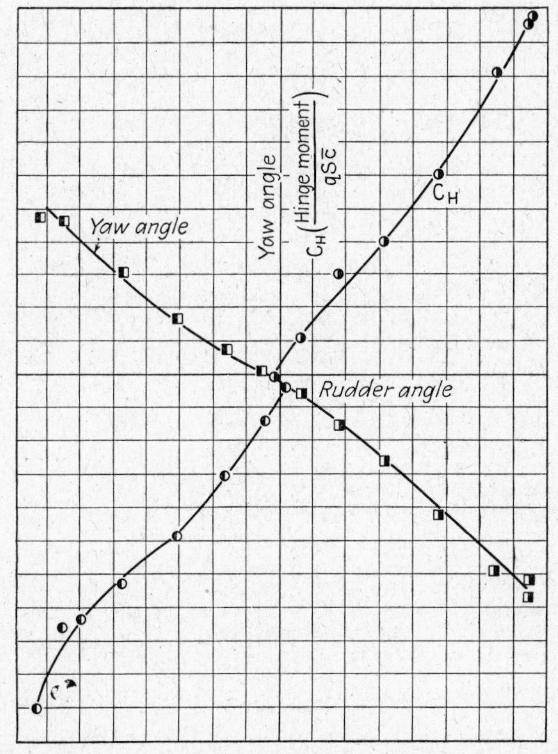

FIG. 11:20.—Rudder hinge moment and airplane yaw angle *vs.* rudder angle.

Similar instrumentation yields directional-control results such as those shown in Fig. 11:20. Allen concludes that flight testing of aircraft is becoming an exact science rather than the almost entirely qualitative study it was a few years ago.

APPENDIX 1

UNITS AND CONVERSION FACTORS[1]

TABLE I.—LENGTH EQUIVALENTS

Centimeters	Inches	Feet	Yards	Meters	Kilo-meters	Miles
1	0.3937	0.03281	0.01094	0.01	10^{-5}	$0.0_5 6214$
2.540	1	0.08333	0.02778	0.0254	$0.0_4 254$	$0.0_4 1578$
30.48	12	1	0.3333	0.3048	$0.0_3 3048$	$0.0_3 1894$
91.44	36	3	1	0.9144	$0.0_3 9144$	$0.0_3 5682$
100	39.37	3.281	1.0936	1	0.001	$0.0_3 6214$
100,000	39,370	3281	1093.6	1000	1	0.6214
160,935	63,360	5280	1760	1609	1.609	1

TABLE II.—AREA EQUIVALENTS

Square meters	Square inches	Square feet	Square yards
1	1550	10.76	1.196
$0.0_3 6452$	1	0.006944	$0.0_3 7716$
0.09290	144	1	0.1111
0.8361	1296	9	1

TABLE III.—VOLUME AND CAPACITY EQUIVALENTS

Cubic inches	Cubic feet	Cubic yards	U.S. quarts, liquid	U.S. gallons, liquid	Liters
1	$0.0_3 5787$	$0.0_4 2143$	0.01732	$0.0_2 4329$	0.01639
1,728	1	0.03704	29.92	7.481	28.32
46,656	27	1	807.9	202.0	764.6
57.75	0.03342	0.001238	1	0.25	0.9464
231	0.1337	0.004951	4	1	3.785
61.02	0.03531	0.001308	1.057	0.2642	1

[1] In the following tables, the subscripts after a cipher, *e.g.*, 0_3, indicate that the cipher is to be repeated the indicated number of times.

TABLE IV.—VELOCITY EQUIVALENTS

Cm per sec	Meters per sec	Meters per min	Km per hr	Ft per sec	Ft per min	Mph	Knots
1	0.01	0.6	0.036	0.03281	1.9685	0.02237	0.01943
100	1	60	3.6	3.281	196.85	2.237	1.943
1.667	0.01667	1	0.06	0.05468	3.281	0.03728	0.03238
27.78	0.2778	16.67	1	0.9113	54.68	0.6214	0.53960
30.48	0.3048	18.29	1.097	1	60	0.6818	0.59209
0.5080	0.005080	0.3048	0.01829	0.01667	1	0.01136	0.00987
44.70	0.4470	26.82	1.609	1.467	88	1	0.86839
51.479	0.51479	30.887	1.8532	1.68894	101.337	1.15155	1

TABLE V.—FORCE AND WEIGHT EQUIVALENTS

Kilograms	Avoirdupois		Tons		
	Ounces	Pounds	Short	Long	Metric
1	35.27	2.205	0.0_21102	0.0_39842	0.001
0.02835	1	0.0625	0.0_43125	0.0_42790	0.0_42835
0.4535	16	1	0.0005	0.0_34464	0.0_34536
907.2	32.000	2000	1	0.8929	0.9072
1016	35.840	2240	1.12	1	1.016
1000	35.274	2205	1.102	0.9842	1

TABLE VI.—PRESSURE EQUIVALENTS

Megabars or mega-dynes per sq cm	Kg per sq cm (metric atmos-pheres)	Lb per sq in.	Atm	Columns of Hg at temperature 0°C and g = 980.665 cm per sec²		Columns of water at temperature 15°C and g = 980.665 cm per sec²		
				Meters	In.	Meters	In.	Ft
1	1.0197	14.50	0.9869	0.7500	29.53	10.21	401.8	33.48
0.9807	1	14.22	0.9678	0.7355	28.96	10.01	394.0	32.84
0.06895	0.07031	1	0.06804	0.05171	2.036	0.7037	27.70	2.309
1.0133	1.0333	14.70	1	0.76	29.92	10.34	407.2	33.93
1.3333	1.3596	19.34	1.316	1	39.37	13.61	535.7	44.64
0.03386	0.03453	0.4912	0.03342	0.02540	1	0.3456	13.61	1.134
0.09798	0.09991	1.421	0.09670	0.07349	2.893	1	39.37	3.281
0.002489	0.002538	0.03610	0.002456	0.001867	0.07349	0.02540	1	0.08333
0.02986	0.03045	0.4332	0.02947	0.02240	0.8819	0.3048	12	1

TABLE VII.—ENERGY AND WORK EQUIVALENTS

Joules = 10^7 ergs	Kilogram-meters	Foot-pounds	Kilo-watt-hours	*Cheval-vapeur*-hours*	Horse-power hours	Kilo-gram-calories	Btu
1	0.10197	0.7376	$0.0_6 2778$	$0.0_6 3777$	$0.0_6 3725$	$0.0_3 2390$	$0.0_3 9486$
9.80665	1	7.233	$0.0_5 2724$	$0.0_5 37037$	$0.0_5 3653$	0.002344	0.009302
1.356	0.1383	1	$0.0_6 3766$	$0.0_6 51206$	$0.0_6 50505$	$0.0_3 3241$	0.001286
3.6×10^6	3.671×10^5	2.655×10^6	1	1.3596	1.341	860.5	3415
2.648×10^6	2.7×10^5	1.9529×10^6	0.7355	1	0.9863	632.9	2512
2.6845×10^6	2.7×10^5	1.98×10^6	0.7457	1.0139	1	641.7	2547
4183	426.6	3086	0.001162	0.001580	0.001558	1	3.968
1054	107.5	777.52	$0.0_3 2928$	$0.0_3 3981$	$0.0_3 3927$	0.25200	

* Metric horsepower.

TABLE VIII.—POWER EQUIVALENTS

Hp	Kw	*Cheval-vapeur**	Meter-kg per sec	Ft-lb per sec	Kg-cal per sec	Btu per sec
1	0.7457	1.014	76.04	550	0.1783	0.7074
1.341	1	1.360	102.0	737.6	0.2390	0.9486
0.9863	0.7355	1	75	542.3	0.1758	0.6977
0.01315	0.009807	0.01333	1	7.233	0.002344	0.009303
0.00182	0.001356	0.00184	0.1383	1	$0.0_3 3241$	0.001286
5.610	4.183	5.688	426.6	3086	1	3.968
1.414	1.054	1.433	107.5	777.5	0.2520	1

* Metric horsepower.

TABLE IX.—SPECIFIC-WEIGHT EQUIVALENTS

Grams per cu cm	Lb per cu in.	Lb per cu ft	Lb per U.S. gal
1	0.03613	62.43	8.345
27.68	1	1728	231
0.01602	$0.0_3 5787$	1	0.1337
0.1198	0.004329	0.1010	1

TABLE X.—LIFT- AND DRAG-COEFFICIENT EQUIVALENTS

$\frac{\text{Lb/sq ft}}{(\text{Ft/sec})^2}$	$\frac{\text{Lb/sq ft}}{\text{Mph}^2}$	$\frac{\text{Kg/sq M}}{(\text{M/sec})^2}$	$\frac{\text{Kg/sq M}}{(\text{Km/hr})^2}$	British $\frac{L}{2qS}$	NACA $\frac{L}{qS}$
1	2.151	52.7	4.05	421	843
0.464	1	24.5	1.88	196	392
0.0190	0.0409	1	0.0769	8.02	16.0
0.247	0.532	13.0	1	104	208
0.00237	0.00510	0.125	0.00958	1	2.0
0.001185	0.00256	0.0622	0.00479	0.500	1

$q = \frac{1}{2}\rho v^2$; ρ = mass density of air, any units; v = speed, same units.

TABLE XI.—TEMPERATURE EQUIVALENTS

1° centigrade = 1.8° Fahrenheit

Deg C = $\frac{5}{9}$(F − 32) Deg C abs. = deg C + 273

Deg F = $\frac{9}{5}$ deg + 32 Deg F abs. = deg F + 460

TABLE XII.—VISCOSITY EQUIVALENTS

1 poise = 100 centipoise = 1 dyne-sec per sq cm

= 0.00209 lb-sec per sq ft

1 lb-sec per sq ft = 478 poise = 47,800 centipoise

APPENDIX 2

PROPERTIES OF SOME LIQUIDS AND GASES

TABLE XIII
Liquids*

Liquid	Formula	Critical points, deg F		Temp. of data, deg F	Spec. wt.		Viscosity		Sp. ht., Btu/(lb)(deg F)	Therm. conduct., Btu/(hr)(ft)(deg F) = k_c	Prandtl number Pr
		melt	boil		Lb per cu ft = w	Lb per gal (U.S.)	Centipoise	$\frac{\text{Lb-sec}}{10^6 \text{ sqft}} = \mu$			
Alcohol	CH_3OH	−145	148	32			0.808	16.8	0.57		
methyl				68	49	6.55	0.593	12.4	0.60	0.124	7.0
				104			0.449	9.35	0.67		
				140			0.349	7.27			
Benzene	C_6H_6	42	175	32			0.90	18.8			
				68	54.4	7.3	0.647	13.5	0.42	0.092	
				104			0.492	10.2	mean	mean	
				140			0.389	8.1			
Gasoline	C_xH_y	Variable		32	43				0.53	0.078	
				68	mean	5.8			mean	mean	
				140							
Glycerine		−40	554	32	78	10.4	4,800	10^5	0.58		
	$C_3H_8O_3$			68	mean		815	17,000	mean	0.164	
Kerosene	C_xH_y	Variable		32			3.0	62.5			
				68	51	6.8	1.9	39.6	0.47	0.086	
				104	mean	mean	1.3	27	mean	0.084	
				140			0.9	19		0.082	
Mercury	Hg	−38	675	32	847		1.7	35.4			
				68	845		1.6	33.3	0.033	4.83	0.027
				104	841		1.5	31.2	mean		
				140	839		1.4	29.1			
Octane	C_8H_{18}	−71	256	32			0.65	13.5			
				68	43.5	5.8	0.55	11.5	0.50	0.084	8.0
				104			0.43	9.0	mean	0.082	6.4
				140			0.36	7.5		0.081	5.4
Lub. oil	C_xH_y	Variable		32							
SAE 10				68	About	About	72.0	1,500	0.5	0.08	
(mean)				104	57	7.6	25.0	520	mean	mean	
				140			12.0	250			
Lub. oil	C_xH_y	Variable		32							
SAE 30				68	About	About	260	5,420	15	0.08	
(mean)				104	57	7.6	70	1,460	mean	mean	
				140			32	670			
Ethylene	$C_2H_6O_2$		290	32	68				0.542	0.153	
glycol				68	mean	9.1			0.573		
Turpentine		14	420	32			2.2	46			
				68	54	7.2	1.54	32	0.42	0.074	21
				104	mean		1.03	21.5			
				140			0.86	18			
Water,	H_2O	32	212	32	62.42	8.34	1.793	37.5	1.009	0.323	13.6
pure				68	62.32	8.32	1.008	21.0	0.998	0.343	7.1
				104	61.96	8.28	0.653	13.7	0.997	0.362	4.36
				140	61.37	8.21	0.469	9.80	0.999	0.377	3.00
				176	60.61	8.10	0.357	7.47	1.002	0.398	2.18
				212	59.76	8.00	0.283	5.92	1.005†		
Water, sea		27.5			64	8.55					

* *Data chiefly from Perry,* "Chemical Engineers' Handbook."
† At saturated pressure.

TABLE XIV
Gases*

Gas	Formula	Temp. of data, deg F	Viscosity, lb-sec/10^6 sq ft $= 10^6\mu$	Spec. ht. per lb		$k = \frac{c_p}{c_v}$	R, ft per deg F abs.	Therm. conduct., Btu/(hr)(ft)(deg F) $= k_c$	Prandtl number Pr
				c_p	c_v				
Air	N_2	−66	0.297					0.0107	
ρ_{32} = 0.00242	+	32	0.357	0.239				0.0128	0.77
	O_2	130	0.413	0.239	0.171	1.405	53.3	0.0149	0.77
		277	0.487	0.240	mean			0.0179	0.75
		425	0.555	0.241				0.0200	0.77
Carbon dioxide	CO_2	−66	0.228					0.005	1.10
ρ_{32} = 0.00383		32	0.286	0.203				0.0061	1.07
		130	0.342	0.211	0.168	1.28	34.9	0.0078	1.10
		277	0.448	0.220	mean			0.0104	1.01
		425	0.526	0.230				0.0138	1.03
Helium	He	−66	0.333	1.26	0.76			0.0698	0.70
32 = 0.000342		32	0.391	1.26	0.76	1.66	386	0.0801	0.715
		130	0.442	1.26	0.76			0.0895	0.725
		277	0.501	1.26	0.76			0.1016	0.725
		425	0.577	1.26	0.76			0.1129	0.745
Hydrogen	H_2	−66	0.148					0.0771	0.775
ρ_{32} = 0.000174		32	0.175	3.48				0.0916	0.77
		130	0.200	3.48	2.48	2.48	767	0.1048	0.77
		277	0.234	3.50	mean			0.1233	0.77
		425	0.263	3.51				0.1385	0.775
Nitrogen	N_2	−66	0.287					0.0110	0.75
ρ_{32} = 0.00242		32	0.344	0.248				0.0131	0.75
		130	0.396	0.248	0.177	1.41	54.9	0.0151	0.76
		277	0.467	0.249	mean			0.0178	0.76
		425	0.531	0.250				0.0203	0.76
Oxygen	O_2	−66	0.357					0.0111	
ρ_{32} = 0.002765		32	0.426	0.217				0.0134	0.80
		130	0.492	0.218	0.156	1.40	48.3	0.0156	0.80
		277	0.583	0.219	mean			0.0189	0.78
		425	0.665	0.220				0.0213	0.80

* Data chiefly from Boelter, Cherry, and Johnson, "Heat Transfer Notes," University of California Press, Berkeley. Data at 29.92 in. Hg absolute pressure.

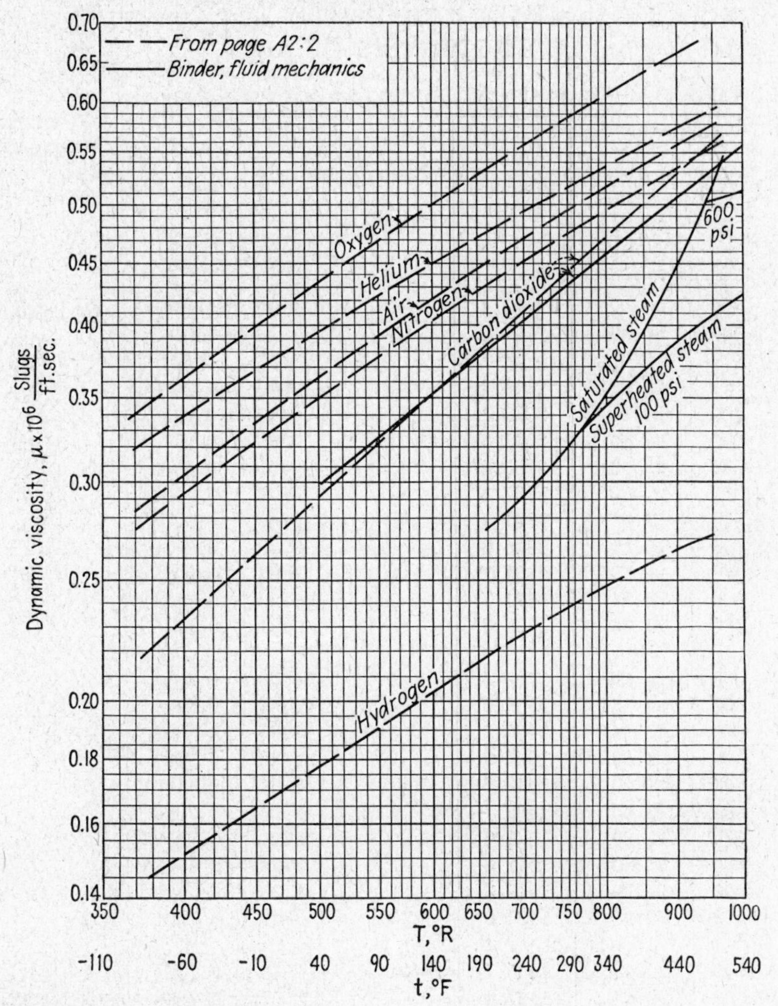

FIG. A1.—Dynamic viscosity of some gases at atmospheric pressure.

APPENDIX 3

PROPERTIES OF AIR

TABLE XV.—STANDARD AIR AT ALTITUDES OTHER THAN SEA LEVEL*

Altitude, ft	Abs. pressure, in. Hg	Abs. pressure, lb per sq ft	Temperature, deg C	$\frac{\rho_0}{\rho} = \frac{1}{\sigma}$	Density ratio $= \sigma$	Reciprocal square root of density ratio $\sqrt{\frac{1}{\sigma}}$
−1,000	31.02	2194.1	17.0	0.9712	1.0296	0.9855
− 500	30.47	2155.2	16.0	......	1.0148	
0	29.921	2116.4	15.0	1.0000	1.0000	1.0000
500	29.38	2078.1	14.0	1.0147	0.9855	1.0074
1.000	28.86	2041.3	13.0	1.0299	0.9710	1.0148
1,500	28.33	2003.8	12.0	1.0451	0.9568	1.0223
2,000	27.82	1967.8	11.0	1.0607	0.9428	1.0299
2,500	27.31	1931.7	10.0	1.0767	0.9288	1.0376
3,000	26.81	1896.3	9.1	1.0928	0.9151	1.0454
3,500	26.32	1861.7	8.1	1.1093	0.9015	1.0532
4,000	25.84	1827.7	7.1	1.1260	0.8881	1.0611
4,500	25.36	1793.8	6.1	1.1431	0.8748	1.0691
5,000	24.89	1760.5	5.1	1.1606	0.8616	1.0773
5,500	24.43	1728.0	4.1	1.1783	0.8487	1.0855
6,000	23.98	1696.2	3.1	1.1965	0.8358	1.0938
6,500	23.53	1664.3	2.1	1.2148	0.8232	1.1022
7,000	23.09	1633.2	1.1	1.2337	0.8106	1.1107
7,500	22.65	1602.1	0.1	1.2528	0.7982	1.1193
8,000	22.22	1571.7	− 0.8	1.2724	0.7859	1.1280
8,500	21.80	1542.0	− 1.8	1.2923	0.7738	1.1368
9,000	21.38	1512.3	− 2.8	1.3125	0.7619	1.1456
9,500	20.98	1484.0	− 3.8	1.3332	0.7501	1.1546
10,000	20.58	1455.7	− 4.8	1.3543	0.7384	1.1637
10,500	20.18	1427.4	− 5.8	1.3757	0.7269	1.1729
11,000	19.79	1399.8	− 6.8	1.3978	0.7154	1.1822
11,500	19.40	1372.2	− 7.8	1.4200	0.7042	1.1916
12,000	19.03	1346.0	− 8.8	1.4428	0.6931	1.2012
12,500	18.65	1319.2	− 9.8	1.4660	0.6821	1.2108
13,000	18.29	1293.7	−10.8	1.4899	0.6712	1.2206
13,500	17.93	1268.2	−11.7	1.5140	0.6605	1.2304
14,000	17.57	1242.8	−12.7	1.5387	0.6499	1.2404
14,500	17.22	1218.0	−13.7	1.5640	0.6394	1.2506
15,000	16.88	1194.0	−14.7	1.5896	0.6291	1.2608
15,500	16.54	1169.9	−15.7	1.6158	0.6189	1.2711
16,000	16.21	1146.6	−16.7	1.6426	0.6088	1.2816

TABLE XV.—STANDARD AIR AT ALTITUDES OTHER THAN SEA LEVEL.—(*Continued*)

Altitude, ft	Abs. pressure, in. Hg	Abs. pressure, lb per sq ft	Temperature, deg C	$\frac{\rho_0}{\rho} = \frac{1}{\sigma}$	Density ratio $= \sigma$	Reciprocal square root of density ratio $\sqrt{\frac{1}{\sigma}}$
16,500	15.89	1123.9	−17.7	1.6700	0.5988	1.2922
17,000	15.56	1100.6	−18.7	1.6975	0.5891	1.3029
17,500	15.25	1078.7	−19.7	1.7262	0.5793	1.3138
18,000	14.94	1056.7	−20.7	1.7550	0.5698	1.3247
18,500	14.63	1034.8	−21.7	1.7848	0.5603	1.3360
19,000	14.33	1013.6	−22.6	1.8152	0.5509	1.3473
19,500	14.04	993.1	−23.6	1.8457	0.5418	1.3586
20,000	13.75	972.6	−24.6	1.8772	0.5327	1.3701
20,500	13.46	952.1	−25.6	1.9095	0.5237	1.3818
21,000	13.18	932.2	−26.6	1.9425	0.5148	1.3937
21,500	12.90	912.4	−27.6	1.9759	0.5061	1.4057
22,000	12.63	893.3	−28.6	2.0104	0.4974	1.4179
22,500	12.36	874.2	−29.6	2.0454	0.4889	1.4302
23,000	12.10	855.9	−30.6	2.0812	0.4805	1.4426
23,500	11.84	837.5	−31.6	2.1182	0.4721	1.4552
24,000	11.59	819.8	−32.5	2.1552	0.4640	1 4681
24,500	11.34	802.1	−33.5	2.1935	0.4559	1.4810
25,000	11.10	785.1	−34.5	2.2321	0.4480	1.4940
25,500	10.86	768.1	−35.5	2.2722	0.4401	1.5074
26,000	10.62	751.2	−36.5	2.3132	0.4323	1.5209
26,500	10.39	734.9	−37.5	2.3546	0.4247	1.5345
27,000	10.16	718.6	−38.5	2.3975	0.4171	1.5484
27,500	9.94	703.1	−39.5	2.4408	0.4097	1.5623
28,000	9.72	687.5	−40.5	2.4857	0.4023	1.5766
28,500	9.50	672.0	−41.5	2.5310	0.3951	1.5910
29,000	9.29	657.1	−42.5	2.5780	0.3879	1.6056
29,500	9.08	642.2	−43.4	2.6254	0.3809	1.6203
30,000	8.88	628.1	−44.4	2.6738	0.3740	1.6352
30,500	8.68	614.0	−45.4	2.7241	0.3671	1.6505
31,000	8.48	599.8	−46.4	2.7755	0.3603	1.6659
31,500	8.29	586.4	−47.4	2.8273	0.3537	1.6814
32,000	8.10	572.9	−48.4	2.8802	0.3472	1.6971
32,500	7.91	559.5	−49.4	2.9351	0.3407	1.7132
33,000	7.73	546.8	−50.4	2.9913	0.3343	1.7295
33,500	7.55	534.0	−51.4	3.0479	0.3281	1.7461
34,000	7.38	522.0	−52.4	3.1075	0.3218	1.7628
34,500	7.20	509.3	−53.4	3.1666	0.3158	1.7795

TABLE XV.—STANDARD AIR AT ALTITUDES OTHER THAN SEA LEVEL.—(*Concluded*)

Altitude, ft	Abs. pressure, in. Hg	Abs. pressure, lb per sq ft	Temperature, deg C	$\frac{\rho_0}{\rho} = \frac{1}{\sigma}$	Density ratio $= \sigma$	Reciprocal square root of density ratio $\sqrt{\frac{1}{\sigma}}$
35,000	7.04	498.0	−54.3	3.2279	0.3098	1.7966
35,500	6.87	485.9	−55.0	3.2971	0.3033	1.8158
36,000	6.71	474.6	−55.0	3.3761	0.2962	1.8374
36,500	6.55	463.3	−55.0	3.4578	0.2892	1.8595
37,000	6.39	452.0	−55.0	3.5411	0.2824	1.8818
37,500	6.24	441.4	−55.0	3.6271	0.2757	1.9045
38,000	6.10	431.5	−55.0	3.7147	0.2692	1.9273
38,500	5.95	420.9	−55.0	3.8037	0.2629	1.9503
39,000	5.81	411.0	−55.0	3.8971	0.2566	1.9738
39,500	5.68	401.8	−55.0	3.9904	0.2506	1.9976
40,000	5.54	391.9	−55.0	4.0866	0.2447	2.0215
40,500	5.41	382.7	−55.0	4.1858	0.2389	2.0459
41,000	5.28	373.5	−55.0	4.2882	0.2332	2.0707
41,500	5.16	365.0	−55.0	4.3917	0.2277	2.0956
42,000	5.04	356.5	−55.0	4.4964	0.2224	2.1207
42,500	4.92	348.0	−55.0	4.6062	0.2171	2.1462
43,000	4.80	339.5	−55.0	4.7170	0.2120	2.1719
43,500	4.69	331.7	−55.0	4.8309	0.2070	2.1979
44,000	4.58	324.0	−55.0	4.9480	0.2021	2.2244
44,500	4.47	316.2	−55.0	5.0684	0.1973	2.2514
45,000	4.36	308.4	−55.0	5.1921	0.1926	2.2785
45,500	4.26	301.4	−55.0	5.3163	0.1881	2.3057
46,000	4.16	294.2	−55.0	5.4437	0.1837	2.3332
46,500	4.06	287.2	−55.0	5.5741	0.1794	2.3609
47,000	3.97	280.8	−55.0	5.7110	0.1751	2.3893
47,500	3.87	273.7	−55.0	5.8479	0.1710	2.4182
48,000	3.78	267.4	−55.0	5.9916	0.1669	2.4478
48,500	3.69	261.0	−55.0	6.1350	0.1630	2.4769
49,000	3.61	255.3	−55.0	6.2854	0.1591	2.5071
49,500	3.52	249.0	−55.0	6.4309	0.1555	2.5359
50,000	3.44	243.3	−55.0	6.5920	0.1517	2.5675

* International standard sea-level air: T = 15°C; w = 0.07651 lb per cu ft; ρ_0 = 0.002378 slug per cu ft; P = 29.921 in. Hg; 1 in. Hg = 70.732 lb per sq ft = 0.4912 lb per sq in.

This table is based on *NACA Tech. Rept.* 218.

For altitudes from 50,000 to 80,000 ft, see *NACA Tech. Rept.* 538.

APPENDIX 4

AIRFOIL DATA

TABLE XVI.—SECTION CHARACTERISTICS, NACA FOUR-DIGIT-SERIES AIRFOILS*

Airfoil	$c_{l\,max}$ scale corr., p. 411	$c_{l\,max}$	α_{l0}, deg	a_0 per deg	$c_{l\,opt}$	$c_{d0\,min}$	$c_{m\,a.c.}$	a.c. % c from $\frac{c}{4}$		$Æ = 6$, round tips	
								Ahead	Above	m_6 per radian	$C_{D\,min}$
0006	A	0.91	0	0.098	0	0.0051	0	0.7	2	4.28	0.0051
0009	BO	1.39	0	0.098	0	0.0058	0	1.0	5	4.28	0.0058
0012	CO	1.66	0	0.099	0	0.0060	0	0.6	3	4.32	0.0060
0015	DO	1.66	0	0.097	0	0.0064	0	1.2	4	4.24	0.0064
0018	EO	1.53	0	0.096	0	0.0070	0	1.7	4	4.20	0.0070
0021	E1	1.48	0	0.093	0	0.0080	0	3.0	6	4.11	0.0080
0025	E2	1.28	0	0.085	0	0.0094	0	2.7	5	3.82	0.0094
2212	C3	1.72	−1.8	0.099	0.12	0.0062	−0.029	0.9	5	4.31	0.0063
2306	A	1.11	−1.8	0.100	0.14	0.0059	−0.036	0.4	4	4.34	0.0060
2309	B2	1.62	−2.0	0.099	0.14	0.0062	−0.037	0.8	5	4.31	0.0064
2312	C2	1.72	−1.9	0.097	0.12	0.0064	−0.039	1.2	4	4.24	0.0065
2315	D2	1.65	−1.7	0.098	0.08	0.0070	−0.034	0.9	3	4.28	0.0070
2406	A	1.04	−1.7	0.099	0.18	0.0056	−0.039	0.4	4	4.31	
2409	B2	1.62	−1.7	0.099	0.08	0.0060	−0.044	0.7	4	4.31	0.0061
2412	C2	1.72	−2.0	0.098	0.14	0.0061	−0.043	0.5	3	4.28	0.0062
2415	D2	1.66	−1.7	0.097	0.10	0.0068	−0.040	1.4	5	4.24	0.0069
2418	E2	1.53	−1.9	0.094	0.06	0.0076	−0.038	1.1	2	4.14	0.0076
2421	E3	1.44	−1.7	0.093	0.06	0.0083	−0.035	1.4	2	4.11	0.0084
2506	A	1.06	−2.0	0.099	0.14	0.0058	−0.048	0	0	4.31	0.0060
2509	B2	1.48	−2.0	0.098	0.13	0.0060	−0.051	0.3	2	4.28	0.0061
2512	C2	1.73	−2.1	0.098	0.18	0.0064	−0.054	1.0	2	4.28	0.0066
2515	D2	1.64	−2.0	0.095	0.09	0.0071	−0.050	0.9	2	4.18	0.0072
2518	E2	1.58	−2.0	0.092	0.06	0.0075	−0.047	1.1	2	4.07	0.0075
2521	E3	1.48	−1.8	0.091	0.02	0.0082	−0.044	2.3	4	4.04	0.0083
2612	C1	1.78	−2.3	0.096	0.16	0.0063	−0.062	1.4	2	4.20	0.0066
2712	CO	1.80	−2.6	0.096	0.16	0.0065	−0.075	1.0	1	4.20	0.0068
4212	C5	1.83	−3.4	0.098	0.28	0.0067	−0.060	0.6	2	4.28	0.0072
4306	A	1.28	−3.8	0.099	0.28	0.0065	−0.075	0.5	2	4.31	0.0073
4309	B5	1.71	−3.6	0.099	0.24	0.0068	−0.073	0.7	3	4.31	0.0071
4312	C5	1.74	−3.9	0.096	0.27	0.0069	−0.076	0.9	3	4.20	0.0073
4315	D4	1.67	−3.6	0.099	0.10	0.0076	−0.069	1.2	4	4.31	0.0076
4318	E4	1.56	−3.5	0.095	0.16	0.0082	−0.065	1.3	3	4.18	0.0083
4321	E5	1.38	−3.6	0.091	0.04	0.0089	−0.058	1.8	3	4.04	0.0090
4406	A	1.32	−3.9	0.100	0.32	0.0062	−0.087	0.4	0	4.34	0.0071
4409	B4	1.77	−3.9	0.096	0.26	0.0066	−0.088	0.6	2	4.20	0.0072
4412	C4	1.74	−4.0	0.098	0.32	0.0071	−0.088	0.8	2	4.28	0.0073
4415	D4	1.72	−4.0	0.097	0.22	0.0076	−0.085	1.0	1	4.24	0.0079
4418	E4	1.57	−3.7	0.092	0.13	0.0079	−0.078	1.4	1	4.07	0.0081
4421	E5	1.41	−3.4	0.089	0.08	0.0088	−0.071	1.9	2	3.96	0.0089

TABLE XVI.—SECTION CHARACTERISTICS, NACA FOUR-DIGIT-SERIES AIRFOILS.*—(*Concluded*)

Airfoil	$c_{l\,max}$ scale corr., p. 411	$c_{l\,max}$	α_{l0} deg	a_0 per deg	$c_{l\,opt}$	$c_{d0\,min}$	$c_{m\,a.c.}$	a.c. % c from $\frac{c}{4}$		$Æ = 6$, round tips	
								Ahead	Above	m_6 per radian	$C_{D\,min}$
4506	A	1.18	− 4.3	0.100	0.34	0.0071	−0.110	0.5	− 1	4.34	0.0081
4509	B3	1.67	− 4.1	0.099	0.27	0.0071	−0.106	0.3	0	4.31	0.0076
4512	C3	1.81	− 4.2	0.093	0.21	0.0070	−0.106	1.1	0	4.11	0.0073
4515	D3	1.73	− 4.1	0.097	0.17	0.0082	−0.097	0.9	0	4.24	0.0083
4518	E3	1.65	− 3.9	0.092	0.13	0.0086	−0.093	1.4	2	4.07	0.0087
4521	E4	1.50	− 3.4	0.091	0.06	0.0093	−0.082	1.6	2	4.04	0.0094
4612	C2	1.88	− 4.6	0.094	0.24	0.0074	−0.124	1.0	0	4.14	0.0077
4712	C1	1.95	− 5.0	0.093	0.26	0.0078	−0.143	1.2	0	4.11	0.0082
6212	C7	1.87	− 5.2	0.096	0.45	0.0077	−0.089	0.8	4	4.20	0.0087
6306	BO	1.65	− 5.2	0.101	0.57	0.0078	−0.109	−0.4	0	4.37	0.0158
6309	B6	1.78	− 5.4	0.100	0.27	0.0079	−0.112	0.6	3	4.34	0.0090
6312	C6	1.78	− 5.5	0.097	0.35	0.0077	−0.111	0.7	1	4.24	0.0086
6315	D6	1.66	− 5.4	0.097	0.22	0.0088	−0.105	0.7	2	4.24	0.0089
6318	E6	1.53	− 5.2	0.094	0.15	0.0091	−0.098	1.3	1	4.14	0.0092
6321	E7	1.41	− 5.2	0.092	0.10	0.0098	−0.090	1.5	2	4.07	0.0100
6406	BO	1.53	− 5.6	0.100	0.50	0.0073	−0.129	−0.7	0	4.34	0.0107
6409	B6	1.80	− 5.9	0.097	0.48	0.0075	−0.133	0	− 2	4.24	0.0087
6412	C6	1.82	− 5.9	0.098	0.33	0.0078	−0.133	0.9	1	4.28	0.0088
6415	D6	1.70	− 5.7	0.095	0.25	0.0087	−0.125	0.7	− 2	4.18	0.0091
6418	E6	1.62	− 5.7	0.095	0.25	0.0093	−0.118	1.3	0	4.18	0.0096
6421	E7	1.51	− 5.2	0.092	0.10	0.0099	−0.110	1.7	0	4.07	0.0101
6506	A	1.38	− 6.3	0.097	0.40	0.0070	−0.159	0	0	4.24	0.0099
6509	B4	1.83	− 6.3	0.099	0.48	0.0075	−0.158	0.1	− 3	4.31	0.0093
6512	C5	1.87	− 6.2	0.097	0.40	0.0079	−0.155	0.8	− 3	4.24	0.0088
6515	D6	1.79	− 6.0	0.095	0.25	0.0094	−0.147	1.0	− 2	4.18	0.0096
6518	E6	1.72	− 5.7	0.091	0.10	0.0099	−0.139	1.6	− 2	4.04	0.0100
6521	E7	1.60	− 5.3	0.090	0.10	0.0106	−0.129	1.8	3	4.00	0.0108
6612	C4	1.96	− 6.6	0.095	0.25	0.0086	−0.185	1.7	− 2	4.18	0.0094
6712	C2	2.05	− 7.3	0.096	0.35	0.0097	−0.199	1.2	− 2	4.20	0.0102
0006T†	A	0.91	0	0.096	0	0.0054	0	1.0	9	4.20	0.0055
0006B†	BO	1.13	0	0.100	0	0.0060	0	0.6	2	4.34	0.0061
0012T	BO	1.10	0	0.095	0	0.0058	0	0.6	4	4.18	0.0058
0012B	DO	1.60	0	0.097	0	0.0069	0	2.0	6	4.24	0.0069
0018T	DO	1.38	0	0 094	0	0.0066	0	0.8	3	4.14	0.0066
0018B	E2	1.50	0	0.093	0	0.0083	0	2.5	3	4.11	0.0083
$2R_112$‡	C3	1.64	− 1.5	0.097	0 15	0.0059	−0.020	1.1	5	4.24	0.0061
$2R_212$‡	C2	1.61	− 0.6	0.098	0.10	0.0063	0.005	1.0	7	4.28	0.0062
$0012F_0$§	CO	1.64	− 0.2	0.107	0	0.0076	0	0	8	4.57	0.0076
$0012F_1$§	CO	2.19	−11.7	0.095	0.66	0.0111	−0.196	−1.5	−16	4.18	0.0060

* Turbulence = 0.025; $V \approx 80$ ft per sec; $p'' \approx 300$ lb per sq in.; $R^a \approx 3{,}500{,}000$; R_e effective $\approx 8{,}000{,}000$.

From *NACA Tech. Rept.* 628 or 610 corrected as specified in *Tech. Rept.* 669.

See pp. 394 to 406 for ordinates of these airfoils.

† T refers to exceptionally thin-nosed sections; B refers to exceptionally blunt-nosed sections.

‡ R_1 and R_2 refer to airfoils with reflexed trailing edge.

§ F_0 and F_1 refer to airfoils with flat trailing edge: F_0 straight, F_1 deflected down.

TABLE XVII.—SECTION CHARACTERISTICS, NACA FIVE-DIGIT-SERIES AIRFOILS*

Airfoil	$c_{l\,max}$, *Re* corr., p. 411	$c_{l\,max}$	α_{l0}, deg	a_0 per deg	$c_{l\,opt}$	$c_{d0\,min}$	$c_{m\,a.c.}$	a.c. % c from $\frac{c}{4}$		$\frac{t}{c}$, max. %	Max. camber, %	Æ = 6	
								Ahead	Above			m_6 per radian	$C_{D\,min}$
22112	D2	1.64	− 0.8	0.100	0.06	0.0062	0.001	1.0	5	12.00	1.6	4.34	0.0063
23112	D2	1.73	− 0.8	0.100	0.08	0.0064	0.002	1.5	8	12.00	2.1	4.34	0.0065
24112	C3	1.67	− 0.9	0.100	0.10	0.0064	0	1.4	8	12.00	2.4	4.34	0.0064
25112	C3	1.62	− 1.2	0.100	0.08	0.0064	−0.002	1.3	7	12.00	2.7	4.34	0.0065
21012	D3	1.63	− 0.6	0.099	0.04	0.0060	0.001	1.5	6	12.00	1.1	4.32	0.0060
22012	D2	1.72	− 0.9	0.100	0.10	0.0061	−0.005	1.3	5	12.00	1.5	4.34	0.0062
23006	A	1.17	− 1.2	0.100	0.15	0.0057	−0.012	1.0	8	6.00	1.8	4.34	0.0058
23009	C2	1.66	− 1.1	0.099	0.08	0.0059	−0.009	0.9	7	9.00	1.8	4.32	0.0060
23012	D2	1.74	− 1.2	0.100	0.08	0.0060	−0.008	1.2	7	12.00	1.8	4.34	0.0061
23012-33	B6	1.52	− 1.2	0.097	0.25	0.0061	−0.010	0.7	7	12.00	1.8	4.24	0.0063
23012-34	B3	1.49	− 1.2	0.094	0.13	0.0062	−0.011	0.9	4	12.00	1.8	4.14	0 0063
23012-64	D2	1.71	− 1.0	0.095	0.10	0.0062	−0.010	1.0	4	12.00	1.8	4.18	0.0063
23015	D2	1.73	− 1.1	0.098	0.10	0.0067	−0.008	1.1	6	15.00	1.8	4.28	0.0068
23018	E2	1.58	− 1.2	0.097	0.08	0.0074	−0.006	1.7	6	18.00	1.8	4.24	0.0074
23021	E2	1.50	− 1.2	0.092	0.07	0.0080	−0.005	2.3	7	21.00	1.8	4.07	0.0080
24012	C3	1.71	− 1.5	0.100	0.08	0.0062	−0.013	1.3	6	12.00	2.1	4.34	0.0063
25012	C3	1.67	− 1.6	0.100	0.10	0.0064	−0.019	1.1	7	12.00	2.3	4.34	0.0065
32012	D3	1.74	− 1.2	0.100	0.15	0.0064	−0.005	1.1	6	12.00	2.3	4.34	0.0066
33012	D3	1.80	− 1.7	0.099	0.10	0.0064	−0.014	1.0	6	12.00	2.8	4.32	0.0065
34012	D3	1.80	− 2.1	0.100	0.20	0.0064	−0.022	0.6	5	12.00	3.1	4.34	0.0066
42012	D4	1.76	− 1.8	0.100	0.20	0.0067	−0.009	1.1	6	12.00	3.1	4.34	0.0068
43009	B4	1.72	− 2.4	0.100	0.18	0.0060	−0.021	0.8	6	9.00	3.7	4.34	0.0065
43012	D4	1.84	− 2.3	0.100	0.26	0.0068	−0.019	1.0	7	12.00	3.7	4.34	0.0071
43012A	E4	1.78	− 2.2	0.102	0.29	0.0070	−0.017	1.2	7	12.00	3.7	4.41	0.0073
43015	D4	1.76	− 2.3	0.101	0.18	0.0070	−0.015	1.2	5	15.00	3.7	4.37	0.0071
43018	E4	1.63	− 2.4	0.096	0.16	0.0078	−0.013	1.8	6	18.00	3.7	4.20	0.0079
43021	E6	1.48	− 2.4	0.093	0.10	0.0085	−0.010	2.4	7	21.00	3.7	4.11	0.0087
44012	D4	1.82	− 2.8	0.098	0.25	0.0069	−0.028	0.5	5	12.00	4.2	4.28	0.0070
62021	E4	1.52	− 3.1	0.094	0.12	0.0087	−0.006	3.2	8	21.00	4.6	4.14	0.0089
63009	C6	1.77	− 3.5	0.098	0.57	0.0071	−0.042	2.6	7	9.00	5.5	4.28	0.0176
63012	D6	1.84	− 3.5	0.100	0.40	0.0075	−0.033	2.7	13	12.00	5.5	4.34	0.0087
63015	E6	1.76	− 3.5	0.098	0.25	0.0078	−0.024	1.6	6	15.00	5.5	4.28	0.0081
63018	E7	1.63	− 3.4	0.097	0.15	0.0080	−0.020	2.1	6	18.00	5.5	4.24	0.0081
63021	E8	1.48	− 3.6	0.097	0.21	0.0089	−0.018	3.1	6	21.00	5.5	4.24	0.0092
64021	E11	1.46	− 4.2	0.094	0.13	0.0091	−0.031	2.7	8	21.00	6.2	4.14	0.0093
0012;60° *f*	CO	2.35	−13.1	0.091	....	0.0141	−0.200	0.6	3	12.00	0	4.04	
23009;60°*f*	C2	2.31	−14.0	0.092	....	0.0144	−0.233	0.9	7	9.00	1.8	4.07	
23012;60°*f*	D2	2.48	−14.3	0.088	....	0.0142	−0.236	1.2	7	12.00	1.8	3.93	
23009;75°*f*	C2	2.30	−15.1	0.089	....	0.0177	−0.210	0.9	7	9.00	1.8	3.96	
23012;75°*f*	D2	2.54	−15.6	0.085	....	0.0172	−0.228	1.2	7	12.00	1.8	3.82	
23015;75°*f*	D2	2.70	−16.2	0.086	....	0.0168	−0.245	1.1	6	15.00	1.8	3.86	
23021;75°*f*	E2	2.74	−16.5	0.094	....	0.0156	−0.300	2.3	7	21.00	1.8	4.14	
43009;75°*f*	B4	2.35	−17.5	0.080	....	0.0178	−0.208	0.8	6	9.00	3.7	3.64	
43012;75°*f*	D4	2.65	−17.3	0.082	....	0.0171	−0.225	1.0	7	12.00	3.7	3.72	
63009;75°*f*	C6	2.40	−19.0	0.078	....	0.0178	−0.230	2.6	7	9.00	5.5	3.57	

* Turbulence ≈ 0.025; $V \approx 80$ ft per sec; $p'' \approx 300$ lb per sq in.; $Re \approx 3{,}500{,}000$; Re effective ≈ 8,000,000.
From *NACA Tech. Rept.* 631 and 610, corrected as specified in *NACA Tech. Rept.* 669.
See p. 407 for ordinates of these airfoils.
f = 0.2-chord split flaps.

TABLE XVIII.—SECTION CHARACTERISTICS MISCELLANEOUS AIRFOILS*

Airfoil	$c_{l\,max}$, R^e corr., p. 411	$c_{l\,max}$	α_{l0}, deg	a_0 per deg	$c_{l\,opt}$	c_{d0}	$c_{m\,a.c.}$	a.c. % c from $\frac{c}{4}$ Ahead	Above	$\frac{t}{c}$ max. % c	Max camber, % c	$Æ = 6$ m_6 per radian	$C_{D\,min}$
B 103	C4	1.76	− 4.8	0.097	0.15	0.0075	−0.065	0.6	7	12.68	4.2	4.24	0.0076
B 103(inv.)	..	0.96	......	0.098	......	......	0.069	0.9	− 2	.....	...	4.28	
B 103A	C3	1.74	− 3.8	0.098	0.17	0.0065	−0.053	0.5	5	10.38	3.2	4.28	0.0067
B 103A(inv.)	..	0.85	......	0.100	......	......	0.058	0.8	0	.....	...	4.34	
B 106	B4	1.64	− 4.4	0.094	0.14	0.0069	−0.052	0.8	5	13.06	3.5	4.14	0.0070
B 106(inv.)	..	0.88	......	0.093	......	......	0.057	1.4	2	.....	...	4.11	
B 106R	B3	1.48	− 1.1	0.095	0.05	0.0065	−0.001	0.3	4	13.06	2.0	4.18	0.0066
B 111	D3	1.68	− 2.1	0.096	0.17	0.0062	−0.033	1.3	6	11.50	3.0	4.20	0.0063
B 111(inv.)	..	0.89	......	0.096	......	......	0.033	0.9	2	.....	...	4.20	
B 112	D2	1.69	− 2.0	0.096	0.20	0.0062	−0.023	0.7	5	11.50	2.8	4.20	0.0064
B 112(inv.)	..	0.70	......	0.096	......	......	0.023	0.7	− 5	.....	...	4.20	
S GS-M	D6	1.69	− 7.9	0.099	0.30	0.0080	−0.105	0.1	6	16.05	5.5	4.31	0.0084
S GS-M(inv.)	..	0.89	......	0.101	......	......	0.105	1.1	1	.....	...	4.37	
S GS-I	D4	1.78	− 6.8	0.097	0.25	0.0070	−0.094	0.4	4	13.98	4.5	4.24	0.0072
S GS-I(inv.)	..	1.16	......	0.100	......	......	0.093	1.2	2	.....	...	4.34	
St Ae. 27A	E8	1.72	−10.2	0.100	0.40	0.0102	−0.177	0	0	19.80	8.0	4.34	0.0111
RAF34	C1	1.58	− 0.8	0.098	0.20	0.0061	−0.006	0.4	5	12.64	1.8	4.28	0.0061
USA27	C6	1.71	− 4.7	0.094	0.30	0.0075	−0.078	1.8	5	11.12	5.6	4.14	0.0084
USA27(inv.)	..	0.52	......	0.094	......	......	0.080	1.9	0	.....	...	4.14	
USA35-A	E6	1.52	− 8.0	0.095	0.38	0.0094	−0.111	0.8	5	18.18	7.3	4.18	0.0099
USA35-B	C5	1.81	− 5.2	0.099	0.35	0.0072	−0.076	0.5	5	11.61	4.6	4.31	0.0075
USA35-B(inv.)	..	0.81	......	0.102	......	......	0.081	1.3	5	.....	...	4.41	
C 62	A	1.06	− 1.8	0.095	0.15	0.0059	−0.038	0.6	4	8.04	1.9	4.18	0.0060
C 72	C4	1.74	− 5.6	0.095	0.23	0.0071	−0.084	1.0	3	11.73	4.0	4.18	0.0075
C 72 (inv.)	..	0.83	......	0.096	......	......	0.085	1.0	− 1	.....	...	4.20	
C 80	A	1.24	− 1.0	0.098	0.05	0.0057	−0.015	0.2	4	8.58	1.3	4.28	0.0058
C 80(inv.)	..	0.81	......	0.100	......	......	0.018	0.4	2	.....	...	4.34	
N 22	C4	1.72	− 5.4	0.096	0.17	0.0075	−0.075	0.6	4	12.37	4.3	4.20	0.0076
N 22(inv.)	..	0.84	......	0.098	......	......	0.082	0.8	0	.....	...	4.28	
N 60	C4	1.73	− 5.5	0.097	0.30	0.0074	−0.078	0	0	12.37	4.0	4.24	0.0077
N 60R	C3	1.50	− 1.5	0.098	0.09	0.0066	−0.001	−0.1	6	12.37	2.8	4.28	0.0067
N 68	A	0.96	0	0.097	0	0.0054	0	0.7	5	8.00	0	4.24	0.0055
N 69	A	1.00	0	0.093	0	0.0058	0	0.8	4	10.94	0	4.11	0.0058
N 71	C2	1.67	− 2.0	0.099	0.18	0.0058	0.029	0.7	6	11.54	2.0	4.31	0.0060
N 71(inv.)	..	1.24	......	0.099	......	......	0.030	0	1	.....	...	4.31	
N 75	C2	1.68	− 2.2	0.097	0.15	0.0065	−0.045	0.9	3	11.50	2.0	4.24	0.0067
N 75(inv.)	..	1.09	......	0.096	......	......	0.046	0.7	2	.....	...	4.20	
N 76	C3	1.63	− 2.1	0.096	0.19	0.0067	−0.032	0.7	4	11.50	2.7	4.20	0.0070
N 76(inv.)	..	0.99	......	0.095	......	......	0.032	0.5	0	.....	...	4.18	
N 80	C2	1.74	− 2.2	0.098	0.16	0.0060	−0.044	−0.1	2	11.54	2.0	4.28	0.0062
N 80(inv.)	..	1.17	......	0.100	......	......	0.043	0	0	.....	...	4.34	
N 81	C2	1.79	− 2.2	0.100	0.14	0.0062	−0.041	0.2	5	11.54	2.0	4.34	0.0064
N 81(inv.)	..	1.26	......	0.101	......	......	0.038	0.1	2	.....	...	4.37	
G 367	D6	1.70	− 6.6	0.097	0.30	0.0076	−0.093	0.7	4	14.85	5.9	4.24	0.0081
G 398	D5	1.68	− 6.0	0.094	0.15	0.0076	−0.081	0.4	1	13.75	4.9	4.14	0.0079
G 398(inv.)	..	0.83	......	0.097	......	......	0.086	1.9	3	.....	...	4.24	
G 398A	A	1.20	− 6.1	0.095	0.40	0.0072	−0.086	1.0	− 2	13.62	4.5	4.18	0.0092
G 398B	A	1.19	− 6.4	0.090	0.45	0.0071	−0.093	1.7	4	13.48	4.5	4.00	0.0104
G 398R	D4	1.46	− 2.2	0.098	0.10	0.0070	−0.005	0.5	10	13.75	3.5	4.28	0.0070
G 413	D5	1.61	− 7.7	0.101	0.35	0.0080	−0.096	0	7	16.45	5.0	4.37	0.0087
G 420	E4	1.51	− 8.3	0.095	0.18	0.0084	−0.084	−0.4	7	18.75	4.5	4.18	0.0086
G 429AG	CO	1.61	0	0.100	0	0.0058	0	0.1	4	11.20	0	4.34	0.0058
G 429J	CO	1.65	0	0.102	0	0.0057	0	0.2	5	11.78	0	4.41	0.0059
G 436	C4	1.68	− 4.4	0.098	0.22	0.0071	−0.061	0.5	5	11.10	3.9	4.28	0.0074
G 436(inv.)	..	0.76	......	0.099	......	......	0.062	0.6	− 6	.....	...	4.31	
G 532	C5	1.91	− 6.1	0.101	0.37	0.0068	−0.095	0.8	6	13.00	4.8	4.37	0.0730
G 532(inv.)	..	0.73	......	0.101	......	......	0.095	2.9	14	.....	...	4.37	

* Turbulence ≈ 0.025; $V \approx 80$ ft per sec; $p'' \approx 300$ lb per sq in.; $Re \approx 3{,}500{,}000$; Re effective ≈ 8,000,000.
From *NACA Tech. Rept.* 628 corrected as specified in *NACA Tech. Rept.* 669.
See page 401 for ordinates of these airfoils.

TABLE XVIII.—SECTION CHARACTERISTICS, MISCELLANEOUS AIRFOILS.—(*Concluded*)

Airfoil	$c_{l\,max}$ *Re* corr. p. 411	$c_{l\,max}$	α_{l0}, deg	a_0 per deg	$c_{l\,opt}$	c_{d0}	$c_{m\,a.c.}$	a.c. % c from $\frac{c}{4}$		$\frac{t}{c}$, max. % c	Max. camber, % c	Æ = 6	
								Ahead	Above			m_6 radian	$C_{D\,min}$
C Y	C4	1.68	− 5.0	0.092	0.12	0.0071	−0.069	1.1	4	11.70	3.9	4.07	0.0073
C Y(inv.)	..	0.92	......	0.098	......	......	0.072	1.7	3	.....	...	4.28	
C Y-B	A	1.14	− 5.4	0.089	0.35	0.0062	−0.075	1.3	− 2	11.46	3.3	4.96	0.0083
C YM-15	D4	1.70	− 5.2	0.094	0.10	0.0076	−0.068	1.1	7	15.00	4.0	4.14	0.0077
C YM-15(inv.)	..	1.23	......	0.097	......	......	0.071	1.3	1	.....	...	4.24	
C YM-18	E4	1.00	− 5.1	0.091	0.07	0.0085	−0.064	1.4	5	18.00	4.0	4.04	0.0084
C YM-18(inv.)	..	1.39	......	0.094	......	......	0.650	2.2	2	.....	...	4.14	
C Y-6	A	1.07	− 2.9	0.098	0.15	0.0055	−0.038	0.7	5	6.00	1.9	4.28	0.0059
C Y-8	B3	1.37	− 3.6	0.096	0.14	0.0054	−0.045	0.7	6	8.00	2.6	4.20	0.0050
C Y-10	C3	1.68	− 4.5	0.098	0.23	0.0065	−0.059	0.7	4	10.00	3.2	4.28	0.0068
C Y-14	D4	1.72	− 6.2	0.096	0.15	0.0076	−0.080	1.2	6	14.00	4.6	4.20	0.0077
C Y-18	E6	1.48	− 7.6	0.092	0.23	0.0095	−0.098	1.5	6	18.00	6.3	4.07	0.0099
C Y-18(inv.)	..	0.89	......	0.089	......	......	0.101	0.3	−10	.....	...	3.96	
C Y-22	E8	1.36	− 9.3	0.088	0.15	0.0111	0.107	1.8	13	22.00	8.0	3.93	0.0113
NACA:													
CYH	C3	1.58	− 2.9	0.095	0.08	0.0065	−0.027	0.7	6	11.70	3.1	4.18	0.0066
CYH(inv.)	..	0.96	......	0.095	......	......	0.032	1.6	− 1	.....	...	4.18	
-M6	C3	1.51	− 0.8	0.095	0.03	0.0066	0.002	−0.4	0	12.01	2.4	4.18	0.0066
-M6(inv.)	..	1.19	......	0.097	......	......	0.007	0	0	.....	...	4.24	
15	A	1.17	− 2.0	0.094	0.15	0.0060	−0.043	0.3	0	12.00	2.0	4.14	0.0061
16	B4	1.64	− 2.1	0.095	0.17	0.0060	−0.045	0.7	3	12.00	2.0	4.18	0.0061
17	B4	1.53	− 1.9	0.095	0.25	0.0060	−0.047	0.4	2	12.00	2.6	4.18	0.0065
18	C2	1.69	− 2.0	0.096	0.25	0.0061	−0.049	0.6	3	12.00	2.6	4.20	0.0064
19	A	1.01	− 1.9	0.093	0.17	0.0056	−0.044	0	0	12.00	2.0	4.11	0.0059
20	A	1.02	− 2.2	0.090	0.24	0.0056	−0.048	1.2	−10	12.00	2.0	4.00	0.0067
21	C2	1.71	− 2.1	0.096	0.20	0.0064	−0.038	0.5	3	12.00	2.4	4.20	0.0066
21(inv.)	..	1.08	......	0.097	......	......	0.040	0.4	1	.....	...	4.24	
23	B2	1.65	− 1.0	0.100	0.18	0.0055	−0.007	0.5	7	9.00	2.0	4.34	0.0057
24	C2	1.67	− 0.8	0.103	0.15	0.0059	0	−0.1	6	12.00	2.0	4.44	0.0060
25	D2	1.54	− 0.8	0.105	0	0.0063	0.008	−0.1	8	15.00	2.0	4.51	0.0062
26	E2	1.46	− 0.9	0.104	−0.05	0.0065	0.008	−0.3	8	18.00	2.0	4.47	0.0065
27	A	1.14	− 1.3	0.102	0.10	0.0053	−0.010	−0.2	6	6.00	2.0	4.41	0.0054

Abbreviations: B = Boeing; S = Sikorsky; G = Goettingen; C = Clark; N = U.S. Navy.

TABLE XIX.—CHARACTERISTICS OF HIGH-SPEED AIRFOILS*

NACA airfoil	α_{l0}, deg	a_0 per deg	c_l opt	c_{d0} min	$c_{m\ a.c.}$	a.c. % c ahead of $\frac{c}{4}$
$M = 0.3, \frac{Re}{10^6} = 0.6$						
16-009	0	0.102	0	0.005	−0.01	6
16-109	−0.8	0.102	0.12	0.005	−0.025	3.5
16-209	−1.4	0.100	0.26	0.005	−0.045	3.5
16-509	−3.8	0.112	0.5	0.005	−0.105	1
16-709	−5.0	0.112	0.52	0.008	−0.140	1
16-1009	−6.5	0.124	0.75	0.011	−0.175	2
16-106	−0.7	0.114	0.1	0.003	−0.025	1
16-506	−3.8	0.110	0.4	0.0045	−0.11	1
16-512	−3.8	0.098	0.4	0.008	−0.11	3
16-515	−3.8	0.090	0.3	0.0105	−0.11	6
16-521	−2.1	0.090	0.02	0.0160	−0.07	6
16-530	+1.7	0.068	−0.12	0.0300	+0.015	8
$M = 0.6, \frac{Re}{10^6} = 1.2$						
16-009	0	0.102	0	0.004	−0.005	5
16-109	−0.8	0.110	0.1	0.0035	−0.03	8
16-209	−1.6	0.106	0.2	0.0045	−0.06	4
16-509	−3.9	0.123	0.5	0.0055	−0.135	2
16-709	−5.1	0.130	0.7	0.008	−0.165	5
16-1009†	−6.5†	0.144	1.1	0.0105	−0.230	−2
16-106	−0.6	0.124	0.05	0.003	−0.030	3
16-506	−3.3	0.132	0.6	0.0045	−0.125	1
16-512	−3.9	0.130	0.5	0.0075	−0.135	2
16-515	−4.2	0.088	0.32	0.0105	−0.145	9
16-521	−1.4	0.104	0.14	0.0195	−0.06	6
16-530	+3.1	0 070	0.17	0.043	+0.06	13
$M = 0.7, \frac{Re}{10^6} = 1.4$						
16-009	0	0 112	0	0.005	−0.005	6
16-109	−0.6	0.130	0.1	0.0035	−0.03	4
16-209	−1.0	0.148	0.25	0.004	−0.07	3
16-509	−3.9	0.142	0.45	0.0055	−0.155	3
16-709	−5.4	0.136	0.7	0.0085	−0.18	1
16-1009†	−6.6†	0.120	0.75	0.0155	−0.22	−6
16-106	−0.9	0.152	0.1	0.003	−0.035	3
16-506	−3.3	0.156	0.8	0.0040	−0.145	0
16-512	−3.6	0.124	0.5	0.0080	−0.150	4
16-515	−4.5	0.088	0.3	0.0130	−0.17	9
16-521	−0.3	0.118	−0.05	0.0295	−0.025	15
$M = 0.75, \frac{Re}{10^6} = 1.5$						
16-009	−0.1	0.124	0	0.005	−0.005	9
16-109	−0 8	0.138	0.1	0.0035	−0.030	1
16-209	−1.7	0.142	0.2	0.004	−0.075	3
16-509	−3.8	0.156	0.5	0.005	−0.175	3
16-709	−5.1	0.126	0.45	0.016	−0.21	5
16-106	−0.9	0.140	0.1	0.003	−0.035	6
16-506	−3.2	0.188	0.7	0.005	−0.160	0
16-512	−4.1	0.090	0.3	0.013	−0.150	5
16-515	−1.3	0.096	0.1	0 0195	−0.080	13

* High-speed tunnel tests reported in *NACA Tech. Note* 976.

† Neglecting lower surface burble.

TABLE XX.—CHARACTERISTICS OF TAPERED WINGS, VARIABLE-DENSITY-TUNNEL TEST RESULTS*

Wings†	Plan-form taper ratio	As-pect ratio	$C_{L\max}$	αL_0, deg	a per deg	$C_{L\,opt}$	$C_{De\,\min}$	$C_{M\,a.c.}$	a.c. fraction ahead of root $\frac{c}{4}$	e
0015-09;0-0	2:1	6	1.53	0	0.075	0.04	0.0065	0	0.014	0.89
2415-09;0-0	2:1	6	1.68	−1.7	0.074	0.14	0.0065	−0.040	+0.022	0.90
2415-09;15-0	2:1	6	1.63	−1.9	0.075	0.19	0.0065	−0.043	−0.352	0.90
2415-09;30-0	2:1	6	1.43	−1.9	0.072	0.16	0.0065	−0.042	−0.775	0.88
2415-09;30-8.5	2:1	6	1.51	0.7	0.076	0.36	0.0071	0.002	−0.786	0.92
$2R_115$-09;15-8.5	2:1	6	1.59	1.2	0.076	0.26	0.0078	0.003	−0.348	0.93
$2R_215$-09;15-0	2:1	6	1.50	−0.7	0.078	0.16	0.0066	0.004	−0.351	0.89
0015-09;15-3.45	2:1	6	1.48	1.0	0.076	0.06	0.0069	0.007	−0.346	0.90
0015-09;15-3.45	4:1	6	1.32	0.7	0.076	0.10	0.0070	0.005	−0.334	0.90
2218-09;0-0	2:1	6	1.60	−1.8	0.071	0.15	0.0074	−0.029	0.028	0.91
M6(18)-(09);0-0	2:1	6	1.49	−1.1	0.070	0.18	0.0071	−0.006	0.017	0.90
CYM-18-09;0-0	2:1	6	1.67	−5.2	0.071	0.22	0.0076	−0.071	0.020	0.91
23015-09;0-0	2:1	6	1.71	−1.3	0.074	0.17	0.0067	−0.007	0.014	0.91
23018-09;0-0	2:1	6	1.66	−1.3	0.073	0.11	0.0071	−0.007	0.020	0.90
23018-09;0-0	3:1	10	1.51	−1.2	0.083	0.04	0.0070	−0.011	0.013	0.80
23016-09;0-0	5:1	10	1.50	−1.2	0.083	0.03	0.0067	−0.009	0.011	0.78
23018-09;0-0	5:1	10	1.49	−1.2	0.083	0.05	0.0071	−0.011	0.013	0.81
23016-09;0-0	5:1	12	1.46	−1.2	0.086	0.02	0.0066	−0.014	0.016	0.76
23020-09;0-0	5:1	12	1.42	−1.2	0.084	0	0.0069	−0.007	0.010	0.74
0018-09;0-0	2:1	6	1.48	.....	0.074	0	0.0069	0	0.020	0.90
23013-43010;0-2	1.6:2	6	1.67	−0.7	0.074	....	0.0064	−0.009		
4412-4412;0-0	Ellip.	6	1.81	−4.0	0.074	0.15	0.0071	−0.100	0.018	0.92

* Reported in *NACA Tech. Rept.* 627, corrected as directed in *NACA Tech. Rept.* 669.

† Numerical designations have the following significance: in the example 2415-09; 30-8.5,

2415 Root airfoil = 2409 tip airfoil; 30 deg sweepback on $\frac{c}{4}$ line = 8.5 deg dihedral on $\frac{c}{4}$ line.

TABLE XXI.—ORDINATES OF AIRFOILS IN TABLE XVI

Sta.	0006		0009		0012		0015		0018	
	Up'r	L'w'r	Up'r	L'w'r	Up'r	L'w'r	Up'r	L'w'r	Up'r	L'w'r
0	0	0	0	0	0	0	0	0	0	0
1.25	0.947	−0.947	1.420	−1.420	1.894	−1.894	2.367	−2.367	2.841	−2.841
2.5	1.307	−1.307	1.961	−1.961	2.615	−2.615	3.268	−3.268	3.922	−3.922
5.0	1.777	−1.777	2.666	−2.666	3.555	−3.555	4.443	−4.443	5.332	−5.332
7.5	2.100	−2.100	3.150	−3.150	4.200	−4.200	5.250	−5.250	6.300	−6.300
10	2.341	−2.341	3.512	−3.512	4.683	−4.683	5.853	−5.853	7.024	−7.024
15	2.673	−2.673	4.009	−4.009	5.345	−5.345	6.681	−6.681	8.018	−8.018
20	2.869	−2.869	4.303	−4.303	5.738	−5.738	7.172	−7.172	8.606	−8.606
25	2.971	−2.971	4.456	−4.456	5.941	−5.941	7.427	−7.427	8.912	−8.912
30	3.001	−3.001	4.501	−4.501	6.002	−6.002	7.502	−7.502	9.003	−9.003
40	2.902	−2.902	4.352	−4.352	5.803	−5.803	7.254	−7.254	8.705	−8.705
50	2.647	−2.647	3.971	−3.971	5.294	−5.294	6.618	−6.618	7.941	−7.941
60	2.282	−2.282	3.423	−3.423	4.563	−4.563	5.704	−5.704	6.845	−6.845
70	1.832	−1.832	2.748	−2.748	3.664	−3.664	4.580	−4.580	5.496	−5.496
80	1.312	−1.312	1.967	−1.967	2.623	−2.623	3.279	−3.279	3.935	−3.935
90	0.724	−0.724	1.086	−1.086	1.448	−1.448	1.810	−1.810	2.172	−2.172
95	0.403	−0.403	0.605	−0.605	0.807	−0.807	1.008	−1.008	1.210	−1.210
100	(0.063)	(−0.063)	(0.095)	(−0.095)	(0.126)	(−0.126)	(0.158)	(−0.158)	(0.183)	(−0.183)
100	0	0	0	0	0	0	0	0	0	0
	L.E. rad. 0.40		L.E. rad. 0.89		L.E. rad. 1.58		L.E. rad. 2.48		L.E. rad. 3.56	

Sta.	0021		0025		2212		2306		2309	
	Up'r	L'w'r	Up'r	L'w'r	Up'r	L'w'r	Up'r	L'w'r	Up'r	L'w'r
0	0	0	0	0	—	0	—	0	—	0
1.25	3.314	− 3.314	3.946	− 3.946	2.44	−1.46	1.16	−0.73	1.69	−1.16
2.5	4.576	− 4.576	5.447	− 5.447	3.35	−1.96	1.70	−0.95	2.39	−1.58
5.0	6.221	− 6.221	7.406	− 7.406	4.62	−2.55	2.43	−1.15	3.38	−2.01
7.5	7.350	− 7.350	8.750	− 8.750	5.55	−2.89	3.01	−1.22	4.09	−2.24
10	8.195	− 8.195	9.756	− 9.756	6.27	−3.11	3.48	−1.22	4.67	−2.38
15	9.354	− 9.354	11.136	−11.136	7.25	−3.44	4.18	−1.18	5.54	−2.50
20	10.041	−10.041	11.953	−11.953	7.74	−3.74	4.85	−1.09	6.08	−2.52
25	10.397	−10.397	12.378	−12.378	7.93	−3.94	4.91	−1.04	6.37	−2.51
30	10.503	−10.503	12.504	−12.504	7.97	−4.03	5.00	−1.00	6.50	−2.50
40	10.155	−10.155	12.090	−12.090	7.68	−3.92	4.86	−0.94	6.32	−2.39
50	9.285	− 9.285	11.029	−11.029	7.02	−3.56	4.49	−0.81	5.82	−2.13
60	7.986	− 7.986	9.507	− 9.507	6.07	−3.05	3.92	−0.65	5.07	−1.78
70	6.412	− 6.412	7.633	− 7.633	4.90	−2.43	3.19	−0.48	4.11	−1.38
80	4.590	− 4.590	5.465	− 5.465	3.52	−1.74	2.30	−0.33	2.96	−0.97
90	2.533	− 2.533	3.016	− 3.016	1.93	−0.97	1.28	−0.19	1.84	−0.54
95	1.412	− 1.412	1.680	− 1.680	1.05	−0.56	0.68	−0.13	0.88	−0.33
100	(0.221)	(−0.221)	(0.262)	(−0.262)	(0.13)	(−0.13)	(0.06)	(−0.06)	(0.10)	(−0.10)
100	0	0	0	0	—	0	—	0	—	0
	L.E. rad. 4.85		L.E. rad. 6.88		L.E. rad. 1.58. Slope of radius through end of chord 2/10		L.E. rad. 0.40. Slope of radius through end of chord 2/15		L.E. rad. 0.89. Slope of radius through end of chord 2/15	

TABLE XXI.—ORDINATES OF AIRFOILS IN TABLE XVI.—(*Continued*)

Sta.	2312		2315		2406		2409		2412		2415	
	Up'r	L'w'r	Up'r	L'w'r	Up'r	L'w'r	Up'r	L'w'r	Up'r	L'w'r	Up'r	L'w'r
0	—	0	—	0	—	0	—	0	—	0	—	0
1.25	2.24	−1.57	2.80	−1.96	1.11	−0.80	1.62	−1.23	2.15	−1.65	2.71	−2.08
2.5	3.11	−2.16	3.85	−2.74	1.57	−1.04	2.27	−1.66	2.99	−2.27	3.71	−2.86
5.0	4.31	−2.85	5.26	−3.66	2.28	−1.29	3.20	−2.15	4.13	−3.01	5.07	−3.84
7.5	5.18	−3.26	6.28	−4.25	2.81	−1.40	3.87	−2.44	4.96	−3.46	6.06	−4.47
10	5.86	−3.52	7.08	−4.66	3.24	−1.45	4.43	−2.60	5.63	−3.75	6.83	−4.90
15	6.89	−3.82	8.25	−5.13	3.90	−1.44	5.25	−2.77	6.61	−4.10	7.97	−5.42
20	7.54	−3.94	8.97	−5.38	4.37	−1.37	5.81	−2.79	7.26	−4.23	8.70	−5.66
25	7.88	−3.99	9.36	−5.48	4.69	−1.25	6.18	−2.74	7.67	−4.22	9.17	−5.70
30	8.00	−4.00	9.50	−5.50	4.88	−1.12	6.38	−2.62	7.88	−4.12	9.38	−5.62
40	7.77	−3.84	9.22	−5.29	4.90	−0.90	6.35	−2.35	7.80	−3.80	9.25	−5.25
50	7.14	−3.45	8.47	−4.77	4.60	−0.70	5.92	−2.02	7.24	−3.34	8.57	−4.67
60	6.21	−2.92	7.36	−4.06	4 08	−0.49	5.22	−1.63	6.38	−2.76	7.50	−3.90
70	5.02	−2.31	5.95	−3.22	3.35	−0.33	4 27	−1.24	5.18	−2.14	6.10	−3.05
80	3.62	−1.63	4.29	−2.28	2.44	−0.20	3.10	−0.85	3.75	−1.50	4.41	−2.15
90	2.00	−0.91	2.36	−1.26	1.35	−0.11	1.72	−0.47	2.06	−0.82	2.45	−1.17
95	1.09	−0.52	1.30	−0.72	0.73	−0.08	0.94	−0.28	1.14	−0.48	1.34	−0.68
100	(0.13)	(−0.13)	(0.16)	(−0.16)	(0.06)	(−0.06)	(0.10)	(−0.10)	(0.13)	(−0.13)	(0.16)	(−0.16)
100	—	0	—	0	—	0	—	0	—	0	—	0
	L.E. rad. 1.58. Slope of radius through end of chord 2/15		L.E. rad. 2.48. Slope of radius through end of chord 2/15		L.E. rad. 0.40. Slope of radius through end of chord 2/20		L.E. rad. 0.89. Slope of radius through end of chord 2/20		L.E. rad. 1.58. Slope of radius through end of chord 2/20		L.E. rad. 2.48. Slope of radius through end of chord 2/20	

Sta.	2418		2421		2506		2509		2512		2515	
	Up'r	L'w'r	Up'r	L'w'r	Up'r	L'w'r	Up'r	L'w'r	Up'r	L'w'r	Up'r	L'w'r
0	—	0	—	0	—	0	—	0	—	0	—	0
1.25	3.28	−2.45	3.87	−2.82	1.08	−0.83	1.57	−1.27	2.09	−1.70	2.63	−2.11
2.5	4.45	−3.44	5.21	−4.02	1.53	−1.09	2.22	−1.72	2.91	−2.33	3.63	−2.94
5.0	6.03	−4.68	7.00	−5.51	2.18	−1.38	3.10	−2.24	4.02	−3.09	4.96	−3.96
7.5	7.17	−5.48	8.29	−6.48	2.67	−1.54	3.75	−2.58	4.83	−3.59	5.91	−4.60
10	8.05	−6.03	9.28	−7.18	3.08	−1.62	4.28	−2.78	5.46	−3.92	6.66	−5.06
15	9.34	−6.74	10.70	−8.05	3.71	−1.65	5.06	−2.98	6.40	−4.30	7.75	−5.83
20	10.15	−7.09	11.59	−8.52	4.16	−1.59	5.60	−3.02	7.03	−4.43	8.48	−5.87
25	10.65	−7.18	12.19	−8.67	4.46	−1.46	5.96	−2.97	7.44	−4.44	8.92	−5.92
30	10.88	−7.12	12.38	−8.62	4.68	−1.33	6.18	−2.84	7.69	−4.33	9.19	−5.84
40	10.71	−6.71	12.18	−8.16	4.82	−0.98	6.27	−2.44	7.72	−3.90	9.16	−5.35
50	9.89	−5.99	11.22	−7.31	4.65	−0.65	5.97	−1.97	7.29	−3.29	8.62	−4.62
60	8.65	−5.04	9.79	−6.17	4.21	−0.36	5.35	−1.50	6.49	−2.63	7.64	−3.76
70	7.02	−3.97	7.94	−4.87	3.52	−0.15	4.44	−1.06	5.35	−1.97	6.28	−2.88
80	5.08	−2.80	5.74	−3.44	2.60	−0.03	3.26	−0.67	3.92	−1.33	4.57	−1.98
90	2.81	−1.53	3.18	−1.88	1.45	−0.00	1.82	−0.36	2.18	−0.72	2.56	−1.07
95	1.55	−0.87	1.78	−1.06	0.79	−0.03	0.99	−0.22	1.19	−0.42	1.41	−0.62
100	(0.19)	(−0.19)	(0.22)	(−0.22)	(0.06)	(−0.06)	(0.10)	(−0.10)	(0.13)	(−0.13)	(0.16)	(−0.16)
100	—	0	—	0	—	0	—	0	—	0	—	0
	L.E. rad. 3.56. Slope of radius through end of chord 2/20		L. E. rad. 4.85. Slope of radius through end of chord 2/20		L.E. rad. 0.40. Slope of radius through end of chord 2/25		L.E. rad. 0.89. Slope of radius through end of chord 2/25		L.E. rad. 1.58. Slope of radius through end of chord 2/25		L.E. rad. 2.48. Slope of radius through end of chord 2/25	

TABLE XXI.—ORDINATES OF AIRFOILS IN TABLE XVI.—(*Continued*)

Sta.	2518		2521		2612		2712		4212		4306	
	Up'r	L'w'r	Up'r	L'w'r	Up'r	L'w'r	Up'r	L'w'r	Up'r	L'w'r	Up'r	L'w'r
0	—	0	—	0	—	0	—	0	—	0	—	0
1.25	3.18	−2.53	3.79	−2.90	2.05	−1.73	2.04	−1.75	3.04	−1.07	1.39	−0.57
2.5	4.33	−3.53	5.06	−4.11	2.86	−2.37	2.82	−2.40	4.13	−1.41	2.05	−0.64
5.0	5.89	−4.79	6.85	−5.61	3.95	−3.17	3.90	−3.23	5.75	−1.63	3.10	−0.54
7.5	7.02	−5.61	8.12	−6.62	4.72	−3.68	4.66	−3.76	6.96	−1.66	3.93	−0.35
10	7.88	−6.20	9.07	−7.33	5.34	−4.03	5.26	−4.12	7.90	−1.61	4.83	−0.12
15	9.12	−6.95	10.47	−8.25	6.25	−4.45	6.13	−4.56	9.15	−1.55	5.72	0.32
20	9.94	−7.31	11.37	−8.72	6.87	−4.61	6.73	−4.75	9.74	−1.74	6.44	0.68
25	10.42	−7.42	11.92	−8.90	7.26	−4.62	7.12	−4.77	9.92	−1.96	6.85	0.89
30	10.68	−7.33	12.19	−8.84	7.51	−4.52	7.36	−4.67	9.94	−2.08	7.00	1.00
40	10.61	−6.79	12.06	−8.24	7.58	−4.03	7.43	−4.18	9.56	−2.05	6.82	1.02
50	9.94	−5.94	11.27	−7.27	7.23	−3.36	7.13	−3.47	8.75	−1.85	6.33	1.03
60	8.78	−4.91	9.93	−6.04	6.56	−2.56	6.52	−2.61	7.59	−1.55	5.56	0.99
70	7.19	−3.80	8.14	−4.70	5.56	−1.77	5.67	−1.67	6.13	−1.21	4.54	0.86
80	5.24	−2.62	5.93	−3.26	4.15	−1.11	4.42	−0.83	4.39	−0.85	3.29	0.65
90	2.92	−1.43	3.28	−1.78	2.34	−0.56	2.57	−0.33	2.41	−0.50	1.79	0.34
95	1.62	−0.82	1.82	−1.01	1.28	−0.33	1.44	−0.19	1.31	−0.31	0.97	0.15
100	(0.19)	(−0.19)	(0.22)	(−0.22)	(0.13)	(−0.13)	(0.13)	(−0.13)	(0.13)	(−0.13)	(0.06)	(−0.06)
100	—	0	—	0	—	0	—	0	—	0	—	0
	L.E. rad. 3.56. Slope of radius through end of chord 2/25		L.E. rad. 4.85. Slope of radius through end of chord 2/25		L.E. rad. 1.58. Slope of radius through end of chord 2/30		L.E. rad. 1.58. Slope of radius through end of chord 2/35		L.E. rad. 1.58. Slope of radius through end of chord 4/10		L.E. rad. 0.40. Slope of eradius throughend of chord 4/15	

Sta.	4309		4312		4315		4318		4321		4406	
	Up'r	L'w'r	Up'r	L'w'r	Up'r	L'w'r	Up'r	L'w'r	Up'r	L'w'r	Up'r	L'w'r
0	—	0	—	0	—	0	—	0	—	0	—	0
1.25	1.98	−0.94	2.64	−1.29	3.32	−1.60	4.07	−1.90	4.84	−2.19	1.25	−0.64
2.5	2.80	−1.21	3.63	−1.75	4.47	−2.26	5.36	−2.74	6.29	−3.18	1.88	−0.79
5.0	4.09	−1.37	5.10	−2.19	6.13	−2.97	7.20	−3.68	8.26	−4.38	2.79	−0.82
7.5	5.05	−1.36	6.22	−2.34	7.37	−3.31	8.56	−4.25	9.75	−5.14	3.53	−0.73
10	5.86	−1.26	7.12	−2.39	8.36	−3.50	9.64	−4.58	10.92	−5.64	4.15	−0.60
15	7.08	−1.01	8.46	−2.31	9.85	−3.62	11.22	−4.92	12.62	−6.19	5.15	−0.25
20	7.88	−0.76	9.34	−2.17	10.80	−3.60	12.25	−5.01	13.72	−6.42	5.90	0.12
25	8.34	−0.60	9.82	−2.07	11.32	−3.55	12.80	−5.04	14.29	−6.50	6.42	0.46
30	8.50	−0.50	10.00	−2.00	11.50	−3.50	13.00	−5.00	14.50	−6.50	6.76	0.74
40	8.29	−0.43	9.75	−1.88	11.18	−3.33	12.64	−4.77	14.09	−6.23	6.90	1.10
50	7.65	−0.29	8.96	−1.61	10.31	−2.93	11.65	−4.24	12.98	−5.56	6.55	1.24
60	6.71	−0.15	7.85	−1.28	9.01	−2.42	10.15	−3.55	11.31	−4.68	5.85	1.27
70	5.46	−0.05	6.39	−0.95	7.31	−1.86	8.24	−2.76	9.18	−3.66	4.85	1.16
80	3.95	0.00	4.62	−0.64	5.29	−1.30	5.95	−1.94	6.64	−2.58	3.56	0.91
90	2.16	−0.02	2.54	−0.38	2.92	−0.74	3.29	−1.08	3.67	−1.43	1.96	0.49
95	1.16	−0.05	1.38	−0.25	1.58	−0.44	1.79	−0.64	2.00	−0.84	1.05	0.24
100	(0.09)	(−0.09)	(0.13)	(−0.13)	(0.16)	(−0.16)	(0.19)	(−0.19)	(0.22)	(−0.22)	(0.06)	(−0.06)
100	—	0	—	0	—	0	—	0	—	0	—	0
	L.E. rad. 0.89. Slope of radius through end of chord 4/15		L.E. rad. 1.58. Slope of radius through end of chord 4/15		L.E. rad. 2.48. Slope of radius through end of chord 4/15		L.E. rad. 3.56. Slope of radius through end of chord 4/15		L.E. rad. 4.85. Slope of radius through end of chord 4/15		L.E. rad. 0.40. Slope of radius through end of chord 4/20	

TABLE XXI.—ORDINATES OF AIRFOILS IN TABLE XVI.—(*Continued*)

Sta.	4409		4412		4415		4418		4421		4506	
	Up'r	L'w'r	Up'r	L'w'r	Up'r	L'w'r	Up'r	L'w'r	Up'r	L'w'r	Up'r	L'w'r
0	—	0	—	0	—	0	—	0	—	0	—	0
1.25	1.81	−1.05	2.44	−1.43	3.07	−1.79	3.76	−2.11	4.45	−2.42	1.21	−0.71
2.5	2.61	−1.37	3.39	−1.95	4.17	−2.48	5.00	−2.99	5.84	−3.48	1.75	−0.88
5.0	3.74	−1.65	4.73	−2.49	5.74	−3.27	6.75	−4.06	7.82	−4.78	2.60	−1.00
7.5	4.64	−1.74	5.76	−2.74	6.91	−3.71	8.06	−4.67	9.24	−5.62	3.25	−0.97
10	5.37	−1.73	6.59	−2.86	7.84	−3.98	9.11	−5.06	10.35	−6.15	3.82	−0.89
15	6.52	−1.55	7.89	−2.88	9.27	−4.18	10.66	−5.49	12.04	−6.75	4.74	−0.64
20	7.33	−1.30	8.80	−2.74	10.25	−4.15	11.72	−5.56	13.17	−6.98	5.45	−0.32
25	7.90	−1.02	9.41	−2.50	10.92	−3.98	12.40	−5.49	13.86	−6.92	5.98	0.02
30	8.25	−0.78	9.76	−2.26	11.25	−3.75	12.76	−5.26	14.27	−6.76	6.36	0.34
40	8.35	−0.35	9.80	−1.80	11.25	−3.25	12.70	−4.70	14.16	−6.16	6.74	0.93
50	7.87	−0.07	9.19	−1.40	10.53	−2.72	11.85	−4.02	13.18	−5.34	6.65	1.35
60	7.00	0.14	8.14	−1.00	9.30	−2.14	10.44	−3.24	11.60	−4.40	6.13	1.56
70	5.76	0.26	6.69	−0.65	7.63	−1.55	8.55	−2.45	9.50	−3.35	5.21	1.53
80	4.21	0.26	4.89	−0.39	5.55	−1.03	6.22	−1.67	6.91	−2.31	3.90	1.25
90	2.33	0.14	2.71	−0.22	3.08	−0.57	3.46	−0.93	3.85	−1.27	2.18	0.72
95	1.26	0.03	1.47	−0.16	1.67	−0.36	1.89	−0.55	2.11	−0.74	1.17	0.35
100	(0.09)	(−0.09)	(0.13)	(−0.13)	(0.16)	(−0.16)	(0.19)	(−0.19)	(0.22)	(−0.22)	(0.06)	(−0.06)
100	—	0	—	0	—	0	—	0	—	0	—	0
	L.E. rad. 0.89. Slope of radius through end of chord 4/20		L.E. rad. 1.58. Slope of radius through end of chord 4/20		L.E. rad. 2.48. Slope of radius through end of chord 4/20		L.E. rad. 3.56. Slope of radius through end of chord 4/20		L.E. rad. 4.85. Slope of radius through end of chord 4/20		L.E. rad. 0.40. Slope of radius through end of chord 4/25	

Sta.	4509		4512		4515		4518		4521		4612	
	Up'r	L'w'r	Up'r	L'w'r	Up'r	L'w'r	Up'r	L'w'r	Up'r	L'w'r	Up'r	L'w'r
0	—	0	—	0	—	0	—	0	—	0	—	0
1.25	1.75	−1.12	2.33	−1.51	2.94	−1.88	3.56	−2.25	4.23	−2.56	2.26	−1.57
2.5	2.47	−1.50	3.22	−2.07	4.00	−2.64	4.79	−3.16	5.60	−3.66	3.13	−2.16
5.0	3.54	−1.84	4.50	−2.67	5.49	−3.48	6.49	−4.27	7.50	−5.05	4.36	−2.81
7.5	4.36	−1.99	5.46	−2.99	6.60	−3.98	7.74	−4.96	8.90	−5.90	5.27	−3.17
10	5.04	−2.05	6.25	−3.18	7.49	−4.30	8.74	−5.41	10.00	−6.50	6.02	−3.40
15	6.12	−1.96	7.46	−3.28	8.85	−4.59	10.25	−5.89	11.63	−7.17	7.17	−3.56
20	6.89	−1.75	8.34	−3.17	9.81	−4.60	11.27	−6.01	12.73	−7.42	8.01	−3.50
25	7.46	−1.47	8.95	−2.95	10.47	−4.43	11.96	−5.91	13.46	−7.38	8.60	−3.31
30	7.85	−1.16	9.37	−2.66	10.88	−4.16	12.37	−5.68	13.88	−7.16	9.01	−3.00
40	8.19	−0.52	9.64	−1.97	11.08	−3.44	12.53	−4.89	13.97	−6.35	9.36	−2.27
50	7.97	0.03	9.29	−1.29	10.62	−2.62	11.94	−3.94	13.27	−5.27	9.18	−1.41
60	7.27	0.42	8.43	−0.70	9.56	−1.85	10.72	−2.98	11.86	−4.12	8.56	−0.56
70	6.12	0.62	7.06	−0.29	7.99	−1.20	8.92	−2.11	9.85	−3.00	7.44	0.10
80	4.56	0.60	5.23	−0.04	5.89	−0.69	6.57	−1.34	7.26	−1.97	5.66	0.40
90	2.56	0.35	2.93	0.00	3.32	−0.35	3.69	−0.71	4.06	−1.−5	3.23	0.31
95	1.38	0.15	1.58	−0.04	1.80	−0.24	2.01	−0.44	2.24	−0.63	1.77	0.14
100	(0.09)	(−0.09)	(0.12)	(−0.12)	(0.16)	(−0.16)	(0.19)	(−0.19)	(0.22)	(−0.22)	(0.12)	−(0.12)
100	—	0	—	0	—	0	—	0	—	0	—	0
	L.E. rad. 0.89. Slope of radius through end of chord 4/25		L.E. rad. 1.58. Slope of radius through end of chord 4/25		L.E. rad. 2.48. Slope of radius through end of chord 4/25		L.E. rad. 3.56. Slope of radius through end of chord 4/25		L.E. rad. 4.85. Slope of radius through end of chord 4/25		L.E. rad. 1.58. Slope of radius through end of chord 4/30	

TABLE XXI.—ORDINATES OF AIRFOILS IN TABLE XVI.—(*Continued*)

Sta.	4712		6212		6306		6309		6312		6315	
	Up'r	L'w'r	Up'r	L'w'r	Up'r	L'w'r	Up'r	L'w'r	Up'r	L'w'r	Up'r	L'w'r
0	—	0	—	0	—	0	—	0	—	0	—	0
1.25	2.21	−1.61	3.70	−0.79	1.63	−0.40	2.32	−0.75	3.05	−1.06	3.38	−1.34
2.5	3.04	−2.22	4.99	−0.94	2.46	−0.34	3.30	−0.88	4.20	−1.38	5.15	−1.84
5.0	4.24	−2.92	6.92	−0.79	3.79	0.05	4.83	−0.76	5.93	−1.56	7.05	−2.27
7.5	5.13	−3.32	8.42	−0.48	4.87	0.50	6.05	−0.50	7.26	−1.47	8.48	−2.39
10	5.84	−3.56	9.56	−0.15	5.80	0.96	7.07	−0.18	8.38	−1.29	9.67	−2.38
15	6.95	−3.79	11.09	0.31	7.26	1.79	8.64	0.46	10.03	−0.83	11.45	−2.13
20	7.74	−3.77	11.74	0.26	8.23	2.45	9.70	1.02	11.14	−0.40	12.60	−1.83
25	8.31	−3.60	11.92	0.03	8.80	2.84	10.29	1.35	11.79	−0.14	13.25	−1.62
30	8.71	−3.33	11.91	−0.10	9.00	3.00	10.50	1.50	12.00	0.00	13.50	−1.50
40	9.06	−2.56	11.44	−0.17	8.78	2.98	10.24	1.53	11.69	0.08	13.15	−1.37
50	8.95	−1.64	10.48	−0.12	8.17	2.86	9.50	1.55	10.84	0.23	12.16	−1.09
60	8.47	−0.65	9.11	−0.05	7.20	2.62	8.35	1.48	9.50	0.35	10.67	−0.77
70	7.67	0.34	7.37	0.01	5.90	2.21	6.83	1.29	7.76	0.39	8.71	−0.50
80	6.21	0.95	5.30	0.02	4.27	1.63	4.94	0.98	5.62	0.34	6.30	−0.30
90	3.73	0.78	2.89	−0.03	2.34	0.86	2.71	0.50	3.08	0.15	3.45	−0.20
95	2.06	0.42	1.55	−0.07	1.24	0.43	1.45	0.23	1.66	0.03	1.87	−0.17
100	(0.12)	(−0.12)	(0.12)	(−0.12)	(0.06)	(−0.06)	(0.09)	(−0.09)	(0.12)	(−0.12)	(0.16)	(−0.16)
100	—	0	—	0	—	0	—	0	—	0	—	0
	L.E. rad. 1.58. Slope of radius through end of chord 4/35		L.E. rad. 1.58. Slope of radius through end of chord 6/10		L.E. rad. 0.40. Slope of radius through end of chord 6/15		L.E. rad. 0.89. Slope of radius through end of chord 6/15		L.E. rad. 1.58. Slope of radius through end of chord 6/15		L.E. rad. 2.48. Slope of radius through end of chord 6/15	

Sta.	6318		6321		6406		6409		6412	
	Up'r	L'w'r	Up'r	L'w'r	Up'r	L'w'r	Up'r	L'w'r	Up'r	L'w'r
0	—	0	—	0	—	0	—	0	—	0
1.25	4.76	−1.57	5.70	−1.79	1.45	−0.52	2.06	−0.88	2.73	−1.23
2.5	6.16	−2.26	7.20	−2.65	2.16	−0.55	2.96	−1.11	3.80	−1.64
5.0	8.19	−2.99	9.38	−3.63	3.32	−0.36	4.30	−1.18	5.36	−1.99
7.5	9.75	−3.30	11.03	−4.15	4.24	−0.06	5.42	−1.08	6.57	−2.05
10	11.00	−3.44	12.35	−4.44	5.06	0.28	6.31	−0.86	7.58	−1.99
15	12.87	−3.40	14.28	−4.64	6.39	0.97	7.78	−0.36	9.18	−1.67
20	14.06	−3.25	15.54	−4.65	7.42	1.61	8.88	0.17	10.34	−1.25
25	14.74	−3.10	16.24	−4.58	8.16	2.16	9.65	0.69	11 14	−0.78
30	15.00	−3.00	16.50	−4.50	8.64	2.62	10.13	1.12	11.65	−0.38
40	14.59	−2.82	16.06	−4.25	8.90	3.10	10.35	1.65	11.80	0.20
50	13.51	−2.41	14.84	−3.71	8.48	3.19	9.81	1.86	11.16	0.55
60	11.84	−1.90	12.99	−3.02	7.64	3.05	8.78	1.92	9.95	0.78
70	9.64	−1.40	10.60	−2.30	6.35	2.66	7.28	1.76	8.23	0.85
80	7.00	−0.95	7.68	−1.60	4.66	2.02	5.34	1.36	6.03	0.73
90	3.84	−0.55	4.22	−0.90	2.58	1.11	2.95	0.74	3.33	0.39
95	2.10	−0.36	2.31	−0.55	1.38	0.55	1.57	0.35	1.79	0.16
100	(0.19)	(−0.19)	(0.22)	(−0.22)	(0.06)	(−0.06)	(0.09)	(−0.09)	(0.12)	(−0.12)
100	—	0	—	0	—	0	—	0	—	0
	L.E. rad. 3.56. Slope of radius through end of chord 6/15		L.E. rad. 4.85. Slope of radius through end of chord 6/15		L.E. rad. 0.40. Slope of radius through end of chord 6/20		L.E. rad. 0.89. Slope of radius through end of chord 6/20		L.E. rad. 1.58. Slope of radius through end of chord 6/20	

TABLE XXI.—ORDINATES OF AIRFOILS IN TABLE XVI.—(*Continued*)

Sta.	6415		6418		6421		6506		6509	
	Up'r	L'w'r	Up'r	L'w'r	Up'r	L'w'r	Up'r	L'w'r	Up'r	L'w'r
0	—	0	—	0	—	0	—	0	—	0
1.25	3.45	−1.53	4.26	−1.82	5.13	−2.08	1.36	−0.60	1.93	−0.99
2.5	4.67	−2.13	5.62	−2.59	6.60	−3.04	2.00	−0.70	2.75	−1.27
5.0	6.44	−2.75	7.53	−3.46	8.65	−4.16	3.01	−0.62	3.99	−1.45
7.5	7.76	−3.00	8.98	−3.91	10.24	−4.81	3.85	−0.43	4.97	−1.45
10	8.88	−3.11	10.16	−4.15	11.52	−5.18	4.58	−0.19	5.82	−1.34
15	10.58	−2.97	12.02	−4.26	13.44	−5.52	5.78	0.37	7.18	−0.96
20	11.81	−2.67	13.32	−4.07	14.79	−5.49	6.74	0.95	8.22	−0.49
25	12.64	−2.29	14.17	−3.75	15.65	−5.23	7.49	1.51	8.97	0.02
30	13.15	−1.91	14.64	−3.40	16.15	−4.91	8.06	2.03	9.56	0.51
40	13.25	−1.25	14.70	−2.70	16.16	−4.16	8.66	2.84	10.11	1.39
50	12.46	−0.76	13.80	−2.08	15.14	−3.40	8.65	3.35	9.97	2.03
60	11.10	−0.34	12.24	−1.47	13.44	−2.59	8.06	3.48	9.20	2.34
70	9.16	−0.04	10.11	−0.94	11.06	−1.83	6.89	3.21	7.81	2.30
80	6.70	0.09	7.40	−0.54	8.08	−1.17	5.17	2.52	5.85	1.87
90	3.72	0.04	4.12	−0.31	4.51	−0.65	2.90	1.43	3.29	1.07
95	2.01	−0.05	2.24	−0.23	2.46	−0.42	1.57	0.73	1.78	0.53
100	(0.16)	(−0.16)	(0.19)	(−0.19)	(0.22)	(−0.22)	(0.06)	(−0.06)	(0.09)	(−0.09)
100	—	0	—	0	—	0	—	0	—	0
	L.E. rad. 2.48. Slope of radius through end of chord 6/20		L.E. rad. 3.56. Slope of radius through end of chord 6/20		L.E. rad. 4.85. Slope of radius through end of chord 6/20		L.E. rad. 0.40. Slope of radius through end of chord 6/25		L.E. rad. 0.89. Slope of radius through end of chord 6/25	

Sta.	6512		6515		6518		6521		6612	
	Up'r	L'w'r	Up'r	L'w'r	Up'r	L'w'r	Up'r	L'w'r	Up'r	L'w'r
0	—	0	—	0	—	0	—	0	—	0
1.25	2.57	−1.34	3.26	−1.68	3.98	−1.95	4.75	−2.22	2.45	−1.43
2.5	3.56	−1.82	4.40	−2.33	5.27	−2.83	6.17	−3.26	3.41	−1.94
5.0	5.02	−2.26	6.04	−3.04	7.10	−3.78	8.20	−4.50	4.78	−2.47
7.5	6.13	−2.43	7.30	−3.39	8.50	−4.33	9.70	−5.24	5.84	−2.70
10	7.06	−2.45	8.34	−3.55	9.62	−4.64	10.93	−5.71	6.70	−2.78
15	8.57	−2.27	9.97	−3.56	11.37	−4.85	12.79	−6.13	8.11	−2.69
20	9.89	−1.91	11.14	−3.33	12.63	−4.74	14.10	−6.14	9.17	−2.41
25	10.50	−1.47	12.00	−2.95	13.52	−4.44	15.05	−5.92	9.95	−2.00
30	11.07	−0.98	12.59	−2.49	14.10	−4.02	15.60	−5.53	10.51	−1.51
40	11.56	−0.06	13.00	−1.52	14.45	−2 98	15.89	−4.44	11.14	−0.49
50	11.29	0.71	12.62	−0.62	13.94	−1.94	15.27	−3.27	11.13	0.53
60	10.35	1.21	11.50	0.08	12.66	−1.05	13.81	−2.20	10.56	1.44
70	8.76	1.39	9.69	0.49	10.63	−0.41	11.57	−1.30	9.33	1.98
80	6.54	1.24	7.22	0.60	7.91	−0.05	8.59	−0.68	7.19	1.90
90	3.68	0.72	4.05	0.36	4.45	0.02	4.85	−0.32	4.16	1.19
95	2.00	0.33	2.22	0.14	2.45	−0.05	2.67	−0.23	2.28	0.60
100	(0.12)	(−0.12)	(0.15)	(−0.15)	(0.18)	(−0.18)	(0.22)	(−0.22)	(0.12)	(−0.12)
100	—	0	—	0	—	0	—	0	—	0
	L.E. rad. 1.58. Slope of radius through end of chord 6/25		L.E. rad. 2.48. Slope of radius through end of chord 6/25		L.E. rad. 3.56. Slope of radius through end of chord 6/25		L.E. rad. 4.85. Slope of radius through end of chord 6/25		L.E. rad. 1.58. Slope of radius through end of chord 6/30	

TABLE XXI.—ORDINATES OF AIRFOILS IN TABLE XVI.—(*Concluded*)

Sta.	6712		0006T		0006B		0012T		0012B	
	Up'r	L'w'r	Up'r	L'w'r	Up'r	L'w'r	Up'r	L'w'r	Up'r	L'w'r
0	—	0	0	0	0	0	0	0	0	0
1.25	2.36	−1.50	0.62	−0.62	1.42	−1.42	1.25	−1.25	2.84	−2.84
2.5	3.28	−2.03	0.94	−0.94	1.85	−1.85	1.88	−1.88	3.69	−3.69
5.0	4.60	−2.59	1.43	−1.43	2.30	−2.30	2.86	−2.86	4.59	−4.59
7.5	5.61	−2.89	1.80	−1.80	2.54	−2.54	3.61	−3.61	5.08	−5.08
10	6.44	−3.02	2.11	−2.11	2.69	−2.69	4.21	−4.21	5.38	−5.38
15	7.75	−3.01	2.55	−2.55	2.87	−2.87	5.09	−5.09	5.74	−5.74
20	8.75	−2.80	2.82	−2.82	2.96	−2.96	5.64	−5.64	5.92	−5.92
25	9.51	−2.43	2.96	−2.96	3.00	−3.00	5.92	−5.92	6.00	−6.00
30	10.07	−1.99	3.00	−3.00	3.00	−3.00	6.00	−6.00	6.00	−6.00
40	10.70	−0.92	2.87	−2.87	2.96	−2.96	5.75	−5.75	5.93	−5.93
50	10.80	0.19	2.56	−2.56	2.79	−2.79	5.11	−5.11	5.59	−5.59
60	10.44	1.31	2.15	−2.15	2.49	−2.49	4.29	−4.29	4.98	−4.98
70	9.67	2.34	1.70	−1.70	2.04	−2.04	3.39	−3.39	4.07	−4.07
80	8.02	2.73	1.22	−1.22	1.46	−1.46	2.43	−2.43	2.91	−2.91
90	4.88	1.88	0.68	−0.68	0.77	−0.77	1.37	−1.37	1.55	−1.55
95	2.71	1.02	0.39	−0.39	0.41	−0.41	0.78	−0.78	0.83	−0.83
100	(0.12)	(−0.12)	(0.06)	(−0.06)	(0.06)	(−0.06)	(0.12)	(−0.12)	(0.12)	(−0.12)
100	—	0	0	0	0	0	0	0	0	0
	L.E. rad. 1.58. Slope of radius through end of chord 6/35		L.E. rad. 0.10		L.E. rad. 1.19		L.E. rad. 0.40		L.E. rad. 3.80	

TABLE XXII.—ORDINATES OF AIRFOILS IN TABLES XVI, XVII, AND XVIII

Sta.	0018T		0018B		2R112		2R212		0012F		0012F	
	Up'r	L'w'r	Up'r	L'w'r	Up'r	L'w'r	Up'r	L'w'r	Up'r	L'w'r	Up'r	L'w'r
0	0	0	0	0	—	0	—	0	0	0	0	0
1.25	1.87	−1.87	4.27	−4.27	2.24	−1.57	2.30	−1.52	1.89	−1.89	1.89	−1.89
2.5	2.83	−2.83	5.54	−5.54	3.10	−2.17	3.16	−2.10	2.61	−2.61	2.61	−2.61
5.0	4.28	−4.28	6.89	−6.89	4.29	−2.86	4.38	−2.76	3.55	−3.55	3.55	−3.55
7.5	5.41	−5.41	7.62	−7.62	5.16	−3.28	5.29	−3.17	4.20	−4.20	4.20	−4.20
10	6.32	−6.32	8.07	−8.07	5.84	−3.57	5.98	−3.42	4.68	−4.68	4.68	−4.68
15	7.64	−7.64	8.61	−8.61	6.82	−3.88	6.97	−3.74	5.35	−5.35	5.35	−5.35
20	8.46	−8.46	8.87	−8.87	7.47	−4.02	7.58	−3.90	5.74	−5.74	5.74	−5.74
25	8.88	−8.88	9.00	−9.00	7.82	−4.06	7.91	−3.97	5.94	−5.94	5.94	−5.94
30	9.00	−9.00	9.00	−9.00	7.98	−4.02	8.00	−4.00	6.00	−6.00	6.00	−6.00
40	8.62	−8.62	8.89	−8.89	7.76	−3.84	7.63	−3.98	5.74	−5.74	5.74	−5.74
50	7.67	−7.67	8.38	−8.38	7.03	−3.55	6.73	−3.87	4.31	−4.31	4.31	−4.31
60	6.44	−6.44	7.47	−7.47	5.94	−3.18	5.49	−3.66	1.96	−1.96	1.96	−1.96
70	5.09	−5.09	6.11	−6.11	4.61	−2.72	4.06	−3.27	0.50	−0.50	0.50	−0.50
80	3.65	−3.65	4.37	−4.37	3.16	−2.10	2.61	−2.64	0.50	−0.50	−0.41	−1.43
90	2.05	−2.05	2.32	−2.32	1.63	−1.26	1.26	−1.63	0.50	−0.50	−3.23	−4.30
95	1.17	−1.17	1.24	−1.24	0.87	−0.74	0.66	−0.95	0.50	−0.50	−5.45	−6.57
96.27	—	—	—	—	—	—	—	—	—	—	—	(−8.41)
98.79	—	—	—	—	—	—	—	—	—	—	(−7.55)	
100	(0.18)	(−0.18)	(0.18)	(−0.18)	(0.13)	(−0.13)	(0.13)	(−0.13)	(0.50)	−(0.50)		
100	0	0	0	0	—	0	0	—	0	0		
	L.E. rad. 0.89		L.E. rad. 7.15		L.E. rad. 1.58. Slope of radius through end of chord 0.131		L.E. rad. 1.58. Slope of radius through end of chord 0.153		L.E. rad. 1.58			

Sta.	103		103A		106		106R	
	Up'r	L'w'r	Up'r	L'w'r	Up'r	L'w'r	Up'r	L'w'r
0	3.56	3.56	2.92	2.92	2.98	2.98	2.98	2.98
1.25	6.10	2.20	5.00	1.80	5.26	1.54	5.26	1.54
2.5	7.17	1.73	5.87	1.42	6.14	1.04	6.14	1.04
5.0	8.56	1.22	7.01	1.00	7.54	0.42	7.54	0.42
7.5	9.55	0.88	7.82	0.72	8.56	0.04	8.56	0.04
10	10.35	0.64	8.48	0.52	9.44	−0.28	9.44	−0.28
15	11.53	0.32	9.44	0.26	10.62	−0.64	10.62	−0.64
20	12.28	0.15	10.00	0.12	11.34	−0.90	11.34	−0.90
30	12.70	0.02	10.40	0.02	11.88	−1.18	11.88	−1.18
40	12.42	0.00	10.17	0.00	11.54	−1.28	11.62	−1.20
50	11.56	0.02	9.47	0.02	10.54	−1.30	10.70	−1.14
60	10.21	0.11	8.36	0.08	9.08	−1.22	9.35	−0.95
70	8.38	0.25	6.86	0.17	7.18	−0.98	7.66	−0.50
80	6.26	0.46	5.13	0.30	4.96	−0.72	5.90	0.22
90	3.84	0.71	3.18	0.45	2.54	−0.42	4.23	1.27
95	2.50	0.85	2.14	0.53	1.29	−0.23	3.48	1.96
100	1.11	1.00	0.87	0.87	0.04	−0.04	2.84	2.76
	L.E. rad. 1.25 T.E. rad. 0.05		L.E. rad. 0.97 T.E. rad. 0.25		L.E. rad. 0.70		L.E. rad. 0.70	

TABLE XXII.—ORDINATES OF AIRFOILS IN TABLES XVI, XVII, AND XVIII.—(*Continued*)

Sta.	111		112	
	Up'r	L'w'r	Up'r	L'w'r
0	0	0	0	0
1.25	2.226	−1.108	2.287	−1.047
2.5	3.083	−1.527	3.180	−1.430
5.0	4.327	−2.044	4.512	−1.858
7.5	5.288	−2.322	5.524	−2.086
10	6.064	−2.522	6.329	−2.257
15	7.163	−2.780	7.431	−2.491
20	7.901	−2.879	8.137	−2.661
25	8.378	−2.919	8.530	−2.782
30	8.608	−2.892	8.637	−2.863
35	8.632	−2.850	8.538	−2.926
40	8.479	−2.800	8.311	−2.949
45	8.168	−2.725	7.972	−2.938
50	7.733	−2.660	7.508	−2.888
55	7.189	−2.563	6.948	−2.804
60	6.555	−2.449	6.318	−2.686
65	5.822	−2.302	6.603	−2.521
70	5.044	−2.132	4.846	−2.330
75	4.209	−1.933	4.049	−2.093
80	3.330	−1.649	3.214	−1.766
85	2.464	−1.331	2.388	−1.406
90	1.618	−0.950	1.574	−0.994
95	0.786	−0.502	0.769	−0.519
100	0	0	0	0
	L.E. rad.		L.E. rad.	
	2.5	0.7	2.5	0.7

Sta.	GS-M	
	Up'r	L'w'r
0	5.58	5.58
0.25	7.03	4.42
0.50	7.56	3.99
0.75	7.98	3.68
1.00	8.31	3.42
1.25	8.61	3.18
2.5	9.73	2.19
5.0	11.30	1.15
7.5	12.60	0.50
10	13.62	0.18
15	15.29	0.00
20	16.25	0.26
25	16.63	0.58
30	16.72	0.89
40	16.10	1.43
50	14.51	1.75
60	12.18	1.80
70	9.42	1.64
80	6.44	1.23
90	3.37	0.65
95	1.77	0.31
100	0.09	0.09
	L.E. rad. 2.77 T.E. rad. 0.09	

Sta.	GS-1		27-A	
	Up'r	L'w'r	Up'r	L'w'r
0	5.00	5.00	5.00	5.00
1.25	7.46	2.83	7.57	2.70
2.5	8.45	2.06	9.10	2.03
5.0	9.79	1.20	11.20	1.20
7.5	10.81	0.69	12.73	0.65
10	11.66	0.38	14.00	0.30
15	12.92	0.08	15.96	0.00
20	13.68	0.00	17.34	0.30
30	14.15	0.25	18.00	1.80
40	13.59	0.66	17.34	3.00
50	12.30	0.97	16.00	3.80
60	10.47	1.11	14.00	4.40
70	8.29	1.05	11.20	4.50
80	5.76	0.83	8.00	3.80
90	2.98	0.49	4.44	2.30
95	1.49	0.26	2.33	1.15
100	0	0	0.12	0.00
	L.E. rad. 2.20		L.E. rad. 2.00	

Sta.	34		27		35-A		35-B		C 62		C 72	
	Up'r	L'w'r	Up'r	L'w'r	Up'r	L'w'r	Up'r	L'w'r	Up'r	L'w'r	Up'r	L'w'r
0	0	0	1.77	1.77	4.33	4.33	2.76	2.76	0	0	3.49	3.49
1.25	1.98	−1.62	3.80	0.50	8.09	1.62	5.15	1.03	—	—	5.55	1.92
2.5	2.82	−2.14	5.07	0.36	9.54	1.00	6.11	0.63	1.88	−1.08	6.51	1.47
5.0	4.11	−2.81	6.94	0.19	11.81	0.46	7.52	0.28	2.96	−1.56	7.89	0.93
7.5	—	—	8.22	0.10	13.58	0.22	8.65	0.14	3.74	−1.80	8.85	0.64
10	5.83	−3.53	9.19	0.02	14.85	0.10	9.45	0.07	4.28	−1.91	9.60	0.43
15	6.97	−3.91	10.50	0.10	16.60	0.00	10.56	0.00	5.08	−2.01	10.69	0.16
20	7.72	−4.16	11.37	0.36	17.73	0.08	11.28	0.05	5.57	−2.12	11.36	0.03
25	8.14	−4.26										
30	8.32	−4.32	11.97	0.93	18.46	0.24	11.76	0.15	5.93	−2.11	11.73	0.00
40	8.08	−4.32	11.68	1.14	17.89	0.40	11.42	0.28	5.83	−2.00	11.41	0.21
50	7.21	−4.11	10.86	0.75	16.21	0.58	10.33	0.39	5.34	−1.84	10.53	0.59
60	5.87	−3.68	9.54	0.28	13.83	0.66	8.81	0.45	4.72	−1.60	9.15	0.85
70	4.31	−3.09	8.08	0.06	11.11	0.60	7.08	0.42	3.88	−1.24	7.36	0.91
80	2.70	−2.30	6.10	0.01	7.88	0.50	5.02	0.35	2.87	−0.84	5.23	0.72
90	1.26	−1.34	3.69	0.12	4.31	0.32	2.72	0.20	1.68	−0.41	2.80	0.40
95	0.64	−0.73	2.26	0.33	2.39	0.19	1.50	0.12	—	—	1.52	0.21
100	0	0	0.67	0.65	0.43	0	0.25	0	0.05	−0.05	0.10	0
	L.E. rad. 1.29 T.E. rad. 0.13										L.E. rad. 1.40	

TABLE XXII.—ORDINATES OF AIRFOILS IN TABLES XVI, XVII, AND XVIII.—(*Continued*)

Sta.	C 80	
	Up'r	L'w'r
0	0	0
1	1.18	−0.81
3	2.54	−1.36
5	3.48	−1.71
7	4.13	−1.97
10	4.83	−2.25
15	5.40	−2.51
20	5.69	−2.71
25	5.73	−2.85
30	5.69	−2.85
40	5.31	−2.66
50	4.69	−2.27
60	3.90	−1.77
70	3.00	−1.21
80	2.00	−0.72
90	1.00	−0.38
95	0.51	−0.21
100	0.05	−0.05
	L.E. rad. 0.5	

Sta.	N 22		N 60		N 60R		N 68		N 69	
	Up'r	L'w'r	Up'r	L'w'r	Up'r	L'w'r	Up'r	L'w'r	Up'r	L'w'r
0	3.37	3.37	3.40	3.40	3.40	3.40	0	0	0	0
0.25	—	—	—	—	—	—	0.50	−0.50	0.47	−0.47
0.50	—	—	—	—	—	—	0.72	−0.72	0.72	−0.72
0.75	—	—	—	—	—	—	0.89	−0.89	0.90	−0.90
1.00	—	—	—	—	—	—	1.02	−1.02	1.06	−1.06
1.25	5.58	1.70	5.60	1.91	5.60	1.91	1.14	−1.14	1.20	−1.20
2.5	6.66	1.15	6.76	1.46	6.76	1.46	1.56	−1.56	1.73	−1.73
5.0	8.25	0.62	8.24	0.96	8.24	0.96	2.18	−2.18	2.50	−2.50
7.5	9.33	0.32	9.33	0.62	9.33	0.62	2.61	−2.61	3.07	−3.07
10	10.13	0.16	10.14	0.40	10.14	0.40	2.97	−2.97	3.53	−3.53
15	11.28	0.03	11.32	0.15	11.32	0.15	3.45	−3.45	4.23	−4.23
20	12.01	0.00	11.98	0.04	11.98	0.04	3.75	−3.75	4.79	−4.79
30	12.42	0.05	12.41	0.04	12.41	0.04	4.00	−4.00	5.32	−5.32
40	12.01	0.15	12.03	0.22	11.95	0.14	3.93	−3.93	5.47	−5.47
50	11.04	0.24	11.06	0.48	10.79	0.21	3.63	−3.63	5.20	−5.20
60	9.57	0.30	9.55	0.71	9.18	0.34	3.16	−3.16	4.57	−4.57
70	7.68	0.32	7.66	0.78	7.42	0.54	2.55	−2.55	3.67	−3.67
80	5.51	0.24	5.50	0.64	5.75	0.89	1.80	−1.80	2.62	−2.62
90	3.06	0.12	3.04	0.37	4.28	1.61	1.00	−1.00	1.45	−1.45
95	1.73	0.05	1.72	0.19	3.66	2.13	0.57	−0.57	0.80	−0.80
100	0.40	0	0.40	0	3.20	2.80	0	0	0	0
			L.E. rad. 1.27		L.E. rad. 1.27		L.E. rad. 0.45 T.E. rad. 0.13		L.E. rad. 0.35 T.E. rad. 0.13	

Sta.	N 71		N 75		N 76		N 80		N 81		387	
	Up'r	L'w'r	Up'r	L'w'r	Up'r	L'w'r	Up'r	L'w'r	Up'r	L'w'r	Up'r	L'w'r
−0.022	—	—	—	—	—	—	—	—	0.24	0.24		
−0.02	—	—	—	—	0.21	0.21						
−0.013	—	—	0.17	0.17	—	—	0.17	0.17				
0	0.62	0.62	0.34	0	0.42	0	0.33	0	0.48	0	3.20	3.20
0.125	1.22	0.05	0.74	−0.37	0.80	−0.34	0.74	−0.38	0.90	−0.38		
0.25	1.50	−0.12	0.97	−0.56	1.03	−0.63	0.98	−0.56	1.14	−0.58		
0.50	1.88	−0.36	1.31	−0.83	1.38	−0.78	1.31	−0.83	1.51	−0.86		
0.75	2.16	−0.55	1.58	−1.03	1.65	−0.97	1.58	−1.03	1.81	−1.07		
1.00	2.40	−0.70	1.81	−1.19	1.89	−1.12	1.81	−1.19	2.06	−1.25		
1.25	2.62	−0.82	2.01	−1.32	2.11	−1.25	2.02	−1.33	2.28	−1.39	6.25	1.50
2.5	3.48	−1.25	2.83	−1.82	2.98	−1.70	2.84	−1.83	3.18	−1.92	7.65	1.05
5.0	4.60	−1.82	4.01	−2.38	4.25	−2.19	4.03	−2.38	4.48	−2.50	9.50	0.55
7.5	5.41	−2.22	4.92	−2.73	5.22	−2.46	4.94	−2.73	5.45	−2.85	10.85	0.25
10	6.06	−2.55	5.65	−2.96	6.01	−2.64	5.68	−2.97	6.20	−3.07	11.95	0.10
15	7.00	−2.99	6.76	−3.23	7.20	−2.80	6.78	−3.24	7.27	−3.33	13.40	0.00
20	7.61	−3.24	7.49	−3.36	8.01	−2.86	7.51	−3.37	7.88	−3.43	14.40	0.00
25	7.95	−3.41	7.92	−3.43	8.47	−2.87	7.92	−3.45	8.07	−3.47		
30	8.06	−3.48	8.05	−3.45	8.63	−2.87	8.07	−3.47	7.99	−3.40	15.05	0.20
40	7.72	−3.35	7.86	−3.36	8.42	−2.84	7.75	−3.25	7.53	−3.10	14.60	0.40
50	6.94	−2.99	7.40	−3.17	7.81	−2.77	7.09	−2.84	6.79	−2.70	13.35	0.45
60	5.89	−2.54	6.60	−2.83	6.79	−2.64	6.13	−2.34	5.83	−2.22	11.35	0.50
70	4.60	−1.98	5.47	−2.35	5.37	−2.46	4.89	−1.78	4.62	−1.67	8.90	0.45
80	3.19	−1.38	4.01	−1.73	3.69	−2.05	3.47	−1.21	3.25	−1.12	6.15	0.30
90	1.69	−0.72	2.23	−0.98	1.97	−1.23	1.82	−0.58	1.72	−0.57	3.25	0.15
95	—	—	—	—	—	—	—	—	—	—	1.75	0.05
100	0	0	0	0	0	0	0	0	0	0	0.40	0
			T.E. rad. 0.10		T.E. rad. 0.10		T.E. rad. 0.05		T.E. rad. 0.10			

TABLE XXII.—ORDINATES OF AIRFOILS IN TABLES XVI, XVII, AND XVIII.—(*Continued*)

Sta.	398		398A		398B		398R		413		420	
	Up'r	L'w'r	Up'r	L'w'r	Up'r	L'w'r	Up'r	L'w'r	Up'r	L'w'r	Up'r	L'w'r
0	3.74	3.74	3.46	3.46	3.20	3.20	3.74	3.74	5.93	5.93	8.05	8.05
1.25	6.20	1.89	5.00	2.50	4.44	2.60	6.20	1.89	8.89	3.23	10.75	5.25
2.5	7.40	1.28	6.43	1.73	5.64	2.04	7.40	1.28	10.24	2.32	12.20	4.40
5.0	9.17	0.69	8.48	0.84	7.77	1.09	9.17	0.69	11.75	1.56	13.95	3.30
7.5	10.37	0.35	9.87	0.46	9.33	0.56	10.37	0.35	12.94	0.95	15.15	2.50
10	11.25	0.18	10.85	0.24	10.43	0.29	11.25	0.18	13.91	0.49	16.10	1.85
15	12.53	0.03	12.23	0.06	11.94	0.07	12.53	0.03	15.31	0.09	17.50	1.00
20	13.34	0.00	13.09	0.00	12.87	0.00	13.34	0.00	16.12	0.00	18.30	0.40
30	13.80	0.05	13.66	0.04	13.51	0.03	13.80	0.05	16.63	0.18	18.75	0.00
40	13.34	0.17	13.25	0.15	13.17	0.15	13.30	0.13	15.85	0.59	17.90	0.10
50	12.27	0.27	12.23	0.27	12.17	0.26	12.08	0.08	14.15	0.97	16.30	0.35
60	10.63	0.33	10.62	0.32	10.57	0.32	10.39	0.09	11.85	1.35	13.90	0.55
70	8.53	0.35	8.51	0.36	8.49	0.34	8.42	0.24	9.22	1.40	10.95	0.75
80	6.12	0.27	6.13	0.28	6.09	0.27	6.50	0.65	6.11	1.34	7.45	0.65
90	3.40	0.13	2.40	0.12	3.37	0.12	4.77	1.50	3.05	0.94	3.70	0.55
95	1.92	0.06	1.91	0.06	1.91	0.06	4.02	2.16	1.56	0.54	1.85	0.40
100	0.40	0	0.40	0	0.40	0	3.40	3.00	0.16	0	0.10	0

Sta.	429AG		429J		436		532		S-Y		Y-B	
	Up'r	L'w'r	Up'r	L'w'r	Up'r	L'w'r	Up'r	L'w'r	Up'r	L'w'r	Up'r	L'w'r
0	0	0	0	0	2.66	2.66	2.45	2.45	3.50	3.50	3.50	3.50
1.25	1.71	−1.71	1.97	−1.97	4.53	1.21	5.81	1.15	5.45	1.93	4.29	2.83
2.5	2.44	−2.44	2.74	−2.74	5.54	0.79	7.05	0.80	6.50	1.47	5.11	2.23
5.0	3.43	−3.43	3.73	−3.73	7.00	0.37	8.55	0.50	7.90	0.93	6.76	1.28
7.5	4.10	−4.10	4.39	−4.39	8.11	0.15	9.65	0.30	8.85	0.63	8.02	0.81
10	4.59	−4.59	4.87	−4.87	8.98	0.05	10.55	0.15	9.60	0.42	8.92	0.57
15	5.19	−5.19	5.49	−5.49	10.16	0	11.60	0.00	10.68	0.15	10.14	0.14
20	5.50	−5.50	5.80	−5.80	10.82	0	12.25	0.00	11.36	0.03	11.00	0.03
25	5.60	−5.60	5.89	−5.89								
30	5.57	−5.57	5.83	−5.83	11.08	0	12.75	0.25	11.70	0	11.46	0
40	5.22	−5.22	5.36	−5.36	10.55	0	12.05	0.65	11.40	0	11.24	0
50	4.45	−4.45	4.56	−4.56	9.60	0	10.70	1.05	10.53	0	10.42	0
60	3.46	−3.46	3.58	−3.58	8.28	0	9.00	1.35	9.15	0	9.09	0
70	2.45	−2.45	2.52	−2.52	6.60	0	7.10	1.50	7.35	0	7.32	0
80	1.58	−1.58	1.46	−1.46	4.70	0	4.90	1.35	5.22	0	5.21	0
90	0.89	−0.89	0.55	−0.55	2.64	0	2.60	0.80	2.80	0	2.81	0
95	0.60	−0.60	0.20	−0.20	1.54	0	1.40	0.45	1.49	0	1.47	0
100	0	0	0	0	0.43	0	0.20	0	0.12	0	0.12	0
	L.E. rad. 1.40		L.E. rad. 1.61						L.E. rad. 1.50			

TABLE XXII.—ORDINATES OF AIRFOILS IN TABLES XVI, XVII, AND XVIII.—(*Continued*)

Sta.	YM-15		M-18		CY-6		CY-8		CY-10		CY-14	
	Up'r	L'w'r	Up'r	L'wr'	Up'r	L'w'r	Up'r	L'w'r	Up'r	L'w'r	Up'r	L'w'r
0	3.50	3.50	3.50	3.50	1.79	1.79	2.39	2.39	2.99	2.99	4.19	4.19
1.25	5.95	1.43	6.40	0.98	2.80	0.99	3.73	1.32	4.66	1.65	6.52	2.31
2.5	7.21	0.76	7.86	0.11	3.33	0.75	4.44	1.00	5.56	1.26	7.78	1.76
5.0	8.88	−0.05	9.78	−0.94	4.05	0.48	5.40	0.64	6.75	0.80	9.45	1.11
7.5	10.01	−0.53	11.06	−1.58	4.54	0.32	6.05	0.43	7.56	0.54	10.59	0.75
10	10.89	−0.87	12.07	−2.05	4.92	0.22	6.56	0.29	8.20	0.36	11.48	0.50
15	12.17	−1.34	13.52	−2.69	5.48	0.08	7.31	0.10	9.14	0.13	12.79	0.18
20	12.96	−1.56	14.41	−3.02	5.82	0.02	7.77	0.02	9.72	0.03	13.60	0.04
30	13.35	−1.65	14.85	−3.15	6.00	0	8.00	0	10.00	0	14.00	0
40	13.01	−1.61	14.47	−3.07	5.85	0	7.80	0	9.75	0	13.64	0
50	12.00	−1.48	13.35	−2.83	5.40	0	7.20	0	9.00	0	12.58	0
60	10.44	−1.29	11.61	−2.46	4.69	0	6.25	0	7.82	0	10.95	0
70	8.39	−1.04	9.33	−1.98	3.77	0	5.03	0	6.28	0	8.80	0
80	5.95	−0.74	6.62	−1.40	2.68	0	3.57	0	4.46	0	6.25	0
90	3.20	−0.40	3.56	−0.75	1.44	0	1.91	0	2.39	0	3.35	0
95	1.70	−0.20	1.90	−0.40	0.76	0	1.02	0	1.27	0	1.78	0
100	0.14	−0.02	0.15	−0.03	0.06	0	0.08	0	0.10	0	0.14	0

Sta.	CY-18		CY-22		CYH		M6		NACA 15		NACA 16	
	Up'r	L'w'r	Up'r	L'w'r	Up'r	L'w'r	Up'r	L'w'r	Up'r	L'w'r	Up'r	L'w'r
0	5.38	5.38	6.58	6.58	3.50	3.50	0	0	—	0	—	0
1.25	8.38	2.97	10.25	3.63	5.45	1.93	1.97	−1.76	1.45	−1.06	1.80	−1.36
2.5	10.00	2.26	12.22	2.77	6.50	1.47	2.81	−2.20	2.22	−1.57	2.59	−1.92
5.0	12.15	1.43	14.85	1.75	7.90	0.93	4.03	−2.73	3.42	−2.31	3.77	−2.66
7.5	13.61	0.97	16.63	1.19	8.85	0.63	4.94	−3.03	4.38	−2.86	4.67	−3.16
10	14.76	0.65	18.05	0.79	9.60	0.42	5.71	−3.24	5.16	−3.28	5.40	−3.52
15	16.45	0.23	20.10	0.28	10.68	0.15	6.82	−3.47	6.36	−3.84	6.49	−3.96
20	17.47	0.05	21.37	0.06	11.36	0.03	7.55	−3.62	7.16	−4.12	7.20	−4.17
25	—	—	—	—	—	—	8.01	−3.71	7.65	−4.20	7.66	−4.20
30	18.00	0	22.00	0	11.70	0.00	8.22	−3.79	7.88	−4.12	7.88	−4.12
40	17.53	0	21.44	0	11.40	0.00	8.05	−3.90	7.80	−3.80	7.80	−3.80
50	16.19	0	19.78	0	10.52	0.00	7.26	−3.94	7.24	−3.34	7.24	−3.34
60	14.07	0	17.20	0	9.15	0.00	6.03	−3.82	6.36	−2.76	6.36	−2.76
70	11.30	0	13.83	0	7.41	0.06	4.58	−3.48	5.18	−2.14	5.18	−2.14
80	8.03	0	9.83	0	5.62	0.38	3.06	−2.83	3.76	−1.50	3.75	−1.50
90	4.31	0	5.27	0	3.84	1.02	1.55	−1.77	2.08	−0.82	2.08	−0.82
95	2.29	0	2.81	0	2.93	1.40	0.88	−1.08	1.14	−0.48	1.14	−0.48
100	0.18	0	0.23	0	2.05	1.85	0.26	−0.26	(0.13)	(−0.13)	(0.13)	(−0.13)
100	—	—	—	—	—	—	—	—	—	0	—	0
					L.E. rad. 1.50				L.E. rad. 0.40. Slope of radius through end of chord 0.10		L.E. rad. 0.80. Slope of radius through end of chord 0.10	

TABLE XXII.—ORDINATES OF AIRFOILS IN TABLES XVI, XVII, AND XVIII.—(*Concluded*)

Sta.	NACA 17		NACA 18		NACA 19		NACA 20		NACA 21		NACA 23	
	Up'r	L'w'r	Up'r	L'w'r	Up'r	L'w'r	Up'r	L'w'r	Up'r	L'w'r	Up'r	L'w'r
0	—	−1.00	—	−1.00	—	0	0	0	—	0	—	0
1.25	0.77	−1.83	1.14	−2.08	1.10	−0.76	0.75	−0.46	1.97	−1.76	1.81	−1.23
2.5	1.68	−2.17	2.09	−2.50	1.82	−1.21	1.45	−0.87	2.81	−2.20	2.58	−1.66
5.0	3.13	−2.66	3.50	−3.00	3.04	−1.97	2.71	−1.62	4.03	−2.73	3.59	−2.14
7.5	4.24	−3.04	4.54	−3.35	4.07	−2.57	3.78	−2.27	4.94	−3.03	4.36	−2.41
10	5.11	−3.35	5.35	−3.60	4.94	−3.05	4.70	−2.80	5.71	−3.24	4.93	−2.54
15	6.36	−3.84	6.49	−3.96	6.23	−3.70	6.12	−3.58	6.82	−3.47	5.74	−2.66
20	7.16	−4.12	7.20	−4.17	7.11	−4.07	7.07	−4.02	7.55	−3.62	6.22	−2.63
25	7.65	−4.20	7.66	−4.20	7.64	−4.19	7.63	−4.18	8.01	−3.71	6.44	−2.57
30	7.88	−4.12	7.88	−4.12	7.88	−4.12	7.88	−4.12	8.22	−3.79	6.44	−2.46
40	7.80	−3.80	7.80	−3.80	7.80	−3.80	7.80	−3.80	8.12	−3.84	5.98	−2.20
50	7.24	−3.34	7.24	−3.34	7.24	−3.34	7.24	−3.34	7.54	−3.66	5.04	−1.92
60	6.36	−2.76	6.36	−2.76	6.36	−2.76	6.36	−2.76	6.58	−3.28	3.83	−1.62
70	5.18	−2.14	5.18	−2.14	5.18	−2.14	5.18	−2.14	5.34	−2.72	2.53	−1.30
80	3.75	−1.50	3.75	−1.50	3.75	−1.50	3.75	−1.50	3.86	−2.02	1.32	−0.91
90	2.08	−0.82	2.08	−0.82	2.08	−0.82	2.08	−0.82	2.15	−1.17	0.38	−0.46
95	1.14	−0.48	1.14	−0.48	1.14	−0.48	1.14	−0.48	1.23	−0.73	0.10	−0.22
100	(0.13)	(−0.13)	(0.13)	(−0.13)	(0.13)	(−0.13)	(0.13)	(−0.13)	0.26	−0.26	0	0
100	—	0	—	0	—	0	—	0				
	L.E. rad. 0.40. Slope of radius through end of chord 0.25		L.E. rad. 0.80. Slope of radius through end of chord 0.25		L.E. rad. 0.20. Slope of radius through end of chord 0.10				L.E. rad. 1.75		L.E. rad. 0.949. Slope of radius through end of chord 0.1448	

Sta.	NACA 24		NACA 25		NACA 26		NACA 27	
	Up'r	L'w'r	Up'r	L'w'r	Up'r	L'w'r	Up'r	L'w'r
0	—	0	—	0	—	0	—	0
1.25	2.43	−1.64	3.03	−2.03	3.66	−2.39	1.26	−0.79
2.5	3.33	−2.27	4.12	−2.89	4.91	−3.43	1.80	−1.02
5.0	4.61	−3.02	5.61	−3.89	6.61	−4.72	2.60	−1.25
7.5	5.52	−3.47	6.66	−4.51	7.81	−5.51	3.21	−1.31
10	6.20	−3.74	7.46	−4.91	8.72	−6.09	3.67	−1.32
15	7.16	−4.03	8.55	−5.42	9.95	−6.75	4.34	−1.29
20	7.70	−4.11	9.17	−5.57	10.63	−7.02	4.75	−1.18
25	7.94	−4.07	9.44	−5.57	10.94	−7.06	4.94	−1.07
30	7.94	−3.94	9.41	−5.43	10.92	−6.90	4.94	−0.97
40	7.36	−3.56	8.74	−4.93	10.14	−6.31	4.60	−0.82
50	6.22	−3.08	7.43	−4.26	8.63	−5.45	3.87	−0.75
60	4.76	−2.54	5.71	−3.47	6.66	−4.39	2.91	−0.72
70	3.19	−1.94	3.87	−2.60	4.53	−3.25	1.89	−0.67
80	1.70	−1.29	2.08	−1.66	2.47	−2.05	0.94	−0.55
90	0.52	−0.59	0.67	−0.74	0.82	−0.88	0.23	−0.31
95	0.15	−0.27	0.20	−0.31	0.25	−0.37	0.06	−0.15
100	0	0	0	0	0	0	0	0
	L.E. rad. 1.670. Slope of radius through end of chord 0.1448		L.E. rad. 2.58. Slope of radius through end of chord 0.145		L.E. rad. 3.66. Slope of radius through end of chord 0.145		L.E. rad. 0.42. Slope of radius through end of chord 0.145	

TABLE XXIII.—ORDINATES OF AIRFOILS IN TABLE XVI

Sta.	22112		23112		24112		25112		21012		22012	
	Up'r	L'w'r	Up'r	L'w'r	Up'r	L'w'r	Up'r	L'w'r	Up'r	L'w'r	Up'r	L'w'r
0	—	0	—	0	—	0	—	0	—	0	—	0
1.25	2.87	−1.09	2.76	−1.19	2.64	−1.29	2.58	−1.34	2.95	−0.90	2.84	−1.10
2.5	3.82	−1.50	3.72	−1.67	3.61	−1.74	3.53	−1.82	3.72	−1.45	3.76	−1.60
5.0	5.07	−2.07	5.07	−2.11	4.99	−2.24	4.90	−2.32	4.67	−2.44	4.97	−2.17
7.5	5.82	−2.56	6.01	−2.45	5.97	−2.51	5.89	−2.59	5.28	−3.12	5.71	−2.68
10	6.33	−3.04	6.65	−2.72	6.70	−2.71	6.65	−2.77	5.72	−3.64	6.22	−3.15
15	6.89	−3.80	7.43	−3.26	7.68	−3.03	7.80	−2.93	6.33	−4.36	6.80	−3.89
20	7.17	−4.31	7.71	−3.77	8.14	−3.33	8.41	−3.07	6.67	−4.80	7.11	−4.38
25	7.26	−4.63	7.74	−4.13	8.26	−3.62	8.68	−3.21	6.82	−5.07	7.23	−4.66
30	7.21	−4.81	7.64	−4.37	8.17	−3.87	8.67	−3.34	6.82	−5.18	7.22	−4.80
40	6.80	−4.82	7.10	−4.52	7.50	−4.12	8.06	−3.57	6.52	−5.10	6.85	−4.76
50	6.07	−4.52	6.28	−4.33	6.58	−4.03	6.98	−3.63	5.89	−4.71	6.17	−4.42
60	5.15	−3.98	5.25	−3.90	5.43	−3.70	5.69	−3.44	5.04	−4.09	5.27	−3.85
70	4.07	−3.27	4.08	−3.23	4.17	−3.15	4.29	−3.04	4.03	−3.30	4.19	−3.14
80	2.87	−2.39	2.85	−2.42	2.87	−2.39	2.88	−2.37	2.86	−2.38	2.99	−2.26
90	1.56	−1.34	1.52	−1.39	1.51	−1.39	1.48	−1.43	1.57	−1.32	1.63	−1.26
95	0.85	−0.76	0.83	−0.78	0.82	−0.79	0.79	−0.82	0.87	−0.75	0.89	−0.71
100	(0.13)	(−0.13)	(0.13)	(−0.13)	(0.13)	(−0.13)	(0.13)	(−0.13)	(0.13)	(−0.13)	(0.13)	(−0.13)
100	—	—	—	—	0	—	—	—	—	0	—	0
	L.E. rad. 1.58. Slope of radius through end of chord 0.416		L.E. rad. 1.58. Slope of radius through end of chord 0.337		L.E. rad. 1.58. Slope of radius through end of chord 0.284		L.E. rad. 1.58. Slope of radius through end of chord 0.252		L.E. rad. 1.58. Slope of radius through end of chord 0.595		L.E. rad. 1.58. Slope of radius through end of chord 0.393	

Sta.	23006		23009		23012		23012-33		23012-34		23012-63	
	Up'r	L'w'r	Up'r	L'w'r	Up'r	L'w'r	Up'r	L'w'r	Up'r	L'w'r	Up'r	L'w'r
0	—	0	—	0	—	0	—	0	—	0	—	0
1.25	1.41	−0.52	2.04	−0.91	2.67	−1.23	1.90	−0.77	1.67	−0.67	2.53	−1.20
2.5	2.08	−0.60	2.83	−1.19	3.61	−1.71	2.89	−1.15	2.54	−0.90	3.41	−1.61
5.0	3.00	−0.61	3.93	−1.44	4.91	−2.26	4.34	−1.70	3.80	−1.25	4.59	−2.00
7.5	3.62	−0.60	4.70	−1.63	5.80	−2.61	5.38	−2.18	4.71	−1.58	5.41	−2.27
10	4.06	−0.63	5.26	−1.79	6.43	−2.92	6.15	−2.62	5.40	−1.91	6.00	−2.50
15	4.51	−0.83	5.85	−2.17	7.19	−3.50	7.08	−3.40	6.34	−2.64	6.70	−3.02
20	4.63	−1.10	6.06	−2.55	7.50	−3.97	7.49	−3.98	6.86	−3.35	7.04	−3.55
25	4.63	−1.32	6.11	−2.80	7.60	−4.28	7.60	−4.30	7.17	−3.90	7.23	−3.96
30	4.56	−1.46	6.05	−2.96	7.55	−4.46	7.55	−4.46	7.34	−4.27	7.37	−4.29
40	4.23	−1.58	5.69	−3.03	7.14	−4.48	7.11	−4.46	7.33	−4.67	7.32	−4.66
50	3.75	−1.54	5.09	−2.86	6.41	−4.17	6.52	−4.30	6.95	−4.71	6.93	−4.70
60	3.17	−1.40	4.32	−2.53	5.47	−3.67	5.81	−3.83	6.20	−4.43	6.21	−4.42
70	2.50	−1.17	3.42	−2.08	4.36	−3.00	4.48	−3.14	5.16	−3.80	5.17	−3.79
80	1.75	−0.87	2.41	−1.51	3.08	−2.16	3.16	−2.26	3.79	−2.87	3.78	−2.86
90	0.95	−0.50	1.31	−0.86	1.68	−1.23	1.70	−1.25	2.10	−1.65	2.09	−1.63
95	0.51	−0.29	0.72	−0.50	0.92	−0.70	0.93	−0.70	1.15	−0.91	1.15	−0.90
100	(0.06)	(−0.06)	(0.10)	(−0.10)	(0.13)	(−0.13)	(0.12)	(−0.12)	(0.12)	(−0.12)	(0.12)	(−0.12)
100	—	0	—	0	—	0	—	0	—	0	—	0
	L.E. rad. 0.40. Slope of radius through end of chord 0.305		L.E. rad. 0.89. Slope of radius through end of chord 0.305		L.E. rad. 1.58. Slope of radius through end of chord 0.305		L.E. rad. 0.40. Slope of radius through end of chord 0.305		L.E. rad. 0.40. Slope of radius through end of chord 0.305		L.E. rad. 1.58. Slope of radius through end of chord 0.305	

TABLE XXIII.—ORDINATES OF AIRFOILS IN TABLE XVI.—(*Continued*)

Sta.	23015		23018		23021		24012		225012		32012	
	Up'r	L'w'r	Up'r	L'w'r	Up'r	L'w'r	Up'r	L'w'r	Up'r	L'w'r	Up'r	L'w'r
0	—	0	—	0	—	0	—	0	—	0	—	0
1.25	3.34	−1.54	4.09	−1.83	4.87	−2.08	2.58	−1.34	2.48	−1.39	3.32	−0.86
2.5	4.44	−2.25	5.29	−2.71	6.14	−3.14	3.50	−1.85	3.37	−1.94	4.36	−1.11
5.0	5.89	−3.04	6.92	−3.80	7.93	−4.52	4.80	−2.37	4.70	−2.49	5.69	−1.50
7.5	6.91	−3.61	8.01	−4.60	9.13	−5.55	5.74	−2.70	5.62	−2.82	6.48	−1.91
10	7.64	−4.09	8.83	−5.22	10.03	−6.32	6.44	−2.95	6.36	−3.04	6.99	−2.38
15	8.52	−4.84	9.86	−6.18	11.19	−7.51	7.37	−3.34	7.39	−3.33	7.53	−3.18
20	8.92	−5.41	10.36	−6.86	11.80	−8.30	7.82	−3.66	7.97	−3.54	7.80	−3.68
25	9.08	−5.78	10.56	−7.27	12.05	−8.76	7.96	−3.92	8.20	−3.68	7.87	−4.00
30	9.05	−5.96	10.55	−7.47	12.06	−8.95	7.89	−4.11	8.21	−3.79	7.81	−4.20
40	8.59	−5.92	10.04	−7.37	11.49	−8.83	7.44	−4.17	7.75	−3.87	7.35	−4.26
50	7.74	−5.50	9.05	−6.81	10.40	−8.14	6.66	−3.93	6.92	−3.67	6.59	−4.00
60	6.61	−4.81	7.75	−5.94	8.90	−7.07	5.67	−3.47	5.87	−3.27	5.60	−3.51
70	5.25	−3.91	6.18	−4.82	7.09	−5.72	4.48	−2.84	4.64	−2.70	4.46	−2.88
80	3.73	−2.83	4.40	−3.48	5.05	−4.13	3.18	−2.07	3.27	−1.97	3.15	−2.10
90	2.04	−1.53	2.39	−1.94	2.76	−2.30	1.73	−1.18	1.78	−1.13	1.71	−1.19
95	1.12	−0.90	1.32	−1.09	1.53	−1.30	0.94	−0.67	0.98	−0.64	0.93	−0.69
100	(0.16)	(−0.16)	(0.19)	(−0.19)	(0.22)	(−0.22)	(0.13)	(−0.13)	(0.13)	(−0.13)	(0.12)	(−0.12)
100	—	0	—	0	—	0	—	0	—	0	—	0
	L.E. rad. 2.48. Slope of radius through end of chord 0.305		L.E. rad. 3.56. Slope of radius through end of chord 0.305		L.E. rad. 4.85. Slope of radius through end of chord 0.305		L.E. rad. 1.58. Slope of radius through end of chord 0.252		L.E. rad. 1.58. Slope of radius through end of chord 0.215		L.E. rad. 1.58. Slope of radius through end of chord 0.589	

Sta.	33012		34012		42012		43009		43012		43012A	
	Up'r	L'w'r	Up'r	L'w'r	Up'r	L'w'r	Up'r	L'w'r	Up'r	L'w'r	Up'r	L'w'r
0	—	0	—	0	—	0	—	0	—	0	—	0
1.25	3.09	−1.03	2.90	−1.10	3.85	−0.63	2.73	−0.51	3.55	−0.82	3.87	−0.81
2.5	4.15	−1.33	3.95	−1.50	4.92	−0.72	3.76	−0.50	4.71	−1.00	5.19	−1.09
5.0	4.62	−1.66	5.46	−1.85	6.40	−0.81	5.30	−0.30	6.33	−1.06	7.02	−1.44
7.5	6.61	−1.87	6.51	−2.00	7.26	−1.15	6.27	−0.13	7.42	−1.09	8.17	−1.71
10	7.34	−2.08	7.34	−2.10	7.75	−1.61	6.98	−0.06	8.20	−1.21	8.96	−1.92
15	8.10	−2.58	8.39	−2.32	8.27	−2.45	7.69	−0.33	9.02	−1.66	9.62	−2.28
20	8.38	−3.10	8.86	−2.62	8.49	−3.00	7.83	−0.78	9.26	−2.22	9.65	−2.57
25	8.41	−3.46	8.97	−2.91	8.52	−3.36	7.78	−1.16	9.25	−2.64	9.43	−2.79
30	8.33	−3.69	8.85	−3.15	8.42	−3.59	7.60	−1.41	9.10	−2.91	9.14	−2.93
40	7.80	−3.81	8.26	−3.38	7.88	−3.73	7.02	−1.70	8.46	−3.15	8.47	−3.15
50	6.96	−3.62	7.35	−3.25	7.02	−3.55	6.19	−1.75	7.53	−3.07	7.52	−3.07
60	5.90	−3.22	6.20	−2.92	5.97	−3.18	5.20	−1.65	6.35	−2.78	6.35	−2.77
70	4.67	−2.65	4.89	−2.42	4.72	−2.62	4.09	−1.41	5.00	−2.32	5.00	−2.31
80	3.29	−1.94	3.45	−1.80	3.32	−1.92	2.88	−1.08	3.52	−1.73	3.52	−1.72
90	1.78	−1.11	1.84	−1.04	1.79	−1.10	1.56	−0.64	1.90	−1.00	1.90	−1.00
95	0.98	−0.63	1.00	−0.60	0.98	−0.62	0.83	−0.39	1.02	−0.58	1.04	−0.59
100	(0.12)	(−0.12)	(0.12)	(−0.12)	(0.12)	(−0.12)	(0.10)	(−0.10)	(0.13)	(−0.13)	(0.13)	(−0.13)
100	—	0	—	0	—	0	—	0	—	0	—	0
	L.E. rad. 1.58. Slope of radius through end of chord 0.458		L.E. rad. 1.58. Slope of radius through end of chord 0.379		L.E. rad. 1.58. Slope of radius through end of chord 0.785		L.E. rad. 0.89. Slope of radius through end of chord 0.610		L.E. rad. 1.58. Slope of radius through end of chord 0.610		L.E. rad. 1.58. Slope of radius through end of chord 0.610	

TABLE XXIII.—ORDINATES OF AIRFOILS IN TABLE XVI.—(*Continued*)

Sta.	43015		43018		43021		44012		62021	
	Up'r	L'w'r	Up'r	L'w'r	Up'r	L'w'r	Up'r	L'w'r	Up'r	L'w'r
0	—	0	—	0	—	0	—	0	—	0
1.25	4.42	−1.03	5.40	−1.23	6.40	−1.36	3.30	−0.93	8.12	−0.70
2.5	5.67	−1.40	6.67	−1.78	7.74	−2.07	4.44	−1.20	9.39	−0.97
5.0	7.41	−1.78	8.50	−2.44	9.61	−3.03	6.11	−1.32	11.05	−1.27
7.5	8.57	−2.02	9.75	−2.91	10.93	−3.75	7.32	−1.30	12.08	−2.14
10	9.41	−2.31	10.63	−3.38	11.90	−4.47	8.21	−1.25	12.80	−3.58
15	10.36	−3.00	11.69	−4.34	13.03	−5.67	9.39	−1.32	13.67	−5.06
20	10.69	−3.67	12.11	−5.10	13.53	−6.57	9.90	−1.57	14.12	−5.97
25	10.73	−4.14	12.22	−5.62	13.70	−7.10	9.97	−1.90	14.26	−6.56
30	10.60	−4.41	12.10	−5.91	13.60	−7.42	9.79	−2.22	14.12	−6.89
40	9.93	−2.60	11.39	−6.04	12.85	−7.49	9.08	−2.56	13.30	−7.02
50	8.86	−4.39	10.20	−5.71	11.52	−7.01	8.02	−2.58	11.92	−6.63
60	7.50	−3.91	8.67	−5.04	9.82	−6.18	6.76	−2.38	10.12	−5.88
70	5.93	−3.22	6.87	−4.12	7.81	−5.02	5.29	−2.01	8.01	−4.80
80	4.19	−2.38	4.87	−3.02	5.51	−3.66	3.71	−1.53	5.70	−3.51
90	2.27	−1.36	2.63	−1.72	2.99	−2.07	2.00	−0.90	3.09	−2.00
95	1.25	−0.79	1.44	−0.99	1.65	−1.18	1.09	−0.54	1.69	−1.14
100	(0.16)	(−0.16)	(0.19)	(−0.19)	(0.22)	(−0.22)	(0.13)	(−0.13)	(0.22)	(−0.22)
100	—	0	—	0	—	0	—	0	—	0
	L.E. rad. 2.48. Slope of radius through end of chord 0.610		L.E. rad. 3.56. Slope of radius through end of chord 0.610		L.E. rad. 4.85. Slope of radius through end of chord 0.610		L.E. rad. 1.58. Slope of radius through end of chord 0.505		L.E. rad. 4.85. Slope of radius through end of chord 1.178	

Sta.	63009		63012		63015		63018		63021	
	Up'r	L'w'r	Up'r	L'w'r	Up'r	L'w'r	Up'r	L'w'r	Up'r	L'w'r
0	—	0	—	0	—	0	—	0	—	0
1.25	3.46	−0.22	4.46	−0.50	5.51	−0.73	6.71	−0.80	7.88	−0.88
2 5	4.79	0.03	5.84	−0.41	6.94	−0.88	8.11	−1.09	9.29	−1.32
5.0	6.62	0.80	7.77	0.03	8.91	−0.62	10.10	−1.24	11.29	−1.77
7.5	7.90	1.31	9.07	0.39	10.29	−0.51	11 46	−1.34	12.71	−2.08
10	8.71	1 61	9.99	0.50	11 21	−0.58	12.48	−1.60	13.70	−2.58
15	9.53	1 52	10.86	0.17	12 20	−1.15	13.54	−2.50	14.86	−3.82
20	9.60	1 00	11.03	−0.48	12.46	−1.91	13.86	−3.37	15.30	−4.83
25	9 44	0 50	10.91	−0.99	12.40	−2.49	13.88	−3.99	15.37	−5.46
30	9.15	0.12	10.66	−1.38	12.16	−2.89	13.67	−4.40	15.18	−5.89
40	8.35	−0.38	9.80	−1.84	11.28	−3.28	12.71	−4.72	14.20	−6.16
50	7.30	−0.68	8.64	−1.97	10.00	−3.30	11.33	−4.60	12.68	−5.91
60	6.10	−0.77	7.24	−1.90	8.40	−3.03	9.58	−4.15	10.75	−5.29
70	4.76	−0.75	5.69	−1.66	6.61	−2.56	7.53	−3.48	8.50	−4.37
80	3.30	−0.63	3.97	−1.28	4.64	−1.94	5.32	−2.58	5.99	−3.21
90	1.77	−0.42	2.12	−0.79	2.49	−1.13	2.89	−1.50	3.22	−1.84
95	0.94	−0.28	1.14	−0.48	1.36	−0.65	1.56	−0.88	1.78	−1.08
100	(0.10)	(−0.10)	(0.13)	(−0.13)	(0.16)	(−0.16)	(0.19)	(−0.19)	(0.22)	(−0.22)
100	—	0	—	0	—	0	—	0	—	0
	L.E. rad. 0.89. Slope of radius through end of chord 0.915		L.E. rad. 1.58. Slope of radius through end of chord 0.915		L.E. rad. 2.48. Slope of radius through end of chord 0.915		L.E. rad. 3.56. Slope of radius through end of chord 0.915		L.E. rad. 4.85. Slope of radius through end of chord 0.915	

TABLE XXIII.—ORDINATES OF AIRFOILS IN TABLE XVI.—(*Concluded*)

Sta.	64021		0012		23009		23012		23009		23012	
	Up'r	L'w'r	Up'r	L'w'r	Up'r	L'w'r	Up'r	L'w'r	Up'r	L'w'r	Up'r	L'w'r
0	—	0	0	0	—	0	—	0	—	0	—	0
1.25	7.49	−1.06	1.89	−1.89	2.04	−0.91	2.67	−1.23	2.04	−0.91	2.67	−1.23
2.5	8.94	−1.64	2.62	−2.62	2.83	−1.19	3.61	−1.71	2.83	−1.19	3.61	−1.71
5.0	11.12	−2.19	3.56	−3.56	3.93	−1.44	4.91	−2.26	3.93	−1.44	4.91	−2.26
7.5	12.74	−2.44	4.28	−4.20	4.70	−1.63	5.80	−2.61	4.70	−1.63	5.80	−2.61
10	13.96	−2.65	4.68	−4.68	5.26	−1.79	6.43	−2.92	5.26	−1.79	6.43	−2.92
15	15.50	−3.20	5.34	−5.34	5.85	−2.17	7.19	−3.50	5.85	−2.17	7.19	−3.50
20	16.28	−3.80	5.74	−5.74	6.06	−2.55	7.50	−3.97	6.06	−2.55	7.50	−3.97
25	16.44	−4.40	5.94	−5.94	6.11	−2.80	7.60	−4.28	6.11	−2.80	7.60	−4.28
30	16.21	−4.88	6.00	−6.00	6.06	−2.96	7.55	−4.46	6.05	−2.96	7.55	−4.48
40	15.09	−5.27	5.80	−5.80	5.69	−3.03	7.14	−4.48	5.69	−3.03	7.14	−4.48
50	13.42	−5.13	5.29	−5.29	5.09	−2.86	6.41	−4.17	5.09	−2.86	6.41	−4.17
60	11.34	−4.69	4.56	−4.56	4.32	−2.53	5.47	−3.67	4.32	−2.53	5.47	−3.67
70	8.96	−3.91	3.66	−3.66	3.42	−2.08	4.36	−3.00	3.42	−2.08	4.36	−3.00
80	6.30	−2.91	2.62	−2.62	2.41	−1.51	3.08	−2.16	2.41	−1.51	3.08	−2.16
90	3.40	−1.70	1.45	−1.45	1.31	−0.88	1.68	−1.23	1.31	−0.86	1.68	−1.23
95	1.87	−0.99	0.81	−0.81	0.72	−0.50	0.92	−0.70	0.72	−0.50	0.92	−0.70
100	(0.22)	(−0.22)	(0.13)	(−0.13)	(0.10)	(−0.10)	(0.13)	(−0.13)	(0.10)	(−0.10)	(0.13)	(−0.13)
100	—	0	0	0	—	0	—	0	—	0	—	0
	L.E. rad. 4.85. Slope of radius through end of chord 0.757		L.E. rad. 1.58		L.E. rad. 0.89. Slope of radius through end of chord 0.305		L.E. rad. 1.58. Slope of radius through end of chord 0.305		L.E. rad. 0.89. Slope of radius through end of chord 0.305		L.E. rad. 1.58. Slope of radius through end of chord 0.305	

Sta.	23015		23021		43009		43012		63009	
	Up'r	L'w'r	Up'r	L'w'r	Up'r	L'w'r	Up'r	L'w'r	Up'r	L'w'r
0	—	0	—	0	—	0	—	0	—	0
1.25	3.34	−1.54	4.87	−2.08	2.73	−0.51	3.55	−0.82	3.46	−0.22
2.5	4.44	−2.25	6.14	−3.15	3.76	−0.50	4.71	−1.00	4.79	0.03
5.0	5.89	−3.04	7.93	−4.52	5.30	−0.30	6.33	−1.06	6.62	0.80
7.5	6.91	−3.61	9.13	−5.55	6.27	−0.13	7.42	−1.09	7.90	1.31
10	7.64	−4.09	10.03	−6.32	6.96	−0.06	8.20	−1.21	8.71	1.61
15	8.52	−4.84	11.19	−7.51	7.69	−0.33	9.02	−1.66	9.53	1.52
20	8.92	−5.41	11.80	−8.30	7.83	−0.78	9.26	−2.22	9.60	1.00
25	9.09	−5.78	12.05	−8.76	7.78	−1.16	9.25	−2.64	9.44	0.50
30	9.05	−5.96	12.06	−8.95	7.60	−1.41	9.10	−2.91	9.15	0.12
40	8.59	−5.92	11.49	−8.83	7.02	−1.70	8.46	−3.15	8.35	−0.38
50	7.74	−5.50	10.40	−8.14	6.19	−1.75	7.53	−3.07	7.30	−0.66
60	6.61	−4.81	8.90	−7.07	5.20	−1.65	6.35	−2.78	6.10	−0.77
70	5.25	−3.91	7.09	−5.72	4.09	−1.41	5.00	−2.32	4.76	−0.75
80	3.73	−2.83	5.05	−4.13	2.88	−1.08	3.52	−1.73	3.30	−0.63
90	2.04	−1.59	2.76	−2.30	1.56	−0.64	1.90	−1.00	1.77	−0.42
100	(0.16)	(−0.16)	(0.22)	(−0.22)	(0.10)	(−0.10)	(0.13)	(−0.13)	(0.10)	(−0.10)
100	—	0	—	0	—	0	—	0	—	0
	L.E. rad. 2.48. Slope of radius through end of chord 0.305		L.E. rad. 4.85. Slope of radius through end of chord 0.305		L.E. rad. 0.89. Slope of radius through end of chord 0.610		L.E. rad. 1.58. Slope of radius through end of chord 0.610		L.E. rad. 0.89. Slope of radius through end of chord 0.915	

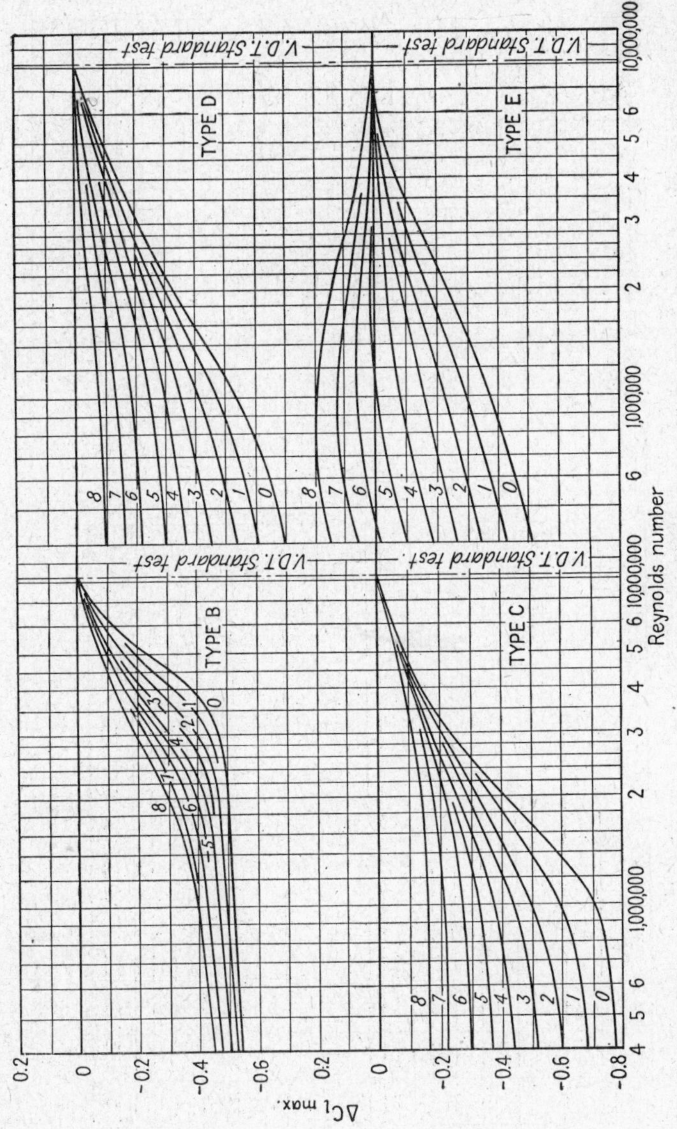

FIG. A2.—Scale effect corrections for $C_{l\,max}$. In order to obtain the section maximum lift coefficient at the desired Reynolds number, apply to the standard-test value the increment indicated by the curve that corresponds to the scale-effect designation of the airfoil.

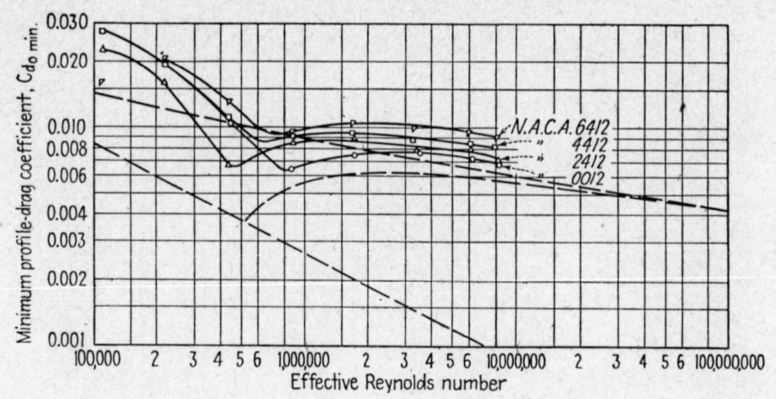

FIG. A3.—Section minimum drag coefficient.

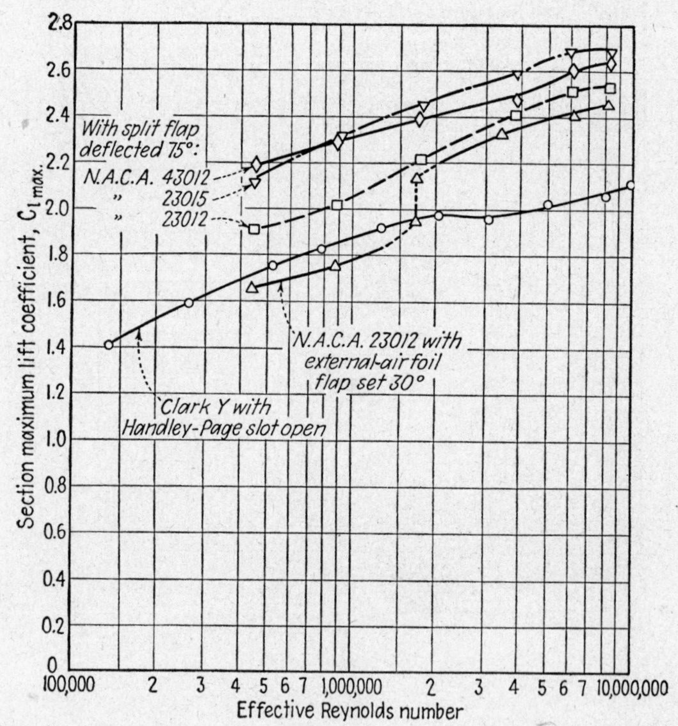

FIG. A4.—Section maximum lift coefficient $C_{l\,\max}$. Airfoils with high-lift devices.

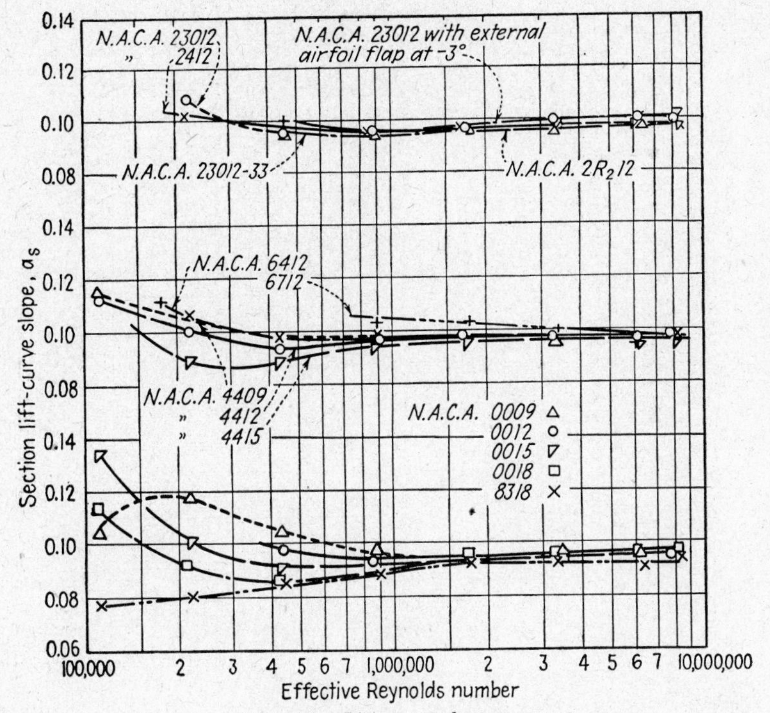

FIG. A5.—Lift-curve slope, a_0.

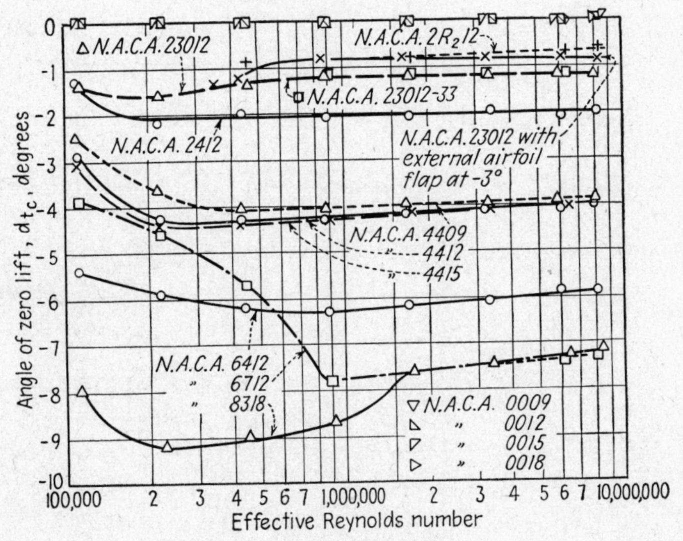

FIG. A6.—Angle of zero lift, α_{l0}.

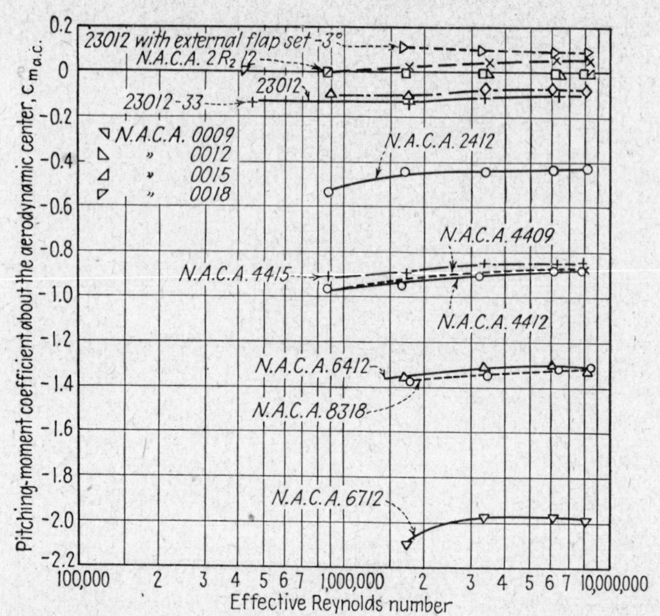

FIG. A7.—Pitching-moment coefficient about the aerodynamic center, $c_{m\ a.c.}$

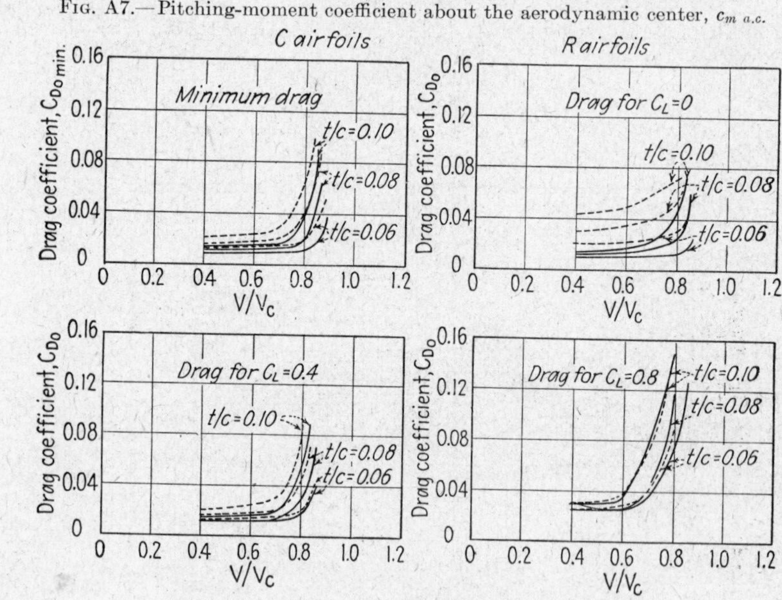

FIG. A8.—Effect of compressibility on drag.

$$V_c = \text{speed of sound in air} = 1{,}120\sqrt{\frac{T}{519}} \text{ ft per sec}$$

where T = absolute Fahrenheit temperature

$$\frac{V}{V_c} = \text{Mach's number}$$

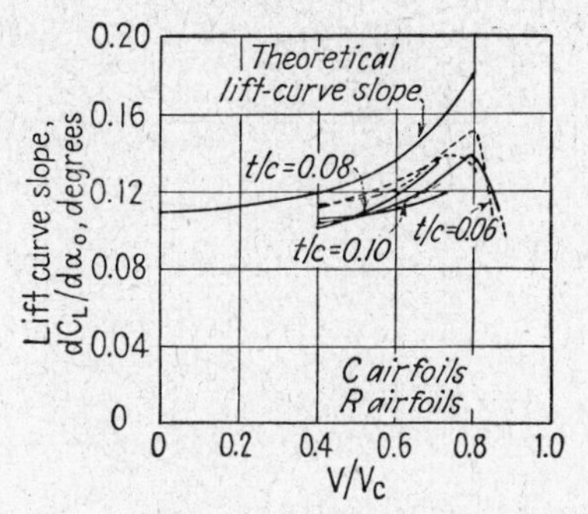

FIG. A9.—Effect of compressibility on lift.

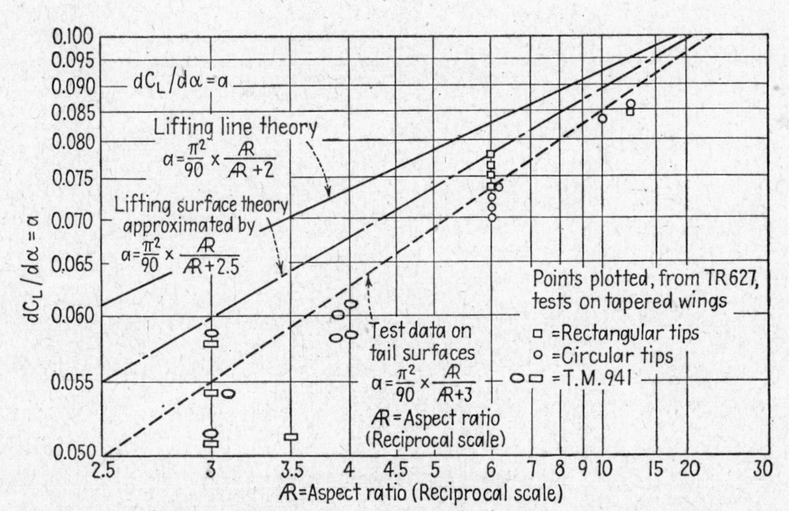

FIG. A10.—Lift-curve slope for wings and tail surfaces as a function of aspect ratio. Theoretical and experimental values. *NACA Tech. Rept.* 116 gives wind-tunnel data that plot nearly as $a = 0.1095 \dfrac{A}{A + 1.8}$, but data in *NACA Tech. Rept.* 116 are believed to be incorrectly corrected for tunnel-wall effect.

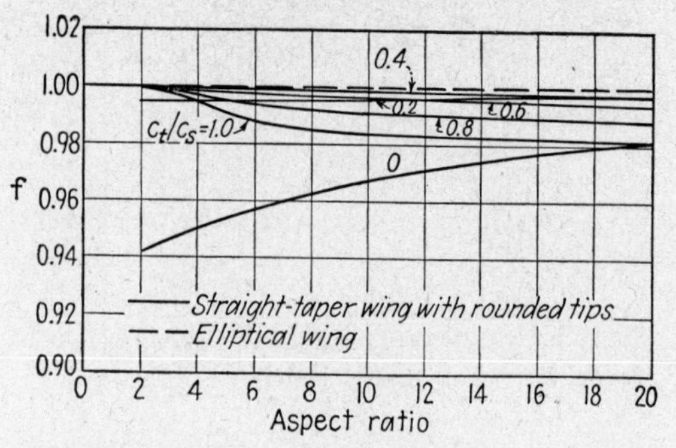

FIG. A11.—Chart for determining lift-curve slope.

$$a = f \frac{a_0}{1 - \frac{57.3a_0}{\pi A}}$$

$$m = 57.3$$

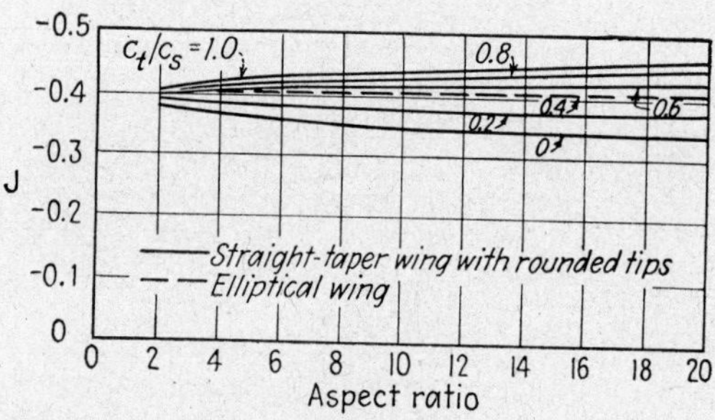

FIG. A12.—Chart for determining angle of attack.

$$\alpha_s = \frac{C_L}{a} + \alpha_{l0s} + J\epsilon$$

$$\alpha s_{(L=0)} = \alpha_{l0s} + J\epsilon$$

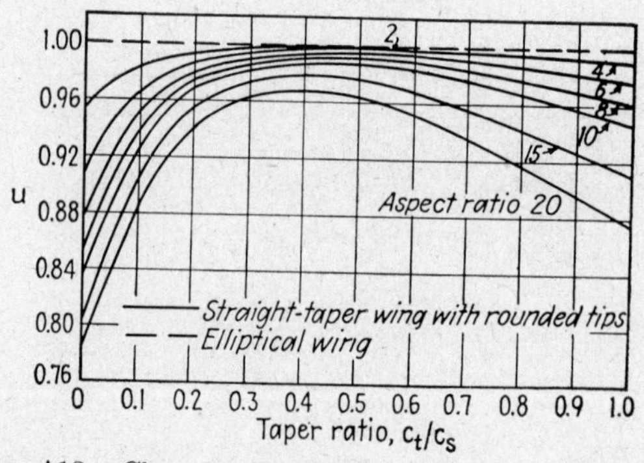

FIG. A13.—Chart for determining induced-drag factor u.

$$C_{Di} = \frac{C_L^2}{\pi A u} = C_L \epsilon a_0 v + (\epsilon a_0)^2 \omega$$

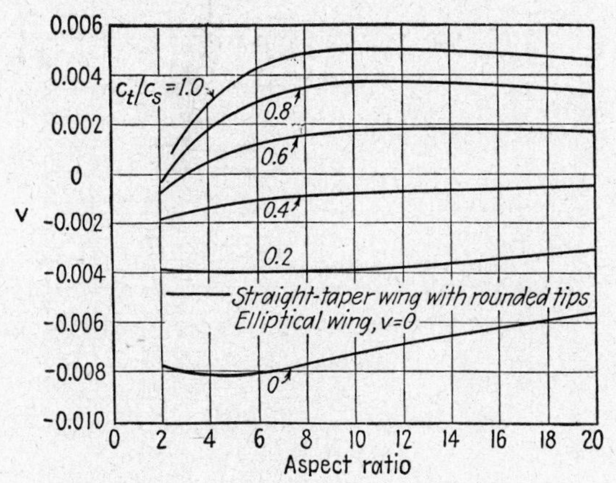

FIG. A14.—Chart for determining induced-drag factor v.

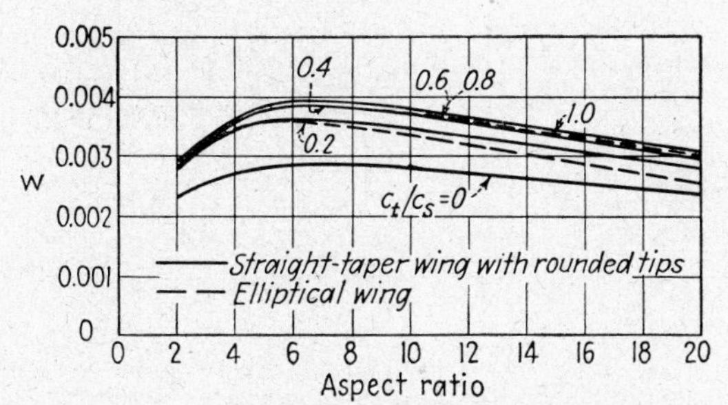

FIG. A15.—Chart for determining induced-drag factor w.

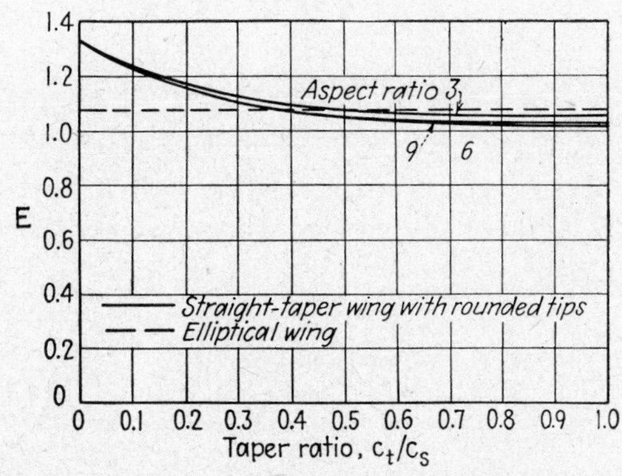

FIG. A16.—Chart for determining pitching moment due to section moment.

$$C_{ms} = Ec_{m\ a.c.}$$

For $c_{m\ a.c.}$ constant across span.

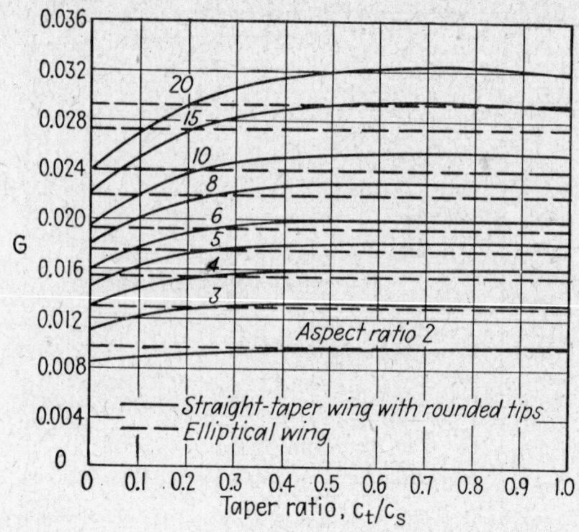

FIG. A17.—Chart for determining pitching moment due to basic lift forces.

$$C_{mlb} = G\epsilon a_0 A \tan \beta$$

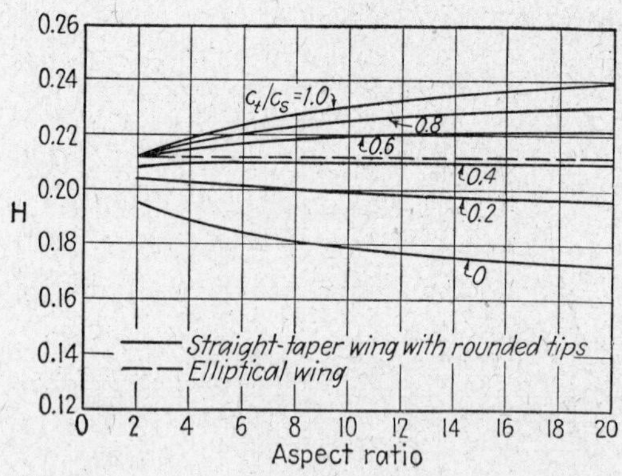

FIG. A18.—Chart for determining aerodynamic-center position.

$$\frac{X_{a.c.}}{S/b} = HA \tan \beta$$

TABLE XXIV.—ADDITIONAL SPAN-LIFT DISTRIBUTION DATA, VALUES OF L_a FOR ROUNDED-TIP WINGS*

$$c_l = c_{lb} + C_L c_{la1} \qquad c_{la1} = \frac{S}{cb} L_s \qquad c_{lb} = \frac{a_0 S}{cb} L_b$$

Spanwise station $\frac{y}{b/2} = 0$

Æ \ c_t/c_s	0	0.1	0.2	0.3	0.4	0.5	0.6	0.7	0.8	0.9	1.0
2	1.439	1.400	1.367	1.339	1.316	1.301	1.298	1.292	1.290	1.287	1.282
3	1.489	1.430	1.385	1.350	1.322	1.302	1.288	1.275	1.263	1.253	1.246
4	1.527	1.452	1.400	1.360	1.329	1.302	1.279	1.260	1.242	1.226	1.211
5	1.559	1.473	1.414	1.369	1.333	1.301	1.272	1.248	1.225	1.204	1.186
6	1.585	1.492	1.428	1.378	1.338	1.300	1.267	1.237	1.211	1.187	1.163
7	1.609	1.510	1.440	1.386	1.340	1.300	1.264	1.232	1.203	1.176	1.149
8	1.629	1.534	1.456	1.392	1.344	1.300	1.264	1.229	1.198	1.165	1.135
10	1.661	1.558	1.473	1.409	1.355	1.306	1.264	1.222	1.187	1.152	1.120
12	1.686	1.578	1.490	1.420	1.361	1.308	1.261	1.219	1.180	1.143	1.109
14	1.708	1.592	1.502	1.429	1.366	1.309	1.260	1.214	1.172	1.136	1.100
16	1.726	1.610	1.513	1.433	1.368	1.309	1.255	1.208	1.165	1.127	1.090
18	1.741	1.623	1.525	1.441	1.370	1.308	1.252	1.203	1.160	1.118	1.080
20	1.755	1.632	1.531	1.446	1.372	1.307	1.250	1.199	1.152	1.109	1.070

Spanwise station $\frac{y}{b/2} = 0.2$

Æ \ c_t/c_s	0	0.1	0.2	0.3	0.4	0.5	0.6	0.7	0.8	0.9	1.0
2	1.369	1.329	1.300	1.279	1.267	1.260	1.258	1.256	1.253	1.250	1.248
3	1.405	1.346	1.308	1.279	1.260	1.248	1.241	1.234	1.228	1.221	1.214
4	1.434	1.363	1.318	1.284	1.260	1.243	1.232	1.220	1.209	1.198	1.186
5	1.459	1.377	1.324	1.288	1.260	1.240	1.223	1.208	1.194	1.181	1.168
6	1.477	1.388	1.329	1.290	1.259	1.236	1.218	1.200	1.184	1.169	1.151
7	1.491	1.393	1.332	1.291	1.259	1.236	1.214	1.193	1.174	1.157	1.138
8	1.502	1.401	1.338	1.294	1.261	1.236	1.212	1.189	1.168	1.148	1.129
10	1.513	1.411	1.347	1.299	1.265	1.236	1.299	1.182	1.158	1.137	1.114
12	1.520	1.417	1.349	1.302	1.265	1.233	1.202	1.172	1.148	1.126	1.102
14	1.527	1.423	1.354	1.307	1.268	1.232	1.201	1.170	1.144	1.119	1.094
16	1.532	1.428	1.358	1.308	1.269	1.232	1.199	1.164	1.135	1.110	1.087
18	1.539	1.429	1.359	1.309	1.270	1.231	1.195	1.160	1.130	1.103	1.078
20	1.547	1.431	1.360	1.311	1.271	1.230	1.190	1.155	1.123	1.098	1.069

Spanwise station $\frac{y}{b/2} = 0.4$

Æ \ c_t/c_s	0	0.1	0.2	0.3	0.4	0.5	0.6	0.7	0.8	0.9	1.0
2	1.217	1.190	1.178	1.172	1.172	1.171	1.170	1.169	1.169	1.168	1.168
3	1.220	1.191	1.176	1.166	1.161	1.160	1.159	1.158	1.157	1.156	1.155
4	1.223	1.192	1.173	1.162	1.156	1.151	1.149	1.148	1.147	1.146	1.145
5	1.226	1.193	1.172	1.159	1.149	1.142	1.140	1.138	1.136	1.134	1.133
6	1.229	1.193	1.171	1.155	1.145	1.138	1.132	1.128	1.127	1.126	1.125
7	1.229	1.193	1.170	1.152	1.140	1.131	1.124	1.121	1.120	1.119	1.118
8	1.229	1.192	1.168	1.150	1.138	1.128	1.120	1.116	1.113	1.111	1.110
10	1.228	1.192	1.167	1.148	1.132	1.121	1.113	1.108	1.104	1.102	1.100
12	1.228	1.192	1.166	1.145	1.125	1.111	1.107	1.102	1.099	1.094	1.090
14	1.228	1.191	1.161	1.136	1.116	1.104	1.100	1.096	1.090	1.087	1.082
16	1.228	1.189	1.158	1.131	1.112	1.101	1.097	1.091	1.086	1.081	1.075
18	1.228	1.186	1.152	1.129	1.111	1.100	1.092	1.087	1.080	1.076	1.070
20	1.228	1.182	1.149	1.127	1.110	1.098	1.089	1.083	1.078	1.071	1.065

Spanwise station $\frac{y}{b/2} = 0.6$

Æ \ c_t/c_s	0	0.1	0.2	0.3	0.4	0.5	0.6	0.7	0.8	0.9	1.0
2	0.970	0.976	0.984	0.992	1.003	1.010	1.012	1.014	1.016	1.018	1.019
3	0.950	0.962	0.975	0.985	0.996	1.004	1.011	1.018	1.023	1.030	1.038
4	0.932	0.948	0.962	0.978	0.992	1.002	1.008	1.014	1.023	1.035	1.050
5	0.920	0.938	0.953	0.971	0.988	1.000	1.008	1.015	1.023	1.038	1.053
6	0.909	0.930	0.949	0.966	0.981	0.993	1.002	1.013	1.024	1.039	1.055
7	0.900	0.920	0.940	0.959	0.975	0.989	1.000	1.012	1.024	1.039	1.054
8	0.891	0.916	0.938	0.956	0.972	0.988	0.999	1.011	1.024	1.039	1.053
10	0.881	0.907	0.929	0.947	0.961	0.976	0.992	1.008	1.023	1.039	1.052
12	0.872	0.901	0.923	0.941	0.958	0.972	0.989	1.006	1.022	1.038	1.051
14	0.868	0.895	0.918	0.937	0.953	0.969	0.986	1.003	1.019	1.035	1.049
16	0.861	0.888	0.912	0.931	0.948	0.966	0.983	1.000	1.017	1.033	1.048
18	0.858	0.883	0.906	0.925	0.944	0.963	0.981	0.996	1.015	1.032	1.047
20	0.851	0.876	0.898	0.920	0.940	0.959	0.978	0.995	1.012	1.028	1.046

* From *NACA Tech. Rept.* 631, Table II.

TABLE XXIV.—ADDITIONAL SPAN-LIFT DISTRIBUTION DATA, VALUES OF L_a FOR ROUNDED-TIP WINGS.—(*Concluded*)

$$c_l = c_{lb} + C_L c_{la1} \qquad c_{la1} = \frac{S}{cb} L_s \qquad c_{lb} = \frac{a_0 S}{cb} L_b$$

$\frac{c_t}{c_s}$ / Æ	0	0.1	0.2	0.3	0.4	0.5	0.6	0.7	0.8	0.9	1.0
Spanwise station $\frac{y}{b/2} = 0.8$											
2	0.615	0.678	0.712	0.731	0.740	0.745	0.746	0.746	0.747	0.747	0.748
3	0.589	0.659	0.700	0.726	0.743	0.754	0.764	0.772	0.782	0.790	0.799
4	0.568	0.644	0.691	0.723	0.746	0.764	0.781	0.795	0.806	0.816	0.824
5	0.548	0.632	0.685	0.720	0.748	0.769	0.790	0.808	0.822	0.834	0.845
6	0.531	0.619	0.675	0.717	0.748	0.775	0.800	0.820	0.838	0.851	0.862
7	0.517	0.609	0.670	0.713	0.748	0.778	0.802	0.827	0.845	0.861	0.875
8	0.504	0.600	0.663	0.710	0.748	0.779	0.808	0.834	0.854	0.872	0.886
10	0.486	0.585	0.653	0.704	0.748	0.783	0.815	0.842	0.868	0.887	0.905
12	0.472	0.576	0.648	0.702	0.748	0.788	0.850	0.850	0.877	0.899	0.919
14	0.462	0.569	0.641	0.699	0.748	0.789	0.825	0.858	0.887	0.911	0.933
16	0.456	0.564	0.638	0.698	0.748	0.791	0.830	0.862	0.894	0.921	0.944
18	0.450	0.559	0.636	0.698	0.750	0.796	0.835	0.870	0.901	0.930	0.953
20	0.444	0.545	0.629	0.698	0.753	0.801	0.842	0.878	0.909	0.937	0.962
Spanwise station $\frac{y}{b/2} = 0.9$											
2	0.378	0.465	0.508	0.525	0.531	0.534	0.535	0.536	0.537	0.538	0.539
3	0.352	0.447	0.500	0.528	0.543	0.552	0.559	0.564	0.568	0.571	0.575
4	0.331	0.435	0.495	0.532	0.554	0.569	0.581	0.590	0.598	0.603	0.609
5	0.314	0.424	0.490	0.531	0.560	0.583	0.600	0.613	0.622	0.630	0.636
6	0.300	0.416	0.487	0.531	0.585	0.595	0.615	0.631	0.643	0.652	0.659
7	0.290	0.410	0.484	0.535	0.572	0.603	0.628	0.646	0.660	0.671	0.678
8	0.282	0.403	0.481	0.536	0.579	0.612	0.638	0.658	0.673	0.686	0.696
10	0.266	0.383	0.472	0.541	0.590	0.628	0.656	0.679	0.698	0.712	0.723
12	0.253	0.376	0.469	0.512	0.597	0.639	0.669	0.698	0.718	0.736	0.751
14	0.245	0.370	0.468	0.545	0.602	0.648	0.684	0.715	0.739	0.759	0.776
16	0.239	0.366	0.468	0.547	0.609	0.659	0.698	0.729	0.756	0.780	0.801
18	0.234	0.367	0.470	0.552	0.618	0.669	0.710	0.743	0.773	0.800	0.822
20	0.231	0.368	0.473	0.560	0.625	0.679	0.722	0.759	0.791	0.819	0.846
Spanwise station $\frac{y}{b/2} = 0.95$											
2	0.231	0.296	0.334	0.358	0.370	0.379	0.381	0.383	0.386	0.388	0.390
3	0.209	0.290	0.339	0.369	0.389	0.401	0.407	0.412	0.416	0.418	0.420
4	0.191	0.286	0.342	0.378	0.402	0.420	0.428	0.434	0.440	0.444	0.446
5	0.176	0.281	0.344	0.384	0.415	0.436	0.449	0.458	0.463	0.469	0.471
6	0.166	0.278	0.346	0.392	0.428	0.451	0.466	0.475	0.482	0.490	0.496
7	0.155	0.272	0.346	0.398	0.438	0.464	0.481	0.491	0.502	0.510	0.515
8	0.148	0.261	0.346	0.403	0.446	0.475	0.495	0.510	0.521	0.529	0.534
10	0.138	0.255	0.346	0.410	0.460	0.495	0.520	0.538	0.553	0.566	0.575
12	0.132	0.254	0.348	0.419	0.473	0.511	0.542	0.566	0.583	0.598	0.608
14	0.129	0.252	0.349	0.423	0.482	0.529	0.562	0.588	0.609	0.628	0.640
16	0.126	0.252	0.351	0.432	0.495	0.546	0.581	0.610	0.635	0.655	0.671
18	0.122	0.254	0.357	0.439	0.503	0.558	0.598	0.629	0.658	0.682	0.702
20	0.121	0.258	0.364	0.449	0.516	0.569	0.613	0.648	0.680	0.707	0.730
Spanwise station $\frac{y}{b/2} = 0.975$											
2	0.132	0.172	0.207	0.239	0.263	0.272	0.274	0.277	0.279	0.281	0.282
3	0.119	0.166	0.210	0.250	0.278	0.289	0.291	0.294	0.298	0.300	0.301
4	0.107	0.163	0.214	0.258	0.288	0.304	0.308	0.311	0.315	0.319	0.322
5	0.098	0.158	0.217	0.269	0.304	0.320	0.322	0.328	0.333	0.338	0.342
6	0.089	0.158	0.219	0.272	0.314	0.332	0.340	0.344	0.350	0.357	0.361
7	0.081	0.158	0.222	0.278	0.320	0.342	0.351	0.359	0.366	0.373	0.384
8	0.077	0.158	0.228	0.283	0.328	0.352	0.363	0.374	0.383	0.391	0.400
10	0.069	0.158	0.233	0.295	0.343	0.373	0.390	0.403	0.415	0.428	0.438
12	0.068	0.161	0.242	0.308	0.360	0.395	0.413	0.430	0.448	0.461	0.473
14	0.066	0.163	0.248	0.320	0.376	0.413	0.438	0.458	0.478	0.495	0.510
16	0.064	0.166	0.255	0.331	0.394	0.435	0.463	0.488	0.510	0.529	0.546
18	0.063	0.169	0.263	0.346	0.412	0.461	0.492	0.518	0.539	0.560	0.580
20	0.082	0.171	0.271	0.363	0.435	0.483	0.515	0.544	0.570	0.593	0.615

TABLE XXV.—BASIC SPAN-LIFT DISTRIBUTION DATA, VALUES OF L_b FOR ROUNDED-TIP WINGS*

Æ \ $\frac{c_t}{c}$	0	0.1	0.2	0.3	0.4	0.5	0.6	0.7	0.8	0.9	1.0
					Spanwise station $\frac{y}{b/2} = 0$						
2	−0.118	−0.121	−0.122	−0.122	−0.122	−0.121	−0.121	−0.121	−0.120	−0.120	−0.120
3	−0.153	−0.160	−0.162	−0.163	−0.175	−0.164	−0.164	−0.163	−0.162	−0.161	−0.160
4	−0.183	−0.192	−0.197	−0.199	−0.199	−0.199	−0.198	−0.197	−0.196	−0.194	−0.192
5	−0.211	−0.221	−0.224	−0.226	−0.225	−0.225	−0.224	−0.224	−0.221	−0.219	−0.218
6	−0.235	−0.248	−0.253	−0.253	−0.252	−0.252	−0.250	−0.247	−0.244	−0.243	−0.242
7	−0.256	−0.269	−0.275	−0.276	−0.274	−0.272	−0.270	−0.268	−0.264	−0.261	−0.258
8	−0.274	−0.288	−0.293	−0.293	−0.291	−0.290	−0.288	−0.285	−0.282	−0.279	−0.276
10	−0.304	−0.318	−0.322	−0.323	−0.321	−0.320	−0.318	−9.315	−0.311	−0.305	−0.299
12	−0.329	−0.342	−0.350	−0.349	−0.348	−0.346	−0.341	−0.337	−0.331	−0.323	−0.317
14	−0.350	−0.364	−0.370	−0.370	−0.368	−0.365	−0.360	−0.355	−0.350	−0.343	−0.334
16	−0.367	−0.380	−0.386	−0.385	−0.382	−0.379	−0.375	−0.370	−0.362	−0.358	−0.348
18	−0.384	−0.399	−0.405	−0.403	−0.400	−0.393	−0.387	−0.380	−0.376	−0.368	−0.360
20	−0.398	−0.411	−0.417	−0.415	−0.410	−0.404	−0.399	−0.392	−0.386	−0.378	−0.369
					Spanwise station $\frac{y}{b/2} = 0.2$						
2	−0.076	−0.080	−0.082	−0.085	−0.086	−0.086	−0.086	−0.085	−0.085	−0.084	−0.083
3	−0.098	−0.108	−0.111	−0.112	−0.113	−0.113	−0.113	−0.113	−0.112	−0.110	−0.108
4	−0.117	−0.130	−0.135	−0.138	−0.137	−0.137	−0.137	−0.137	−0.137	−0.135	−0.132
5	−0.131	−0.148	−0.156	−0.159	−0.159	−0.158	−0.158	−0.158	−0.157	−0.156	−0.152
6	−0.145	−0.162	−0.173	−0.176	−0.176	−0.176	−0.176	−0.176	−0.175	−0.172	−0.170
7	−0.156	−0.178	−0.189	−0.192	−0.192	−0.192	−0.191	−0.191	−0.190	−0.190	−0.189
8	−0.168	−0.189	−0.200	−0.204	−0.204	−0.205	−0.205	−0.206	−0.205	−0.204	−0.204
10	−0.182	−0.207	−0.220	−0.224	−0.225	−0.225	−0.226	−0.226	−0.225	−0.225	−0.225
12	−0.197	−0.226	−0.239	−0.240	−0.239	−0.238	−0.238	−0.238	−0.237	−0.237	−0.237
14	−0.206	−0.234	−0.248	−0.249	−0.248	−0.248	−0.248	−0.248	−0.248	−0.248	−0.248
16	−0.212	−0.242	−0.256	−0.258	−0.257	−0.256	−0.256	−0.256	−0.256	−0.256	−0.255
18	−0.219	−0.247	−0.260	−0.264	−0.265	−0.265	−0.265	−0.265	−0.265	−0.264	−0.262
20	−0.222	−0.255	−0.269	−0.271	−0.271	−0.271	−0.252	−0.252	−0.252	−0.252	−0.270
					Spanwise station $\frac{y}{b/2} = 0.4$						
2	−0.006	−0.011	−0.013	−0.015	−0.016	−0.016	−0.016	−0.016	−0.016	−0.016	−0.015
3	−0.002	−0.010	−0.012	−0.015	−0.016	−0.016	−0.016	−0.016	−0.017	−0.018	−0.018
4	0	−0.006	−0.011	−0.012	−0.016	−0.016	−0.018	−0.019	−0.020	−0.020	−0.021
5	0.004	−0.004	−0.010	−0.012	−0.016	−0.018	−0.020	−0.021	−0.021	−0.022	−0.023
6	0.009	−0.002	−0.008	−0.012	−0.016	−0.018	−0.020	−0.021	−0.022	−0.024	−0.026
7	0.012	−0.001	−0.010	−0.013	−0.017	−0.018	−0.020	−0.022	−0.025	−0.027	−0.029
8	0.014	0	−0.008	−0.012	−0.017	−0.019	−0.021	−0.025	−0.029	−0.030	−0.030
10	0.021	0.007	−0.002	−0.010	−0.017	−0.020	−0.022	−0.027	−0.030	−0.032	−0.032
12	0.028	0.009	−0.001	−0.010	−0.017	−0.021	−0.025	−0.029	−0.032	−0.036	−0.038
14	0.036	0.013	0	−0.010	−0.017	−0.021	−0.028	−0.031	−0.035	−0.040	−0.042
16	0.043	0.019	0.002	−0.008	−0.016	−0.022	−0.029	−0.034	−0.038	−0.041	−0.045
18	0.049	0.022	0.004	−0.008	−0.015	−0.022	−0.031	−0.038	−0.041	−0.043	−0.046
20	0.050	0.023	0.006	−0.006	−0.014	−0.022	−0.031	−0.038	−0.041	−0.046	−0.049
					Spanwise station $\frac{y}{b/2} = 0.6$						
2	0.052	0.052	0.051	0.050	0.050	0.050	0.050	0.050	0.049	0.049	0.048
3	0.070	0.069	0.068	0.068	0.068	0.068	0.068	0.068	0.068	0.068	0.068
4	0.085	0.082	0.081	0.080	0.080	0.080	0.080	0.080	0.080	0.080	0.080
5	0.099	0.095	0.092	0.091	0.091	0.091	0.091	0.091	0.091	0.090	0.090
6	0.109	0.107	0.104	0.102	0.101	0.101	0.100	0.100	0.100	0.100	0.100
7	0.119	0.117	0.114	0.112	0.111	0.110	0.110	0.110	0.110	0.109	0.108
8	0.128	0.122	0.121	0.120	0.120	0.119	0.119	0.118	0.118	0.117	0.116
10	0.139	0.138	0.135	0.132	0.131	0.130	0.130	0.129	0.128	0.126	0.124
12	0.148	0.145	0.141	0.140	0.140	0.139	0.137	0.135	0.134	0.132	0.130
14	0.155	0.152	0.150	0.148	0.145	0.142	0.141	0.140	0.139	0.138	0.135
16	0.160	0.158	0.154	0.151	0.149	0.146	0.143	0.141	0.140	0.139	0.136
18	0.165	0.162	0.160	0.158	0.152	0.148	0.145	0.142	0.140	0.139	0.138
20	0.170	0.169	0.165	0.159	0.152	0.148	01147	0.143	0.141	0.140	0.140

TABLE XXV.—BASIC SPAN-LIFT DISTRIBUTION DATA, VALUES OF L_b FOR ROUNDED-TIP WINGS.*—(*Concluded*)

c_s/c_t / Æ	0	0.1	0.2	0.3	0.4	0.5	0.6	0.7	0.8	0.9	1.0
Spanwise station $\frac{y}{b/2} = 0.8$											
2	0.072	0.079	0.080	0.082	0.083	0.085	0.085	0.086	0.086	0.084	0.081
3	0.088	0.098	0.101	0.102	0.104	0.108	0.109	0.110	0.110	0.108	0.106
4	0.100	0.113	0.120	0.123	0.126	0.128	0.128	0.130	0.130	0.130	0.129
5	0.109	0.125	0.135	0.138	0.140	0.143	0.147	0.148	0.148	0.148	0.149
6	0.115	0.135	0.148	0.152	0.156	0.160	0.160	0.162	0.163	0.164	0.165
7	0.121	0.142	0.158	0.163	0.169	0.172	0.173	0.173	0.174	0.174	0.175
8	0.126	0.149	0.164	0.174	0.180	0.182	0.182	0.183	0.183	0.184	0.184
10	0.136	0.160	0.178	0.188	0.195	0.200	0.201	0.202	0.203	0.201	0.198
12	0.145	0.170	0.188	0.200	0.208	0.212	0.214	0.216	0.216	0.214	0.210
14	0.152	0.182	0.200	0.210	0.216	0.221	0.223	0.227	0.228	0.225	0.220
16	0.159	0.186	0.205	0.216	0.222	0.229	0.232	0.233	0.236	0.232	0.229
18	0.161	0.197	0.215	0.224	0.230	0.235	0.239	0.242	0.243	0.242	0.238
20	0.166	0.201	0.220	0.232	0.237	0.241	0.243	0.248	0.248	0.248	0.247
Spanwise station $\frac{y}{b/2} = 0.9$											
2	0.059	0.068	0.072	0.073	0.075	0.076	0.075	0.075	0.075	0.075	0.075
3	0.068	0.083	0.092	0.098	0.099	0.100	0.100	0.100	0.100	0.100	0.100
4	0.074	0.098	0.111	0.118	0.121	0.122	0.123	0.123	0.123	0.123	0.123
5	0.081	0.107	0.122	0.131	0.138	0.140	0.141	0.141	0.142	0.142	0.142
6	0.087	0.117	0.136	0.148	0.154	0.159	0.160	0.160	0.160	0.160	0.160
7	0.090	0.123	0.146	0.160	0.167	0.171	0.171	0.171	0.172	0.172	0.172
8	0.092	0.131	0.153	0.170	0.179	0.182	0.183	0.184	0.185	0.186	0.187
10	0.098	0.139	0.166	0.184	0.197	0.201	0.203	0.205	0.207	0.209	0.210
12	0.100	0.147	0.178	0.198	0.210	0.218	0.221	0.225	0.228	0.229	0.230
14	0.102	0.156	0.188	0.208	0.220	0.231	0.238	0.241	0.243	0.245	0.246
16	0.103	0.161	0.197	0.219	0.231	0.241	0.249	0.253	0.258	0.259	0.260
18	0.105	0.166	0.202	0.228	0.243	0.252	0.260	0.263	0.269	0.271	0.275
20	0.107	0.172	0.211	0.238	0.248	0.260	0.268	0.273	0.279	0.282	0.285
Spanwise station $\frac{y}{b/2} = 0.95$											
2	0.038	0.051	0.058	0.059	0.060	0.060	0.060	0.060	0.059	0.059	0.058
3	0.044	0.063	0.073	0.078	0.069	0.080	0.080	0.080	0.080	0.079	0.078
4	0.050	0.072	0.076	0.092	0.095	0.097	0.099	0.100	0.100	0.100	0.099
5	0.052	0.083	0.100	0.107	0.110	0.112	0.113	0.114	0.116	0.117	0.116
6	0.054	0.088	0.109	0.119	0.122	0.128	0.130	0.132	0.132	0.131	0.130
7	0.056	0.093	0.116	0.130	0.135	0.140	0.144	0.148	0.150	0.149	0.145
8	0.057	0.100	0.125	0.140	0.146	0.152	0.158	0.160	0.161	0.160	0.159
10	0.058	0.107	0.138	0.152	0.162	0.171	0.178	0.182	0.186	0.187	0.183
12	0.059	0.112	0.143	0.165	0.169	0.189	0.198	0.200	0.202	0.205	0.204
14	0.060	0.116	0.151	0.174	0.190	0.202	0.214	0.215	0.218	0.221	0.222
16	0.061	0.121	0.159	0.184	0.203	0.218	0.222	0.229	0.233	0.236	0.238
18	0.061	0.126	0.166	0.194	0.213	0.229	0.236	0.241	0.248	0.251	0.255
20	0.061	0.128	0.173	0.203	0.225	0.239	0.245	0.251	0 259	0.265	0.271
Spanwise station $\frac{y}{b/2} = 0.975$											
2	0.019	0.030	0.035	0.037	0.037	0.037	0.037	0.036	0.036	0.035	0.064
3	0.022	0.039	0.045	0.049	0.050	0.051	0.052	0.054	0.053	0.052	0.051
4	0.026	0.043	0.054	0.060	0.062	0.064	0.068	0.069	0.069	0.068	0.067
5	0.029	0.051	0.065	0.070	0.071	0.075	0.078	0.081	0.082	0.083	0.083
6	0.030	0.055	0.071	0.079	0.082	0.088	0.091	0.094	0.097	0.097	0.097
7	0.030	0.060	0.078	0.087	0.091	0.098	0.101	0.107	0.110	0.110	0.110
8	0.030	0.062	0.081	0.091	0.100	0.107	0.112	0.120	0.121	0.121	0.121
10	0.031	0.067	0.090	0.105	0.115	0.124	0.132	0.138	0.141	0.142	0.143
12	0.031	0.069	0.095	0.115	0.131	0.141	0.149	0.153	0.160	0.161	0.162
14	0.031	0.071	0.102	0.127	0.143	0.155	0.163	0.171	0.175	0.177	0.178
16	0.031	0.077	0.111	0.138	0.156	0.169	0.178	0.182	0.188	0.190	0.191
18	0.032	0.083	0.121	0.150	0.169	0.182	0.191	0.197	0.200	0.201	0.202
20	0.032	0.086	0.128	0.158	0.178	0.193	0.202	0.208	0.210	0.212	0.213

* From *NACA Tech. Rept.* 631, Table, III.

DETERMINATION OF THE CHARACTERISTICS OF TAPERED WINGS[1]

An illustrative example is here worked out for a wing with straight taper and rounded tips having the following characteristics:

$$\mathcal{R} = 6$$
$$\frac{c_t}{c_s} = 0.5$$
$$b = 40 \text{ ft}$$
$$S = 266.7 \text{ sq ft}$$
$$\beta = 10°$$
$$C_L = 1.2$$
$$q = 10 \text{ lb per sq ft}$$

Root section:
NACA 4415

$$a_{0_s} = 0.097$$
$$\alpha_{l0_s} = -3.8°$$
$$c_{m\ a.c._s} = -0.083$$

Construction tip section:
NACA 2409

$$a_{0_t} = 0.099$$
$$\alpha_{0_t} = -1.7°$$
$$c_{m\ a.c._t} = -0.044$$

The angle of twist measured between the chords of the root and construction tip sections is -5 deg (washout). Then, by the use of the angles of zero lift of the root and tip sections, the angle of aerodynamic twist is determined to be -7.1 deg.

The chord at several stations along the semispan and the calculation of the lift distribution are given in Table XXVII. In the table, a_0 and $c_{m\ a.c.}$ are assumed to have a linear variation along the semispan. Values of L_b and L_a were obtained from Tables XXV and XXVI for an aspect ratio of 6 and a taper ratio of 0.5 and the basic, additional, and total lift distributions were computed and plotted in Fig. A10. The pitching-moment coefficient $c_{m\ a.c.}$ varies so much along the semispan that C_{m_s} cannot be found by use of the factor E but must be found by use from (4). Accordingly, $c_{m\ a.c.}\ c^2$ is plotted against y in Fig. A19, and C_{m_s} is found from the area under the curve to be -0.072.

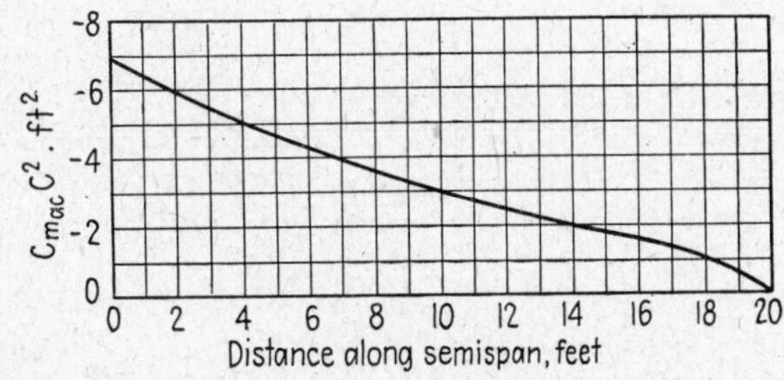

FIG. A19.—Graphical determination of section pitching moment.

$$C_{m_s} = \frac{2b}{S^2}\int_0^{b/2} c_{m\ a.c.}\ c^2 dy = -0.072$$

[1] *NACA Tech. Rept.* 572.

From Figs. A11 to A18 the remaining factors and characteristics are determined to be

$$f = 0.989 \qquad a = 0.0755$$
$$J = -0.408 \qquad \alpha_s = 15.0$$
$$u = 0.995 \qquad s(L = 0) = -0.9$$
$$v = 0.0001 \qquad C_{D1} = 0.0786$$
$$w = 0.0039 \qquad C_{mlb} = 0.015$$
$$G = 0.0190 \qquad f_{a.c.} = 0.057$$
$$H = 0.214$$
$$C_{m\,a.c.} = 0.072 + 0.015 = -0.057$$

Table XXVI.—Calculation of Lift Distribution for Illustrative Example

$\frac{y}{b/2}$	c	a_0	L_b	L_a	C_{lb}*	C_{la1}†	$C_L \times c_{la1}$	c_l	l_b	l_a	l	$c_{m\,a.c.}$	$c_{m\,a.c.} \times c^2$
0	9.13	0.097	−0.252	1.300	0.127	0.950	1.140	1.267	11.59	104.0	115.6	−0.083	−6.92
0.2	8.22	0.097	−0.176	1.236	0.098	1.003	1.205	1.303	8.05	99.0	107.2	−0.075	−5.06
0.4	7.30	0.098	−0.018	1.138	0.012	1.039	1.248	1.260	0.88	91.0	92.0	−0.067	−3.57
0.6	6.39	0.098	0.101	0.993	−0.073	1.036	1.242	1.169	−4.66	79.6	74.7	−0.060	−2.45
0.8	5.42	0.099	0.160	0.775	−0.138	0.954	1.145	1.007	−7.48	62.0	54.6	−0.052	−1.53
0.9	4.49	0.099	0.159	0.595	−0.165	0.884	1.061	0.896	−7.41	47.7	40.3	−0.048	−0.97
0.95	3.43	0.099	0.128	0.451	−0.175	0.877	1.053	0.878	−6.01	36.2	30.1	−0.046	−0.54
0.975	2.47	0.099	0.088	0.332	−0.167	0.896	1.076	0.909	−4.13	26.6	22.4	−0.045	−0.27
1.0	0	(0.099)	0	0	0	0	0	0	0	0	0	(−0.044)	0

* $c_{lb} = (\epsilon a_0 S/cb)L_b = -47.3(a_0/c)L_b$.

† $c_{la1} - (S/cb)L_a = (6.67/c)L_a$.

TABLE XXVII.—PRESSURE DISTRIBUTION—ADDITIONAL

Station	$P_{a.c.}$	P_{a1}			
		Class B	Class C	Class D	Class E
0	0	0	0	0	0
1.25	3.2	5.93	4.96	4.32	3.37
2.5	4.5	4.37	4.23	4.02	3.81
5	5.5	3.20	3.22	3.25	3.27
7	5.9	2.63	2.68	2.76	2.31
10	5.7	2.26	2.32	2.39	2.44
15	5.0	1.77	1.85	1.90	1.95
20	4.3	1.47	1.54	1.58	1.62
30	2.9	1.10	1.14	1.16	1.18
40	1.4	0.86	0.87	0.88	0.89
50	0	0.67	0.68	0.68	0.69
60	−1.4	0.51	0.51	0.51	0.51
70	−2.9	0.38	0.37	0.37	0.36
80	−4.3	0.25	0.24	0.24	0.23
90	−5.7	0.13	0.12	0.12	0.11
95	−5.5	0.06	0.06	0.06	0.06
100	0	0	0	0	0

NOTE: Type A distributions have not yet been determined.

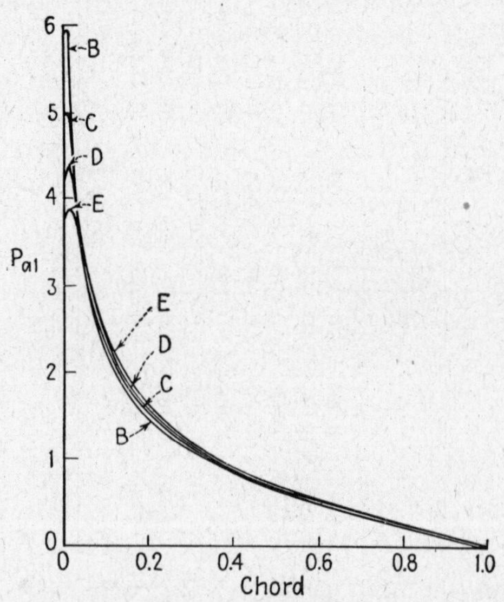

FIG. A20.—Pressure distribution—additional.

TABLE XXVIII.—PRESSURE DISTRIBUTION—BASIC

Station	P_{bm}		P_{bc}	
	Class 1	Class 0	Class 1	Class 2
0	0	0	0	0
1.25	2.85		2.5	32.5
2.5	4.25		5.5	47.0
5	6.05		10.0	56.5
7.5	7.10		14.5	59.0
10	7.80		18.0	57.5
15	8.80		23.0	47.5
20	9.30		25.0	37.0
30	9.50		25.0	24.5
40	8.80		20.5	18.0
50	7.75		14.0	13.0
60	6.60		6.0	9.0
70	5.30		−2.5	5.5
80	3.75		−5.5	3.5
90	2.05		−4.5	1.5
95	1.10		−2.5	1.0
100	0		0	0
$(c_n)_{bm}$ =	6.30	0	9.70	18.75 = $(c_n)_{bc}$

$$P_b = -c_{m\ a.c.}P_{bm} + \frac{Z_c}{c} P_{bc}.$$

$$c_{nb} = c_{m\ a.c.}(c_n)_{bm} + \frac{Z_c}{c} (c_n)_{bc}.$$

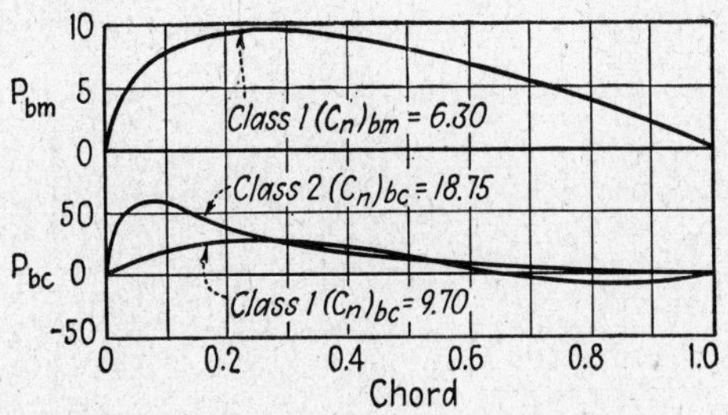

FIG. A21.—Pressure distribution—basic.

TABLE XXIX.—CLASSIFICATION OF AIRFOIL PRESSURE DISTRIBUTION DATA*

Airfoil	Class	Airfoil	Class	Airfoil	Class	Airfoil	Class
NACA:		NACA:		NACA:		N 69	B10
0006	A10	4712	C10	23015	D12	N 71	C10
0009	B10	6212	C10	23018	E12	N 75	C10
0012	C10	6306	A10	23021	F12	N 76	C10
0015	D10	6309	B10	24012	C12	N 80	C10
0018	E10	6312	C10	25012	C12	N 81	C10
0021	F10	6315	D10				
		6318	E10	32012	C12	G 387	D10
2212	C12	6321	F10	33012	C12	G 398	D10
2306	A10			34012	C12	G 398A	C10
2309	B10	6406	A10			G 398B	C10
2312	C10	6409	B10	42012	C12	G 398R	D11
2315	D10	6412	C10	43009	B12	G 413	D10
		6415	D10	43012	C12		
2406	A10	6418	E10	43012A	C12	G 420	E10
2409	B10	6421	F10			G 429AG	C10
2412	C10			43015	D12	G 429J	C10
2415	D10	6506	A10	43018	E12	G 436	C10
2418	E10	6509	B10	43021	F12	G 532	C10
2412	F10	6512	C10	44012	C12		
		6515	D10			C Y	C10
2506	A10	6518	E10	62021	F12	C Y-B	C10
2509	B10	6521	F10	63009	B12	C YM-15	D10
2512	C10	6612	C10	63012	C12	C YM-18	E10
2515	D10	6712	C10				
2518	E10			63015	D12	C Y-6	A10
2521	F10	0006T†	A10	62018	E12	C Y-8	B10
2612	C10	0006B	B10	63021	F12	C Y-10	B10
		0012T	B10	64021	F12	C Y-14	D10
2712	C10	0012B	D10			C Y-18	E10
4212	C10	0018T	D10	B 103	C10	C Y-22	F10
4306	A10	0018B	F10	B 103A	B10		
4309	B10	$2R_1 12$†	C11	B 106	C10	NACA:	
4312	C10	$2R_2 12$	C11			CYH	C11
4315	D10			B 106R	C11	−M6	C11
4318	E10	22112	C11	B 111	C10		
4321	F10	23112	C11	B 112	C10	15	C10
		24112	C11			16	C10
4406	A10	25112	C11	S GS-M	D10	17	C10
4409	B10			S GS-I	D10	18	C10
4412	C10	21012	C12			19	B10
4415	D10	22012	C12	S.T. Ae27a	F10	20	B10
4418	E10	23006	A12	RAF34	C11	21	C11
4421	F10	23009	B12				
		23012	C12	USA27	C10	23	B11
4509	B10			USA35A	E10	24	C11
4512	C10	23012-33	B12	USA35B	C10	25	D11
4515	D10	23012-34	B12			26	E11
4518	E10	23012-64	C12	C 62	D10	27	A11
4521	F10			C 72	C10		
4612	C10			C 80	B10		
				N 22	C10		
				N 60	C10		
				N 60R	C11		
				N 68	B10		

Abbreviations: B = Boeing; S = Sikorsky; G = Goettinger; C = Clark; N = U.S. Navy.

* Classifications refer to data on pp. 423 to 429.

† See footnote, p. 388.

TABLE XXX.—P_a DISTRIBUTION DATA FOR CLASSIFIED AIRFOILS

Chord station	P_{ac1}	P_{at}					
		Class A*	Class B	Class C	Class D	Class E	Class F*
0	0	0	0	0	0	0	0
0.0125	3.2	6.00	5.93	4.98	4.32	3.87	
0.025	4.5	4.58	4.37	4.23	4.02	3.81	3.64
0.05	5.5	3.18	3.20	3.22	3.25	3.27	3.29
0.075	5.9	2.56	2.63	2.68	2.76	2.81	2.87
0.10	5.7	2.20	2.26	2.32	2.39	2.44	2.51
0.15	5.0	1.72	1.77	1.85	1.90	1.95	2.01
0.20	4.3	1.42	1.47	1.54	1.58	1.62	1.68
0.25	3.6	1.23	1.25	1.30	1.35	1.39	1.43
0.30	2.9	1.08	1.10	1.14	1.16	1.18	1.22
0.40	1.4	0.85	0.86	0.87	0.88	0.89	0.90
0.50	0	0.67	0.67	0.68	0.68	0.69	0.70
0.60	−1.4	0.51	0.51	0.51	0.51	0.51	0.51
0.70	−2.9	0.37	0.38	0.37	0.37	0.36	0.36
0.80	−4.3	0.24	0.25	0.24	0.24	0.23	0.23
0.90	−5.7	0.13	0.13	0.12	0.12	0.11	0.12
0.95	−5.5	0.06	0.06	0.06	0.06	0.06	0.06
1.00	0	0	0	0	0	0	0

* These distributions were not given in *NACA Tech. Rept.* 631. Values presented here were obtained as outlined in paragraph 1.33 of the Army–Navy–Civil Committee on Design publication ANC-1(2), Chordwise Air-load Distribution.

Classes A, B, C, D, E, and F correspond to airfoils having the same thickness distribution as the NACA 0010 series and having values of t of 6, 9, 12, 15, 18, and 21%, respectively.

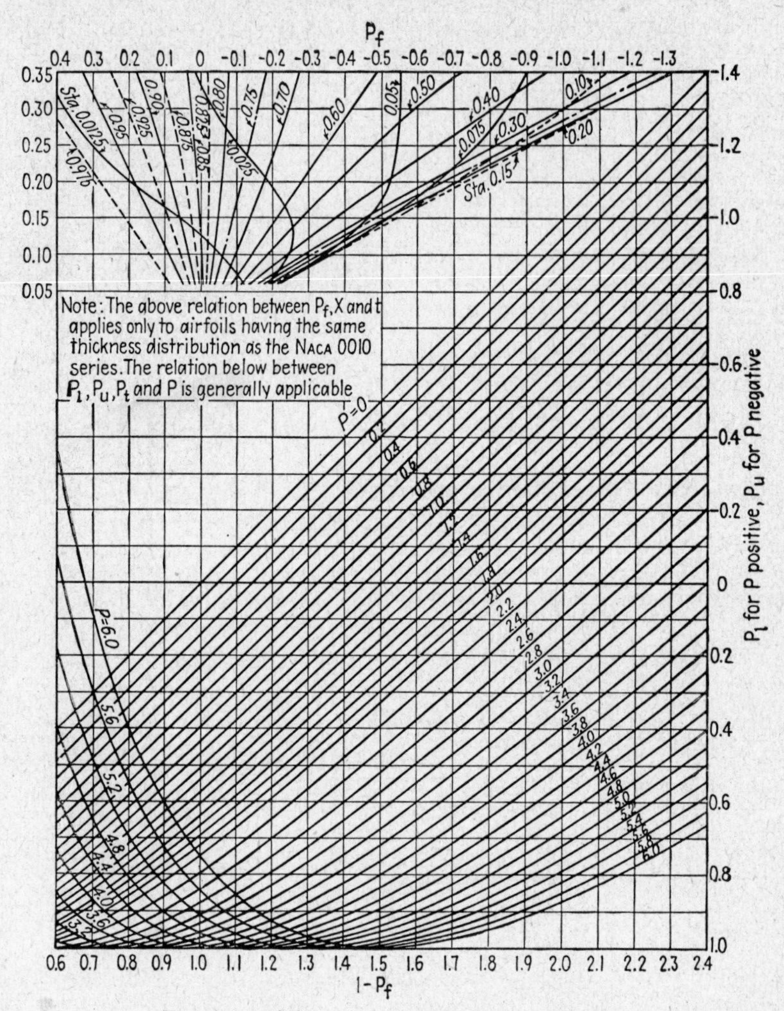

FIG. A22.—Chart for determination of P_u and P_l.

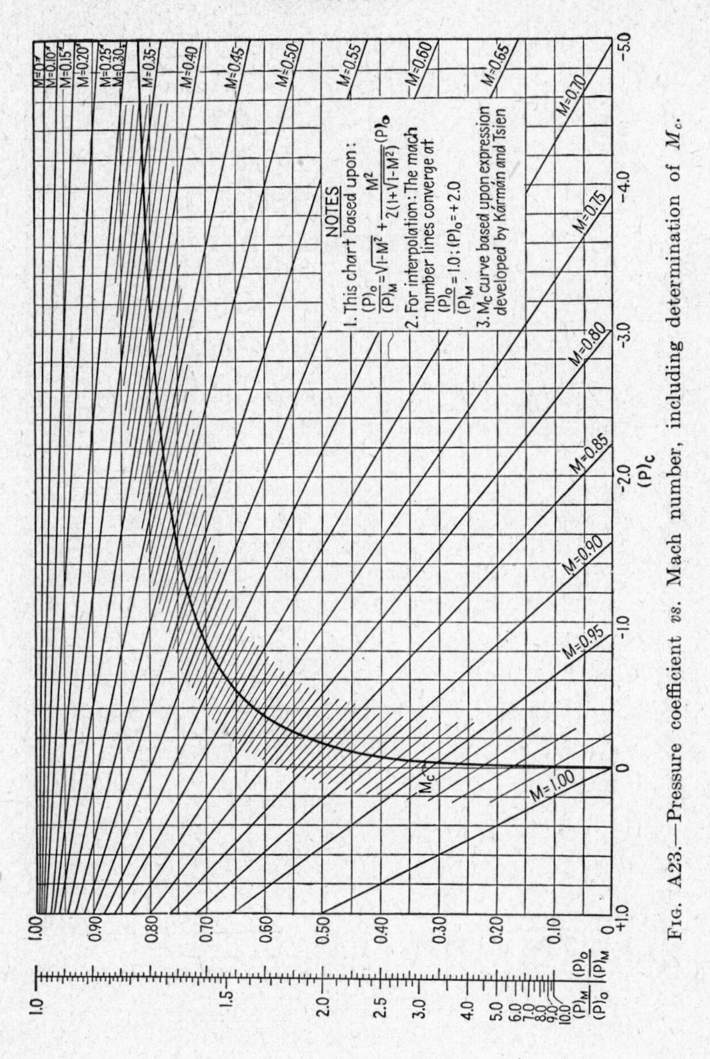

Fig. A23.—Pressure coefficient *vs.* Mach number, including determination of M_c.

APPENDIX 5

PARASITE DRAG DATA

TABLE XXXI.—FUSELAGE-DRAG DATA—FUSELAGES ALONE*

Station	Round fuselage dia.	Rectangular fuselage		Station	Round fuselage dia.	Rectangular fuselage		Sketch
		Height	Width			Height	Width	
−0.156	0.000	0.000 diameter		8.000	3.440	3.440	2.702	
0.000	0.772	0.772 diameter		10.000	3.406	3.406	2.675	
0.250	1.242	1.242 diameter		12.000	3.268	3.268	2.567	
0.500	1.572	1.572 diameter		14.000	2.990	2.990	2.348	
0.719	.....	1.795 diameter		16.000	2.516	2.516	1.976	
1.000	2.044			17.000	2.170	2.175	1.704	
1.500	.....	2.380	2.240	18.000	1.698	.....	1.334	
2.000	2.650	.....	.....	19.000	1.000	.....	0.785	
2.312	.....	2.790	2.370	19.500	0.548	.....	0.430	
3.406	.....	3.090	2.470	20.000	0.000	1.125	0.000	
4.000	3.238	3.238	2.543					
6.000	3.410	3.410	2.678					Fuselage sketch, NACA TR 640 Wing $c/4$ at fuselage $L/4$.

* Fuselage dimensions, NACA TR 540 (1935) 575 (1936), and 678 (1939).
Drag of above fuselages alone at $\alpha = 0$, VDT $Re = 14{,}000{,}000$ based on fuselage length.

Round fuselage, $C_{D\pi} = 0.066$
Rectangular fuselage, $C_{D\pi} = 0.079$

GALCIT data on $\Delta C_{D\pi}$ due to fuselages, $Re = 1{,}000{,}000$ to $8{,}000{,}000$ based on fuselage length See Millikan, "Aerodynamics of the Airplane," p. 98.

Dirigible hull alone, $C_{D\pi} = 0.072$
Large transports or bombers, no nose engine $\Delta C_{D\pi} = 0.070$ to 0.105
Small airplane, closed cockpit + nose engine, $\Delta C_{D\pi} = 0.090$ to 0.130

TABLE XXXII.—DRAG OF WING-FUSELAGE COMBINATIONS*

Diagrams representing combinations	Vert. position $\frac{k}{c}$	a, AR = 6.86	Eff. factor e	C_{De} min	A.c.	C_{m0}	C_{Lib}	$C_{L\,max}$ Re = 8.2	$C_{L\,max}$ Re = 3.7	$\Delta C_{D\pi}$ fuselage
	Tapered NACA 0018–0009 airf il with rectangular fuselage									
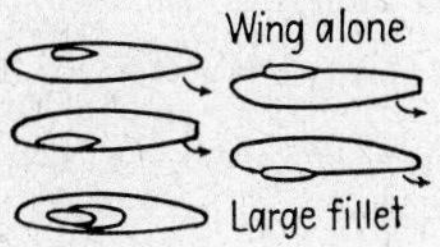		0.077	0.90	0.0093	0.020	0.000	1.4	1.48	1.23	0
Wing alone	0.22	0.078	0.85	0.0124	0.030	0.005	1.6	1.62	1.34	0.050
	0.34	0.078	0.85	0.0128	0.027	0.004	1.4	1.49	1.34	0.057
	−0.22	0.080	0.90‡	0.0124	0.027	−0.005	1.5	1.51	1.27	0.050
	−0.34	0.079	0.80‡	0.0128	0.023	−0.004	0.9	1.26	1.10	0.057
Large fillet	0.00	0.079	0.85	0.0127	0.030	0.000	1.5	1.53	1.26	0.055
	Tapered NACA 0018–0009 airfoil with round fuselage									
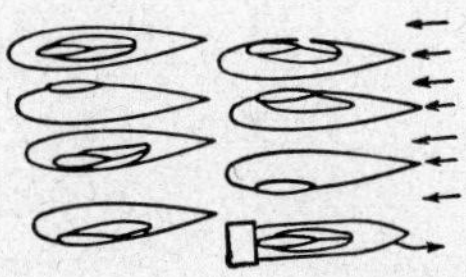	0.00	0.080	0.85†	0.0117	0.026	0.000	1.5	1.52	1.27	0.039
	0.22	0.079	0.85§	0.0124	0.023	−0.001	1.6	1.65	1.37	0.050
	0.34	0.076	0.85	0.0139	0.034	0.006	1.6	1.61	1.31	0.075
	0.34	0.078	0.85	0.0135	0.027	−0.003	1.6	1.69	1.38	0.068
	−0.22	0.080	0.90§	0.0124	0.028	0.001	1.4	1.48	1.22	0.050
	−0.34	0.076	0.60‡	0.0139	0.028	−0.006	0.3	1.28	1.09	0.075
	−0.34	0.080	0.90§	0.0135	0.024	0.003	1.5	1.54	1.22	0.068
	0.00	0.080	0.80	0.0142	0.040	−0.003	1.5	1.53	1.28	0.063

* From *NACA Tech. Rept.* 575, 0018–0009 wing. Wing incidence = 0; horizontal location, $c/4$ of wing at $L/4$ of fuselage. Vertical wing locations noted.

† Poor agreement in high-speed range.

‡ Poor agreement over whole range.

§ Poor agreement in high-lift range.

TABLE XXXIII.—FUSELAGE-DRAG DATA*

Sketch	Fuselage no.	$C_{D\pi}$
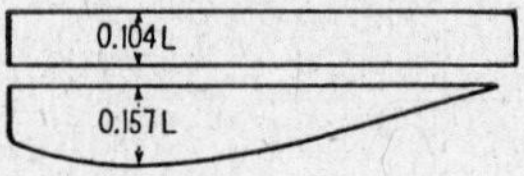 0.104L 0.157L	1	0.353
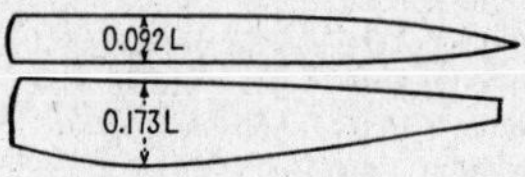 0.092L 0.173L	2	0.266
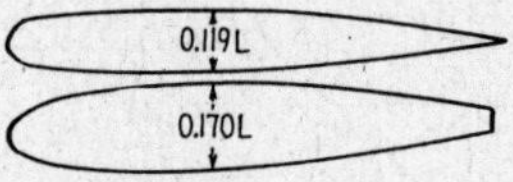 0.119L 0.170L	3	0.062
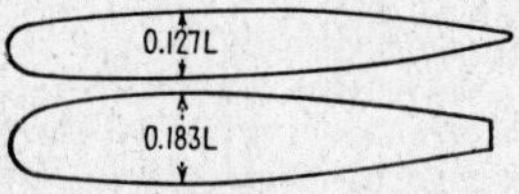 0.127L 0.183L	4	0.071
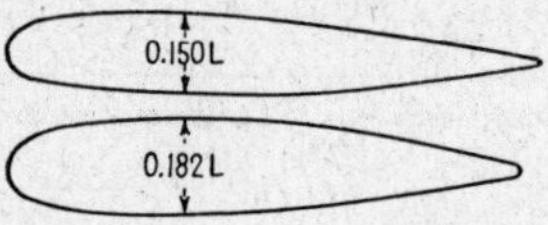 0.150L 0.182L	5	0.063
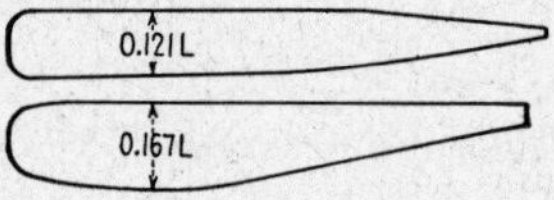 0.121L 0.167L	6	0.116

* Data on drag of fuselage models in Washington Navy Yard tunnel at Re = 400,000 based on fuselage length. From Diehl, "Engineering Aerodynamics," rev. ed., p. 284.

TABLE XXXIV.—NACELLE-DRAG DATA

Nacelles alone. $C_{D\pi}$ = 0.13 for nacelle shown, which was one of the best tested prior to 1940. See *NACA Tech. Rept.* 592.

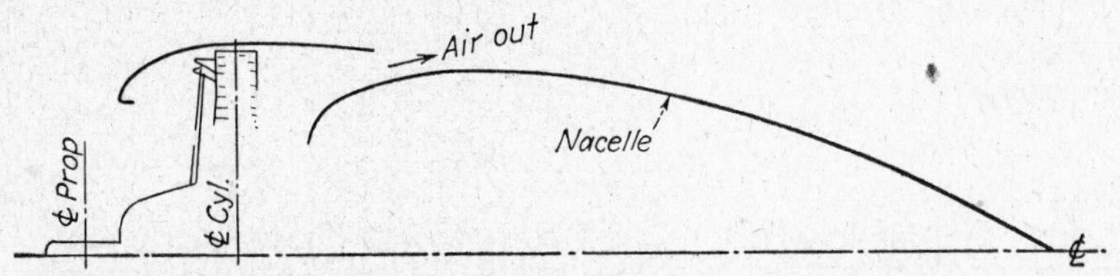

Nacelle-wing combinations. See Diehl, "Engineering Aerodynamics," rev. ed., p. 300; *NACA Tech. Rept.* 415 (1932); *NACA Tech. Rept.* 507 (1934).

GALCIT data:

Nacelle above wing,	$\Delta C_{D\pi}$ = 0.250
Relatively large leading-edge nacelles, small airplane,	$\Delta C_{D\pi}$ = 0.120
Relatively small leading-edge nacelles, large airplane,	$\Delta C_{D\pi}$ = 0.080
Improved nacelles, no cooling air flow,	$\Delta C_{D\pi}$ = 0.050
Improved nacelles, typical cooling air flow,	$\Delta C_{D\pi}$ = 0.100

Relative drag contours of a cowled tractor nacelle. Free air drag = 1.00. Center of propeller hub is reference point. Data from *NACA Tech. Rept.* 415, as plotted by Diehl, "Engineering Aerodynamics," rev. ed.

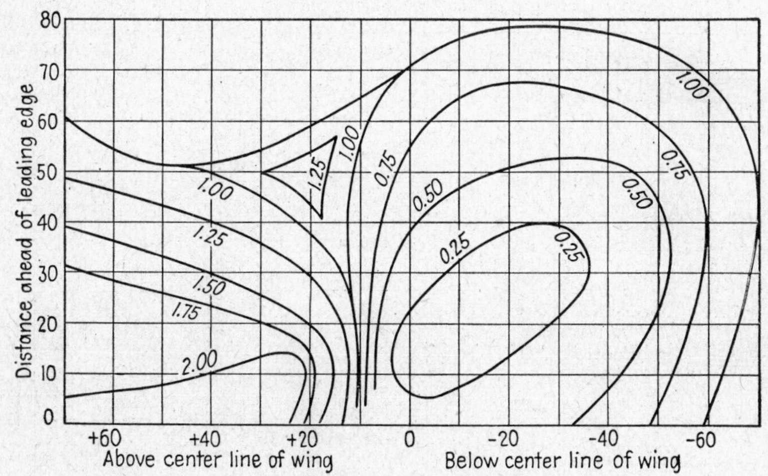

FIG. A24.—Relative drag contours of a cowled tractor nacelle.

Tail-surface-drag Data

For tail surfaces alone, see wing data, Appendix A4.

GALCIT data on $C_{D\pi}$ for tail surfaces (see Millikan, "Aerodynamics of the Airplane," p. 98):

Single-engine low-wing monoplane,	$\Delta C_{D\pi}$ = 0.0085 to 0.0120
Multiengine low-wing monoplane,	$\Delta C_{D\pi}$ = 0.0060 to 0.0110
Multiengine high-wing monoplane,	$\Delta C_{D\pi}$ = 0.0120 to 0.0180

TABLE XXXV.—WING-FUSELAGE-TAIL COMBINATIONS*

Diagrams representing combinations	Remarks	Vert. pos. $\frac{k}{c}$	i_w	a, Æ = 6.86	Eff. factor e	C_{De} min	a.c.	C_{m0}	C_{Lib}	$C_{L\max}$ Re = 8.2	$C_{L\max}$ Re = 3.7	$\Delta C_{D\pi}$ tail
	Tapered NACA 0018–09 airfoil with round fuselage											
	Wing alone			0.077	0.90	0.0093	0.020	0.000	1.4	1.48	1.23	
250	Tapered fillets. Plaster finish	0	0	0.080	0.85†	0.0117	0.026	0.000	1.5	1.52	1.27	
314	Tapered fillets. Vertical horizontal tapered surfaces. i_s = 0°	0	0	0.086	0.85§	0.0128	−0.100§	0.002	1.7	1.73	1.47	0.0043
315	$i_s = -4°$; same as combination 314	0	0	0.087	0.90§	0.0133	−0.156§	0.102	1.6	1.62	1.34	0.0063
316	Tapered fillets. Tail surfaces with end plates, i_s = 0°	0	0	0.086	0.85‡	0.0132	−0.098‡	0.001	1.6	1.67	1.40	0.0058
317	$i_s = -4°$; otherwise same as combination 316	0	0	0.087	0.90§	0.0134	−0.122§	0.086	1.6	1.62	1.33	0.0065
318	Washed-out. Vertical and horizontal tail surfaces. i_s = 0°	0	4	0.086	0.85§	0.0142	−0.129§	−0.044	1.4	1.42	1.38	
319	Symmetrical tapered fillets	0	4	0.080	0.85‡	0.0117	0.027	−0.021	1.5	1.55	1.25	
320	Same as combination 319 but with vertical and horizontal tail surfaces. i_s = 0°	0	4	0.087	0.85§	0.0132	−0.115§	−0.033	1.6	1.66	1.36	0.0059

TABLE XXXV.—WING-FUSELAGE-TAIL COMBINATIONS.*—(*Concluded*)

Diagrams representing combinations	Remarks	Vert. pos. $\frac{k}{c}$	i_w	a, $\text{Æ} =$ 6.86	Eff. factor e	C_{De} min	a.c.	C_{m0}	C_{Lib}	$C_{L\max}$ $Re =$ 8.2	$C_{L\max}$ $Re =$ 3.7	$\Delta C_{D\pi}$ tail
	Tapered NACA 0018–09 airfoil with round fuselage											
321		0	4	0.080	0.85‡	0.0120	0.034	−0.021	1.5	1.50	1.22	
322	Vertical and horizontal tail surfaces. $i_s = 0°$	0	4	0.087	0.85‡	0.0133	−0.116‖	−0.039	1.6	1.67	1.35	0.0051
323	$i_s = -4°$; otherwise same as combination 322	0	4	0.086	0.85†	0.0138	−0.110‖	0.062	1.6	1.60	1.31	0.0070
324	Tail surfaces with end plates. $i_s = 0°$	0	4	0.086	0.85‡	0.0135	−0.114‖	−0.032	1.6	1.65	1.34	0.0058
325	Tapered fillets. Horizontal tail surfaces. $i_s = 0°$	0	0	0.086	0.85‡	0.0127	−0.087	0.005	1.7	1.72	1.41	0.0056
306	Tapered fillets.	0.22	0	0.080	0.85	0.0122	0.032	−0.001	1.6	1.65	1.36	
312	Tapered fillets. Horizontal tail surfaces. $i_s = 0°$	0.22	0	0.087	0.85§	0.0129	−0.133	0.019	1.8	1.84	1.50	0.0039
326	$i_s = -4°$; otherwise same as combination 312	0.22	0	0.085	0.85‡	0.0137	−0.166‖	0.116	1.7	1.76	1.46	0.0083
327	$i_s = 4°$; otherwise same as combination 312	0.22	0	0.086	0.80‡	0.0133	−0.125§	−0.077	1.7	1.81	1.50	0.0061

* *NACA Tech. Rept.* 678 (1939). Wing $c/4$ at fuselage $L/4$.

† Poor agreement in high-speed range.

‡ Poor agreement over whole range.

§ Poor agreement in high-lift range.

‖ a.c. $= dC_{mc/4}/dC_L$ at $C_{mc/4} = 0$ for combinations with tail surfaces.

i_w = incidence of wing.

C_{Lib} = lift coefficient at interference burble.

TABLE XXXVI.—LANDING-GEAR-DRAG DATA

(Full-scale landing gears tested at about 100 mph)

1. Wheels alone, S_π = rectangle circumscribed on wheel (from *NACA Tech. Rept.* 485 except where noted):

	$C_{D\pi}$
Low-pressure wheel and tire	0.24
Streamlined wheel and tire	0.18
Extra-low-pressure tire (includes Goodyear Airwheels)	0.24
Disk wheel and high-pressure tire	0.32
High-pressure tires, completely faired (British data, 1930)	0.24 to 0.32

2. Cowled wheels, S_π = rectangle circumscribed on wheel and cowl

Fairing *A*	0.120
Fairing *B*	0.080
Fairing *C*	0.095
Fairing *D*	0.170

For mudguards; add for each wheel, sq ft .... f_e = 0.2 to 0.4

3. Complete landing gears (*NACA Tech. Repts.* 485, 518, 522): Fig. A25 Arrangements as sketched on p. 439.

Sketch no. in Fig. A25	Sq ft f_e	Sketch no. in Fig. A25	Sq ft f_e
1. 8.50-10 wheels, not faired	1.67	4. 8.50-10 wheels	0.51
1. 8.50-10 wheels, faired	1.50	5. 8.50-10-wheels, not faired	1.52
1. 8.50-10 wheels, no streamline members	3.83	5. 8.50-10 wheels, faired	1.02
2. 8.50-10 wheels, faired	0.74	6. 8.50-10 wheels, not faired	1.60
2. 27-in. streamlined wheels, not faired	0.98	7. 24-in. streamlined wheels, intersections filleted	0.86
3. 27-in. streamlined wheels, not faired	0.84	7. 8.50-10 wheels, no fillets	1.13
3. 8.50-10 wheels, faired	0.68	8. 8.50-10 wheels	1.05
3. 21-in. streamlined wheels, not faired	0.53	9. Low-pressure wheels, intersections filleted	0.31
		9. Low-pressure wheels, no wheel fairing	0.47
		9. Streamlined wheels, round strut, half fork, no fairing	1.25

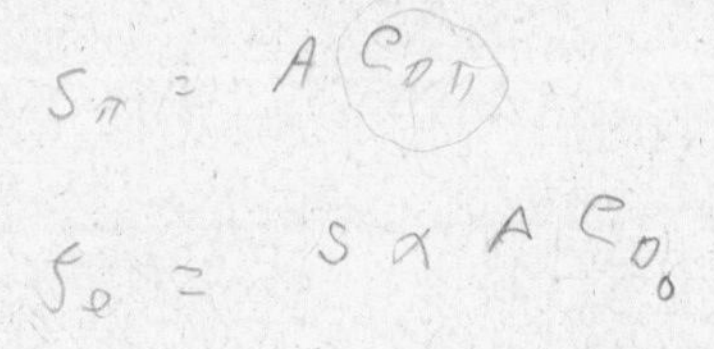

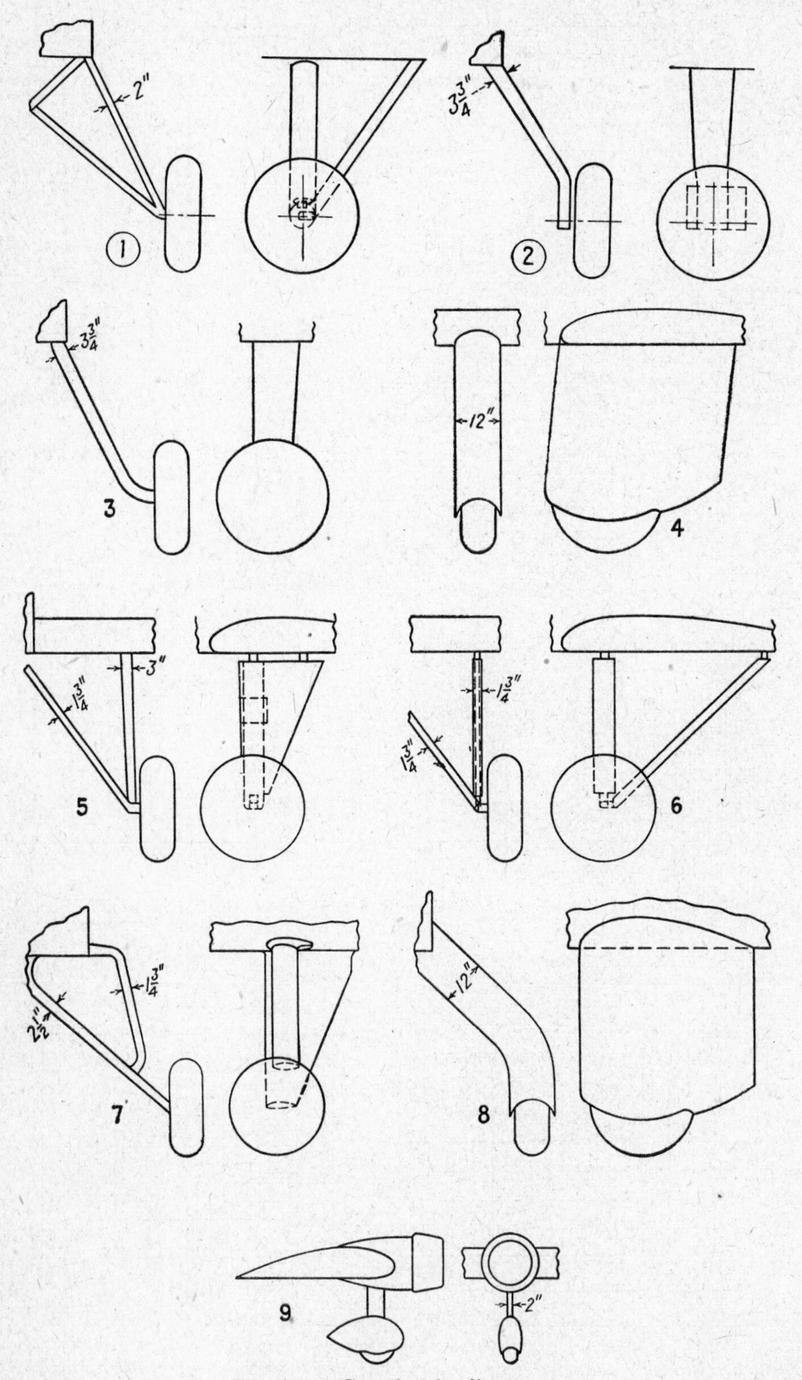

FIG. A25.—Complete landing gears.

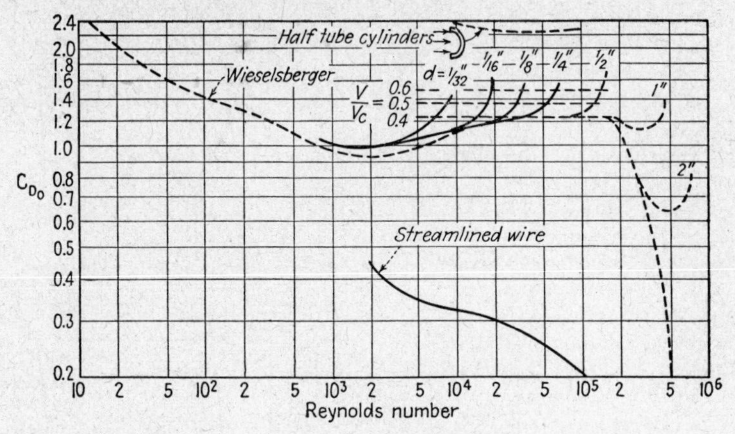

FIG. A26.—Drag of circular cylinders as a function of *Re* and *M*. (*From NACA Tech. Rept.* 619.)

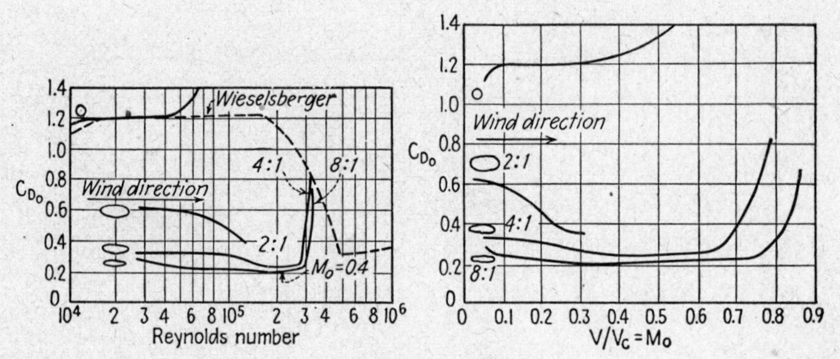

FIG. A27.—Drag of circular and elliptic cylinders as a function of *Re* and *M*. (*From NACA Tech. Rept.* 619.)

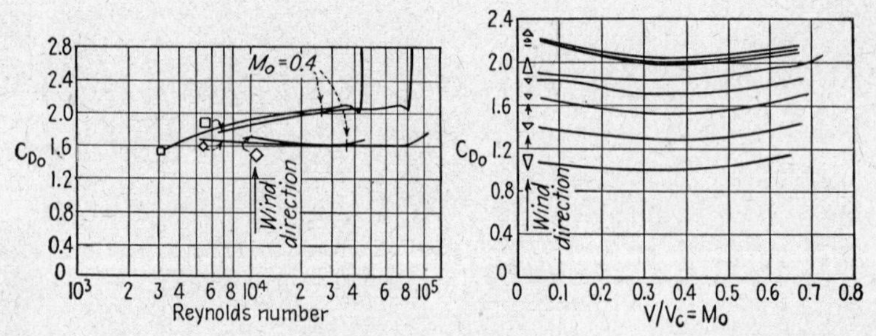

FIG. A28.—Drag of square and triangular cylinders as a function of *Re* and *M*. (*From NACA Tech. Rept.* 619.)

Drag of Wires, Struts, and Miscellaneous Items

1. Smooth round wires and struts. S_π = frontal area.
   Use infinite-cylinder data, page 440, for *Re* and *M* corrections to get drag per foot of length.
   For wires ($d \leq 1/4$ in.) assume two end fittings equivalent to 3 ft of wire.
   For struts ($d \geq 5/16$ in.), assume two end fittings equivalent to 1 ft of strut.
2. Stranded aircraft cable. S_π = frontal area.
   Add 20 to 30 per cent to round-wire data.
3. Smooth elliptical wire. S_π = frontal area.
   Use 4:1 elliptical-cylinder data, page 440, for *Re* and *M* corrections. Assume two end fittings equivalent to 10 to 15 ft of wire. For standard streamlined wire use special graph on page 440.
4. Square wire. S_π = frontal area.
   Use infinite-square-cylinder data, page 440, for *Re* and *M* corrections. Assume two end fittings equivalent to 2 ft of wire.
5. Streamlined struts. S_π = frontal area.
   Use Fig. A29 for *Re* correction. Mach number corrections not available (usually not important below 200 mph). Assume two end fittings equivalent to 5 ft of strut if faired, 10 ft if not. Use Fig. A30 for fineness-ratio correction if strut data of desired fineness ratio are not available.
6. Miscellaneous items. S_π = frontal area.
   See *NACA Tech. Note* 480. Re = 120,000 for items *a* to *d*.

Item	$C_{D\pi}$
a. Hollow sphere, anemometer cup, or parachute (Wind →)	1.4
b. Hollow sphere or anemometer cup, reversed	0.4
c. Hollow-cone anemometer cup	1.3
d. Hollow-cone anemometer cup, reversed	0.5
e. Radiator cores	0.7
f. Radiators, complete, exposed	1.0
g. Radiators, cowled	0.3 to 0.5
h. Control horns on lower surface or on rudder	0.3 to 0.6
i. Control horns on upper surface	0.6 to 1.2
j. External hand holds, steps, air scoops, etc	1.5 to 2.0

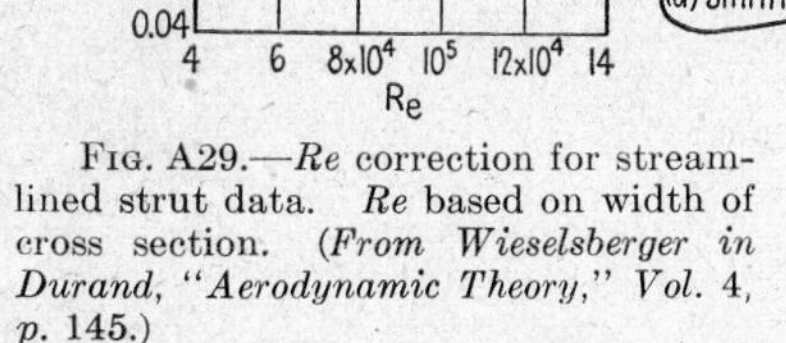

Fig. A29.—*Re* correction for streamlined strut data. *Re* based on width of cross section. (*From Wieselsberger in Durand, "Aerodynamic Theory," Vol.* 4, *p.* 145.)

Fig. A30.—Fineness-ratio correction for streamlined struts. (*From Diehl.*) Thick-airfoil data shown dotted for comparison.

APPENDIX 6

AIRPLANE, PROPELLER, AND ENGINE DATA

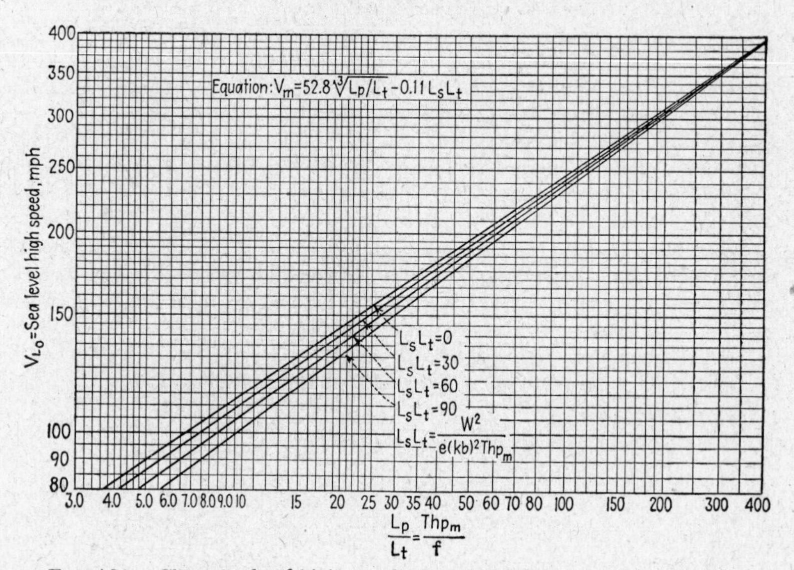

FIG. A31.—Chart for level high speed at sea level. (*Frp. NACA Rept.* 408).

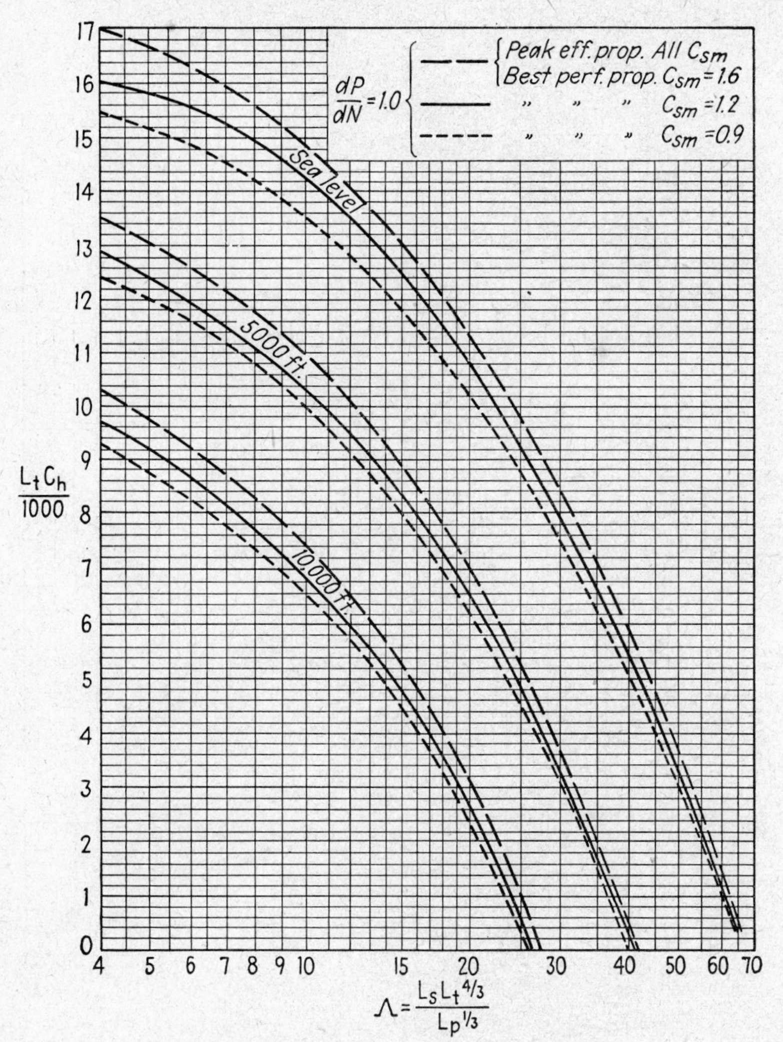

FIG. A32.—Climb chart. (*From NACA Rept.* 408.)

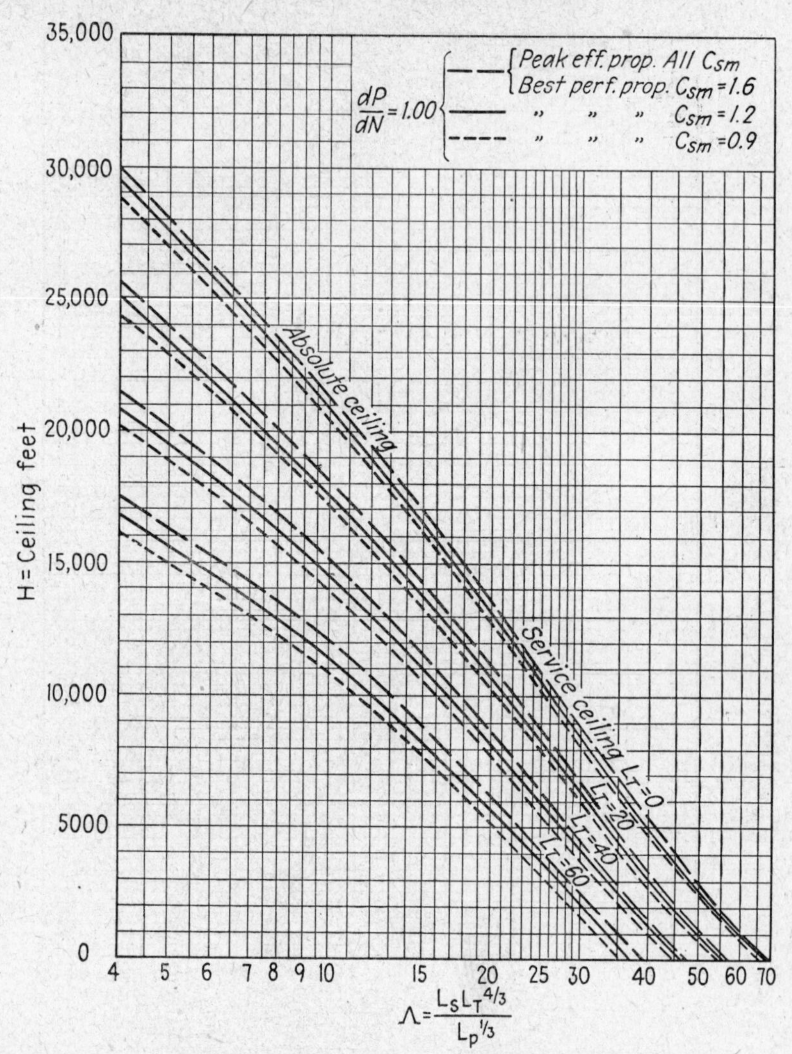

FIG. A33.—Ceiling chart. (*From NACA Rept.* 408.)

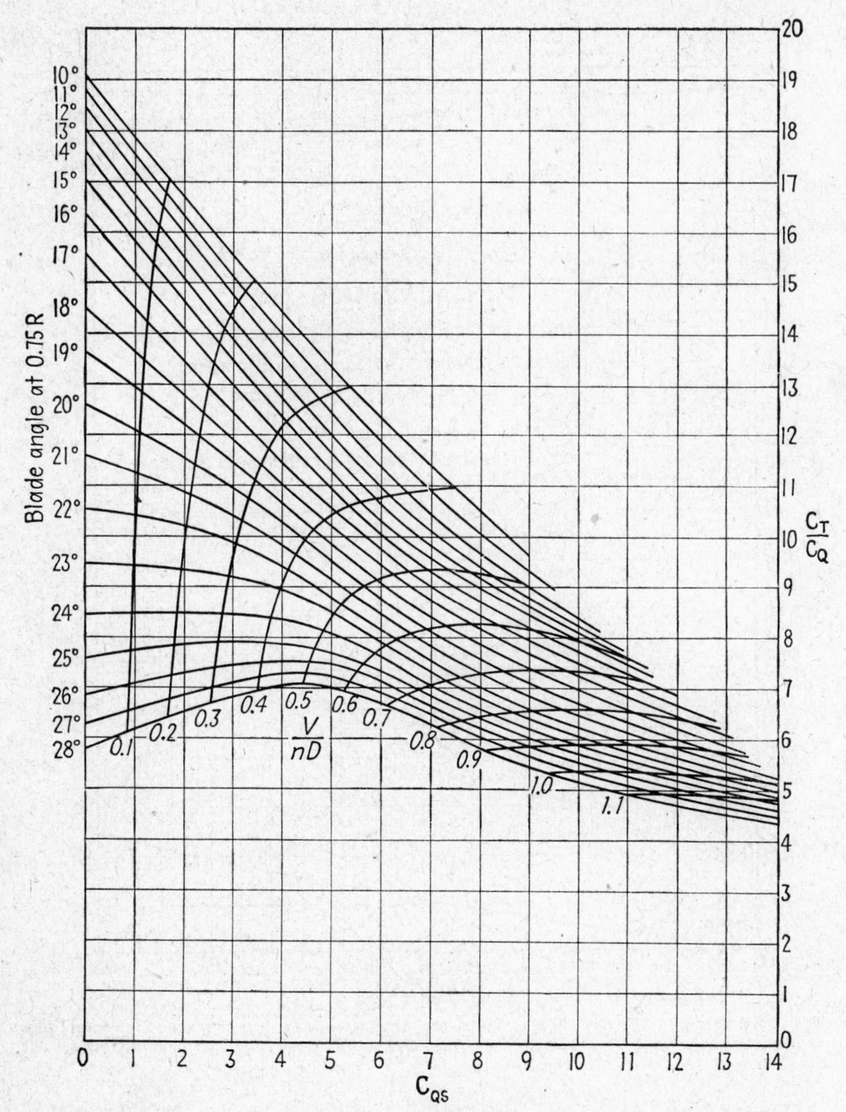

FIG. A34.—Propeller-performance chart for a cabin fuselage with J-5 engine and NACA engine cowling. C_{QS} is proportional to V; C_T/C_Q is proportional to T.

$$C_{QS} = V\sqrt{\frac{\rho D^3}{Q}} = \frac{J}{\sqrt{C_Q}}$$

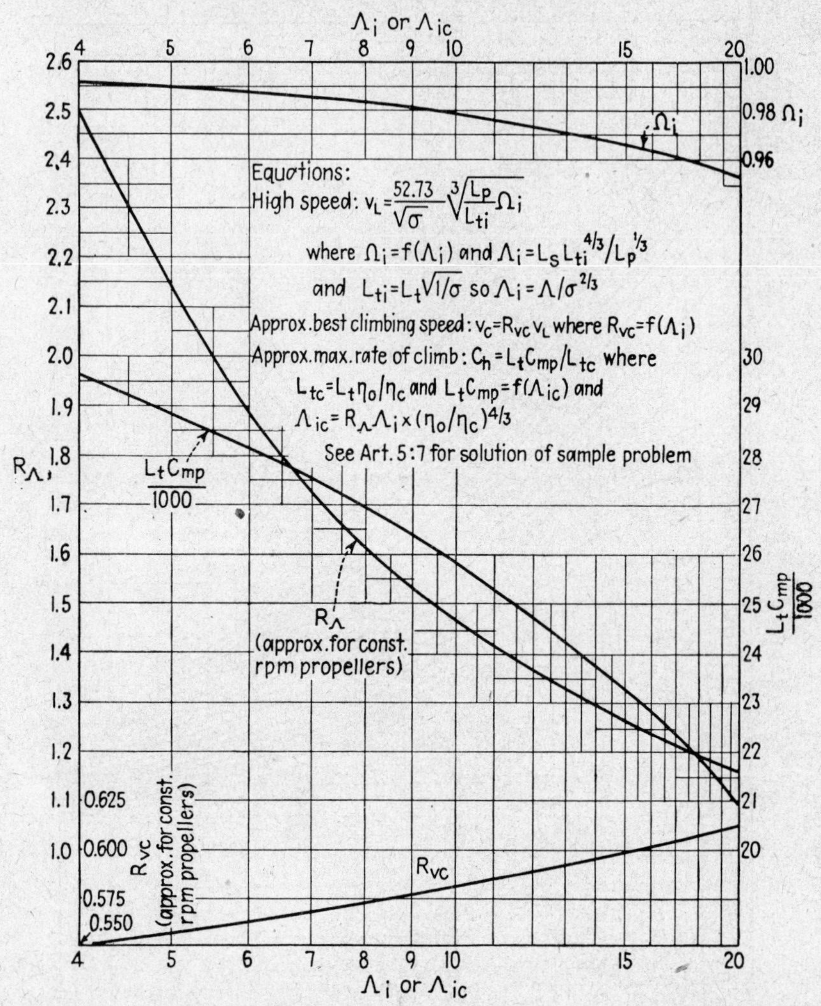

FIG. A35.—Speed and climb chart for airplanes with supercharged engines and constant-rpm propellers. (*Replotted from GALCIT composite performance chart in Millikan, "Aerodynamics of the Airplane."*)

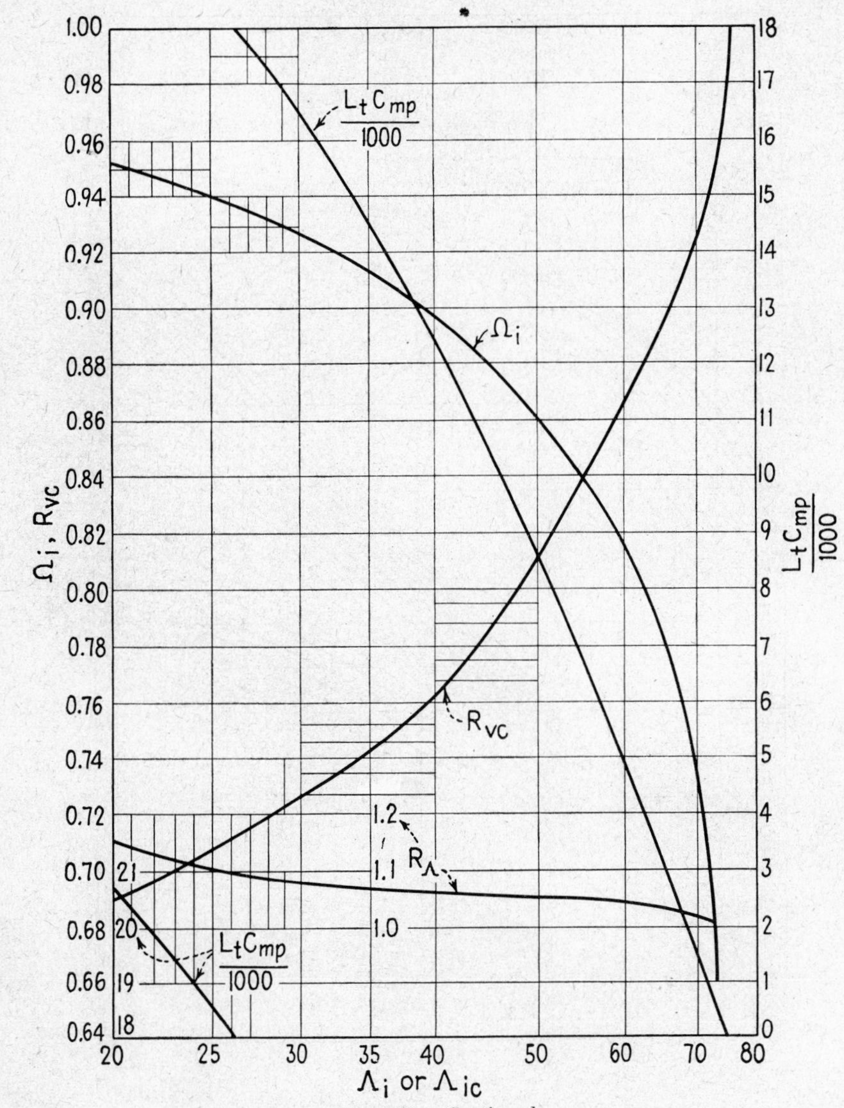

FIG. A35.—*Continued.*

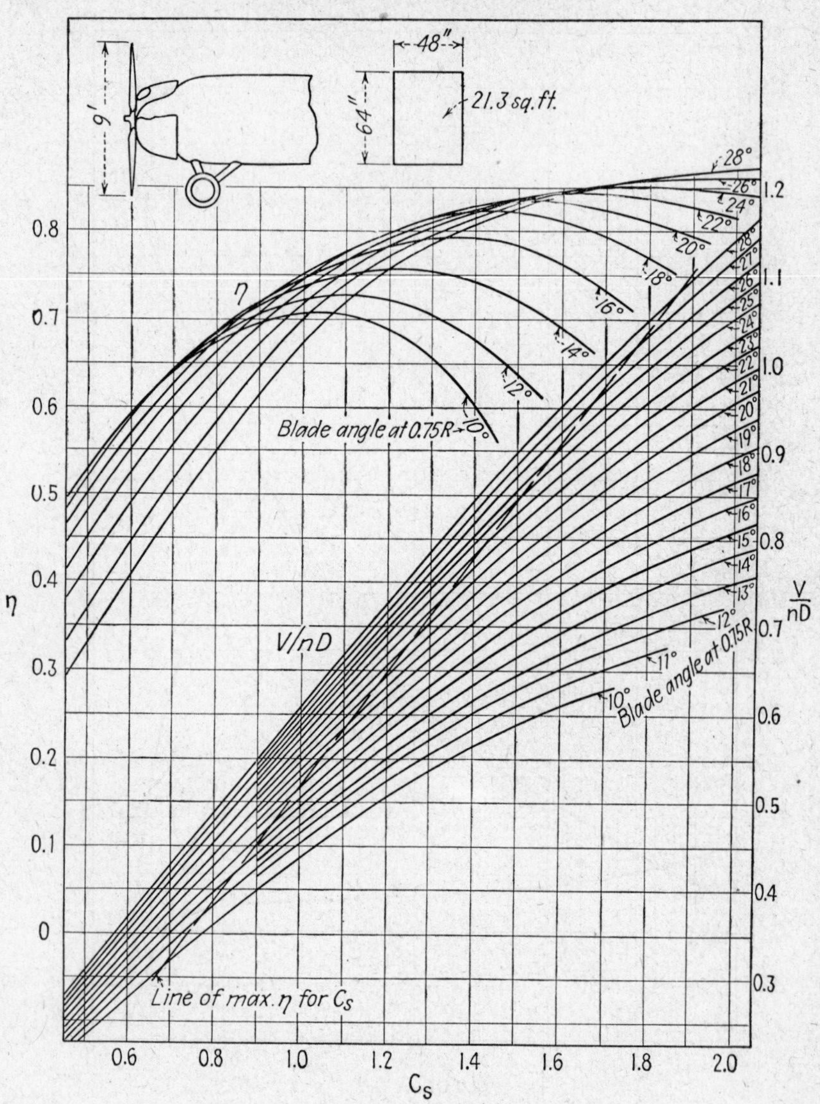

FIG. A36.—Design chart corresponding to take-off chart.

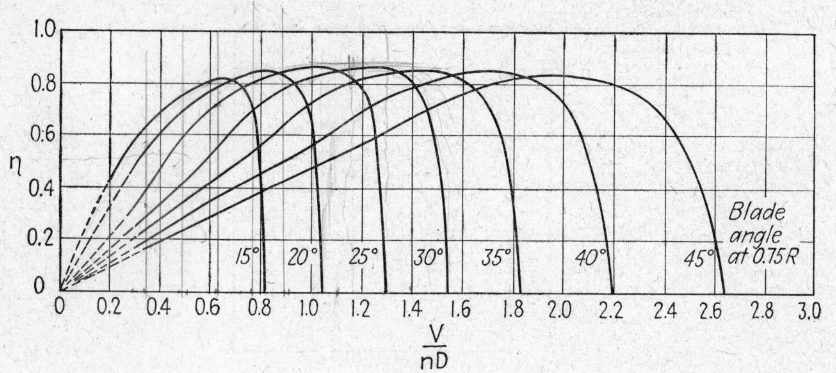

FIG. A37.—Efficiency curves for propeller 5868-9, Clark Y section, two blades.

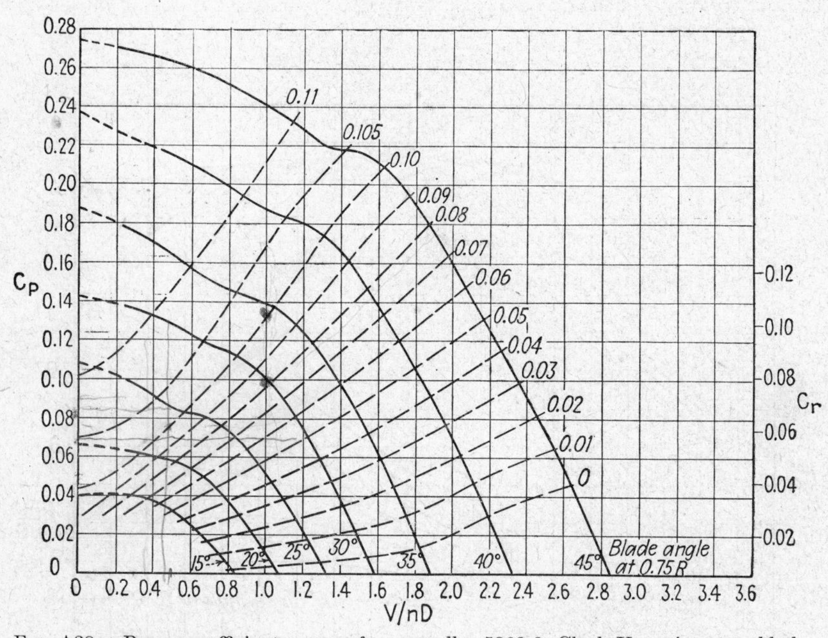

FIG. A38.—Power-coefficient curves for propeller 5868-9, Clark Y section, two blades.

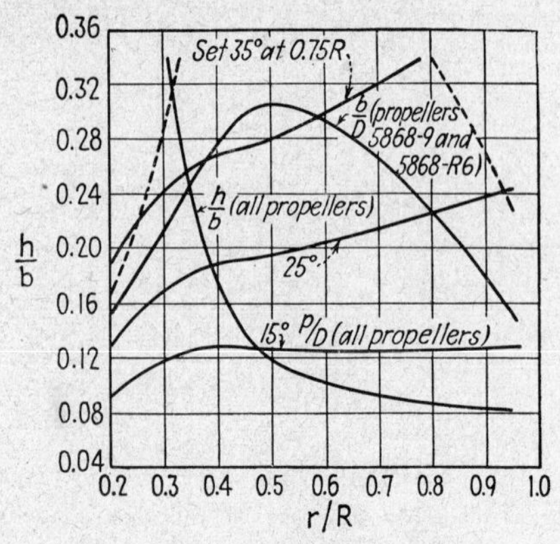

FIG. A39.—Blade-form curves for propellers 5868-9, 5868-R6, and 37-3647. D. diameter; R, radius to the tip; r, station radius; b, section chord; h, section thickness; p, geometric pitch.

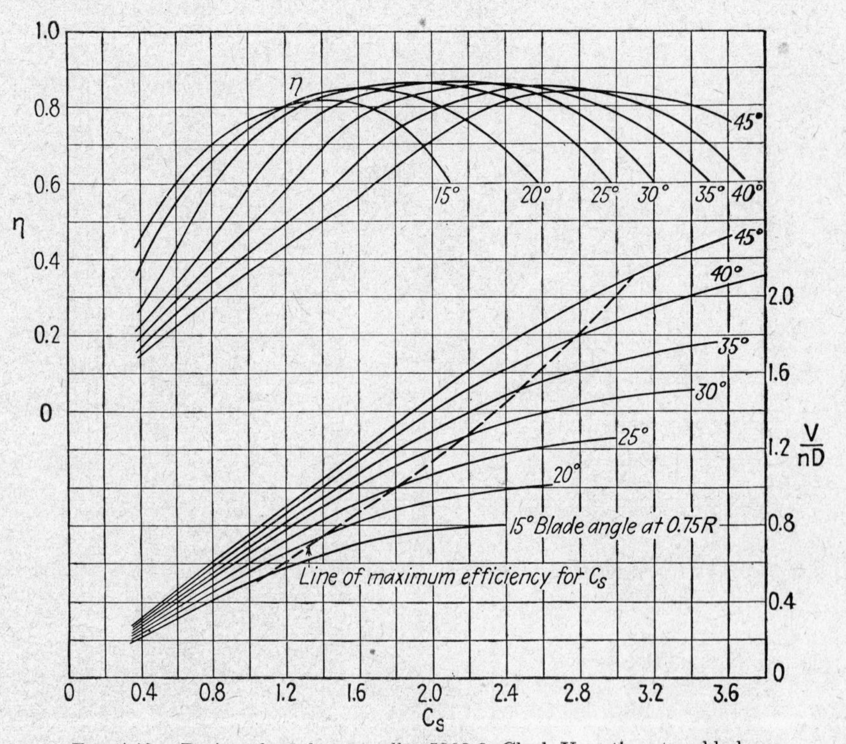

FIG. A40.—Design chart for propeller 5868-9, Clark Y section, two blades.

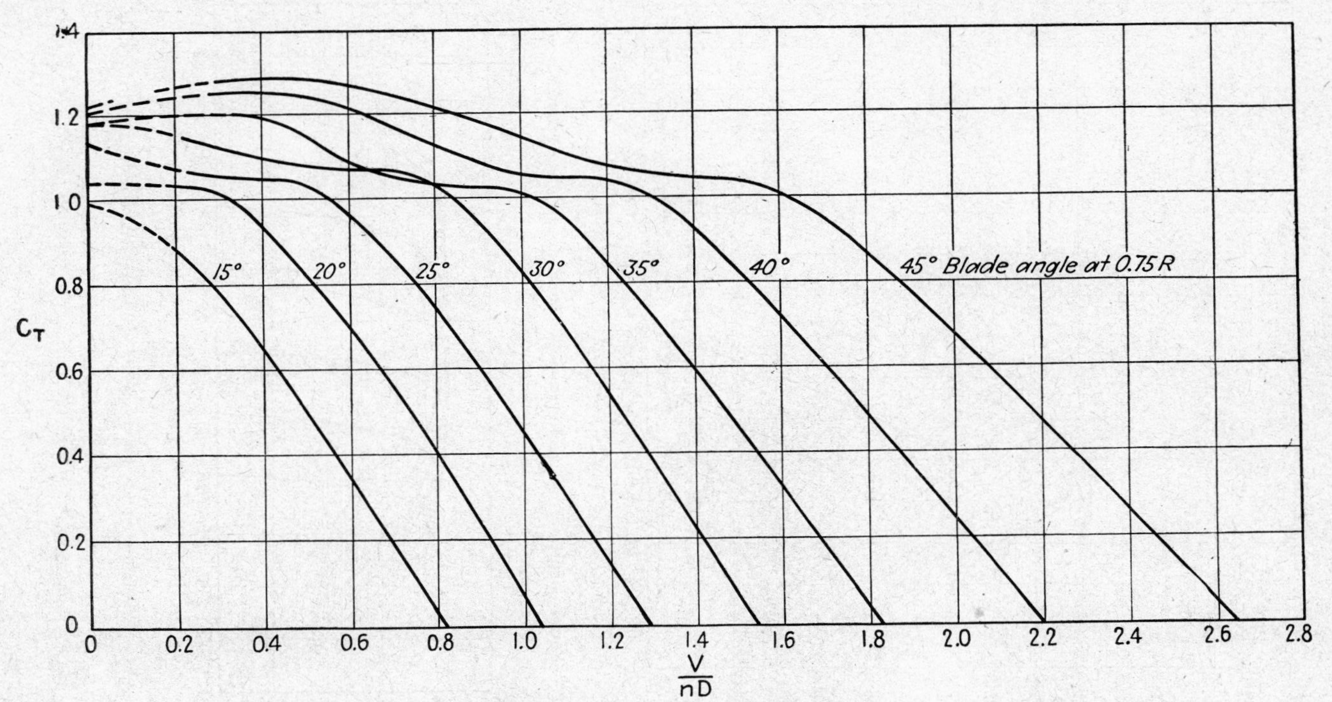

FIG. A41.—Thrust-coefficient curves for propeller 5868-9, Clark Y section, two blades.

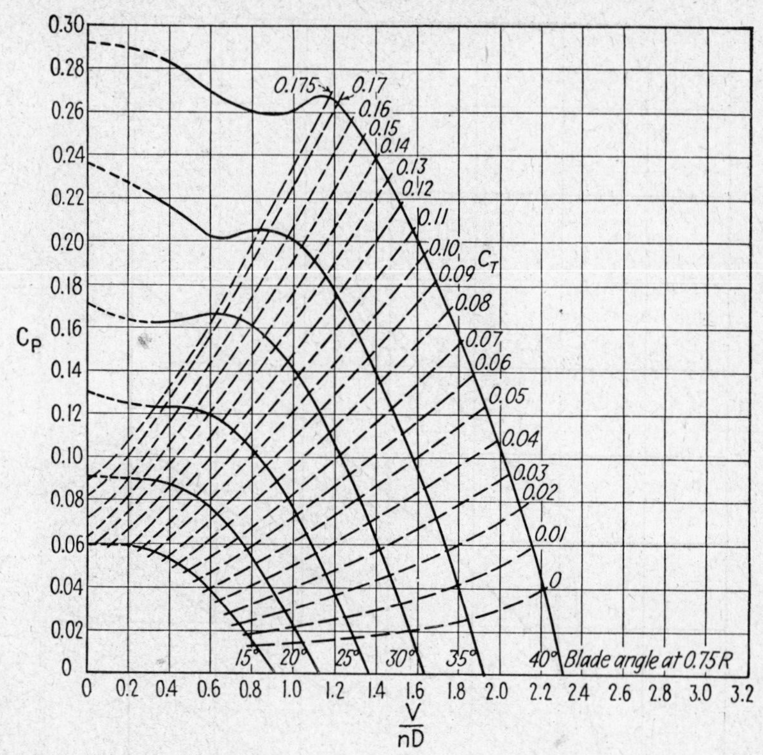

FIG. A42.—Power-coefficient curves for propeller 5868-R6, RAF6 section, three blades.

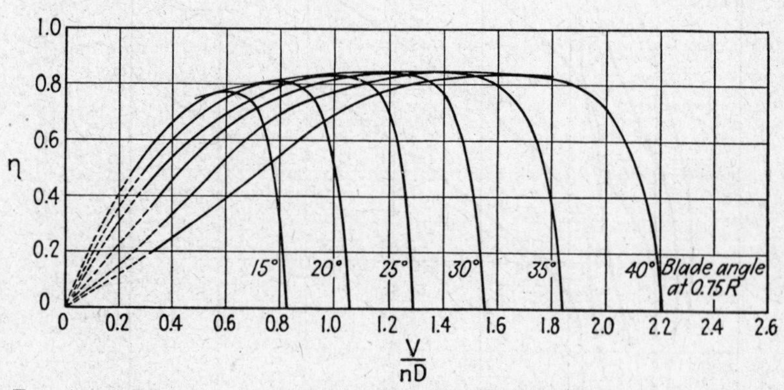

FIG. A43.—Efficiency curves for propeller 5868-R6, RAF6 section, three blades.

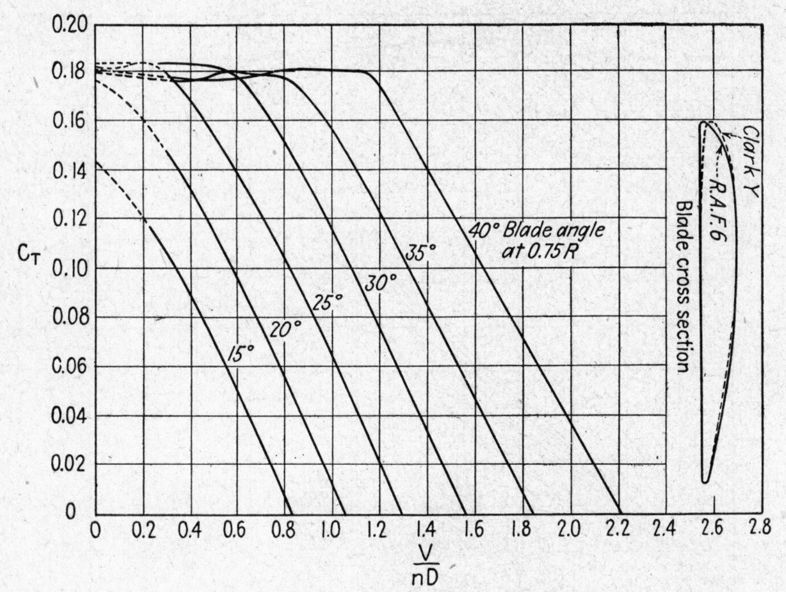

FIG. A44.—Thrust-coefficient curves for propeller 5868-R6, RAF6 section, three blades.

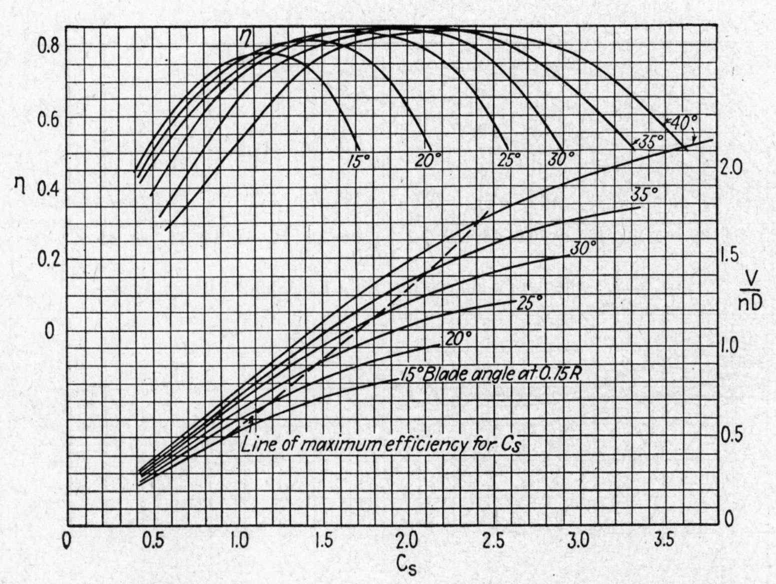

FIG. A45.—Design chart for propeller 5868-R6, RAF6 section, three blades.

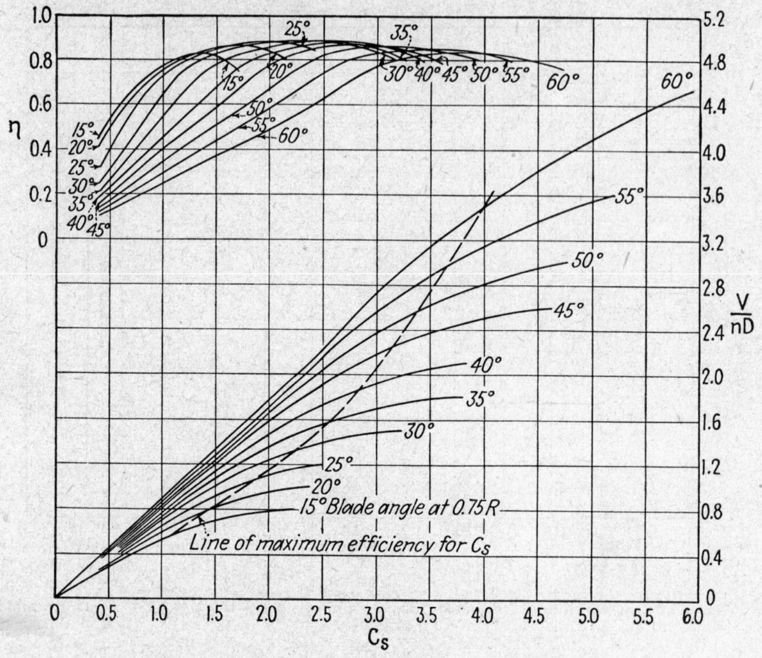

FIG. A46.—Design chart for propeller 5868-9 with spinner.

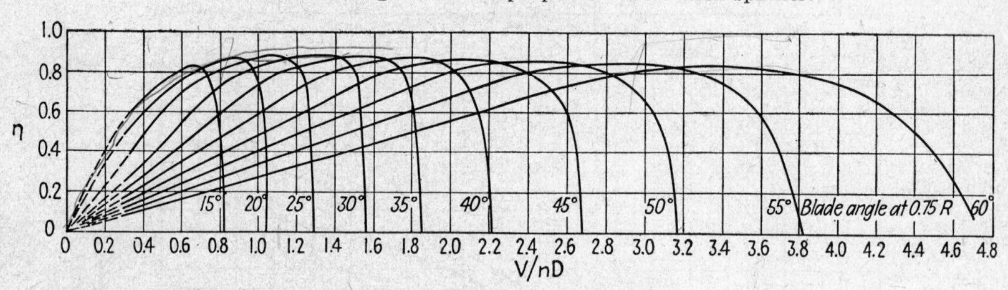

FIG. A47.—Efficiency curves for propeller 5868-9 with spinner.

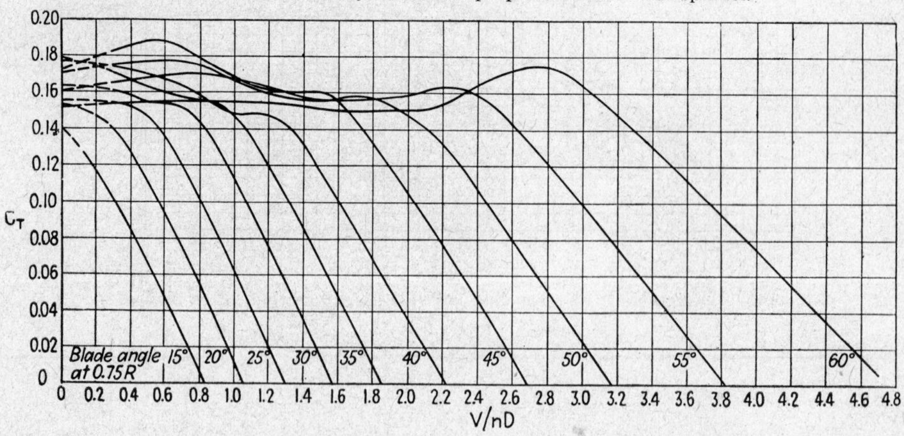

FIG. A48.—Thrust coefficient for propeller 5868-9 with spinner.

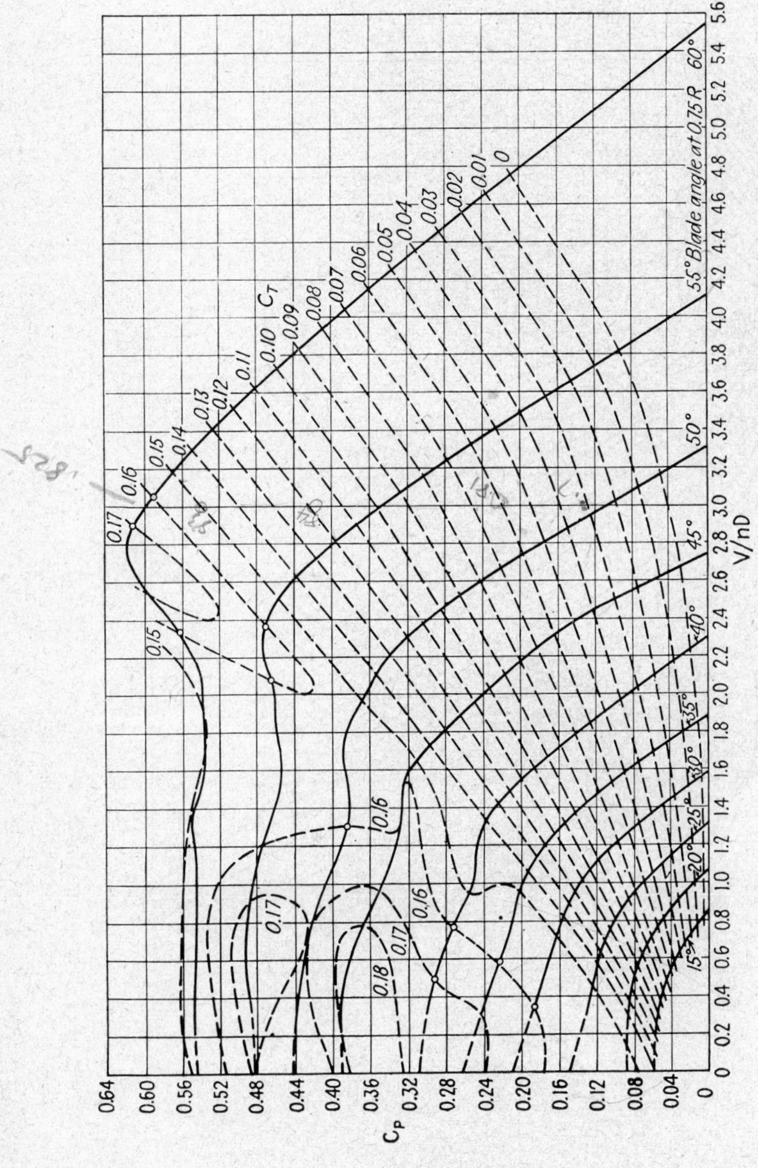

FIG. A49.—Power-coefficient curves for propeller 5868-9 with spinner.

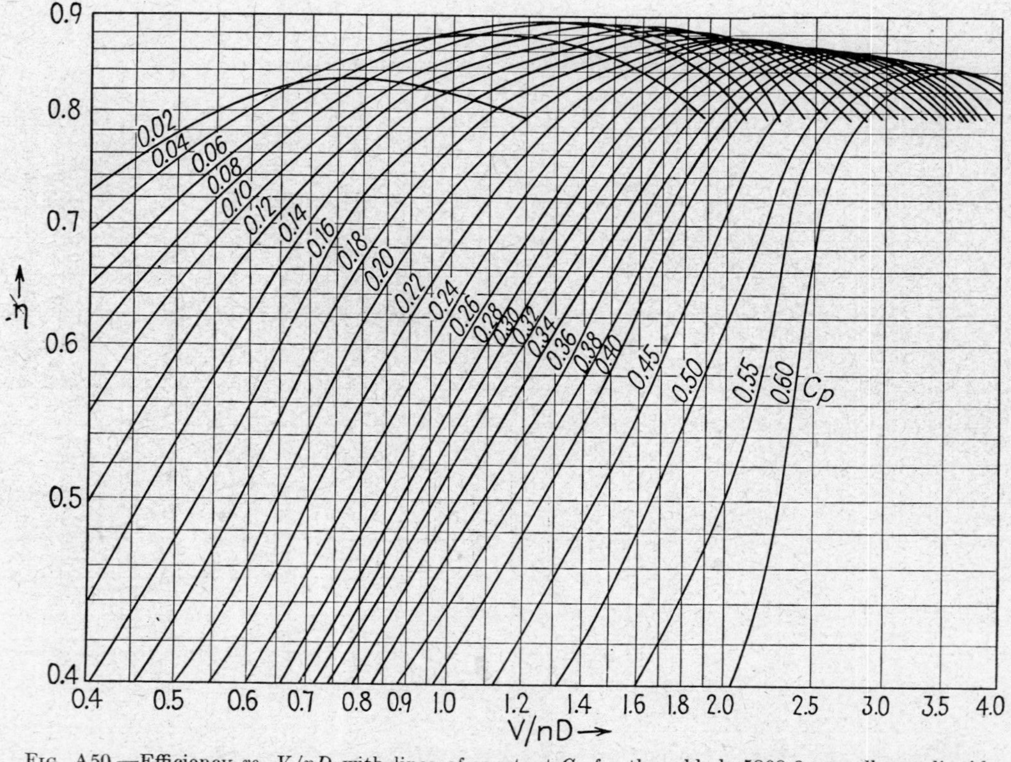

FIG. A50.—Efficiency *vs.* V/nD with lines of constant C_P for three-blade 5868-9 propeller on liquid-cooled nacelle, with spinner. (*Replotted from NACA Tech. Rept.* 658.)

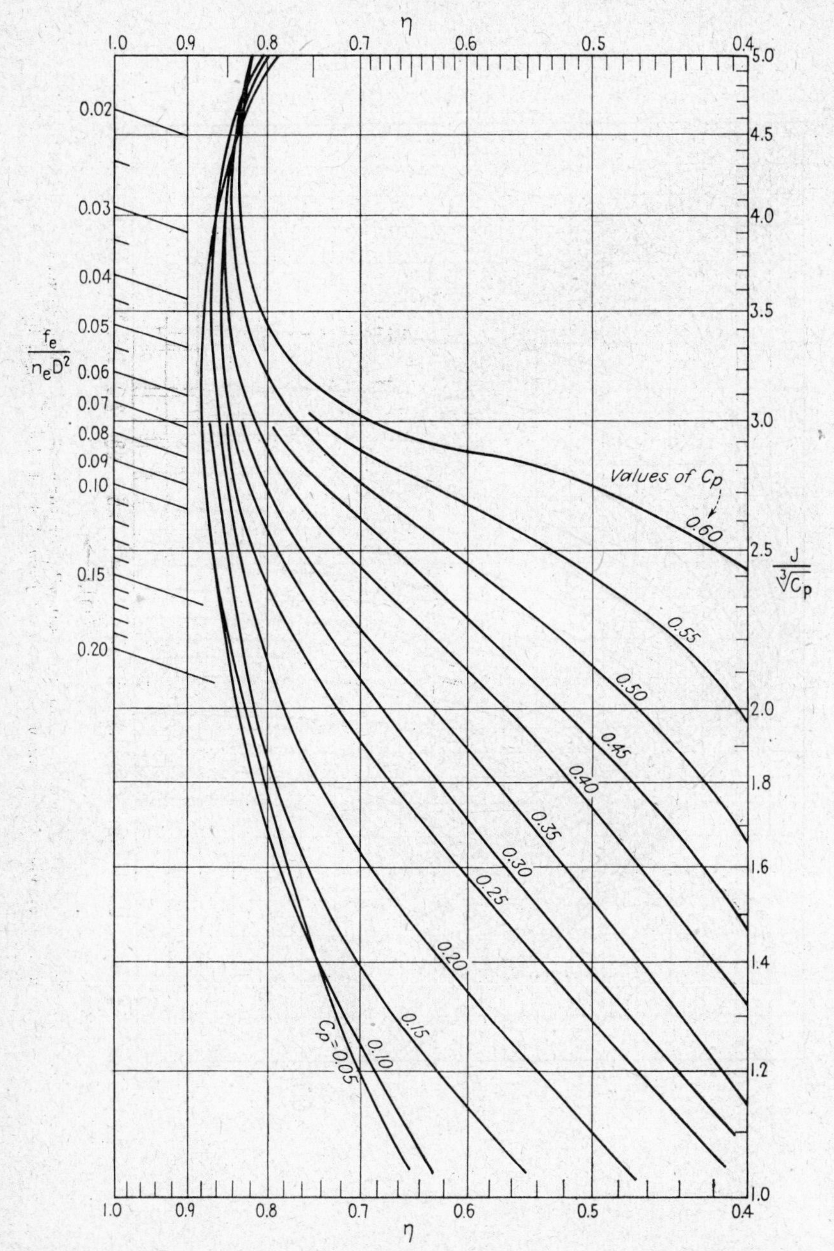

FIG. A51.—General logarithmic plot of full throttle power available from engine-propeller unit. (*From NACA Tech. Rept.* 658, *Fig.* 16, *replotted.*) Three-blade 5868-9 propeller with spinner in front of liquid-cooled nacelle. To be traced onto Chart C.

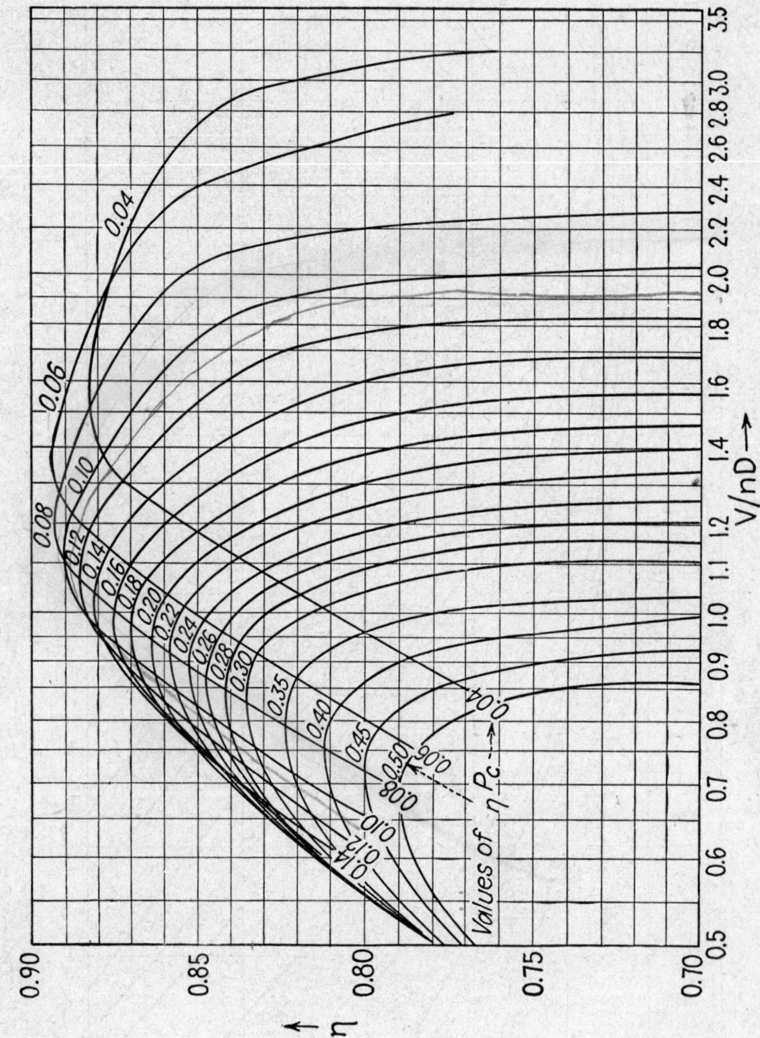

FIG. A52.—Efficiency *vs.* V/nD with lines of constant ηP_c, for three-blade 5868-9 propeller on liquid-cooled nacelle with spinner. (*Replotted from NACA Tech. Rept.* 658.)

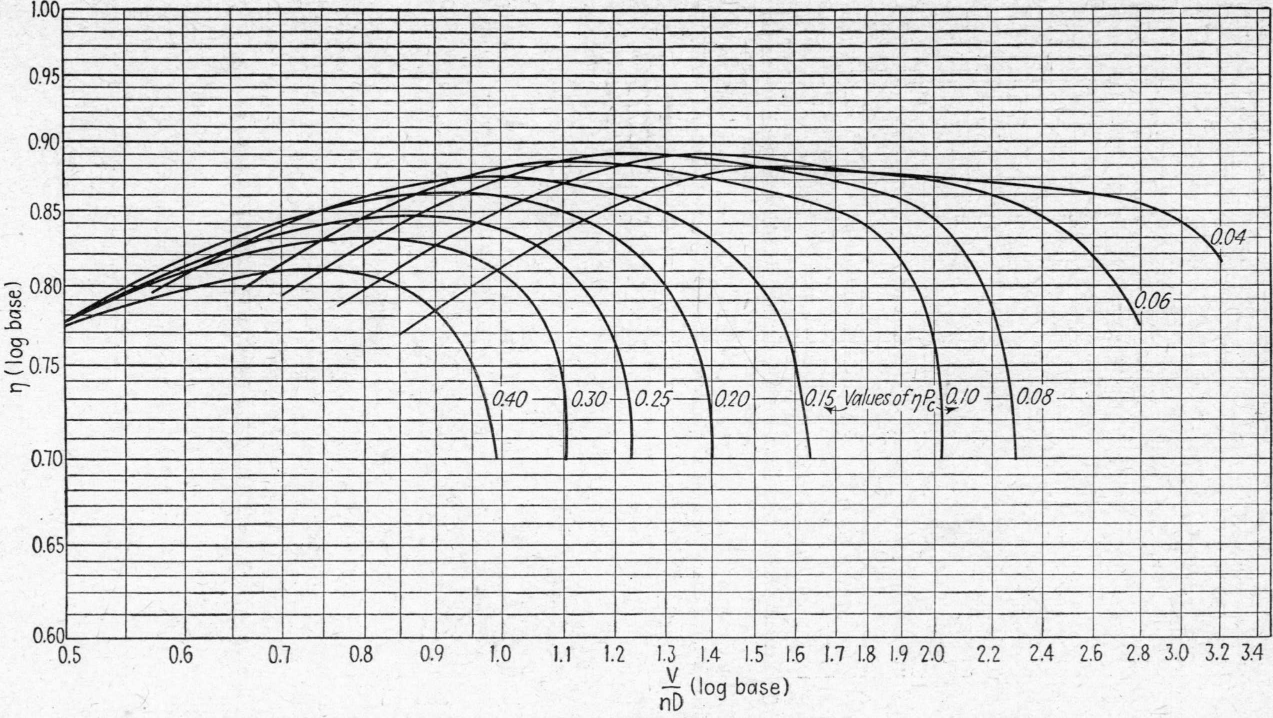

FIG. A53.—Logarithmic plot of propeller efficiency. (For cruising performance calculations. To be used in connection with Chart D as directed in Art. 5:9.)

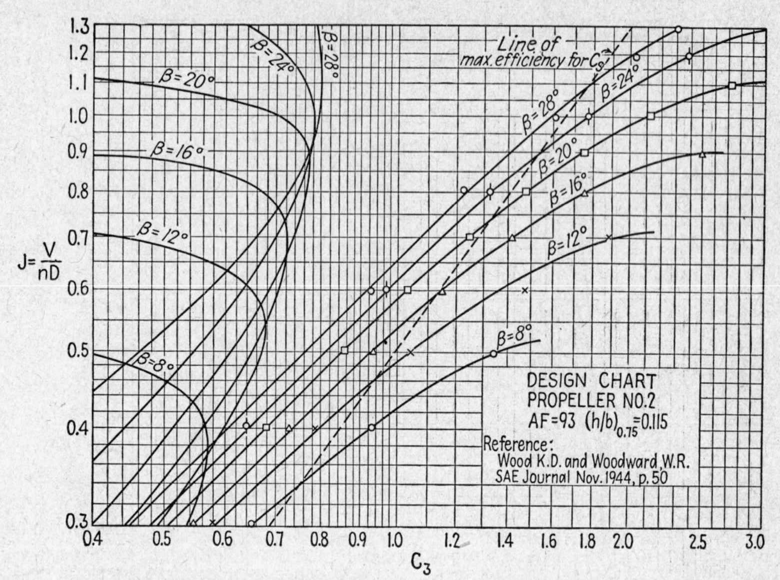

FIG. A54.—Design chart for light airplane propellers. (*Wood, K. D., and W. H. Woodward*, SAE *Journal, November*, 1944, *p.* 50.)

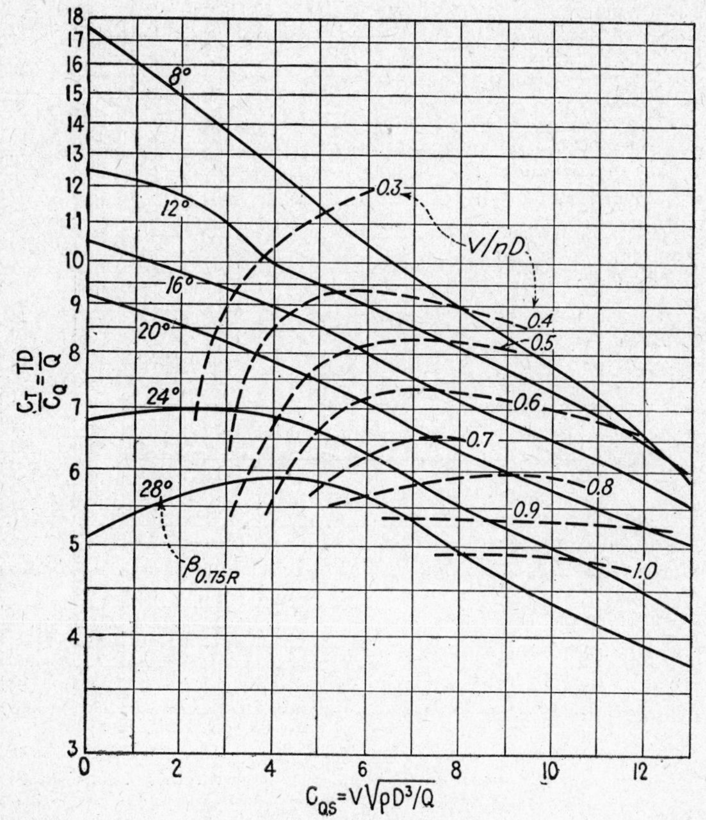

FIG. A55.—Estimated thrust-speed characteristics of special Freedman-Burnham propeller on Piper cruiser airplane.

$$\text{A.F.} = 93$$

$$\left(\frac{h}{b}\right)_{0.75R} = 0.115$$

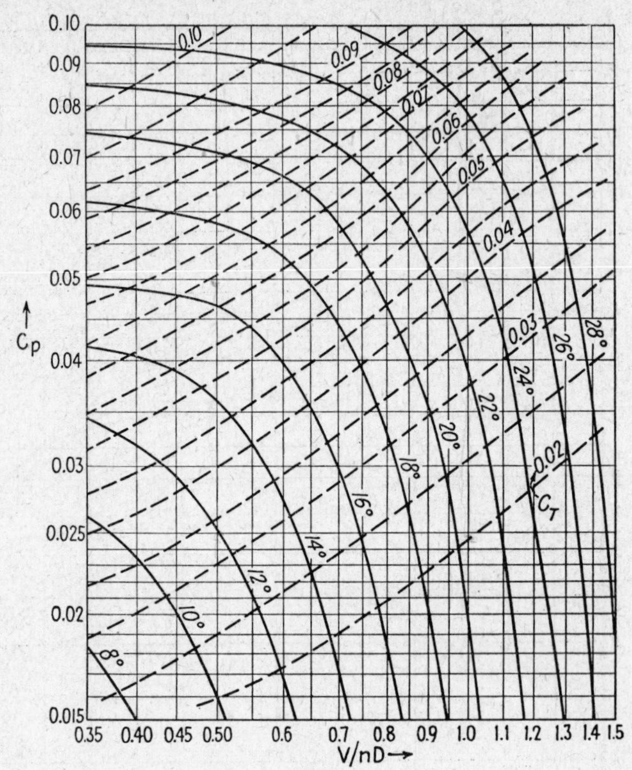

Fig. A57.—C_P *vs.* V/nD for light airplane propeller with lines of constant C_T.
A.F. = 93

$$\left(\frac{h}{b}\right)_{0.75R} = 0.115$$

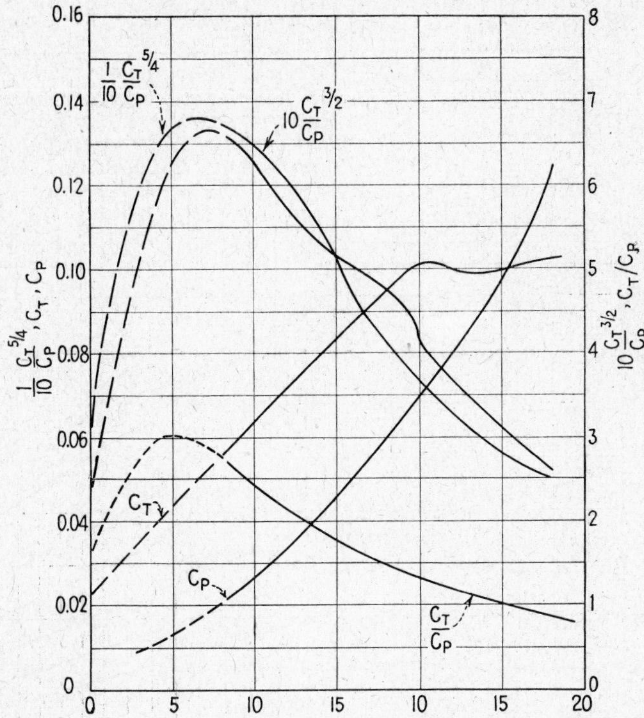

FIG. A58.—Static thrust of two-blade propeller on light airplane. Same propeller and airplane as in Figs. A54 to A56.

Hypothetical 3660 S1C3-G engine		
Ratios: Blower	7.15:1	Fuel: 90 octane
Pistons	6.7:1	
Propeller .500, .5625, .666		

Maximum power limits

Take-off	2400 hp at 2700 rpm
Normal or climb	2100 hp at 2550 rpm
Continuous emergency operation, multi-engine aircraft (not for high-speed performance or military operation)	2300 hp at 2600 rpm
Cruising	1400 hp at 2350 rpm

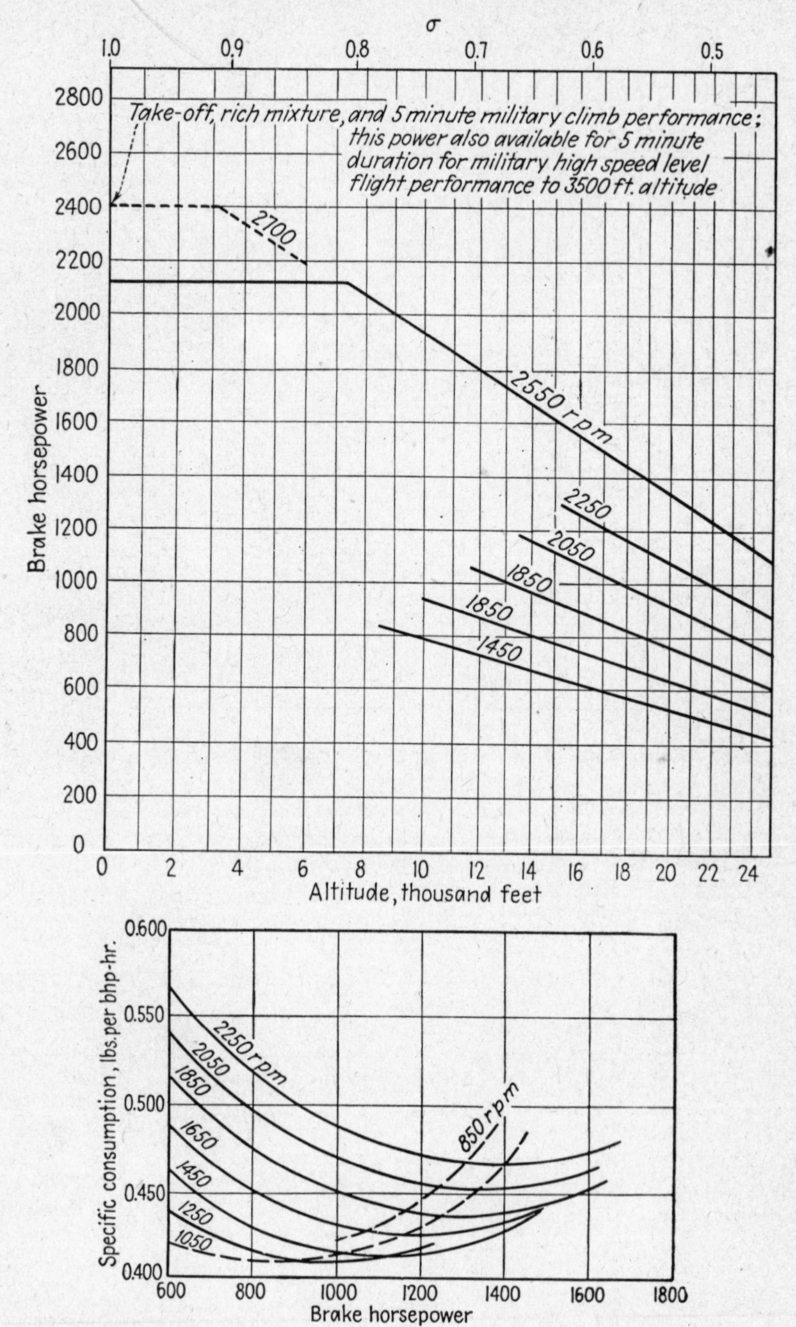

FIG. A59. (*continued*).—Hypothetical aircraft-engine data, R3660, S1C3-G.

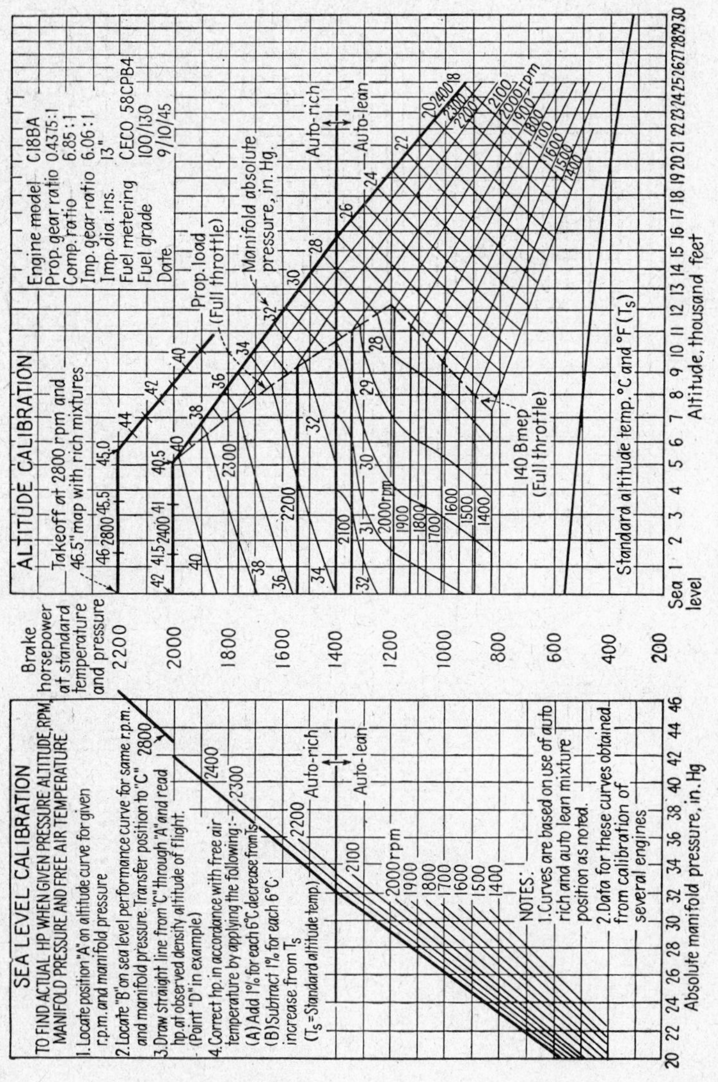

FIG. A60.—Engine-power chart for Constellation airplane. (*From Lockheed Rept.* 5527.)

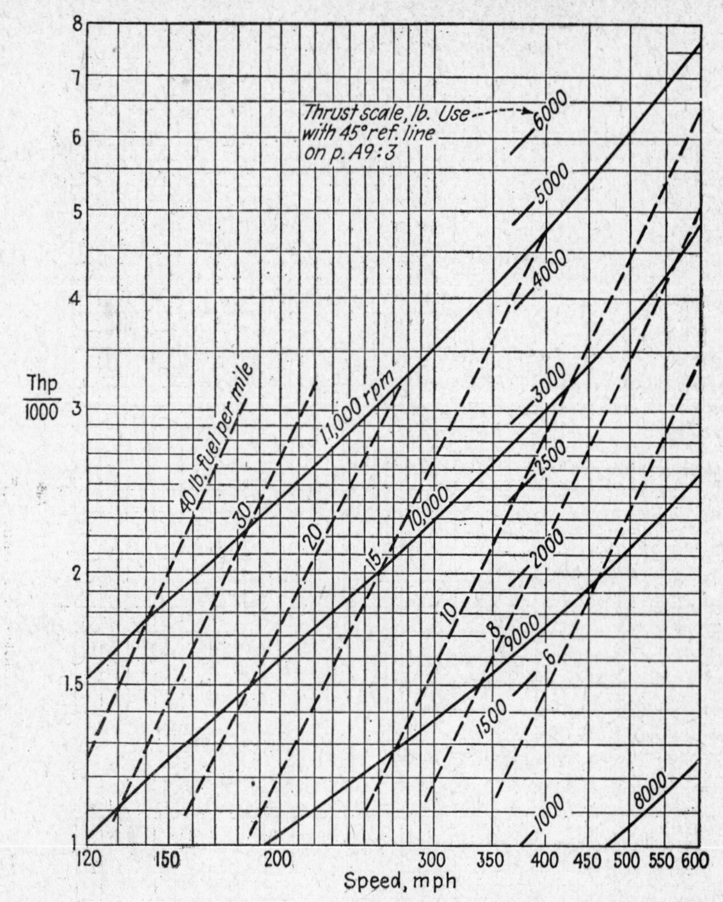

FIG. A61.—Hypothetical turbo-jet characteristics at 35,000 ft altitude (four times the thrust of Fig. 4:7.3) plotted for use with general power-required chart.

INDEX